W9-CQM-010

PATHWAYS OF HUMAN DEVELOPMENT

Normal Growth and Emotional Disorders in Infancy, Childhood, and Adolescence

Mohammad Shafii, M.D.
Professor of Psychiatry
Director of Child Psychiatric Services
Department of Psychiatry and Behavioral Sciences
University of Louisville School of Medicine

Sharon Lee Shafii, B.S.N., R.N.
Editor-in-Residence
Formerly Assistant Head Nurse, Adolescent Service
Neuropsychiatric Institute
University of Michigan Medical Center

1982
Thieme-Stratton Inc.
New York

Georg Thieme Verlag
Stuttgart • New York

Publisher: Thieme-Stratton Inc.
381 Park Avenue South
New York, New York 10016

Cover illustration by M. Losaw.

Pathways of Human Development:
Normal Growth and Emotional Disorders in Infancy, Childhood and Adolescence
Mohammad Shafii and Sharon Lee Shafii

Printed in the United States of America.   TSI ISBN 0-86577-049-2
GTV ISBN 3-13-631101-9

Copyright © 1982 by Thieme-Stratton Inc. All rights reserved. No part of this publication may be revised or republished without written permission from the publisher. Library of Congress catalog card number   82-80780.

Last digit is print number   5   4   3   2   1

To Kay and Joyce
with warmest regards,

Mohammed

To
JALEH AND TARANEH

Our Children,
Our Teachers

CONTENTS

Part III
ASSESSMENT AND TREATMENT

CONTRIBUTING AUTHORS

Richard J. Cowen, Ph.D.
Kennedy Memorial Hospital for Children
Boston, Massachusetts

Nuhad D. Dinno, M.D.
Professor of Pediatrics
Department of Pediatrics
University of Louisville
School of Medicine

David Carson Dolen, M.D.
Assistant Professor of Psychiatry
Department of Psychiatry and Behavioral
    Sciences
University of Louisville
School of Medicine

Sherman C. Feinstein, M.D.
Director, Child Psychiatry Research
Psychosomatic and Psychiatric Institute
Michael Reese Hospital
Clinical Professor of Psychiatry
Pritzker School of Medicine
University of Chicago

Susan Feldman-Rotman, Ph.D.
Research Psychologist
Psychosomatic and Psychiatric Institute
Michael Reese Hospital

James F. Kennedy, Ph.D.
Assistant Professor
Department of Psychiatry and Behavioral
    Sciences
Director of Group Psychotherapy for
    Children and Adolescents
Child Psychiatric Services
University of Louisville
School of Medicine

Lovick C. Miller, Ph.D.
Professor of Clinical Psychology
Department of Psychiatry and Behavioral
    Sciences
University of Louisville
School of Medicine

Alice Woolsey, A.C.S.W
Clinical Social Worker
Psychosomatic and Psychiatric Institute
Michael Reese Hospital

PREFACE

The infinite path of human development begins at the moment of conception—a physiological union of two minute cells, and, hopefully, the psychological and spiritual communion of two human beings. From this moment, the possibilities of physiological and psychological growth and development of the new human being are boundless, the ways of reaching maturity and personality integration are infinite.

As the mysteries of human development in health and disorder gradually unfold, discoveries and new insights emerge which expand the horizons of our imagination. The psychology of human development is the basic science of psychopathology and treatment, just as anatomy, physiology, and biochemistry are to the health sciences. Knowledge of human development is essential for understanding emotional disorders and finding effective methods of treatment.

In this book, the stages of human development are discussed from the moment of conception through late adolescence in an interwoven tapestry of relevant information from anatomical, physiological, biochemical, cognitive, behavioral, psychodynamic, and psychoanalytic perspectives. We have attempted to present a holistic picture of the child and adolescent at each specific developmental stage, integrating information from a variety of sources and schools of thought so that the reader will be able to form a gestalt of a healthy child as a baseline for observation. We hope that the reader will allow himself to freely associate to the material, reviving personal experiences as a child, a sibling, a peer, and perhaps a parent, in order to gain a deeper and more meaningful perspective of the world of children and youth.

Emotional disorders, assessment, and treatment are conceptualized from an integrated developmental perspective. A holistic approach synthesizes the significant contributions of clinicians and scientists in each specific area. In the discussion of emotional disorders, the criteria of the *Diagnostic and Statistical Manual of Mental Disorders, Third Edition* (DSM-III) are, for the most part, incorporated.

For the majority of subjects, a brief historical perspective gives the reader an idea of the gradual evolution of thought within a particular topic. Direct reference to the pioneers in human development, psychopathology, and treatment, facilitates the reader's familiarity with their major contributions. These references provide ready access for exploration of the original works.

Undergraduate and graduate students, practitioners in the health sciences, particularly those in the mental health field, and educators will find this book useful for a concise, but comprehensive review, which we hope will enhance daily practice, teaching, and preparation for national and state licensure and specialty board examinations.

The germination of this book began while we were students at, and later teaching and practicing as faculty and staff in the Department of Psychiatry, University of Michigan Medical Center, Ann Arbor, Michigan. The quality of excellence and scholarship at Michigan, under the leadership of Raymond W. Waggoner, Sr., M.D., who was then Professor and Chairman, has inspired us throughout the years.

We wrote most of this book while on sabbatical, residing in the small, mountainous, and peaceful village of St. Jeannet, Cote d'Azure, France, where we were free from the telephone, television, and radio. This retreat helped us totally devote our hearts and minds to the task at hand. From the moment of inception to completion, this writing has been a joint venture—a labor of agony and ecstasy.

PREFACE ix

We are indebted to John J. Schwab, M.D., Professor and Chairman of the Department of Psychiatry and Behavioral Sciences, University of Louisville School of Medicine, who suggested the idea of writing this book, encouraged us to take a sabbatical, and also generously devoted time to reading a number of chapters and offering constructive suggestions.

We deeply appreciate the enthusiastic dedication and caring commitment of Carolyn Gero, Administrative Assistant, who efficiently coordinated and was actively involved in the preparation of the manuscript. Mrs. Gero's contributions were beyond all expectations. We also acknowledge the tireless efforts of Sara Sue Niemann, Nancy VanCleave, Marilynn Rufer, Jane Scott, and other members of the Child Psychiatric Services' support staff in making this book a reality.

A heartfelt thank you to Pamela Holden, Business Administrator, for her continuous, effective assistance with, and attention to a myriad of details related to our sabbatical. We especially appreciate her conscientious and careful response to communications and numerous mailings of the manuscript without delay or loss.

We are grateful to John F. Ice, M.D., Associate Professor of Psychiatry, who assumed the responsibilities of Acting Director of the Child Psychiatric Services during our sabbatical, and to Russell Whittinghill, A.C.S.W., Chief Psychiatric Social Worker, for his selfless dedication. Vernon Pearson, Research Assistant, helped in the tedious task of obtaining relevant reference material and verifying the references and bibliographies. The hard work and commitment of the faculty, professional staff, fellows, and residents of the Child Psychiatric Services greatly contributed to the completion of this book.

We acknowledge the contributions of Jesse W. Wright, M.D., Associate Professor of Psychiatry, who read chapter 7 and made several constructive suggestions.

We are grateful to the Board of Directors of the Bingham Child Guidance Clinic, to the Metro United Way, and to Norton Hospital and Kosair-Children's Hospital for the continuous support which has helped make research and scholarship possible within an active child psychiatric setting.

Mohammad and Sharon Shafii

St. Jeannet, France
Spring 1981
Louisville, Kentucky
Summer 1981

And a woman who held a babe against
her bosom said, Speak to us of Children.
    And he said:
    Your children are not your children.
    They are the sons and daughters of Life's
longing for itself.
    They come through you but not from
you,
    And though they are with you yet they
belong not to you.

    You may give them your love but not
your thoughts,
    For they have their own thoughts.
    You may house their bodies but not
their souls,
    For their souls dwell in the house of to-
morrow, which you cannot visit, not even
in your dreams.
    You may strive to be like them, but seek
not to make them like you.
    For life goes not backward nor tarries
with yesterday.

    You are the bows from which your chil-
dren as living arrows are sent forth
    The archer sees the mark upon the path
of the infinite, and He bends you with His
might that His arrows may go swift and far.
    Let your bending in the archer's hand
be for gladness;
    For even as He loves the arrow that flies,
so He loves also the bow that is stable.

—Kahlil Gibran*

* Reprinted from THE PROPHET, by Kahlil Gibran,
by permission of Alfred A. Knopf, Inc. Copyright
1923 by Kahlil Gibran and renewed 1951 by
Administrators C.T.A. of Kahlil Gibran estate and
Mary G. Gibran.

Part I

Human Development

Chapter 1

HUMAN BONDING: Pregnancy and the First Hours of Life*

Among the enormous changes adopted by our technologically oriented medical care system during the past 50 to 100 years, the elimination of immediate contact between mother and infant following delivery is of major psychological impact. This separation completely disregards biological timing and programming and may have harmful effects on infant development and bonding within the family.

BONDING: DEFINITION

Konrad Lorenz (1966) defined bonding as "...behavior patterns of an objectively demonstrable mutual attachment [which] constitute the personal tie." (p. 159) Bonding, or attachment, is not unique to human relationships. Some species of fish, birds, and mammals also develop and sustain strong bonds with each other. Bonding effectively ensures the care of infants and the perpetuation of species. According to Lorenz, bonding also provides inhibition against destructive aggression within a species.

PSYCHOBIOLOGY OF MOTHERING

What are the psychobiological and psychophysiological roots of human relationships? What contributes to the parents' deep love and commitment to their newborn infant? What is the infant's contribution to this reciprocal relationship?

Recently, a number of exciting studies have been conducted to explore the development of human bonding. The study of normal and pathological development during pregnancy and in-

---

* An earlier version was published in *Current Concepts in Psychiatry*, 5(2):2–8, April 1979, under the title "Human Bonding and Child Development."

fancy is becoming a fertile meeting ground for the disciplines of biochemistry, psychophysiology, pediatrics, child psychiatry, developmental psychology, behavioral sciences, and psychoanalysis. From the synthesis of these diverse research endeavors, a new scientific perspective is evolving, which transcends the duality of body and mind—a dichotomy that has plagued Western sciences for centuries. For the first time, hard data exist to verify the influence of love and human relationships on the physical, biochemical, and physiological development of not only the infant's body and mind, but also that of the parents. What was known throughout the ages in the heart, now is being substantiated in the laboratory setting.

Attachment

Inspired by Darwin's *On the Origin of Species by Natural Selection* (1859), Freud's (1920) concepts of instinct, Spitz and Wolf's (1946) work on the genesis of emotional disorders in infancy, and observations of ethologists, such as Harlow (1960), Bowlby (1958) suggested that *attachment behavior* is a major biological instinct. Infant behavior patterns, such as sucking, crying, clinging, following with the eyes, and smiling, stimulate the expression of parenting instincts, especially in the mother. The expression of mothering behavior is essential for the care and development of the infant.

How does mothering behavior develop? In her classic article, "The Psychosomatic Implications of the Primary Unit: Mother-Child," Theresa Benedek (1949) discussed the psychology of motherhood and related the proclivity toward motherhood to the menstrual cycle, particularly to "the post-ovulative progestin phase," during which a follicle of the ovary ruptures and luteinization occurs. (p. 643) The function of progesterone is to prepare the mucous membrane of the uterus for the nesting of the impregnated ovum.

According to Benedek (1949), during this time, "...the psychic apparatus seems to register the somatic preparation for pregnancy by a change of emotional attitude; the woman's attention shifts from extraverted activities to her body and its welfare." (p. 643) Around this time, the desire for pregnancy, preoccupation with care of a child, or regression to be taken care of as a child become prevalent in women's thoughts, behaviors, and fantasies.

"The interaction between mother and child—*the symbiosis*—begins after conception."(ibid., p. 643) Although some women may experience morning sickness or other physical discomforts, pregnancy frequently enhances feelings of well-being, joy, energy, and security.

The bonding and attachment between mother and child and between father and child have roots in the parents' early childhood experiences, which are frequently unavailable to consciousness. The experience of courting, dating, and marriage and the fantasies about being a mother or father are the conscious precursors of human bonding. Pregnancy brings into focus the actualization of these fantasies and dreams.

The psychology of pregnancy and the nesting behavior of mother and father in preparation for their baby have not been explored in depth. In a brief discussion, Rubin (1977)—who has written extensively from a nursing perspective on the psychology of pregnancy and maternal behavior—likens the bonding process to "...the weaving of a tapestry. Not a cord, nor a bond, nor a welding job, rather a large creative work, framed between the child and the mother's own significant social world..." (p. 67) which gradually and continuously unfolds against all odds, and all internal and external stress, to further the identity of the mother and the development of the child.

The relationship between the fetus and the mother is reciprocal and interdependent. The experience of knowing and sensing a heart beating within the mother's own body is one of the first physical and concrete manifestations of the presence of another being. The mother carries on a constant silent dialogue with her baby. Quickening, usually occurring between the fourth and fifth months of pregnancy, is a moment of unforgettable excitement for both mother and father. The mother now relates more to the unborn child—at times talking to him or her.

The fetus responds to external auditory stimuli, such as quieting music, independently from the mother's reaction. Sudden loud noises have increased the heartbeat of the fetus indepen-

dently from the change in the mother's heartbeat. Excitement, tension, and the mother's physical discomfort and food intake evoked independent responses from the intrauterine fetus. These fetal reactions, which have been experienced by the mother enteroceptively or on the visceral level, are significant building blocks of the human bond.

Biological Rhythms

We are becoming increasingly aware of the role of hidden rhythmic fluctuations that underlie our daily psychobiological functions. Behavioral aspects of physiological processes have been correlated with a spectrum of periodicities along a continuum. These rhythmic fluctuations include the microrhythms of heartbeats, respiration, and electrical brain activity, the 90-minute rapid-eye-movement cycle of dreaming, deep and quiet sleep within the circadian cycle (the 24-hour sleep and wakefulness cycle), and the ultradian (less than 24 hours) and infradian (seasonal) cycles. The study of biological rhythms is a new field of science called chronobiology.

According to Luce (1971), "...perhaps rhythm is actually one of the earliest and most inherent pleasures." (p. 37) Some authorities postulate that the sound of the heartbeat, the gurgle of the stomach and the intestine, the pulsation of the vessels, the noise of inspiration and expiration, and the talking of the mother create a noisy but rhythmic environment for the fetus. The fetus senses and responds to maternal stimulation and contributes to the mother's well-being, ambivalence, hope, and despair. In this partnership, the unborn infant is not as helpless and passive as was previously thought.

DISORDERS OF ATTACHMENT AND MOTHERING

After reports on the battered-child syndrome were published by Kempe *et al.* (1962) and Fontana *et al.* (1963), a number of studies, conducted during the 1960's and 1970's, revealed that premature infants were battered more often than full-term infants when they were returned home following a few weeks or months of hospitalization. Elmer and Gregg (1967) reported that 30% of the 20 severely battered children in their study were prematurely born. In the large series of premature infants seen by Skinner and Castle (1969) and Klein and Stern (1971), 13 to 23% were severely abused after painstaking, long-term hospital care. Most mothers in these samples who battered their children wanted to have their babies and were concerned about them. Why, then, did these mothers batter their children? Did the immediate separation of the children from their mothers after birth and the long-term hospitalization in high-risk nurseries contribute to these abuses?

Klaus and Kennell (1976) responded to these questions in their important work *Maternal-Infant Bonding: The Impact of Early Separation or Loss on Family Development.* This book should be required reading for all clinicians and those caring for infants and children. Klaus and Kennell stated that in 70% of the hospitals in the United States mothers are not permitted to enter nurseries after the birth of their babies. Among the 30% of the hospitals that allow mothers into the nursery, only 40% permitted them to touch their babies, and "...it is apparent that most normal births in the United States are associated with several days of deprivation for the mother. A woman who delivers a premature infant suffers complete separation from her infant for at least the first day...even after the first day she only sees her infant through a glass window." (pp. 7–8) After this initial deprivation, many of the mothers were not allowed to feed their infants.

ATTACHMENT BEHAVIOR IN ANIMALS

In some animal species, if a newborn is taken from its mother even for a short time, it is entirely rejected by the mother. Klopfer (1971) discovered that, if a kid is removed from a mother goat immediately after birth for even an hour, the mother will not only reject the kid, but will also butt it. When a mother goat was allowed to have contact for as short a time as 5 minutes immediately after birth, she accepted the kid even after 3 hours of separation, although there was some difficulty in nursing and mothering behavior that lasted 2 or 3 months. Half of the kids did not nurse at all, and the other half nursed with any mother goat in the community. In a control group with no postpartum separation, all the kids were nursing with their mothers, and none nursed indiscriminately.

Is there a sensitive or critical period immediately after birth when the bond between mother and child is established? Will separation at this early and crucial time disrupt the bonding process?

To probe this question, another interesting study, conducted by Rosenblatt and Lehrman (1963), focused on the maternal behavior of laboratory rats. After being exposed to pups, male and female rats displayed characteristics similar to those of human beings. The rats developed maternal behavior toward their pups. When the separation of the pups from the mother occurred immediately after birth and lasted 4 days, the impact on the mother was devastating and debilitating. After the pups were reintroduced to their mothers, the mothers were not able to look after them and completely ignored them; all the pups died within the next 5 days. (Klaus and Kennell, 1976, p. 23) After all separations, the deprived mothers' nesting and maternal care behavior declined sharply and disappeared after a short period.

Shaikh (1971) discovered that blood serum concentration of estradiol increased significantly before parturition in rats. It is postulated that some hormonal substances, including estradiol, are responsible for the development of maternal behavior before delivery and immediately after delivery. But the presence of pups immediately after birth is essential for sustaining and further developing maternal behavior. Separation of the pups from the mother immediately after birth permanently extinguishes maternal behavior.

In studying the behavior of primates, Sackett and Ruppenthal (1974) observed that mothers separated from their babies for one hour after birth maintained a visual interest in their babies while they were separated by a see-through cage. If the separation lasted longer than 24 hours, the deprived mothers lost interest.

SENSITIVE PERIOD

In an attempt to investigate the sensitive period in the development of human bonding and attachment behavior between mother and child, Klaus *et al.* (1972) studied 28 primiparous mothers. They placed their sample into two groups.

The 14 mothers in the control group had the traditional contact with their infants: a glimpse of the baby shortly after birth, brief contact and identification at six to 12 hours, and then visits for 20 to 30 minutes every four hours for bottle feedings. In addition to this routine contact, the 14 mothers in the extended-contact group were given their nude babies, with a heat panel overhead, for one hour within the first three hours after birth, and also five extra hours of contact each afternoon of the three days after delivery.

pp. 460–461.

Other variables were similar in both groups.

Within 28 to 32 days postpartum, a standardized interview, a carefully structured monitoring of the mother's interaction with her baby during a physical examination of the infant, and a film taken of the mother feeding her baby were systematically evaluated. Analysis of all of these data showed that the extended-contact mothers engaged in more eye-to-eye contact, fondling, and soothing behavior. They were more reluctant to leave the baby with someone else during physical examination, in contrast to the control group mothers. In the same groups, one and 2 years later, Kennell *et al.* (1974) found that extended-contact mothers had more extensive verbal exchanges and richer communicative interaction with their children than the control group mothers.

In a recent study, Hales *et al.* (1977) tried to define "the limits" of the maternal sensitive period. They studied 60 primiparous mothers in Guatemala. The mothers were placed into three groups.

In the early-contact group, immediately after birth, the nude infants were placed skin to skin with their mothers under a heat panel for 45 minutes.

In the delayed-contact group, 12 hours after delivery, the nude infant was placed skin to skin with the mother under a heat panel for 45 minutes.

In the control group, following the practice of the hospital, the mother was allowed to glance at her baby after birth; 12 hours later, a nurse brought the wrapped infant to the mother's bed.

All of the infants remained with their mothers during the day and were breast-fed during the 2-day hospital stay. An independent observer, who did not know anything about the groups, observed the mothers 36 hours after delivery through a window while they were breast-feeding and caring for their infants. Observations were made in the first 15 seconds of every minute for 15 minutes.

Hales and co-workers (1977) concluded that statistically significant differences existed in affectionate behavior, body closeness, and caretaking behavior between the early-contact group and the other two groups. The mothers "...who received 45 minutes of private skin-to-skin contact with their infants immediately after birth showed significantly more affectionate behavior than those who had no...skin-to-skin contact."(p. 457) These mothers gave something extra to their babies. "They cuddled them more, looked at them face-to-face more, and held them a little closer." (p. 457)

De Chateau and Wiberg (1977) conducted a similar study in Sweden. In one group, the mother and infant had skin-to-skin contact immediately after delivery for 15 to 20 minutes, and the baby suckled the mother's breast while she was still on the delivery table. In the control group, the babies were separated from the mothers for about 30 minutes after birth, while the baby was weighed, examined, and dressed. Then, in both groups, the babies were taken to their mothers and stayed with them in their rooms.

The observations of both groups 36 hours after delivery showed that the extra-contact mothers held their infants significantly more often than the mothers in the other groups, and their infants cried significantly less frequently. Three months later, "In the extra contact group, mothers spent more time looking en face and kissing, and their infants laughed or smiled more frequently." (p. 149)

It is interesting to note that, at the 3-month follow-up, 58% of the extra-contact mothers and only 26% of control mothers were still breast-feeding their babies.

Peterson and Mehl (1978) have found that maternal attachment was directly related to the following variables in order of significance.

1. The shorter the separation of the mother from the infant, the greater the attachment.
2. The greater the degree of satisfaction and involvement of the mother and father in the birth experience, the greater the attachment.
3. The longer the labor, the greater the attachment.
4. The more positive the prenatal attitudes and expectations, the greater the attachment.

THE FIRST HOURS OF LIFE

Eye-to-Eye Contact

Until recently, knowledge about the first 2 weeks of life, and especially the first few hours of life, was limited. There was, for example, question about the newborn's ability to see, hear, and respond to environmental stimuli. It was thought that most newborns slept during the first 20 hours of life. This may be true in cases where the mothers received large doses of sedatives or analgesics during labor; however, Desmond *et al.* (1966), Brazelton *et al.* (1966), and Emde *et al.* (1975) demonstrated that infants are quite awake and alert during birth and the first hour afterward. The infants showed exploratory behavior, could follow objects with their eyes and heads, and could fix their eyes on a face. Robson's (1967) studies at the National Institute of Mental Health show that the infant's eye contact with a face is a genetically programmed behavior, present at the time of birth. Eye-to-eye contact is a powerful innate releaser of maternal and attachment behavior in the mother. The child communicates effectively with the mother and the care-givers through eye contact. The eye contact of a child can resonate the deepest cord within the mother's heart and mind and can prepare her for the love and care of her baby.

The precursors of all human bonds in later life—including the love relationship, which frequently begins with a look or a glance—may have their roots in these early moments of life. When the infant's and mother's eyes meet, human bonding and existential communion between the body, mind, and soul of the two begin.

Vision is the most effective and efficient means of data reception, processing, and communication. The significance of eye contact in health and illness, particularly in mental health and psychopathology, has not been wholly understood and explored.

Could it be that this early eye contact reactivates microbiological and microphysiological processes of the lateral geniculate body of the midbrain and the occipital area of the cortex? The occipital area of the cortex, with its extensive connection with the angular gyrus and the visual area of the frontal cortex, contributes to the synthetic and integrative function of the ego and the enhancement of object relationships. Perhaps one day we will decipher the mystery of the biochemistry and the psychophysiology of loving and empathy within the context of the mother-infant bond.

Touch and Skin Contact

Embryological studies have documented a direct relationship between the skin and the central nervous system. The licking behavior of newborn animals, grooming behavior of primates, and touching behavior of humans are all of the same origin. Klaus and Kennell (1976) observed that when nude infants were placed with their mothers a few minutes or hours after birth, the mothers

> ... began with fingertip touching of the infant's extremities and proceeded in 4 to 8 minutes to massaging, stroking, and encompassing palm contact of the trunk. In the first 3 minutes mothers maintained fingertip contact 52% of the time and palm contact 28% of the time.
>
> pp. 68–69.

Three to 6 minutes later, fingertip contact had decreased to 26%, and palm contact increased to 62%. Skin, kinesthetic, and embracing contact between mother and child reactivates intrauterine experiences for the child and gives concrete proprioceptive experience to the mother regarding the actuality of her baby.

Talking

Adults, especially mothers, automatically talk in a high-pitched voice to babies. A number of studies show that babies are extremely receptive to high-pitched sounds immediately after birth.

In an excellent study, Condon and Sander (1974) reported that "...as early as the first day of life, the human neonate moves in precise and sustained segments of movement that are synchronous with the articulated structure of adult speech." (p. 99) These infants did not respond to random noises or disconnected vowel and tapping sounds. This finding is extremely significant, because it gives evidence that infants, even within the first few hours of their lives, are selective in their body communication and are receptive to verbal communication.

Breast-Feeding

Body odor, heat, kinesthetic movement, in the form of rocking and holding, and, of course, breast-feeding—which encompasses all of these sensory-motor contacts between mother and child—contribute significantly to the strengthening of human bonds.

In bonding, infants contribute to the mother's psychophysiological development and well-being. For example, Lind et al. (1972) showed through thermal photography of the breast that, after hearing the hunger cries of their newborns, mothers had a significant increase in the amount of blood flow to their breasts. Lind et al. postulated that the cry of the baby prepares mothers physiologically to nurse. (Klaus and Kennell, 1976, p. 78)

Infants, when they begin to lick and later on to suck the breast, stimulate the release of oxytocin in the mother. The release of oxytocin helps in contraction of the uterus and decreases uterine bleeding, another proof of the psychophysiological bond between mother and infant.

Hwang et al. (1971) demonstrated that concentration of serum prolactin in the mother increases significantly during pregnancy and decreases rapidly afterward. Anytime the nipple is touched by the infant's lips or fingers, serum prolactin in the mother increases 400 to 600%. It decreases after breast-feeding begins. Preliminary studies of Klaus and Kennell (1976) show that even physical contact of mothers with their infants, without nursing or touching of the mothers' breasts, significantly increases the level of prolactin in her blood. (pp. 78–79) It is known that prolactin induces secretion of the milk in the alveoli of the breast. Prolactin also is a "love hormone" in birds, activating close attachment between the mother bird and her young.

BIOCHEMISTRY OF EARLY MATERNAL DEPRIVATION

A recent study by Kuhn *et al.* (1978) opens up an exciting vista in the area of biochemistry of maternal deprivation. In a careful study of the effects of maternal deprivation on rat pups, they showed that 9- to 11-day-old pups that "...were deprived for 1, 2, or 6 hours [of their mothers] and then killed..." had significantly lower serum growth hormone (GH) and activity of ornithine decarboxylase (ODC) in the brain than the control pups. The pups that "...were deprived for 2 hours and put back with the mother for 15 minutes, 1, 2, or 4 hours before being killed..." also showed these lower levels throughout the deprivation period, but GH and ODC "...rapidly increased to normal levels when the pups were returned to the mother." (p. 1035) These hormonal changes were independent of food intake, and there were no changes in the concentration of prolactin, thyrotropin, or corticosterone in the serum. The investigators concluded

...that maternal deprivation elicits a neuroendocrine response involving a decline in serum GH levels and that this decrease in GH is responsible for the decrease in brain ODC activity.

p. 1036.

ODC activity is "...a sensitive index of organ growth and differentiation." (p. 1034)

CONCLUSION

A major breakthrough in the field of psychiatry and behavioral sciences could come from the study of human development. At the time of birth, the brain of a human infant weighs approximately 350 grams, and the brain of a chimpanzee, 170 grams. At the time of adulthood, the human brain has increased 400%, and weighs approximately 1,450 grams, but the chimpanzee brain only doubles to a weight of 370 grams.

Conel's histological studies of the cerebral cortex in infants and young children have demonstrated the enormous growth in the number and branching of dendrites and the multiplication of synaptic junctions, all occurring while the organism is subject to shaping by the environment.

Freedman *et al.*, 1975, p. 2041.

In the perspective of child psychiatry, the maximal development of intelligence, emotion,

and adaptability to internal and environmental stress is directly related to the type of care human beings receive from the moment of conception through adolescent years. Prenatal care and early infant care for the first 3 years are most essential for primary prevention and for the treatment of potentially high-risk children.

The care and stimulation provided to the infant by the mothering person is not a theoretical or abstract issue. A warm hug, a touch, a loving look, and a genuine smile make immediate imprints on the infant's mind and brain. They activate new pathways in the brain cells. They stimulate the development of new dendrites and new connections for reception of information, data processing, integration of the information, and data retrieval.

If we might use the simplistic analogy of computer sciences, a bit of human contact is a bit of software that helps in programming and enriching the magnificent computer of the brain, with its more than 14 billion nerve cells ready and eager to receive, develop, and store billions and billions of bits of sensory-motor and affective information. When a child is deprived of such informational input, he will not be able to use his integrative, cognitive, and affective abilities to cope effectively with environmental demands and stresses.

From these data, it is evident that the first hour of life is one of the most crucial and sensitive times between a mother and child for the development of maternal behavior and the strengthening of bonds between the child and the family. Bonding is essential for the growth, development, and unfolding of the human being.

REFERENCES

Benedek, T. (1949). The psychosomatic implications of the primary unit: Mother-child. *Am. J. Orthopsychiatry, 19,* 642–654.

Bowlby, J. (1958). The nature of the child's tie to his mother. *Int. J. Psychoanal., 39,* 350–373, (Sept–Oct).

Brazelton, T.B., Scholl, M.L., Robey, J.S. (1966). Visual responses in the newborn. *Pediatrics, 37,* 284–290.

Condon, W.S., Sander, L.W. (1974). Neonate movement is synchronized with adult speech: Interactional participation and language acquisition. *Science, 183,* 99–101.

Darwin, C. (1859). *On the Origin of Species by Natural Selection.* London: J. Murray.

De Chateau, P., Wiberg, B. (1977). Long-term effect on mother-infant behaviour of extra contact during the first hour post partum. I. First observation at 36 hours and II. A follow-up at three months. *Acta Paediatr. Scand., 66,* 137–151.

Desmond, M.M., Rudolph, A.J., Phitaksphraiwan, P. (1966). The transitional care nursery: A mechanism for preventive medicine in the newborn. *Pediatr. Clin. North. Am., 13,* 651–668.

Elmer, E., Gregg, G.S. (1967). Developmental characteristics of abused children. *Pediatrics, 40,* 596–602.

Emde, R.N., Swedberg, J., Suzuki, B. (1975). Human wakefulness and biological rhythms after birth. *Arch. Gen. Psychiatry, 32,* 780–783.

Fontana, V.J., Donovan, D., Wong, R.J. (1963). The "maltreatment syndrome" in children. *N. Engl. J. Med., 269,* 1389–1394.

Freedman, A.M., Kaplan, H.I., Sadock, B.J. (Eds.) (1975). *Comprehensive Textbook of Psychiatry,* II. Baltimore: Williams and Wilkins, p. 2041.

Freud, S. (1920). Beyond the pleasure principle. *Standard Edition of the Complete Psychological Works of Sigmund Freud,* Vol. 18. London: Hogarth Press, 1968, pp. 3-64.

Hales, D.H., Lozoff, B., Sosa, R., *et al.* (1977). Defining the limits of the maternal sensitive period. *Dev. Med. Child Neurol., 19,* 454–461.

Harlow, H. (1960). Primary affectional patterns in primates. *Am. J. Orthopsychiatry, 30,* 676–684.

Hwang, P., Guyda, H., Friesen, H. (1971). A radioimmunoassay for human prolactin. *Proc. Natl. Acad. Sci. USA, 68,* 1902–1906.

Kempe, C.H., Silverman, F.N., Steele, B.F., *et al.* (1962). The battered child syndrome. *J.A.M.A., 181,* 17–24.

Kennell, J.H., Jerauld, R., Wolfe, H., *et al.* (1974). Maternal behavior one year after early and extended post-partum contact. *Dev. Med. Child Neurol., 16,* 172–179.

Klaus, M., Kennell, J. (1976). *Maternal-Infant Bonding: The Impact of Early Separation or Loss on Family Development.* St. Louis: C.V. Mosby Co.

Klaus, M.H., Jerauld, R., Kerger, N.C., *et al.* (1972). Maternal attachment. Importance of the first post-partum days. *N. Engl. J. Med., 286,* 460–463.

Klein, M., Stern, L. (1971). Low birth weight and the battered child syndrome. *Am. J. Dis. Child, 122,* 15–18.

Klopfer, P.H. (1971). Mother love: What turns it on? *Am. Sci., 59,* 404–407.

Kuhn, C.M., Butler, S.R., Schanberg, S.M. (1978). Selective depression of serum growth hormone during maternal deprivation in rat pups. *Science, 201,* 1034–1036.

Lind, J., Vuorenkoski, V., Wasz-Hockert, O. (1972). The effect of cry stimulus on the temperature of the lactating breast of primipara: A thermographic study. In Morris, N. (Ed.), *Psychosomatic Medicine in Obstetrics and Gynecology.* Basel: S. Karger, pp. 293–295.

Lorenz, K. (1966). *On Aggression.* New York: Harcourt, Brace, and World, p. 159.

Luce, G. (1971). The development of rhythms: Youth and age. In *Biological Rhythms in Human and Animal Physiology.* New York: Dover, pp. 35–42.

Peterson, G.H., Mehl, L.E. (1978). Some determinants of maternal attachment. *Am. J. Psychiatry, 135,* 1168–1173.

Robson, K.S. (1967). The role of eye-to-eye contact in maternal-infant attachment. *J. Child Psychol. Psychiatry, 8,* 13–25.

Rosenblatt, J., Lehrman, D. (1963). Maternal behavior in the laboratory rat. In Rheingold, H.L. (Ed.), *Maternal Behavior in Mammals.* New York: John Wiley, pp. 8–57.

Rubin, R. (1977). Binding-in in the post-partum period. *Matern. Child Nurs. J., 6,* 67–75.

Sackett, G.P., Ruppenthal, G.C. (1974), Some factors influencing the attraction of adult female macaque monkeys to neonates. In Lewis, M., Rosenblum, L.A. (Eds.), *The Effect of the Infant on Its Caregiver.* New York: John Wiley, pp. 163–185.

Shaikh, A.A. (1971). Estrone and estradiol levels in the ovarian venous-blood from rats during the estrous-cycle and pregnancy. *Biol. Reprod., 5,* 297–307.

Skinner, A., Castle, R. (1969). *Seventy-eight Battered Children: A Retrospective Study.* London: National Society for the Prevention of Cruelty to Children (Battered Child Research Department).

Spitz, R.A., Wolf, K.M. (1946). Anaclitic depression: An inquiry into the genesis of psychiatric conditions in early childhood, II. *Psychoanal. Study Child, 2,* 313–342.

Chapter 2

THE WORLD OF ACTION, PERCEPTION AND TRUST: First Year of Life

The first year of life is, without a doubt, the most important period of human development. The infant is at work constantly in the miracle of growth. The physical, physiological, and psychological growth achieved at this time is unparalleled.

ALL MOUTH, EARS, AND EYES: The First Two Months

In pediatric practice, the first 28 days of life are referred to as the "neonatal" or "newborn" period. However, from a developmental perspective, the first 2 months of life are qualitatively different from those that follow. Therefore, in this book, the terms "neonate" and "newborn" will refer to infants in the first 2 months of life.

Until recently, clinicians perceived the neonate as being a passive, sleeping entity, awakening only for hunger or discomfort. Careful research by Brazelton (1961, 1962, 1973), Brazelton *et al.* (1974), Wolff (1959, 1963, 1969), Emde and Koenig (1969), Emde and Harmon (1972), Emde and Robinson (1979), Anders and Hoffman (1973), Anders (1974), Call (1964), Ainsworth (1967), Ainsworth and Bell (1969), Ainsworth *et al.* (1974), and others have dispelled this assumption. We now know that the neonate is an active, complex organism, constantly changing and evolving.

Behavioral States

An average, healthy newborn, with approximately 40 weeks gestation, manifests the following five behavioral states: active sleep, quiet sleep, alert-active state, quiet wakefulness, and crying. (Wolff, 1959, 1966, 1969; Prechtl, 1965, 1974; Brazelton, 1961, 1962, 1969, 1973; Brazelton *et al.* 1974, 1975)

Sleep States

Newborns spend about 70% of their time sleeping. Earlier, it was thought that sleep was a passive state. However, electroencephalogram studies of infants by Kleitman and Engelmann (1953), Aserinsky and Kleitman (1955), Dement and Kleitman (1957), and Metcalf (1969, 1972, 1977) led to the discovery and differentiation of rapid eye movement (REM) sleep (active sleep) from non-REM sleep (quiet sleep). These sleep states were first observed in infants, and later in adults.

ACTIVE SLEEP. REM, frowning, smiling, body movement, mastication, swallowing, erection, and increase in heartbeat, pulse, and respirations occur during active sleep. EEG studies show fast waves of low amplitude. Dreaming is associated with this stage. In older children and adults, this stage is referred to as Stage I-REM sleep. The neonate's sleep is 50% active (REM) sleep.

Does the fetus experience REM sleep? It is generally agreed that the EEG of a premature neonate resembles the EEG of a fetus of the same gestation age. EEG studies of premature neonates, along with rare EEG recordings of fetuses of the same age, have convincingly shown the existence of REM sleep in the eighth month of gestation.

Why do the fetus and the neonate require REM sleep? REM sleep is a basic and primitive form of sleep, originating from the midbrain area. From a neurophysiological point of view, REM sleep provides an endogenous source of stimulation for the central nervous system. This stimulation contributes significantly to the growth of the central nervous system, particularly the forebrain and cortex. As the infant grows, the developing forebrain exerts an inhibitory function over the midbrain area, and decreases the *amount* of REM sleep, although throughout life the quality of REM sleep stays the same.

QUIET SLEEP. EEG recordings of the remaining sleep, or non-REM sleep (quiet sleep), in neonates shows dysrhythmic, poorly organized, and poorly formed slow waves with brief intervals of wakefulness. Deep sleep, or, what in older children and adults is referred to as Stages III and IV sleep, does not exist during the first month of life.

Quiet sleep, or non-REM sleep, gradually increases as the newborn develops. In non-REM sleep, there is no rapid eye movement or body movement. Heartbeat, pulse, and respiration rates are slower than in REM sleep. After the second month of life, significant qualitative changes occur in the EEG patterns during quiet sleep. At the same time, the amount of quiet sleep increases gradually. These changes represent the growth and development of the cortex and forebrain.

In the EEG of a full-term infant during the first month following birth, *tracé alternant* is present. *Tracé alternant* is an intermittent, sharp, slow burst of activity rarely present after the age of 6 weeks. *Tracé alternant* is the pathognomic feature of the EEG in a premature infant. *Tracé alternant* reflects unmodulated and unorganized electrical activities of the cortex.

By the age of 4 weeks, sleep spindles (12 to 16 cycles per second, of low amplitude and fast frequency) appear in the neonate's EEG—a major developmental milestone. The decrease of *tracé alternant* and the appearance of sleep spindles represent the evidence of Stage II quiet sleep and reflect further organization and development of the dendritic and axial connections in the infant's brain.

Sleep-Wakefulness Cycle

The sleep-wakefulness cycle is endogenous in the newborn. Its duration of approximately 3½ hours is related to the hunger-satiation cycle. During one sleep-wakefulness cycle, the infant goes through several active and quiet sleep cycles. The duration of the newborn active-quiet sleep cycle is 45 to 50 minutes. As the infant grows, this cycle lengthens. By age one year, it is about 60 minutes, and from age 3 years and onward, it is about 90 minutes.

Between ages 6 and 8 weeks, because of the growth of the forebrain and the qualitative changes in quiet sleep, the neonate begins to adapt to the circadian (day and night) rhythm. At this time, parents are usually delighted to find that their newborn "sleeps through the night."

Wakeful States

Wakeful states are divided into active wakefulness and quiet wakefulness.

ACTIVE WAKEFULNESS OR ALERT-ACTIVE STATE. The newborn is alert, active, bright-eyed, attentive, and at his best in receiving and responding to environmental stimulation. Most learning occurs in this state.

QUIET WAKEFULNESS OR INACTIVE WAKEFULNESS. The newborn is quiet, relaxed, peaceful, and content. Usually, this state leads to drowsiness or sleep. But, at times, through mother's stimulation, it may lead to active wakefulness.

Crying

Crying, an innate response, usually is the first behavior manifested by mammals, including the human neonate. Crying stimulates the mother to care for her newborn.

Crying in newborns and infants was studied by Lynip (1951), Wolff (1969), and Wasz-Hockert *et al.* (1968). They differentiated a hunger cry, or "basic cry," from a "pain cry." Emde and Robinson (1979) noted that a

...hunger cry is 250–400 cycles per second; a typical sequence begins with a cry followed by a brief silence, and expiratory whistle, another brief rest, and then a cry again. The pain cry is characterized by the sudden onset of a loud, long cry with extended breath holding and expiration afterward.

p. 90.

A "mad cry," "pleasure cry," "impatient cry," and an "angry cry" have also been described. Studies show that, with the exception of the "pain cry," it is very difficult for mothers to distinguish clearly between the various cries on the basis of sound alone.

Human contact decreases newborn crying. Studies by Freedman (1974) demonstrated that almost all newborns were calmed when held or carried.

In the human, we have demonstrated that within hours after birth most crying infants will quiet when held and carried, and of the 252 crying newborns in our study only three could not be quieted in this way.

p. 29.

The calming of newborns after crying significantly decreased the anxieties and tension of the mothering person.

FUSSINESS. Infants in the first 2 months of life have still another form of crying, which is referred to as "fussiness." This crying is not related to the "hunger" and "pain" cries; it creates feelings of restlessness and helplessness in the mother. Infants with severe "fussiness" are referred to as "colicky babies."

Studies by Tennes *et al.* (1972) and Emde *et al.* (1976) revealed that approximately 25% of all infants develop extreme fussiness in the first 2 months of life.

Fussiness is now thought to be independent of mothering ability. It usually begins at age 3 weeks and declines by 3 months, with the development of the social smile. Emde *et al.* (1976) observed that between ages 1 and 3 months, the infant has a tendency toward prolonged "non-hunger fussiness." Emde *et al.* postulated that this fussiness may be adaptational and enhance attachment behavior between the mother and child independent of feeding and other care-giving activities. With the emergence of smiling by 3 months, episodes of fussiness and crying decrease significantly. Smiling, a new modality of communication, seems to replace fussiness.

Reflexes

A reflex is an automatic and involuntary response to a stimulus. The stimulus initiates electric impulses in the afferent nerve fibers, which are then transmitted to the nerve center (central arc), and, via the efferent fibers, stimulate the effectors, such as muscles and glands. Reflexes are the building blocks for human adaptation and survival.

The newborn comes into the world with a repertoire of developed reflexive responses. In examining and assessing the newborn, the clinician needs to be aware of the following behavioral states: active sleep, quiet sleep, alert-active state, quiet wakefulness, and crying. These states significantly influence the neonate's reflexive and behavioral responses.

Reflexes are divided into proprioceptive reflexes (deep reflexes) and extroceptive skin reflexes (superficial reflexes), postural reflexes, and auditory, visual, and vestibular responses.

Proprioceptive Reflexes

Proprioceptive or deep reflexes result from the stimulation of deep structures beneath the skin, such as tendons and bones. In newborns, the following proprioceptive reflexes are present and somewhat exaggerated in the states of quiet sleep and quiet wakefulness (Prechtl, 1974).

JAW JERK. Stroking or tapping the lower jaw results in clonic movement of the jaw. The central arc of this reflex is the pons in the midbrain area.

BICEPS JERK. Tapping the tendon on the biceps contracts the biceps muscle and flexes the forearm. The central arc is cervical 5-6.

KNEE JERK. Tapping the patellar tendon contracts the quadriceps muscle of the thigh and extends the leg. The central arc is lumbar 3-4.

ANKLE CLONUS. Sudden dorsiflexion of the ankle produces a rapid and rhythmic movement of extension-flexion of the ankle. Ankle clonus exists in quiet sleep in infants, but disappears in quiet wakefulness. It reflects lack of inhibitory control of the upper motor neurons (pyramidal tract) on the lower motor neurons. The central arc is sacral 1-2.

MORO REFLEX OR STARTLE REFLEX. Classified also as one of the postural reflexes it is elicited by a loud noise, or more accurately by supporting the head and shoulders of the infant with the hand at a 30° angle to the trunk, while the infant is in a supine position. The head is allowed to drop back 10 to 15°, and the following responses appear: extension of the trunk and extension and abduction of the limbs, followed by adduction and flexion. This reflex represents irritability of the nervous system and usually exists from birth to age 3 months. After further myelinization of the nervous system, and the infant's adaptation to external stimuli, the Moro reflex disappears.

TONIC NECK REFLEX. While the infant is in the supine position, the examiner turns the infant's head sharply to one side. The infant's arm and leg extend on the side the head is turned toward, and the arm and leg on the opposite side flex (fencing position). Tonic neck reflex is present at birth and diminishes by ages 4 to 6 months.

Extroceptive Skin Reflexes

TACTILE.
Sucking Reflex. Stroking the newborn's lips produces sucking.
Rooting Reflex. Gentle stimulation of the cheek or the lips results in the infant's turning the mouth and face toward the stimulus, which is followed by a snapping movement of the mouth. The rooting reflex is also called cardinal points response and is present during quiet wakefulness and sleep. The sucking and rooting reflexes together contribute to the development of sucking behavior in infants. These two reflexes are present from the time of birth up to age 4 months when the infant is awake and continue to exist during sleep until age 7 months.
Palmar Grasp Reflex. Stroking the palm of the hand toward the joints of the fingers results in a sudden grasp reflex from birth to age 6 months.
Plantar Reflex. Stroking the lateral margin of the foot from the heel forward results in flexion of the toes downwardly in children older than 1 to 2 years of age and in adults during wakefulness.

In infants under age 1 to 2 years, and in individuals suffering from an upper motor neuron lesion (pyramidal tract lesion), the great toe flexes dorsally (dorsiflexion), with fanning of the other toes. In some cases, the fanning may be absent. Dorsiflexion of the toes in this situation is called Babinski's sign. Babinski's sign may be present in older children and adults during sleep, but *not* during wakefulness.

CORTICOSPINAL TRACT REFLEXES (NOCICEPTIVE)

Plantar Reflex—Babinski's Sign. Already discussed

Finger Flexion Reflex (Hoffman's Method). The clinician "depresses the distal phalanx and allows it to flip up sharply." (DeMyer, 1974, p. 194) The action results in flexion of the thumb and fingers. This sign is present from birth to ages 1 to 2 years, and in cases of upper motor neuron damage.

Abdominal Reflex. Stroking the abdominal wall with a blunt object results in the contraction of the abdominal muscle on that side. Abdominal reflexes may not be easily elicited until after the infant is between ages 6 and 12 months. Absence or reduction of abdominal reflexes in older children and adults signifies acute pyramidal tract lesions.

Cremasteric Reflex. Stroking the medial aspects of the thigh results in retraction of the testes. This reflex is present in quiet and active sleep and in quiet wakefulness.

Postural Reflexes

SUPPORTING REFLEX. When the infant is held upright with feet touching a flat surface, extension of the legs occurs. This reflex disappears between ages 1 to 2 months.

STEPPING REFLEX. When the infant is held upright with the feet touching a flat surface, stepping movements occur between ages 2 and 6 months, and walking movements after 10 to 11 months.

LANDAU REFLEX. When the infant is placed in the prone position, the neck and spine hyperextend. Flexion of the head results in flexion of the extremities and spine. The reverse occurs when the infant is held in the supine position. The Landau reflex can be elicited between ages 10 and 28 months. The same response can be seen when the infant is learning to sit.

Auditory, Visual, and Vestibular Responses

Auditory-orienting and vestibulo-ocular responses are present in active sleep and quiet wakeful states. Visual pursuit is only present in wakeful states.

Motor Behavior

Soon after birth, the neonate is able to lift his head 90° and balance it when in a prone position. Movement of the hands and legs are asymmetrical and unsynchronized. Hands are usually held in a fisted or half-fisted position. The neonate brings his thumb to his mouth and sucks it, but does not have the ability to bring the hands together or to coordinate their movements.

Because of the lack of myelinization of the pyramidal tract and the relative absence of the inhibitory motor cortex (precentral gyrus of the frontal lobe), there is spasticity in body movement. Lack of motoric control is observable by the presence of the corticospinal reflexes, such as the plantar reflex (Babinski's sign).

Mouth: Perception

The fetus in utero has been observed thumb-sucking and swallowing amniotic fluid. In the newborn, when the external part of the mouth and cheek are stimulated, the head rotates toward the stimulus, and this is "followed by a snapping movement of the mouth." (Spitz, 1964, p. 62) This "rooting reflex" facilitates taking the nipple into the mouth and initiates sucking.

Spitz observed that the newborn has sensory ability, but not perceptive ability (interpretation of physical sensation based on past experience). He felt that the development of perception evolves gradually and is related to the quality of mothering and environmental factors. The only exceptions he noted were the mouth and oral cavity, which at the time of birth already have perceptive ability. Spitz hypothesized that "...all perception begins in the oral cavity, which serves as the primeval bridge from inner reception to external perception." (ibid, p. 62)

Recent microbehavioral analyses of the newborn have documented that the neonate's perceptual repertoire extends far beyond the mouth and oral cavity. However, it is still believed that the skin, mouth, and mucosa of the mouth and oral cavity play significant roles in the development of perception and the sensory-motor growth of the infant.

Ears: Hearing

The newborn comes into the world with a highly developed sense of hearing and is able to discriminate between the high-pitched sounds of human voices (500 to 900 Hertz) and random sounds. From a neurophysiological point of view, auditory-evoked responses of the brain's electrical activities (as recorded in EEG studies of newborns) demonstrate the auditory receptivity of infants. (Goodman *et al.,* 1964; Akiyama *et al.,* 1969)

Preference for Human Communication

The 12-hour-old newborn shows a distinct preference for and responsiveness to human communication. (Condon and Sander, 1974) Studies by Wolff (1963) and Eisenberg *et al.* (1964) demonstrated that a woman's high-pitched voice is the neonate's most preferred auditory stimulus; by age one month, the infant smiles when hearing the human voice.

Vocalization

The neonate begins gurgling, grunting, and cooing between ages 1 and 2 months. Even on the first day after birth, neonates have a special preference for the syntactic patterns of human speech over random sounds. (Condon and Sander, 1974) Such innate receptivity facilitates the neonate's reponse to the mother's verbal communication.

Developmentally, the act of speech evolves from the newborn's early cries. By the age of 2 or 3 weeks, the neonate is able to "verbally" communicate—through cries—internal states of pain, hunger, physical distress, and anger. The neonate's "fussiness cry" seems to be a request for social interaction.

Between the ages of 1 and 2 months, the neonate begins to respond verbally to mother's voice by cooing. The mother reinforces her newborn's vocalization by frequently imitating cooing and by repeating monosyllabic sounds and words.

Eyes: Vision

From the viewpoint of developmental neurology, the newborn's visual system is relatively advanced as compared to the visual systems of other mammals. (Haith, 1976) The human newborn's pupils respond to light, although more slowly than do the pupils of older infants. Visual fixation and visual tracking are fairly developed at the time of birth. The newborn can perceive brightness, intensity, angle, contour, and movement.

Studies conducted by Haith (1969, 1976), in which infrared light and videotaping were used,

convincingly demonstrated that newborns are visually active, even in darkness, manifesting eye movement, visual scanning, looking, and searching. The researchers postulated that the newborn actively seeks visual stimulation to maximize the "firing rate of neurons in the visual cortex" (Emde and Robinson, 1979, p. 86)

Fantz' (1961) classical studies demonstrated that the newborn has visual preferences. Newborns prefer visual stimuli of moderate complexity over simple or very complex stimuli. Also, newborns are capable of distinguishing one pattern from another. The visual acuity of newborns is estimated to be 20/150. (Dayton *et al.,* 1964) Visual accommodation does not become efficient and accurate until age 2 months

Search for the Human Face

Preference for Human Face

Extensive research assesses the newborn's preference for the human face. According to Freedman, the "...overall trend in these studies indicates that young infants show a general preference for looking at cards, or models, in the likeness of the human face." (1974, p. 29) It is now well-documented that the newborn's visual preference is for the eyes rather than any other part of the human face. (Jirari, 1970)

Freedman, in a study of 272 newborns found that 75% of the babies (average age was 42 hours) "...followed a moving object, 68% turned to a voice, 72% followed a silent moving face, while 80% followed a moving and speaking human face." (1974, pp. 29–30)

In Jirari's (1970) studies, a newborn held on the lap functioned more optimally than when kept at the same angle off the lap. The newborn performed best when it was stimulated by a human face while being held and talked to.

Affective Differentiation Between Animate and Inanimate Objects

Until recently, most clinicians and researchers postulated that neonates, especially during the first month, lived in a state of "undifferentiation." This meant that neonates had not as yet developed the ability to differentiate between animate and inanimate objects. Condon and Sander's (1974) studies of the auditory differentiated response of 12-hour-old newborns to the human voice over random sound have dispelled this assumption, opening a new and exciting area of investigation.

Brazelton *et al.* (1975) reported on a fascinating study of 12 mother-infant pairs who were seen regularly and frequently for research purposes during the first 5 months following birth. The mother-child interactions were video taped and, through a microbehavioral analysis technique, ten classes of behaviors in the infants and six classes of behaviors in the mothers were observed and scored. The behaviors observed in the infants included vocalization, direction of gaze, head orientation and position, facial expressions, amount of body movements, specific hand and foot movements, and tongue placement. Behaviors in the mothers noted were vocalization, head position, body position, specific handling of the infant, direction of gaze, and facial expressions.

The researchers found that neonates, even at 2 to 3 weeks of age, during successful interactions with their mothers were involved in synchronic and coordinated rhythmical behavior. Such behavior exhibits five distinct phases: initiation, mutual orientation, greeting, play dialogue, and disengagement. The infants, in short and intense interactions with human beings, demonstrated

...repeated cycles consisting of acceleration from initiation to greetings and then deceleration to disengagement. The pattern is smooth and rhythmical, whereas with objects there is the jaggedness of intense periods of attention interrupted by brief bursts of inattention and of activity. This performance indicates that the infant—as young as two or three weeks of age—is able to differentiate inanimate as opposed to animate events, and that he can appropriately pattern his attention and actions in relation to their unique qualities.

pp. 144–145.

Brazelton *et al.* concluded that the neonate's goal with an inanimate object is

...the exploration of its qualities through vision and prehension. With people, the goal is the achievement of affective synchrony. In both, the infant would be acting intentionally and modifying his behaviour in response to the feedback from the environment.

ibid., p. 145.

In the same laboratory, in another study of infants aged 2 to 20 weeks, Tronick *et al.* (1978) attempted to control the feedback response of the mothers to their infants. The researchers instructed the mothers to have a face-to-face interaction with their infants,

...but remain facially unresponsive [for 3 minutes]. The infants studied reacted with intense wariness and eventual withdrawal, demonstrating the impor-

tance of interactional reciprocity and the ability of infants to regulate their emotional displays.

p. 1.

Physical Contact

Kinesthetic, skin, and other forms of physical contact, such as holding, touching, rocking, caressing, and patting, are sought out by the newborn through crying or fussiness independent of hunger or other forms of discomfort. Physical contact is a building block and important component of human relationships throughout life.

Stimulus Barrier

Some of the neonate's behaviors, such as sleeping or quietness, were believed to be attempts to avoid stimulation, thus serving as a "stimulus barrier." (Bergman and Escalona, 1949) It was thought that hypertrophy of the stimulus barrier, through improper mothering, contributed to the development of severe forms of childhood psychopathology, such as childhood autism. However, careful observation has not shown any evidence that a stimulus barrier exists. In actuality, neonates actively seek stimulation, whether in sleep, in darkness, or in wakefulness.

Attachment Behavior

From a psychological point of view, the development of attachment behavior is essential for the newborn's survival and growth. John Bowlby (1958), the British psychiatrist and psychoanalyst, in a paper entitled "The Nature of the Child's Tie to His Mother," challenged the prevailing idea of the time: that the development of attachment in infants is secondary to hunger needs and libidinal drives.

Inspired by contributions of ethologists (who study animal behavior in natural settings), Bowlby suggested that five "instinctual responses," or "behaviour patterns,"—namely, sucking, clinging, following, crying, and smiling—make up the innate "attachment behaviour" which is species specific to humankind.

Development of Intelligence (Cognitive Development)

In human beings the nature and origin of intelligence or cognition has been of interest throughout the ages. In France, Itard (1820s) and, later, Simone and Binet (1890s) were given the task of distinguishing mentally subnormal (retarded) children from other children. This effort resulted in the development of tests to measure the intelligence of children. (see chapter 20)

Jean Piaget, a Swiss biologist, had an interest in epistemology (a branch of philosophy which explores the origin, nature, and limits of human knowledge). Inspired by the works of Jean Jacques Rousseau on the education of children and by Darwin's observations on the behavior of his son, Piaget became interested in observing and documenting the origin and development of intelligence in children.

Piaget meticulously observed and recorded the behavior of his own three children. Among his significant contributions to the study of the intellectual development of children are: *Judgement and Reasoning in the Child* (1928), *The Child's Conception of the World* (1929), *The Language and Thought of a Child* (1932), and *The Origins of Intelligence in Children* (1952).

Piaget's findings are increasingly being applied to the fields of education, developmental psychology, child psychiatry, and psychoanalysis. James Anthony (1957) began integrating Piaget's concepts of human cognition with psychodynamic theories of childhood psychopathology. Peter Wolff (1960) compared Piaget's developmental stages of intelligence with psychoanalytic theories of personality development. Decari (1965) studied the interrelationship of the development of affect and cognition. Flavell (1963) carefully summarized Piaget's work in a single readable volume, *The Developmental Psychology of Jean Piaget.*

What is Intelligence?

Piaget applied biological concepts to describe the development of intelligence, or cognitive development, which he sometimes referred to as "mental embryology." (Flavell, 1963, pp. 41–42) According to Piaget, the basic and fundamental function of living matter is adaptation in the form of "...incorporating into its structure nutrition-providing elements from the outside." (ibid., p. 45)

The process of adaptation includes two functions: (1) *assimilation,* meaning "...changing elements in the milieu in such a way that they can become incorporated into the structure of the organism...," and (2) *accommodation,* or "adjustment to the object," meaning "...the organism must accommodate its functioning to the specific contours of the object it is trying to assimilate." (ibid., p. 45)

Piaget (1962) perceived intelligence as being

an evolutionary process following specific phases of development. He defined intelligence "...as a form of equilibration, or forms of equilibration, toward which all cognitive functions lead." (Harrison and McDermott, 1972, p. 158) Piaget further explained equilibration, or adaptation, as "...a compensation for an external disturbance." (ibid., p. 158) The subject, through activity, succeeds in compensating for an external disturbance. Equilibration is not static and "...implies the fundamental idea of reversibility, and this reversibility is precisely what characterizes the operations of intelligence." (ibid., p. 158)

Piaget observed that intelligence originates in the infant as a motoric or action response to a sensory stimulus. Such motoric responses are based on reflexes—innate patterns of response, which are referred to as *schemas.* The concept of *schema* plays a significant role in Piaget's developmental psychology, especially in the sensory-motor period. Piaget used the term "schema" for a variety of functions: e.g., birth reflexes (schema of sucking), innate structures within organisms, innate patterns of response, and a plan of action. Flavell (1963) defined schema as "...a cognitive structure which has reference to a class of similar action sequences, these sequences of necessity being strong, bounded totalities in which the constituent behavioral elements are tightly interrelated." (pp. 52–53)

The processes of assimilation and accommodation help the infant adapt and develop new behavioral patterns based on innate schemas. According to Piaget, the development of intelligence progresses through the following sequential periods:

1. Sensory-motor period (birth to 2 years of age)
2. Preoperational period (2 to 7 years of age)
3. Concrete operations (7 to 11 years of age)
4. The period of formal operations (11 to 15 years of age)

In each of these periods, there is a *qualitative* difference in intelligence.

Sensory-Motor Period

The sensory-motor period of intelligence covers the first 2 years of life and comprises six stages.

STAGE 1: THE USE OF REFLEXES (Birth to One Month). The neonate is involved primarily in reflexlike behaviors, such as crying, sucking, swallowing, and gross bodily movement. Environmental stimuli are assimilated by the newborn and go through simple forms of accommodation or adaptive change, based on schemas. Schemas are the building blocks of intelligence. New sensory-motor experiences, through the process of assimilation and accommodation, add to the endowed schemas and lead to more adaptive and complex behavior expressions.

Sensorimotor intelligence rests mainly on actions, on movements and perceptions without language, but these actions are coordinated in a relatively stable way [schemas of action].
Harrison and McDermott, 1972, p. 159.

STAGE 2: THE PRIMARY CIRCULAR REACTION (1 to 4 Months).

The infant's experience begins to influence and change innate reflexes: "...the first simple habits, the most elementary of sensory-motor acquisitions, really come into existence" (Flavell, 1963, p. 91)

Piaget introduced the idea or concept of circular reaction, which contributes to the development and establishment of new schemas. Piaget defines circular reaction as the infant "...stumbling upon a new experience as a consequence of some act," and "...trying to recapture the experience by reenacting the original movements again and again in a kind of rhythmic cycle." (ibid., p. 93) For example, the infant may accidentally discover that making a noise through the mouth is a pleasurable experience, so he gradually produces this noise, and within 2 to 3 months becomes "quite a babbler."

According to Piaget, there are three types of circular reactions: primary (1 to 4 months of age), secondary (4 to 8 months of age), and tertiary (12 to 18 months of age). Secondary and tertiary circular reactions will be discussed later in this chapter and in chapter 3.

Primary circular reaction is called primary because it is the earliest manifestation of such behavior in infants and defines Stage 2 of sensory-motor intelligence (1 to 4 months of age). Primary circular reaction is "...more centered on and around the infant's own body then directed outward towards the manipulation of surrounding objects." (ibid., p. 93)

Learning

Learning during the first 2 months of life occurs through the processes of assimilation, accommodation, adaptation, and reciprocal interaction. Learning through the methods of classical avoidance conditioning and experimental habituation does not occur before age 3 months.

Operant conditioning may occur temporarily without lasting effect. These qualitative differences in learning abilities help to differentiate the first 2 months of life from those that follow.

ALL SMILES, BABBLES, AND LAUGHTER: Three to Six Months

Between 3 and 6 months of life, the infant begins to interact with others in a more obvious way and becomes, according to parents, "human," because of the infant's newly developed ability to establish regular and predictable *eye contact* with other human beings. Following the emergence of regular eye contact by the end of the second month, the infant begins to smile at other human beings indiscriminately. Between the ages of 4 and 5 months, the infant develops a distinct, discriminate smile for mother, and, to a lesser degree, for father, siblings, and other familiar people.

By the beginning of the third month, the infant starts to babble, predictably reproducing sounds repetitively and rhythmically. By 4 months, the infant begins to laugh aloud. As a result, mother spontaneously spends more time with "her baby." She cuddles and rocks the baby while looking at and talking with him and tries to make him smile "just one more time." The baby beams a smile, and this warms the mother's heart. The mother's devotion increases, and the human bond is strengthened. Eye contact, smiling, cooing, and babbling are powerful forces in enhancing the human bond.

Physical Development

Most infants double their birth weight by 5 months. Head circumference increases from 34 to 35 centimeters at birth to an average of 44 centimeters at 6 months. Also, by 6 months, the infant can hold his head erect. He can support most of his weight if held in a standing position and can bounce up and down. The infant begins to roll over, both from front to back and from back to front.

Eye Contact

By the end of the second month, the infant is able to focus on the human face, specifically on the human eyes, in a distinct, "bright-eyed" manner. Wolff (1963), Robson (1967, 1979), Haith (1969), and Haith et al. (1977) conducted extensive studies on infant eye contact.

Haith, *et al.* (1977) examined the visual fixation of infants at ages 3 to 5 weeks, 7 weeks, and 9 to 11 weeks. The researchers used infrared light and television cameras to document the young infant's visual fixations on various features of the human face, especially the eyes. Eight infants were examined from each age group. Each infant was presented with the mother's face and a stranger's face, under three different experimental conditions; the faces were either stationary, moving, or talking. Haith *et al.* observed, "Whereas 3- to 5-week-olds fixated the face only 22.1 percent of the time, 7-week-olds and 9- to 11-week-olds fixated 87.5 and 89.9 percent of the time, respectively." (p. 854) The 7-week-olds and 9- to 11-week-olds both fixated primarily on the eye region.

Haith *et al.* concluded that by age 7 weeks, eyes become very attractive and have a significant "signal value" for social interaction. The infant's development of eye contact at this stage "...carries special social meaning for the infant's caretakers and plays an important role in the development of the social bond." (ibid., p. 854)

The authors found that the infant's visual perceptual activity is not only triggered by visual stimulation, but also by the mother's voice. The mother's voice gives a signal to the 2-month-old infant to look for and expect to see a face. The infant's visual scanning and searching reinforces the mother-child interaction, increases the frequency of eye contact, and contributes significantly to the development of the social smile.

The infant constantly scans mother's face while he is nursing. Under age 2 months, the infant may randomly glance at mother's eyes, but by 2 months he focuses specifically on her eyes more than any other part of her face. For the first time, the mother feels that her baby really recognizes her. She feels elated by this powerful human contact and increases her social interaction with the baby. This reciprocal relationship and mutual feedback strengthens the bond, triggers unspoken love, and becomes the foundation of "basic trust."

Smiling

Peter Wolff (1959, 1963, 1969) made extensive microbehavioral observations of smiling in neonates. Wolff observed that the newborn smiles while in sleep or when drowsy. He described two types of smiling.

Endogenous Smile

This form of smiling is present at birth and frequently noticed when the newborn is in the state of active sleep (REM state), or when drowsy, and it is not related to what is commonly referred to as the "gas smile." Endogenous smiles are directly related to REM states—not to the feeding cycle. It is postulated that endogenous or REM smiling also occurs in utero. REM smile is associated with brain stem functions rather than with the cerebral cortex.

Exogenous Smile or Social Smile

This type of smile is related to outside stimuli. Rene Spitz and Katherine Wolf's (1946) classic study of 145 children, from birth to age 12 months, demonstrated that the smiling response, or the exogenous, social, or interactional smile, "...appears as an age-specific behavioral manifestation of the infant's development from the age of two months to the age of six months." (Spitz, 1965, p. 87) Spitz and Wolf found that 98% of the infants smiled during this period in response to seeing the face of another human being *(en face);* the human face could be that of the mother, a relative, or a friend. Only 2% of the infant population in these studies smiled "...between birth and the end of the second month." (ibid., p. 88)

In 3-month-old infants, Spitz (1965) tried to decipher what "...specific configuration *within* the face...triggers the infant's smiling." (p. 94) He used masks to control for various facial features and clearly documented that the infant smiles at the upper part of the face, particularly the eyes, and, most frequently, at the nodding human face. The infant does not smile at the human profile. (ibid., pp. 92–93)

It is now well-documented that the newborn does not exhibit exogenous smiling. During the first month, the newborn, in an unpredictable and irregular fashion, may randomly smile to a variety of external stimuli—tactile, auditory, visual, or kinesthetic. Between ages 2 and 3 months, the regular consistent, predictable, exogenous smile occurs through visual stimulation, particularly when the infant sees a human face *(en face).*

RECOGNITION SMILE. By age 4 months, the infant shows a distinct, discriminative smile for the mother and, to a lesser extent, for the father and siblings. This is called the preferential, or recognition smile. The baby's smile is contagious, disarming, and uplifting, It touches the deepest chord within all of us, especially the mother.

Sleep

In the third month of life, a significant brain electrical development occurs. This process is referred to as "switchover"—the infant switches over and changes sleep patterns. During the first 2 months, when the infant becomes drowsy or sleepy, he goes immediately into Stage I REM sleep, or active sleep. By 3 months, similar to older children and adults, the infant goes into Stage I non-REM sleep, then to Stage II quiet sleep, and finally, to the lighter Stage I REM sleep. Metcalf and Spitz "...suggest that both physiologically and psychologically, the psychic precursors and prototypes of dreaming, commence during this switchover period." (Metcalf, 1979, p. 66)

By ages 3 to 6 months, the wakeful EEG of the infant shows more organization and rhythmicity. Dysrhythmic EEG patterns decrease. The dominant waves are of 3 to 5 cycles per second, with medium amplitude. Precursors of alpha rhythm (7 to 12 cycles per second) emerge. Increase of eye contact and social smiling occur concomitantly with the maturation of the brain electro-neurophysiological activities.

Prespeech: Babbling

Early in the third month of life, the infant begins a new experimentation by producing cooing and babbling monologues.

> ...the infant produces sounds, mostly of the rhythmic, repetitive variety, linguals and labials, carefully listens to them and repeats them again and again, creating his own echo, the first acoustic imitation. Six months later, he will use this experience when he imitates sounds heard from his mother.
>
> Spitz, 1965, p. 98.

Loud laughter, which begins at around age 4 months, adds significantly to the infant's prespeech repertoire. The baby's laughter brings unbounded joy to the parents and family. This laughter is contagious and, like the earlier social smile, increases parental interaction.

A number of studies confirm that the more a mother is attentive to her baby through physical contact and vocal utterances, the more the baby replaces crying and fussiness with smiles, cooing, and laughter. The neglected child and children brought up in institutions continue to use crying and fussiness as major forms of communication for a longer period of time and have delayed cooing, smiling, and laughter. (Ainsworth and Bell, 1969, pp. 133–170)

Motor Behavior

Between ages 2 and 6 months, the flexion of the hand gradually decreases, and the palm of the hand becomes a major apparatus for sensory contact. By 4 to 6 months, the infant is not only able to hold objects in his hands and mouth for exploration, but is also able to hold objects with both hands at the midline. This is the beginning of efficient exploration and manipulation of the environment with both hands.

Anthropologists believe that the primary difference between human beings and other primates is the ability of human beings to make tools. Toolmaking occurs because of the ability to bring the hands together in the midline position, along with effective eye-hand coordination. Perhaps, because of this, in the homunculus representation of various parts of the body in the motor cortex (precentral gyrus), the thumb and hand occupy a proportionately larger area.

Between ages 4 and 5 months, the infant's body posture becomes symmetrical. There is synchrony and rhythmicity between the movement of both hands. The startle and moro reflexes have subsided, and there is a gradual decrease in corticospinal tract reflexes due to increased myelination.

Rhythmicity and Synchrony of Behavior

Between ages 3 and 6 months, the infant's behavior patterns gain stability, rhythmicity, and predictability. The mother is now able to anticipate her baby's reactions in most situations. The baby has made a major adaptational change, moving from the endogenous rhythm of intrauterine life to the exogenous rhythm of daily life.

The infant usually sleeps through the night except when in distress. He is awake in the daytime for longer periods, actively seeking social interaction with his mother.

Separation-Individuation: The Birth of the Self

Mahler and her co-workers (Mahler and Goslinger, 1955; Mahler and LaPerriere, 1965; Mahler, 1968, 1972; Mahler et al., 1975) observed mother-child interactions during the first 3 to 4 years of life, and, in so doing, contributed significantly to the exploration of the different phases of the child's relationship with mother. Mahler (1972) wrote:

> The biological birth of the human infant and the psychological birth of the individual are not coincident in time. The former is a dramatic and readily observable, well-circumscribed event; the latter, a slowly unfolding intrapsychic process.
>
> p. 333.

Mahler observed that the infant and the child go through the following phases of psychological and affective emotional development before becoming independent and individuated.

Normal Autism (The First Month of Life)

During the first month of life, the "...sleeplike states far outweigh in proportion the states of arousal." (1968, p. 7) This resembles the primal state of intrauterine life. The neonate is in "...a state of primitive hallucinatory disorientation, in which need satisfaction belongs to his own omnipotent, *autistic* orbit." (ibid., pp. 7–8) The newborn's life in the first month is primarily concerned with reducing tension and achieving homeostasis.

Normal Symbiosis (Ages 2 to 4 Months)

Mahler borrowed the term "symbiosis" from biology. According to her, symbiosis is a metaphor for describing the infant's behaviors and functions "...as though he and his mother were an omnipotent system—a dual unity with one common boundary." (ibid., p. 8) Mahler carefully chose this term to describe "...the state of undifferentiation, of fusion with mother, in which the 'I' is not yet differentiated from the 'not-I,' and in which inside and outside are only gradually coming to be sensed as different." (ibid., p. 9) According to Mahler, the symbiotic phase continues until the child is 4 to 5 months old. The infant's recognition smile by age 4 months is considered "...the peak of the symbiotic phase." (ibid., p. 12)

Subphases of the Separation-Individuation Process (Ages 4 to 36 Months)

Mahler conceptualized that the psychological birth of the self, or individuation, progresses through the following subphases of the separation-individuation process.

DIFFERENTIATION. At the peak of symbiosis (ages 4 to 5 months), when the infant is starting clearly to differentiate mother from others, the subphase of differentiation begins.

Differentiation generally covers ages 4 to 7 months. The sensorium moves entero-proprioceptive processes toward outer sensory perception. This is the beginning of the "perceptual-conscious system." (1972, p. 334) During wakefulness, the infant intensely explores his own body, his mother's body, and his physical surroundings. The infant, by ages 4 to 5 months, becomes aware of being in strange situations and begins to show quiet discomfort when mother leaves him even temporarily. This is discussed further later in this chapter and in chapter 3.

Development of Intelligence (Cognitive Development)

The origin and nature of intelligence were discussed earlier in this chapter. According to Piaget, intelligence is an evolutionary process, beginning with the sensory-motor period (birth to 2 years). Piaget divides the sensory-motor period of intelligence into six stages. Stages 1 and 2 were discussed earlier.

Sensory-Motor Period

STAGE 3: THE SECONDARY CIRCULAR REACTION (4 to 8 months). The infant now makes a deliberate effort to change or modify his behavior according to the external situation. This process is called secondary circular reaction. In primary circular reaction, Stage 2, the infant is primarily concerned with bodily activities and has little interest in the "...effects of these activities on the external environment..." (Flavell, 1963, p. 102), for example, "...sucking for the sake of sucking, grasping for the sake of grasping." (ibid., p. 102)

In secondary circular reaction, Stage 3, the "...infant swings, strikes, rubs, and shakes objects with intense interest in the sights and sounds which these actions elicit in the objects." (ibid., p. 102) Primary circular reaction is autocentric *(centered on the self)*, and secondary circular reaction is allocentric *(beyond the self)*.

Although Piaget was more concerned with the infant's interaction with inanimate objects, his findings may also be applied to the infant's interaction with other human beings. At this stage, the infant shows "intentionality" and has a special interest in seeing the consequences of his actions. He creates situations and "procedures" to lengthen interesting events. Intentionality is a precursor of contemplative recognition.

Between ages 5 and 6 months, the infant intently focuses on inanimate objects, particularly objects that the parents have given to him. He enthusiastically explores these objects and, at times, is totally absorbed in the contemplation of them. Contemplative recognition is the precursor of learning, exploration, and differentiation of the environment.

JOYS AND SORROWS OF ATTACHMENT:
Six to Twelve Months

Triumph Over Gravity: Physical Growth

Between ages 6 and 12 months, the infant passes several developmental milestones. Birth weight triples by the end of the first year, and the child grows an additional 25 to 30 centimeters in height. Head circumference has increased by 10 to 12 centimeters. At the time of birth, the brain weighed 350 grams, and by the end of the first year its weight has increased to 900 grams. (Matson, 1969) Between ages 6 and 12 months, most infants grow 6 to 8 teeth.

By the sixth month, the infant is able to sit alone without support, reflecting the orderly integration of the central nervous system. The infant crawls by 10 months and stands without support between 10 and 12 months. Standing is a concrete expression of the child's triumph over gravity.

By 7 months, the infant pats his own image in a mirror and by 10 months is an active participant in social games, such as pat-a-cake and peek-a-boo. By the end of the first year, the infant cooperates with his mother while she is dressing him. At age 10 to 14 months, the infant takes a few steps without assistance; the infant becomes a toddler.

Attachment Behavior

Bowlby (1958) suggested that, as the child grows during the first year of life, specific components of attachment behavior unfold: for instance, the instinctual responses of crying and sucking manifest themselves at birth, followed by eye contact at age 2 months, smiling by 2 to 4 months, and clinging to and following mother by 6 to 12 months. These instinctual responses become integrated as attachment behavior between ages 6 to 12 months.

Stranger Anxiety

By age 4 months, the infant differentiates mother from others and smiles specifically upon seeing her. This is the beginning phase of differentiation. (Mahler, 1971)

Between ages 4 and 5 months, the infant becomes aware of strangers and of being in a strange situation. The infant, when seeing a stranger, pauses and curiously looks with puzzlement and quiet apprehension. Then the infant looks away from the stranger to his mother. When the infant sees mother's face, he smiles, as if to say "I know you!"

According to Spitz (1965), "a decisive change" occurs between ages 6 and 8 months:

The child now clearly distinguishes friend from stranger. If a stranger approaches him, this will release an unmistakable, characteristic and typical behavior in the child; he shows varying intensities of apprehension or anxiety and rejects the stranger. Still, the individual child's behavior varies over a rather wide range. He may lower his eyes "shyly," he may cover them with his hands, lift his dress to cover his face, throw himself prone on his cot and hide his face in the blankets, he may weep or scream. The common demoninator is a refusal of contact, a turning away, with a shading, more or less pronounced, of anxiety.

p. 150.

Spitz called this behavior "...*eight-month anxiety*...the earliest manifestation of *anxiety proper*." (ibid., p. 151) It is also called "stranger anxiety." Stranger anxiety, according to Spitz, is the "second major psyche organizer," or "ego organizer," smiling being the first one.

Memory, Fear, and Stranger Anxiety

Infants during the first 3 months of life experience discomfort, unpleasure, hunger, and pain in the form of distress and tension, without any attachment of memory to these experiences. By age 4 months, with the manifestation of the recognition smile, memory traces are laid down. Between 4 and 6 months, the reactivation of a pleasurable experience brings smiles, and the reactivation of unpleasant experience brings fear. Spitz noted that:

...fear is provoked by a percept which the child has connected with a previous experience of unpleasure. When the child reexperiences this unpleasure-cathected percept he responds by flight.

ibid., p. 154.

Spitz postulated that a child's anxiety reaction to strangers is totally different from fear, because the child has never seen the stranger before and, therefore, does not have memory traces attached to the stranger. Spitz felt that seeing a stranger stimulates the idea in the child's mind that "this is not...mother." (ibid., p. 155) This is experienced as absence of the mother, i.e., the mother has left him, and this brings about apprehension and more or less pronounced anxiety.

Age and Stranger Anxiety

Bronson studied the reaction of 32 infants, ages 3 to 9 months, to strangers while the infants were in their own homes. He noticed that by age 4 months most of the infants occasionally reacted to a stranger by a frown, whimper, or cry. At the same time, indiscriminate smiling at strangers was waning. Infants aged 6 months and older responded to strangers consistently and predictably in a definitely aversive manner, "...so that the term fear becomes more applicable." (Bowlby, 1973, p. 101)

Mother's Presence and Stranger Anxiety

According to Schaffer (1971), the earliest manifestation of fear of strangers occurs when mother is present. The infant looks at the stranger and then at mother, compares the two, and then reacts. It is only later that the infant is able to react to a stranger in the absence of mother.

Age and Fear of Strange Objects

Meili (1959), in a longitudinal study of infants, noticed that many became afraid of strange objects (e.g., a jack-in-the-box) by age 10 months, even though the same infants had not been afraid earlier.

Scarr and Salapatek (1970) repeated Meili's experiment on infants between ages 5 and 18 months. They noticed that more than one-third of the subjects, between ages 9 and 12 months, were frightened by the jack-in-the-box test, and also by a moving mechanical dog. The younger and older subjects were much less afraid.

Role of Mother in Alleviating Stranger Anxiety

Morgan and Ricciute (1969) studied fear of strangers in 80 infants. The infants were divided by age into five groups:

Group I — 4½ months
Group II — 6½ months
Group III — 8½ months
Group IV — 10½ months
Group V — 12½ months

Each infant's reactions to a strange person were tested under two different experimental conditions: (1) when the infant was sitting on mother's lap and (2) when the infant was seated in a chair 4 feet from mother.

Seventy-five percent of the infants in groups I and II did not show any fear of strangers and responded to them by smiling, cooing, or reaching out, when the infants were seated alone or on their mothers' laps. Only one infant manifested fear of strangers. In groups III and IV, 25% manifested signs of fear of and withdrawal from strangers. In group V, no fewer than 50% of the infants were afraid of or withdrew from strangers. In the same group, while seated on their mothers' laps, the 12½-month-old infants welcomed strangers, but all showed fear when seated 4 to 5 feet away from their mothers. (Bowlby, 1973, pp. 120–121)

Ainsworth and Bell (1970) examined the reaction of 56 white middle-class infants, ages 49 to 51 weeks, to strange situations. They found that the presence of the mother encouraged exploratory behavior in the infant, while the absence of the mother depressed exploration and heightened attachment behavior. (p. 49)

Schaffer's (1971) findings regarding the role of mothers in alleviating the fear of strange objects in one-year-old infants are significant. Schaffer discovered that one group of 6-month-old infants were "spellbound" by stimulus objects while their mothers sat behind them. They did not turn to look at their mothers. In contrast, 12-month-old infants "...turned frequently from the objects to mother and back again, apparently well able to keep mother in mind despite her being perceptually absent." (Bowlby, 1973, p. 102)

Bowlby concluded:

...just as attachment to a mother figure is becoming steadily better organized during the latter half of the first year, so also is withdrawal from a fear-arousing situation. Furthermore, because by twelve months a child's cognitive equipment has developed sufficiently for him to be well able to take account of objects and situations briefly absent, he has become able so to organize his behaviour that he moves simultaneously both away from one type of situation and toward another type. Hence he enters his second year equipped to respond in the dual way that is typical of well-organized fear behaviour.

ibid., p. 122.

Biological Roots of Stranger Anxiety

Freedman (1974) suggested that stranger anxiety is biologically determined. It is the outcome of strong attachment behavior and phylogenetically necessary for the survival of the species: "...many mammals and birds show similar fear responses to strangers and strange places after they have formed their initial attachments." (p. 44) Fear of strangers, according to Freedman, is related to fear of predators.

Separation Anxiety

When the infant cannot see or hear mother, he becomes quiet, subdued, and apprehensive. Then, suddenly, the infant cries loudly and shows moderate to severe signs of physical and psychological distress, such as agitation, increase in heartbeat and respiration, sweating, pupil dilation, and at times panic reaction. This reaction to separation from mother is called separation anxiety. It subsides with mother's return.

Separation anxiety is a form of signal anxiety and has alerting and adapting qualities. Usually it is temporary and short-lived. Separation anxiety in the child is alleviated by mother's presence, reinforces attachment behavior between mother and child, and contributes to the child's differentiation of himself from mother and mother from others. It enhances the development of object relationship.

Separation anxiety is dramatically expressed at ages 8 to 10 months, although it usually begins by 6 months and continues to play a dominant role until ages 30 to 36 months. Throughout life, separation anxiety is reactivated in different forms and intensity whenever a loss is experienced, whether it be the loss of a loved one, of self-esteem, or of a cherished possession.

Historical Perspective

Bowlby (1973), in *Separation Anxiety and Anger,* reported that William James wrote in 1890 that "The great source of terror in infancy is solitude." (p. 31) Later, Sutti (1935) and Hermann (1936) recognized that the "rapture" of attachment between mother and child contributed significantly to the development of apprehension in infants, which is now called separation anxiety.

Separation: Protest, Despair, and Detachment

According to Bowlby (1960), in any form of separation from a love object (mothering person), the individual goes through the phases of *protest, despair,* and *detachment* concomitantly. Protest expresses itself in the form of separation anxiety, despair in the form of grief and mourning, and detachment in the form of a psychological defense that may become pathological withdrawal. Bowlby stated, "... separation anxiety, grief and mourning, and defense—are phases of a single process and that only when they are treated as such is their true significance grasped." (Bowlby, 1973, p. 27)

Loss and Psychopathology

According to Bowlby:

Young children are upset by even brief separations. Older children are upset by longer ones. Adults are upset whenever a separation is prolonged or permanent, as in bereavement. A pile of clinical reports,...starting with Freud's early studies of hysteria and swelling to increasing volume in recent years, shows that experiences of separation and loss, occurring recently or years before, play a weighty role in the origin of many clinical conditions.

ibid., p. 30.

Bowlby's findings (1960) in the area of loss of love object and the subsequent development of psychopathology have had significant impact on the fields of human development and child psychiatry. Loss of love object in infancy and childhood may result in pathological grief and mourning and contribute to the development of pathological anxiety, depression, antisocial behavior, disorders of attachment, and possible psychosis in later childhood and adulthood.

Differentiation Between Fear and Anxiety

In recent years, Bowlby has used the concept of "fear" interchangeably with "anxiety." Some clinicians, including Anna Freud, distinguish these two concepts from each other. Anna Freud (1977) wrote:

We have always distinguished between the terms "fear" and "anxiety," using the former exclusively for the attitude toward real dangers threatening from external sources and the latter exclusively for reactions to threats located within the mind, due to clashes between drives and internal opposing forces. While fears, however strong they are, do not develop into phobias, anxiety does so under certain conditions.

p. 86.

Summary

The integration of attachment behavior with cognitive development and the differentiation process, in a normal and healthy infant, expresses itself in the form , of stranger and separation anxiety. The manifestation of stranger and separation anxiety is a major developmental milestone.

Spitz perceived stranger and separation anxiety as being the same phenomenon, although some authors separate them. They feel that stranger anxiety occurs earlier, at around ages 6 to 7 months, and that separation anxiety comes to full expression at ages 8 to 9 months.

The absence of some form of stranger or separation anxiety between ages 6 to 12 months may reflect disturbances in object relationship, disorders of attachment, and even severe forms of psychopathology, such as childhood autism. (see chapter 16)

Separation-Individuation: The Birth of the Self

In describing the infant's development from ages 3 to 6 months, Margaret Mahler's observations on the separation-individuation process were already discussed. Mahler (1972) observed that the infant's interaction with mother is the cornerstone of the psychological birth of the self through the separation-individuation process. Mahler described the following phases in the process of separation-individuation: normal autism (the first month of life), normal symbiosis (ages 2 to 4 months), and subphases of separation-individuation process (ages 4 to 36 months).

Subphases of the Separation-Individuation Process (Ages 4 to 36 Months)

DIFFERENTIATION (Ages 4 to 7 Months). Between ages 4 and 5 months, the infant begins to differentiate mother from others, exhibiting apprehension and discomfort when mother leaves even for a short time (beginning of stranger anxiety).

In the infant between ages 6 and 7 months, the differentiation subphase peaks, and the following behaviors are observed:

> ...hair-pulling, face-patting, manual, tactile and visual exploration of the mother's mouth, nose, face, as well as the covered (clad) and unclad *feel* of parts of the mother's body...
>
> Mahler, 1972, p. 334.

The infant will play peek-a-boo when initiated by mother. Now, the infant does not like to sit passively on mother's lap. He begins pushing his legs and arms against mother as though trying to separate himself physically from her. He ventures away from mother by "slipping down" from her lap. At the same time, he keeps close physical proximity to her by "playing at her feet."

Stranger anxiety and separation anxiety appear by the end of the subphase of differentiation. According to Mahler, the more secure the relationship between mother and child, the more the infant is able to respond optimally to stranger and separation anxiety. The less satisfactory his relationship with mother, the more overwhelming these anxieties will be.

PRACTICING (Ages 7 to 16 months). Mahler divides this subphase into two parts.

Early Practicing Subphase. This usually occurs between ages 7 and 10 months and overlaps the subphase of differentiation. This period is "...characterized by the infant's earliest ability to move away physically from mother by crawling, climbing and righting himself, yet still holding on." (ibid., p. 335) The infant gradually differentiates himself from mother, with whom he has established a special bond. At the same time, he becomes more autonomous from her, while still maintaining close proximity.

The infant becomes more interested in inanimate objects, particularly objects mother has given to him, such as a bottle, blanket, or teddy bear. The infant examines these objects visually and also mouths, smells, touches, and feels them. One of these objects may become a "transitional object." (Winnicott, 1953)

A *"transitional object"* is usually an inanimate object dearly prized by the infant, toddler, or older child. This object gives security and comfort. Usually, the child carries this object whenever he is away from the mother or when he is going to sleep. The transitional object symbolically and psychologically represents the child's love and attachment to the mother. This is one of the ways infants and children cope with the joys and sorrows of separation.

During the early practicing period, the infant tentatively begins to form relationships with persons other than mother. Occasionally, the infant may accept substitutes for mother for a brief period of time. However, this is more the exception than the rule.

During the entire practicing subphase, the child crawls away from mother, but rapidly returns to touch her or to lean against her. These frequent returns are called *"emotional refueling."* After having close physical contact with mother, the child becomes re-energized and continues to explore the surrounding environment.

During the early practicing subphase, there is a temporary increase of separation anxiety. The infant needs frequent perceptual contact with mother. This contact does not always have to be physical; hearing mother's voice or seeing mother from a distance is often sufficient.

A young mother may be bewildered and annoyed to find that, although she could leave her baby alone for a short time when he was younger, now when he is older (7 to 10 months) she cannot be out of his sight, even for a minute! The clinician should prepare the mother for the onset of stranger and separation anxiety and explain that it is a part of a normal developmental process. Understanding may decrease the mother's insecurity, frustration, and annoyance.

The early practicing subphase is a critical and sensitive period. Undue pressure on the infant for separation from the mother may arrest infant emotional development or contribute to regression. Separation from mother, even for a few days during the whole period of practicing and also the next phase, *rapprochement* (ages 16 to 25 months), may be severely traumatic. (see chapter 3)

Practicing Subphase Proper (Ages 10 to 16 Months). The child is now in upright locomotion and generally can walk or take a few steps alone. He is in love with the world and has become a "junior toddler!"

The development of motility and walking ability give the child feelings of security, autonomy, strength, power, and "omnipotence." The child is impervious "...to knocks and falls and other frustrations," in his tremendous desire for mastery of body motility. (Mahler, 1972, p. 336)

As the child ventures

...farther and farther away from the mother's feet, he is often so absorbed in his own activities that for long periods of time he appears to be oblivious of the mother's presence. However, he returns periodically to the mother seeming to need her physical proximity and refueling from time to time.

ibid., p. 336.

The child's feelings of security and elation are related to his newly acquired ability for locomotion and his ability to free himself from mother temporarily. The child has turned the passive experience of separation anxiety into an active process of physically separating himself from mother. He invites mother to chase him, to follow him, and to catch him. The mother should let her child wander away, while keeping a watchful eye to protect him from potential dangers, because the child at this age is oblivious to danger.

The successful experience of the practicing subphase is the foundation for developing assertiveness, independence, curiosity, and the thirst for discovery throughout life.

Concerning elation and depression, Mahler observed:

Most children in the practising subphase appeared to have major periods of exhilaration, or at least of relative elation; they became *low-keyed* only when they became aware that mother was absent from the room. At such times, their gestural and performance motility slowed down; their interest in their surroundings diminished; and they appeared to be preoccupied once again with inwardly concentrated attention...called "imaging."

ibid., p. 336.

In discussing the child's "low-keyed" state when aware of mother's absence, Mahler observed that he was not comforted by another person. The more another person tried to comfort the child, the more apprehensive he would become and would burst into tears. This "toned-down" state visibly terminated when mother returned. Mahler referred to this "toned-down" state as "...reminiscent of a miniature anaclitic depression."(ibid., p. 337) (see chapters 7 and 8)

Development of Intelligence
(Cognitive Development)

According to Piaget, Stage 3 of sensory-motor intelligence spans ages 4 to 8 months. The secondary circular reaction and the development of intentionality are the highlights of this stage and were discussed earlier.

Sensory-Motor Period

STAGE 4: THE COORDINATION OF SECONDARY SCHEMAS (Ages 8 to 12 Months). Through the coordination of secondary circular reactions, which developed in Stage 3 (ages 4 to 8 months), totally new behaviors emerge. Intentionality becomes firmly established. The infant develops the ability to anticipate events by becoming sensitive to preceding signs and signals. For example, when mother begins to get up from her chair, the infant anticipates her leaving and begins to cry.

Another major cognitive development in this stage is the emergence of *"object permanency."* Object permanency means that in the infant's mind inanimate objects begin to have their own separate and permanent existence. For example, if an observer places the infant's favorite toy in front of him when he is 6 to 7 months old, he will make an effort to reach and get the toy. But, if the toy is covered with a cloth while the infant is looking, he will not make any attempt to recover it. According to Piaget, the infant has not yet developed the idea that the object has a permanency outside of his sphere of sensory perception. "Out of sight" is not only "out of mind," but also "out of existence."

If the same experiment is performed when the infant is between ages 8 and 12 months, he will remove the cloth and reach for the hidden object. According to Piaget, this is the beginning of object permanency. If the experiment is complicated by putting the toy first under one cloth and then removing it and putting it under a second cloth, the infant at this stage will reach only under the first cloth for the toy. (Fraiberg, 1969) For further discussion on the development of intelligence, see chapter 3.

Battle of the Spoon—Eating Behavior

Between ages 6 and 12 months, significant changes occur in the infant's eating behavior. He begins to feed himself. Teething may cause crankiness, irritability, and pickiness in eating, and gastrointestinal distress. Accidental biting of mother's breast while sucking brings annoyance and anger from mother and temporary withdrawal of the breast. The infant reacts with frustration, anger, and crying.

The 9- to 10-month-old infant likes to play with food and tries to feed himself. Most infants can feed themselves a cracker by age 10 months. The infant's attempts for autonomy in feeding can become a source of conflict with mother. Infants at this age are very "messy." They take their food into their hands, squeeze it and rub it, while touching their face, hair, body, highchair, and anything within reach, including mother. By ages 10 to 12 months, the infant enjoys smearing food as much as eating it. This is the way he learns about food. Parents should be aware of the infant's developmental need for sensory-motor experimentation.

Eating can become a continuous source of pleasure if the parents allow the infant to experiment with food with all of his sensory-motor modalities. "Messiness" at this stage is to be expected. It is much easier to put a square of plastic under the infant's highchair than constantly to try to force him to be "neat." Some parents react violently to the infant's messiness and deprive him of playing with food. Some try to feed the infant by force and do not allow him to touch his food. The battle of the spoon begins. The infant refuses to eat, and the mother forces. Feeding becomes a power struggle between mother and infant. This can lead to feeding disturbances.

Infants in the latter part of the first year like to imitate their mothers. They want to feed someone and mother is the prime candidate! Parents should be sensitive and receptive to this new development and enjoy the game of being fed by the baby. The more the infant experiences pleasure in eating, through all sensory modalities, the easier it will be for him to develop healthy eating habits. The healthy infant has an innate ability to know when he is hungry and when he is filled. The major problem is that anxious parents usually overfeed their children.

Sleep

Infants between ages 6 and 12 months usually sleep through the night. If there has been minor separation from mother, or if the infant is in distress, there may be transitory sleep disturbances in the form of waking up and crying. Between 8 and 12 months, the infant's average sleep time during 24 hours is 12½ hours, as opposed to the newborn's average of 16½ to 17 hours. The infant has longer and longer periods of daytime wakefulness. Only 10 to 15% of the infant's total sleep time is in the daytime, during two periods of brief napping. (Anders and Weinstein, 1972; Webb, 1974)

Sleep EEG

By age 6 months, the EEG recording during sleep shows a significant change with the appearance of K-complex. K-complex is a high voltage, sharp EEG slow wave, which occurs spontaneously during Stage II non-REM sleep. Stages III and IV—deep sleep with slow EEG waves—become differentiated from Stage II sleep, which is a lighter sleep with faster waves and sleep spindles. The EEG recordings of Stage IV sleep, the deepest level of sleep, are characterized by slow waves and high voltage (delta waves). Stage IV sleep does not appear well organized until the infant is at least one year old. EEG recordings show the emergence of Stage IV sleep between ages 6 and 12 months.

Sleep spindles, which emerge at 3 months,

...become sharp, comblike, very well formed, and often show scalp-positive sharp components. The sharp sleep spindles can be mistaken for electroencephalographic abnormality.... Hemispheric voltage asymmetry begins to develop at about age six months...

Metcalf, 1979, p. 67.

According to Metcalf, at approximately 6 months, when the infant is drowsy, there is another new development in EEG recordings: "...medium- to high-amplitude delta and theta activity." (ibid., p. 68) This phenomenon is called "drowsy hypersynchrony" and lasts until the child is 5 or 6 years old.

Between ages 9 and 10 months, "EEG sleep stages become well differentiated from each other and show the classical sleep stages that are seen thereafter throughout life." (ibid., p. 68) By age 12 months, the amount of REM sleep has decreased significantly to about 20% of the sleep time, which is similar to an adult. During wakefulness, the EEG begins to show regular emergence and development of alpha rhythms (7 to 12 cycles per second).

Baby's First Words: Speech

The cooing and babbling of the 2- to 6-month-old infant becomes more refined and differentiated. The infant can express himself through vocalization, pleasure, surprise, recognition, discomfort, unhappiness, joy, and particularly imitation of mother's voice. The infant expresses a variety of feelings through changes in intonation, intensity, rhythm, and amplitude of his voice. He "talks" without words!

Body movement becomes more synchronized with vocalization. Between ages 9 and 12 months, the infant extensively imitates the intonation of adult speech. The infant responds differently to male and female voices and to friendly or unfriendly approaches.

The First Word

Around age 7 months, the infant vocalizes "m-m-m" when crying. Around 9 to 10 months, one hears the first recognizable words, for instance, "da-da." By 12 months, the infant uses expressive jargon and can give toys on request.

Responding to "No-No"

According to Spitz (1965), a few weeks after "eight-month anxiety" the infant begins to understand

...social gestures and their use as a vehicle of reciprocal communication.... This is most impressive in the child's understanding of, and response to, prohibitions and commands.

p.174.

For instance, if a rubber ball is rolled to the infant, he will roll it back. If you extend your hand and say "hello" to him

...he will put his hand into yours. If you intrude on his activities by energetically saying "No! No!" and at the same time shake your head or wag your finger in sign of prohibition, he will stop whatever he is doing. His face may even express consternation.

ibid., p. 174.

By the end of the first year,

...subtle shadings of emotional attitudes begin to emerge. Jealousy, anger, rage, envy, possessiveness on the one hand, love, affection, attachment, joy, pleasure, etc., on the other...

ibid., p. 177.

PSYCHOANALYTIC CONCEPTS OF HUMAN DEVELOPMENT:
The First Year of Life

Oral Stage

One of the major contributions of Sigmund Freud (1905), Abraham (1916), Erikson (1950), and Anna Freud (1965) to the understanding of human development has been the construction of the libido theory and its application to all phases of human development from birth onward. Sigmund Freud concluded that, from the moment of birth, different zones of the body are endowed with libido, a pleasure-seeking energy. Before Freud, libido as a sexual energy was attributed only to adolescents and adults. Infants and children were not thought to have any sexual thoughts or desires. They were thought to be totally "innocent." Freud, in his famous work, *Three Essays on The Theory of Sexuality* (1905), attacked this myth and associated libido energy with different anatomical orifices of the body. Abraham (1916), and later Erikson (1950), described psychosexual developments in infancy and childhood.

In the oral stage, or oral sensory stage, according to psychoanalytic theory, the mouth and skin of the infant is cathected (invested) with libidinal energy. The stimulation of the mouth and the touch of the skin, in the form of caressing or hugging, by mother or another human being, give comfort and pleasure to the infant beyond satiating hunger.

According to Erikson (1963), the oral-sensory stage expresses itself in the form of oral-receptivity phase.

Oral-Receptivity Phase

From birth to 6 months, the infant openly receives what is given. The infant is relaxed and receptive to mother's giving. This helps in the development of "basic trust." A "mutuality of relaxation" between the infant and mother and others around evolves. The infant is totally trusting and receives pleasure by "...being held, warmed, smiled at, talked to, rocked." (p. 76) At this stage, there is' no ambivalence (love-hate relationships). When the infant is hungry or in pain, he cries, soon learning that this brings the loving and caring provider, namely, mother, who will attend to all of his needs. The development of the sense of basic trust, which is the foundation of human development, is related to this oral-sensory phase.

Oral-Incorporative or Oral-Aggressive Phase

This phase spans ages 6 to 18 to 24 months. The infant starts to develop teeth between ages 5 and 8 months. Biting on hard things and biting through things becomes a pleasurable experience. Also at this time, the infant is able to reach out and grasp objects with both hands, and "... *taking* and *holding on to* things..." becomes a social modality. (ibid., p. 77)

In the oral-aggressive stage, "... 'good' and 'evil' enter the baby's world." (ibid., p. 78) Until teething, the oral cavity was the source of pleasure. Now, the experience of teething brings pain and discomfort. The biting of the breast brings mother's anger and the withdrawal of the nipple. The child feels frustrated, angry, and helpless.

These developmental events contribute to destroying the child's

...unity with a maternal matrix. This earliest catastrophe in the individual's relation to himself and to the world is probably the ontogenic contribution to the biblical saga of paradise, where the first people on earth forfeited forever the right to pluck without effort what had been put at their disposal; they bit into the forbidden apple, and made God angry.

ibid., p. 79.

Erikson concludes:

The oral stages, then, form in the infant the springs of the *basic sense of trust* and the *basic sense of mistrust* which remain the autogenic source of both primal hope and of doom throughout life.

ibid., p. 80.

Development of Defense Mechanisms

Anna Freud (1936), in her classic book, *Ego and the Mechanisms of Defense,* described a number of psychological defense mechanisms. These defense mechanisms are part of the ego functions and help in the individual's adaptation to the environment and channelization of the instinctual drives of sex and aggression. Some of the major psychological defense mechanisms are: introjection, projection, denial, identification, repression, displacement, reversal, reaction formation, isolation, intellectualization, and sublimation. According to Melanie Klein (1957), a neonate manifests from birth the defense mechanisms of introjection and projection. Swallowing and spitting out are biological precursors of introjection and projection.

According to Spitz (1965), imitation behavior, which emerges in infants between ages of 8 and 10 months, is the foundation of the defense mechanism of identification.

The acquisition of action patterns, the mastery of imitation, and the functioning of identification are the devices which permit the child to achieve increasing autonomy from the mother. Imitating the mother's actions enables the child to provide himself with all that his mother had provided before.

p. 179.

REFERENCES

Abraham, K. (1916). The first pregenital stage of the libido. In *Selected Papers of Karl Abraham.* London: Hogarth, 1948, pp. 248–279.

Ainsworth, M. (1967). *Infancy in Uganda: Infant Care and the Growth of Attachment.* Baltimore: Johns Hopkins University Press.

Ainsworth, M., Bell, S. (1969). Some contemporary patterns of mother-infant interaction in the feeding situation. In Ambrose, A. (Ed.), *Stimulation in Early Infancy.* London: Academic Press, pp. 133–170.

Ainsworth, M., Bell, S. (1970). Attachment, exploration, and separation: Illustrated by the behavior of one-year-olds in a strange situation. *Child Dev., 41,* 49–67.

Ainsworth, M., Bell, S., Stayton, D. (1974). Infant-mother attachment and social development: Socialization as a product of reciprocal responsiveness to signals. In Richards, M. (Ed.), *The Integration of the Child into a Social World.* Cambridge: Cambridge University Press.

Akiyama, Y., Schulte, F.J., Schultz, M.A., Parmelee, A.H. (1969). Acoustically evoked responses in premature and full term newborn infants. *Electroencephalogr. Clin. Neurophysiol., 26,* 371–380.

Anders, T. (1974). The infant sleep profile. *Neuropaediatrie, 5,* 425–442.

Anders, T., Hoffman, E. (1973). The sleep polygram: A potentially useful tool for the clinical assessment in human infants. *Am. J. Ment. Defic., 77,* 506–514.

Anders, T., Weinstein, P. (1972). Sleep and its disorders in infants and children: A review. *Pediatrics, 50,* 312–324.

Anthony, E.J. (1957). An experimental approach to the psychopathology of childhood: Encopresis. *Br. J. Med. Psychol., 30,* 156-162, 172–174.

Aserinsky, E., Kleitman, N. (1955). A motility cycle in sleeping infants as manifested by ocular and gross bodily activity. *J. Appl. Physiol., 8,* 11–18.

Bergman, P., Escalona, S.K. (1949). Unusual sensitivities in very young children. *Psychoanal. Study Child, 3,4,* 333–352.

Bowlby, J. (1958). The nature of the child's tie to his mother. *Int. J. Psychoanal., 39,* 350–373.

Bowlby, J. (1960). Grief and mourning in infancy and early childhood. *Psychoanal. Study Child, 15,* 9–52.

Bowlby, J. (1973). *Separation Anxiety and Anger.* New York: Basic Books.

Brazelton, T.B. (1961). Psychophysiological reactions in the neonate. I: The values of observation of the neonate. *J. Pediatr., 58,* 508–512.

Brazelton, T.B. (1962). Crying in infancy. *Pediatrics, 29,* 579–588.

Brazelton, T.B. (1969). *Infants and Mothers: Differences in Development.* New York: Delacorte.

Brazelton, T.B. (1973). *Neonatal Behavior Assessment Scale.* Philadelphia: Lippincott.

Brazelton, T.B., et al., (1974). The origins of reciprocity: The early mother-infant interaction. In Lewis, M., Rosenblum, L. (Eds.), *The Effect of the Infant on Its Caregiver*, Vol. 1. New York: John Wiley, pp. 49–76.

Brazelton, T.B., Tronick, E., Adamson, L., Als, H., Wise, S. (1975). *Parent-Infant Interaction.* Ciba Foundation Symposium. New York: American Elsevier, pp. 137–154.

Call, J.D. (1964). Newborn approach behaviour and early ego development. *Int. J. Psychoanal., 45,* 286–294.

Condon, W.S., Sander, L.W. (1974). Neonate movement is synchronized with adult speech: Interactional participation and language acquisition. *Science, 183,* 99–101.

Dayton, G.O., Jones, M.H., Aiu, P., Rawson, R.A., Steele, B., Rose, M. (1964). Developmental study of coordinated eye movements in the human infant. *Arch. Ophthalmol., 71,* 865–870.

Decarie, T.G. (1965). *Intelligence and Affectivity in Early Childhood.* New York: International Universities Press.

Dement, W.C., Kleitman, N. (1957). Cyclic variations in EEG during sleep and their relation to eye movements, body motility and dreaming. *Electroencephalogr. Clin. Neurophysiol., 9,* 673–690.

DeMyer, W. (1974). *Techniques of Neurologic Examination— A Programmed Text.* Second Edition. New York: McGraw-Hill Book Co., p. 194.

Eisenberg, R.B., Griffin, E.G., Coursin, D.B., Hunter, M.S. (1964). Auditory behavior in the human neonate: A preliminary report. *J. Speech Hear. Res., 7,* 245–269.

Emde, R., Koenig, K. (1969). Neonatal smiling and rapid eye movement states. *J. Am. Acad. Child Psychiatry, 8,* 57–67.

Emde, R., Harmon, R. (1972). Endogenous and exogenous smiling systems in early infants. *J. Am. Acad. Child Psychiatry, 11,* 177–200.

Emde, R, Gaensbauer, T.G., Harmon, R.J. (1976). Emotional expression in infancy: A biobehavioral study. *Psychol. Issues,* Monograph no. 37, Vol. 10.

Emde, R., Robinson, J. (1979). The first two months: Recent research in developmental psychobiology and the changing view of the newborn. In Noshpitz, J. (Ed.), *Basic Handbook of Child Psychiatry,* Vol. 1. New York: Basic Books, pp. 72–105.

Erikson, E. (1950). *Childhood and Society.* Second Edition. New York: Norton. 1963.

Fantz, R.L. (1961). The origin of form perception. *Sci. Am., 204,* 66–72.

Flavell, J.H. (1963). *The Developmental Psychology of Jean Piaget.* New York: D. Van Nostrand.

Fraiberg, S. (1969). Libidinal object constancy and mental representation. *Psychoanal. Study Child, 24,* 9–47.

Freedman, D. (1974). *Human Infancy: An Evolutionary Perspective.* New Jersey: Lawrence Erlbaum Associates, pp. 23–50.

Freud, A. (1936). *The Ego and the Mechanisms of Defense.* New York: International Universities Press.

Freud, A. (1965). The assessment of normality in childhood. In *Normality and Pathology in Childhood: Assessments of Development.* New York: International Universities Press, pp. 54–92.

Freud, A. (1977). Fears, anxieties, and phobic phenomena. *Psychoanal. Study Child, 32,* 85–90.

Freud, S. (1905). Three essays on the theory of sexuality. *Standard Edition of the Complete Psychological Works of Sigmund Freud,* Vol. 7. London: Hogarth Press, 1968, pp. 125–243.

Goodman, W.S., Appleby, S.V., Scott, J.W., Ireland, P.E. (1964). Audiometry in newborn children by electroencephalography. *Laryngoscope, 74,* 1316–1328.

Haith, M. (1969). Infra-red television recording and measurement of ocular behavior in the human infant. *Am. Psychol., 24,* 279–285.

Haith, M. (1976). Visual competence in early infancy. In Held, R., Leibowitz, H.H., Teuber, H.C. (Eds.), *Handbook of Sensory Physiology,* Vol. 8. New York: Springer.

Haith, M., Bergman, T., Moore, M. (1977). Eye contact and face scanning in early infancy. *Science, 198,* 853–855.

Harrison, S., McDermott, J.F. (Eds.) (1972). *Childhood Psychopathology: An Anthology of Basic Readings.* New York: International Universities Press.

Hermann, I. (1936). Sich-anklammern-auf-suche-gehen. *Int. Z. Psychoanal., 22,* 349–370.

Jirari, C. (1970). Form perception, innate form preferences and visually-mediated head-turning in human neonates. Unpublished doctoral dissertation, Committee on Human Development, University of Chicago.

Klein, M. (1957). The psycho-analytic play technique: Its history and significance. In Klein, M., Heinmann, P., Money-Kyrle, R.E. (Eds.), *New Directions in Psychoanalysis.* New York: Basic Books, pp. 3–22.

Kleitman, N., Engelmann, T. (1953). Sleep characteristics of infants. *J. Appl. Physiol., 6,* 269–282.

Lynip, A. (1951). The use of magnetic devices in the collection and analysis of the preverbal utterances of an infant. *Genet. Psychol. Monogr., 44,* 221–262.

Mahler, M.S. (1968). *On Human Symbiosis and the Vicissitudes of Individuation: Infantile Psychosis,* Vol. 1. New York: International Universities Press.

Mahler, M.S. (1971). A study of the separation-individuation process: And its possible application to borderline phenomena in the psychoanalytic situation. *Psychoanal. Study Child, 26,* 403–424.

Mahler, M. (1972). On the first three subphases of the separation-individuation process. *Int. J. Psychoanal., 53,* 333–338.

Mahler, M.S., Gosliner, B.J. (1955). On symbiotic child psychosis: Genetic, dynamic, and restitutive aspects. *Psychoanal. Study Child, 10,* 195–212.

Mahler, M.S., LaPerriere, K. (1965). Mother-child interaction during separation-individuation. *Psychoanal. Q., 34,* 483–498.

Mahler, M.S., Pine, F., Bergman, A. (1975). *The Psychological Birth of the Human Infant: Symbiosis and Individuation.* New York: Basic Books.

Matson, D.D. (1969). *Neurosurgery of Infancy and Childhood.* Springfield, Il.: Charles C. Thomas, p. 123.

Meili, R. (1959). A longitudinal study of personality development. In Jessner, L., Pavenstedt, E. (Eds.), *Dynamic Psychopathology in Children.* New York: Grune and Stratton, pp. 106–123.

Metcalf, D.R. (1969). Effect of extrauterine experience on ontogenesis of EEG sleep spindles. *Psychosom. Med., 31,* 393–399.

Metcalf, D.R. (1972). Development of states in infants. In Clemente, D.C., Purpura, D.P., Mayer, R.E. (Eds.), *Sleep and the Maturing Nervous System.* New York: Academic Press, pp. 216–219.

Metcalf, D.R. (1977). Sleep and dreaming: Protodream and predream. In Wolman, B.D. (Ed.), *International Encyclopedia of Neurology, Psychiatry, Psychoanalysis, and Psychology,* Vol. 10. New York: Van Nostrand Reinhold, pp. 246–257.

Metcalf, D.R. (1979). Organizers of the psyche and EEG development: Birth through adolescence. In Noshpitz, J. (Ed.), *Basic Handbook of Child Psychiatry,* Vol. 1., New York: Basic Books, pp. 63–71.

Morgan, G.A., Ricciuti, H.N. (1969). Infants' responses to strangers during the first year. In Foss, B.M. (Ed.), *Determinants of Infant Behaviour,* Vol. 4. London: Methuen.

Piaget, J. (1928). *Judgement and Reasoning in the Child.* London: K. Paul.

Piaget, J. (1929). *The Child's Conception of the World.*

London: K. Paul, Trench, Trubner, and Co., Ltd.; New York: Harcourt, Brace, and Co.

Piaget, J. (1932). *The Language and Thought of a Child.* London: Routledge and Kegan Paul.

Piaget, J. (1952). *The Origins of Intelligence in Children.* New York: International Universities Press.

Piaget, J. (1962). The stages of the intellectual development of the child. *Bull. Menninger Clin., 26,* 120–128.

Prechtl, H. (1965). Prognostic value of the neurological signs in the newborn infant. *Proc. R. Soc. Med., 58,* 3–4.

Prechtl, H. (1974). The behavioural states of the newborn infant (A review). *Brain Res., 76,* 185–212.

Robson, K.S. (1967). The role of eye-to-eye contact in maternal-infant attachment. *J. Child Psychol. Psychiatry, 8,* 13–25.

Robson, K. (1979). Development of the human infant from two to six months. In Noshpitz, J. (Eds.), *Basic Handbook of Child Psychiatry,* Vol. 1. New York: Basic Books, pp. 106–117.

Scarr, S., Salapatek, P. (1970). Patterns of fear development during infancy. *Merrill-Pal., 16,* 55–90.

Schaffer, H.R. (1971). *The Growth of Sociability.* London: Penguin Books.

Spitz, R. (1965). *The First Year of Life.* New York: International Universities Press.

Spitz, R.A., Wolf, K. (1946). The smiling response: A contribution to the ontogenesis of social relations. *Genet. Psychol. Monogr., 34,* 57–125.

Suttie, I.D. (1935). *Origins of Love and Hate.* London: Kegan Paul.

Tennes, K., *et al.* (1972). The stimulus barrier in early infancy: An exploration of some formulations of John Benjamin. In

Holt, R.R., Peterfreund, E. (Eds.), *Psychoanalysis and Contemporary Science,* Vol. 1. New York: Macmillan, pp. 206–234.

Tronick, E., Als, H., Adamson, L., Wise, S., Brazelton, T.B. (1978). The infant's response to entrapment between contradictory messages in face-to-face interaction. *J. Am. Acad. Child Psychiatry, 17,* 1–13.

Wasz-Hockert, O., Lind, J., Vuorenkoski, V., Partenan, T., Valanne, E. (1968). *The Infant Cry: A Spectrographic and Auditory Analysis.* London: Heinemann.

Webb, W. (1974). The rhythms of sleep and waking. In Scheving, L.E., Halberg, F., Pauly, J.E. (Eds.), *Chronobiology.* Tokyo: Igaku Shoin Ltd., pp. 482–486.

Winnicott, D.W. (1953). Transitional objects and transitional phenomena. *Int. J. Psychoanal., 34,* 89–97.

Wolff, P.H. (1959). State and neonatal activity. In Stone, L., Smith, H., Murphy, L. (Eds.), *The Competent Infant, Research and Commentary.* New York: Basic Books, 1973, pp. 257–268.

Wolff, P.H. (1960). The developmental psychologies of Jean Piaget and psychoanalysis. *Psychol. Issues,* Monograph no. 5.

Wolff, P.H. (1963). Observations on the early development of smiling. In Foss, B.M. (Ed.), *Determinants of Infant Behaviour,* Vol. 2. London: Methuen.

Wolff, P.H. (1966). The Role of Biological Rhythms in Early Psychological Development. Unpublished manuscript.

Wolff, P.H. (1969). The natural history of crying and other vocalizations in early infancy. In Foss, B.M. (Ed.), *Determinants of Infant Behaviour,* Vol. 4. London: Methuen, pp. 81–109.

Chapter 3

THE WORLD OF MASTERY: One to Three Years of Age

During the second and third years of life, the child masters major developmental tasks: walking and running; recognition of object permanency; symbolic language; internalization of the maternal image in the form of object constancy; establishment of gender identity; and toilet training. These developmental events prepare the child for peer interaction, relative independence, and socialization.

MOTOR BEHAVIOR

Between ages 12 and 15 months, most children take their first steps independently. Now they are called toddlers. Through trial and error, and the encouragement and support of his parents, the toddler gradually becomes a walker.

By the age of 15 months, the toddler can point to or vocalize his wants. He is able to throw objects in play. By the age of 18 months, he is partially able to feed himself, although he still spills. He may carry or hug a special toy, doll, or blanket. This is called a "transitional object." He can scribble.

By the age of 2 years, the child imitates mother in her household tasks. He is able to kick large balls, go up and down stairs alone, and runs well. The newly acquired mastery of walking and running has its own perils. The toddler does not have any sense of danger. He runs everywhere and gets into everything. He is like a traveler in a foreign country, who wants to go everywhere, see everything, do everything, and taste everything.

The toddler is annoyed and frustrated when his parents try to control and limit his exploratory excursions. The toddler tests and defies parental prohibitions to assert his own independence. Parents, who were delighted when their baby took his first steps and said his first words, are now at their wit's end to know what to do with this little tornado, who has his own mind and who wants to do everything his own way.

TERRIBLE TWOS: OPPOSITIONAL BEHAVIOR

The parent's reaction to newly acquired motor behavior influences the degree and intensity of the child's responses. Sensitive parents are aware that the child needs room for maneuvering and needs to be able to exert his independence in a safe environment.

Between the ages of one and 2 years, the parents need physically to protect their toddler from potential dangers by creating a safe environment for him. For instance, drugs, cleaning products, spray cans, and other potentially dangerous items must be kept in a high, locked cabinet. Sharp, breakable, precious, and sentimental objects should be temporarily removed. The child is not yet able totally to internalize parental prohibitions. When parents say "no, no," the child usually will respond, but, shortly afterward, the strong and healthy urge for exploration and discovery will take precedence. Then the battle of "no, no" begins, which can result in mutual frustration and unhappiness. It is much easier to prepare the home environment by making it a safe and inviting place for the toddler's explorations, than constantly to worry about his getting into things. Between ages 2 and 3 years, the child is gradually able to internalize parental prohibitions and begins to develop an internal sense of danger.

The toddler phase is referred to as the "terrible twos" because of oppositional behavior. Toddlers do assert their independence. However, the "terribleness" of their behavior is frequently related to the parents' lack of appreciation for and overreaction to the toddler's need for independence. The more vehemently an angry and frustrated parent "asserts" his or her will over the toddler's, the more defiant and oppositional the toddler becomes.

Some negativism and oppositional behavior is healthy and developmentally appropriate for this age. David Levy (1955), in his classical work, "Oppositional Syndromes and Oppositional Behavior," asserted that, "The use of negativism as a protective barrier against submissive tendencies should be given consideration." (Harrison and McDermott, 1972, p. 353) Regarding the developmental significance of the period of negativism and resistance, Levy stated:

The period of resistance [terrible twos] might better be called the first period of independence or even, as some writers have named it, the first puberty, and there are notable resemblances between it and the puberty of adolescence. Evidently the "no-no's" have been more impressive than the words "I do it myself."

ibid., p. 351.

DEVELOPMENT OF INTELLIGENCE

Sensory-Motor Intelligence

The sensory-motor period of intelligence, from birth to age 2 years, is comprised of six stages. We have discussed stages one through four (birth through 12 months of age) in the previous chapter.

Stage 5: Tertiary Circular Reaction (12 to 18 Months)

This stage emerges gradually from the secondary circular reaction (Stage 3) on a more advanced level. The child discovers "...new means through active experimentation." (Flavell, 1963, p. 114)

The child moves closer to the development of object permanency—the recognition that objects have their own independent permanence and existence outside of visual perception.

The child, now, is able to "...search for an object under two or more screens, provided he has *seen* the object disappear under successive screens." (Fraiberg, 1969, p. 30) If the child does not see the hiding of the object under the screens, he is not able to search for it. The permanency of the object depends on the child's visual perception. The child is *not yet able to deduce* that the object exists in some hidden place.

Stage 6: Invention of New Means Through Mental Combinations (18 to 24 Months)

In this stage, the child begins "internal experimentation" and "inner exploration" of new ways of achieving his goals, which are not based on earlier habitual schemas.

By the age of 18 months, the child is able to search for an object in a hidden place, even when an invisible displacement has occurred. *He is able to deduce* that an object might be hidden. According to Piaget, the object now has permanency in the child's mind independent of visual perception. The child has developed the *memory* for the object and can evoke the image of the object in his mind when the object is absent.

There are two types of memories in childhood. The first is *recognition memory,* which means that the infant needs outside sensory stimuli or perceptual clues to recognize past experiences or objects. The development of the social smile by age 2 months and, particularly, the recognition smile for mother by age 4 months are examples of recognition memory.

The second type is *evocative memory,* which means that the child is able to evoke the memory of an object or experience without external stimuli and in the absence of the object. Piaget perceived that the use of symbols and the development of thought processes, fantasies, and language begin with the development of object permanency and evocative memory.

The Period of Preoperational Thought (Ages 1½ to 7 Years)

Development of Symbolic Function

According to Piaget:

From one and one-half to two years of age, a fundamental transformation in the evolution of intelligence takes place in the appearance of symbolic functions....The appearance of symbols in a children's game is an example of the appearance of new significants. At the sensorimotor level the games are nothing but exercises; now they become symbolic play, a play of fiction; these games consist in representing something by means of something else.

Harrison and McDermott, 1972, p. 161.

Another example of symbolization or the development of mental image in the 2- to 3-year-old child is the beginning of delayed imitation. The child does imitate the mother or someone else in her absence. This is another step toward consolidation of the ego defense of identification.

By the time symbols appear, "...the child acquires language; that is to say...verbal signals or collective signals. This symbolic function then brings great flexibility into the field of intelligence."(ibid., p. 161) The development of symbols and language enable the child to use evocative memory to reproduce past events or construct future plans. In short, the thought processes, or the stage of representation of thought, has begun.

Preoperation

Piaget conceptualized the essence of intelligence as the ability to perceive "reversibility in actions" and awareness of "conservation of matter." He refers to these abilities as "operations." The child between the ages of 1½ and 7 years has not developed these abilities. Because of this, Piaget called this phase preoperation period of intelligence.

The early period of preoperation of intelligence (1½ to 3 years of age) is devoted to extensive development of symbolic language, enrichment of fantasy, and play. For further discussion on the development of intelligence, see chapter 4.

LANGUAGE DEVELOPMENT

The ability to use symbols in the early preoperational period of intelligence, ages 18 to 24 months, is prerequisite for language development. According to Lewis (1977):

The generic term *language* is used to include its symbolic, semantic, and verbal speech components. Clearly, the most distinguishing human function is symbolic language: the ability to use signifiers to refer to significates.... A *symbol* is truly representational in that it enables a discourse about things independent of the things themselves.

p. 646.

There are many theories regarding the development of language. Chomsky (1957, 1972) postulated the theory of "generative transformational grammar," which means that the child has the innate ability to use basic grammar and, through that, to construct infinite sentences.

Another theory based on Piaget's concepts of sensory-motor intelligence postulates the development of language based on the development of various schemas, such as imitation, object permanency, symbolic thought representation, and, finally, language.

During the early phase of symbolic language development, the infant uses a word like "da-da" for food, mother, father, and everything else. Gradually, through environmental interaction and differentiation, he becomes more specific in applying the word "da-da" to father. This occurs in the second year of life. Children comprehend the words and sentences of adults and other children before they are able to reproduce them. At this time, the child communicates effectively non-verbally through vocalizations, gestures, play and rhythm.

Children frequently use phrases, sentences, and "big" words accurately, without understanding or comprehending them. This unevenness of expression, as opposed to language comprehension, according to Piaget, is called *décalage*.

The toddler points to or vocalizes wants and usually can say three to five words meaningfully by age 15 months; he can say 10 words, including people's names, by 18 months. The child can use three word sentences and refer to himself by name by 2 years of age. Between 2 and 3 years, the child becomes efficient in using pronouns. However, the use of "me" and "mine" usually occurs before age 2. On the other hand, the pronoun "I" occurs a bit later, at about 2½ years. The use of the abstract word "yes," which signifies moving beyond oppositional behavior and the "no, no" phase, occurs between 2½ and 3 years of age.

Lack of stimulation, maternal deprivation, lack of emphasis on verbalization, and central nervous disturbances or severe psychopathology contribute to delayed development of symbol formation and language in children. Some troubled children may not use language at all, or use only words instead of sentences with pronouns to communicate. (see chapter 16)

SEPARATION-INDIVIDUATION: THE BIRTH OF THE SELF

According to Mahler, the child passes through a number of phases to achieve psychological birth of the self: normal autism (first month of life); normal symbiosis (ages one to 4 months); and the subphases of separation-individuation, such as differentiation (ages 4 to 7 months), practicing (ages 7 to 15-16 months), rapprochement (ages 16 to 25 months), and, finally, individuation, or object constancy (ages 25 to 36 months). The discussion of separation-individuation will continue with a description of the subphases of rapprochement and object constancy.

Subphases of Separation-Individuation

Subphase of Rapprochement (Ages 16 to 25 Months)

Between ages 16 and 25 months, the toddler gradually becomes more efficient in locomotion and gains mastery of walking and running. This new-found freedom has its perils. The child, while he is away from mother, suddenly becomes aware of her absence and becomes frightened and panic-stricken. There is an upsurge in the intensity of separation anxiety, similar to that experienced by the child at ages 8 to 10 months. The child demands mother's presence and wants mother to follow him everywhere. According to Mahler (1972), "...the practicing subphase is now replaced by *active approach behaviour,* and by a seemingly constant concern with the mother's whereabouts." (p. 337) The child not only wants physical contact with mother, but also seeks constant interaction with her, father, and siblings through newly acquired language ability and symbolic play.

At the same time, the child becomes aware of his physical limitations. The omnipotent elation of the practicing subphase gradually gives way to a recognition of reality and the realization that "...he must cope..." with the world "...more or less 'on his own,' very often as a relatively helpless, small and separate individual" (ibid., p. 337)

The child actively woos his mother and other meaningful people around him for human contact. The quality and quantity of wooing behavior gives the clinician clues as to the health or pathology of the individuation process. There is a significant decrease in earlier imperviousness to frustration and relative obliviousness to mother. The more the child is able to woo mother into participating with him in his interests, the more he will venture into exploring the environment and expanding his sense of reality.

The child becomes more possessive of mother, and the words "me" and "mine" gain affective and emotional significance. (Mahler, 1967) Along with this, the child begins directly to express hostile, aggressive behavior toward mother, in the form of hitting, kicking, biting, or opposing her. Ambivalence, or the love-hate relationship of the child toward mother, gains full expression in the phase of rapprochement.

POTENTIAL DANGER. Rapprochement is a critical subphase. The danger signals to watch for are intensive and greater than average separation anxiety, or more than average shadowing of mother. Some children may continue to use "the daring away behavior" of the practicing subphase to provoke their mothers to run after them constantly, and thereby show delayed growth. Many young mothers naturally are bewildered by their child's new clinging, demanding, and shadowing behavior. They may feel angry and frustrated at the child, and doubt their mothering abilities. The child was "as happy as a lark" when he was 11 to 12 months old, and now at 17 to 18 months he becomes more demanding and cries when mother leaves for a moment. Clinicians should explain simply the various phases of separation-individu-ation to the mother and assure her that, in most circumstances, this increased approach toward her is a normal and healthy development.

Undue physical or emotional separation from mother may have a significant regressive or psychopathological impact on the child. At this stage, the child needs the mother's continuous presence and the assurance of stability and consistency in family life to help him master the anxieties of separation. If it is possible, elective surgery and parental vacations without the child should be postponed during this time.

Object Constancy—Individuation (Ages 25 to 36 Months)

The final subphase of separation-individuation process is called the subphase of object constancy or individuation. This usually occurs between ages 25 and 36 months. During this period, the child begins to accept separation from mother. Now, he prefers to play alone rather than to shadow mother constantly. There is a decrease in the intensity of separation anxiety. When mother leaves to go out, the child may express some unhappiness and whimper a bit, but, with reassurance, he usually quiets down and resumes play activities.

Verbal communication increases significantly and replaces, more or less, other modes of communication, although the child continues to use body language and gestures effectively. There is the beginning of fantasy play and "make believe." The child observes the real world carefully and incorporates these observations into play. The child begins to show interest in other adults and playmates.

The child begins to develop a sense of time with an increased ability for frustration tolerance and endurance of separation. The child begins to understand the idea of "later," or "mommy will come back soon," or "...at suppertime, when daddy comes home." This development of the sense of time is often related to either the times of eating or to mother's coming and going.

BEGINNING OF FANTASY LIFE. Between the ages of 2½ and 3 years, the child verbalizes an active and rich fantasy life, composed of symbolic thought and primary process thinking. The child expresses his own fantasies about food, clothes, and body parts, which are usually quite different from reality. The child, without any inhibition, shares his fantasies with others. It is important for parents to enjoy and "go along" with the child's newly acquired internal imagery and rich fantasy life. Premature and insensitive focusing on reality may inhibit the child's creative development and force inward withdrawal.

Object Constancy—Object Permanency

Mahler's concept of object constancy is different from Piaget's concept of object permanency. Object permanency, as we discussed earlier, is achieved when the child, by the age of 18 months, is able to retrieve hidden inanimate objects through one invisible displacement. The child uses evocative memory to find the object. Object constancy, on the other hand, is the ability to internalize the parental image, particularly of mother. The frustrating and pleasure-giving, "good" and "bad," qualities of mother are integrated and internalized in the form of a mental representation of mother. Object constancy is usually reached later than object permanency— usually by ages 2 or 3 years. In childhood psychosis, object constancy is not achieved at all, and in borderline personality disorder (borderline psychosis) only part object relationship (splitting objects into "good" or "bad") is achieved. When the child, by the age of 3 years, has developed object constancy, the process of individuation comes to full expression. The psychological self is born.

By 3 years of age or older, the child can leave mother for a few hours to go to nursery school, or, with proper preparation, can leave mother for a few days without a major developmental crisis. By then, the child has been able to internalize a relatively constant perception of the mother. In the absence of mother, particularly at the time of need or frustration, the child is able to evoke the maternal image to give him comfort, assurance, hope, and security.

PSYCHOANALYTIC CONCEPTS OF HUMAN DEVELOPMENT: One to Three Years of Age

Id, Ego, Superego

Freud, after 30 years of psychoanalytic writing, proposed in *The Ego and the Id* (1923) a major theoretical construct, known as the structural theory. According to Strachey, the translator of Freud's work from German to English:

The Ego and the Id is the last of Freud's major theoretical works. It offers a description of the mind and its workings which is at first sight new and even revolutionary; and indeed all psycho-analytic writings

that date from after its publication bear the unmistakable imprint of its effects...

Freud, 1923, p. 4.

According to the structural theory, the mind is comprised of three parts: *id, ego,* and *superego.* "These are called 'structures' because of the relative constancy of their objects and consistency in modes of operation." (Moore and Fine, 1968, p. 90)

The *id* is the totally unconscious part of the mind, representing the instinctual drives of sex and aggression. The term *id,* or as it is called in German,

"das Es"...was derived in the first instance from Georg Groddeck, a physician practising at Baden-Baden, who had recently become attached to psychoanalysis and with whose wide-ranging ideas Freud felt much sympathy.... But, as Freud also points out, the use of the word certainly goes back to Nietzsche.

Freud, 1923, p. 7.

The *id* represents the passionate, irrational, and driven part of the mind. By calling it the *id,* or the *it,* Freud specifically underlines the animalistic nature of these forces. Freud expanded on the idea of instincts that form the *id:*

I have lately developed a view of the instincts.... According to this view we have to distinguish two classes of instincts, one of which, the sexual instincts or Eros, is by far the more conspicuous and accessible to study.... The second class of instincts was not so easy to point to; in the end we came to recognize sadism as its representative. On the basis of theoretical considerations supported by biology, we put forward the hypothesis of a death instinct, the task of which is to lead organic life into the inanimate state.

ibid., p. 40.

The concept of the death instinct proved to be controversial and later was modified and enlarged by Hartmann (1949) and Anna Freud (1965), and it was conceptualized as the aggressive drive.

The word *ego* means I. It is sometimes referred to as the self. A part of the *ego* is the conscious part of the personality, such as the thought processes and intellectual reasoning. Another part, referred to as the autonomous function of the *ego,* is related to sensory perceptions, such as vision, hearing, touching, tasting, smelling, body movement, coordination, and speech. Some parts of the *ego* are unconscious, such as the defense mechanisms. *Ego,* in psychoanalytic theory, refers to the reasoning and adaptive part of the personality.

Freud (1923) wrote, "The ego represents what may be called reason and common sense, in

contrast to the id which contains the passions."
(p. 25) In another place, Freud stated:

Thus in its relation to the id it is like a man on horseback, who has to hold in check the superior strength of the horse; with this difference, that the rider tries to do so with his own strength while the ego uses borrowed forces. The analogy may be carried a little further. Often a rider, if he is not to be parted from his horse, is obliged to guide it where it wants to go; so in the same way the ego is in the habit of transforming the id's will into action as if it were its own.

ibid., p. 25.

The *superego* is originally derived from the *ego*. It is that part of the personality that deals with moral and religious values and inhibitions against sexual and aggressive wishes. Most of the *superego* functions are unconscious. The *ego* usually mediates between the *id* and *superego* to find a healthy or compromised solution for adaptation.

According to Freud (1923), *superego* and *ego* ideal

...answers to everything that is expected of the higher nature of man. As a substitute for a longing for the father, it contains the germ from which all religions have evolved. The self-judgement which declares that the ego falls short of its ideal produces the religious sense of humility to which the believer appeals in his longing. As a child grows up, the role of father is carried on by teachers and others in authority; their injunctions and prohibitions remain powerful in the ego ideal and continue, in the form of conscience, to exercise the moral censorship. The tension between the demands of conscience and the actual performances of the ego is experienced as a sense of guilt.

p. 37.

Moore and Fine (1968) define *superego* as

A theoretical concept designating those psychic functions which, in their manifest expression, represent moral attitudes, conscience, and the sense of guilt.... In neuroses, symptoms arise as compromises in the conflict between *instinctual drives* (*id* derivatives) and the forces seeking to forbid or restrain their expression (the superego).

p. 90.

Development of the Superego

In early psychoanalytic writing and psychotherapeutic practice, it was thought that children developed and internalized the *superego* between the ages of 5 and 7 years, after experiencing the phallic-oedipal phase. The prohibitions of the internalized *superego* and the *id* as experienced in the *ego* were thought to be prerequisite for the development of psychoneurotic disturbances in children and adults. This theoretical position has been modified.

It is now believed that the oppositional and "no, no" behavior that the toddler shows are early expressions of infantile *superego*. By the age of 2 or 3 years, an early form of an organized *superego* becomes evident in most healthy children. The *superego* continues to go through changes, modifications, and further integration during the phallic-oedipal stage, adolescence, and parenthood, middle age, and aging.

The Conscious, Preconscious, and Unconscious Systems

In the early development of psychoanalysis (1900–1923), Freud divided the mind into three distinct regions: the Conscious System, C.S., the Preconscious System, P.C.S., and the Unconscious System, U.C.S. Later, this theoretical construct was referred to as the topographical theory.

CONSCIOUS SYSTEM. The Conscious System, which is also referred to as consciousness, is a "...state of awareness of *perceptions* coming from the outside world and from within the body and mind." (Moore and Fine, 1968, p. 28) The Conscious System is a very small part of the mind.

PRECONSCIOUS SYSTEM. In psychoanalysis and dynamic psychotherapy, the preconscious refers to "...memories, ideas, and images, and their verbal symbols as well as motor habits, which are for the most part capable of achieving *consciousness* by the act of focusing *attention*." (ibid., p. 74)

Between the Conscious and Unconscious Systems is a border, or phase, called the Preconscious System, P.C.S. The Preconscious System is like a border between two countries. Everything that passes from the land of the conscious to the land of the unconscious has to go through the Preconscious System and vice versa.

Unconscious memories, fantasies, and perceptions are reawakened by daily sensory or experiential events. They are attached to thoughts or body sensations in the preconscious state and finally come to the level of consciousness and awareness.

UNCONSCIOUS SYSTEM. The Unconscious System, or simply the unconscious, is that part of the mind of which one is unaware. Sensory and perceptual experiences, memories, thoughts, and fantasies, after being perceived consciously, go through the process of repression and are stored in the unconscious. This is particularly true for painful events, traumatic experiences, and their mental contents "...which are unacceptable, threatening or abhorrent to the moral, ethical and intellectual standards of the individual." (ibid., p. 94) These repressed fantasies and wishes continuously strive for expression, resulting in intrapsychic conflicts and feelings of anxiety or guilt. When the defense mechanism of repression fails, neurotic and other psychopathological symptoms manifest in the individual.

The contents of the unconscious are irrational and are regulated by the forces of the *id*—sexual and aggressive drives, pleasure principle, and primary process. The *primary process* is "...a primitive, irrational type of wishful thought, dominated by the emotions and close to the *instinctual drives.* (ibid., p.76) The primary process is closely associated with the unconscious. Manifestations of the primary process are symbolic representations. These representations are frequently preverbal, early verbal, and sensory-visual and have the quality of timelessness and spacelessness. The primary process does not follow Aristotelian logic, causality, or reasoning. It is inclusive and holistic, rather than deductive. A symbol in primary process has multiple representations and meanings. Dreaming, daydreaming, fantasies, and spontaneous creative expressions are manifestations of the primary process. The primary process in the true sense is the language of the unconscious. In a pathological situation, for example, hallucinations, delusions, illusions, loose associations, and irrational thought processes are also expressions of the primary process and the unconscious.

Human Development and the Unconscious

Extensive debate exists among psychoanalysts and child psychiatrists as to when the unconscious develops with its components of primary process and organized fantasies. Melanie Klein (1931, 1932, 1935, 1940), the British psychoanalyst, and her followers believed that the neonate, immediately after birth, has the ability to differentiate between "good objects" and "bad objects" in the mothering person. They believed that the neonate internalizes the "good" mothering qualities through the defense of introjection, and discards and externalizes the "bad" mothering qualities through the defense mechanism of projection. They referred to this as the "paranoid state" of early infancy (birth to age 3 months), which is later followed by a "depressive" phase (ages 3 to 6 months). The acceptance of this hypothesis means that, at the time of birth, the neonate comes to the world with organized thought processes in the form of fantasies and primary process thinking. It also means that the child comes to the world with

recognition memory, evocative memory, and symbolic thought processes.

Anna Freud (1935, 1936, 1945, 1949, 1951, 1965) and her followers, along with a large number of child psychiatrists in the United States, do not agree with Klein's theoretical position. They rely heavily on Piaget's observation of the sensory-motor stage of intelligence. As the reader may recall, according to Piaget, the ability for evocative memory, the development of object permanency, and the use of symbols, whether verbal or visual, occur by ages 18 to 24 months.

Based on the observations of Piaget and ego psychologists, it appears that the unconscious processes, in the form of organized memories and fantasies, evolve from sensory-motor intelligence, mother-child interaction, and environmental experiences sometime during the second year of life.

Primary Process

According to psychoanalytic theory, primary process, or primary process thinking, is the language of the unconscious. Reasoning and logical thinking are called secondary process thinking and originate from the primary process. The development of evocative memory by the age of 18 months is the foundation for the development of primary process, in the form of organized fantasies, mental images, and symbolic representation. Instinctual drives and impulses find affective expression in the form of wishes and fantasies, dreams, and daydreams of the primary process.

Development of the Ego

Regarding the development of the *ego,* we now know that some of the major ego functions are present at birth or soon after, such as sensory-motor behavior, discriminatory response to animate versus inanimate objects, and specific response to the syntax of human language.

According to Rene Spitz (1965), during the first 18 months of life, three major developments facilitate the integration and organization of the *ego:* (1) the development of the social smile by age 3 months, (2) the full expression of stranger-separation anxiety by age 8 months, and, (3) the ability to say "no, no" for assertion and expression of aggression by age 15 to 16 months.

By the age of 18 to 24 months, the development of symbolic thought processes and language add further to the functions of the *ego* and enhance human adaptation. Between 2 and 3 years of age, the following autonomous functions of the *ego* can be clearly observed: perception—visual, auditory, tactile, olfactory, taste; motility, control of body functions; development of thought processes in the preoperational level, with an abundance of primary process fantasy; and the development of early reality testing.

Most of the *ego* defense mechanisms, such as introjection, projection, denial, displacement, reversal, repression, and an elementary form of sublimation, are observable. In an intellectually precocious child, or a child who has experienced traumatic toilet training, one might see evidence of obsessional defenses, such as doing-undoing, isolation of affect, and rudimentary forms of rationalization.

STAGES OF PSYCHOSEXUAL DEVELOPMENT

The *oral stage* (birth to ages 18 to 24 months) of psychosexual development was discussed in chapter 2.

Anal Stage

The anal stage in psychoanalysis, or Erikson's muscular-anal stage, spans from 18 months to 3 years of age. This stage is related to the development of eliminative organs and the musculature of the body. Libidinal and erotic energy become cathected to the anal zone. The developmental milestones of this stage are the achievement of voluntary release and control of bowel function (in the form of expelling and withholding), further strengthening of the muscles, and improvement in body coordination. Orderliness, punctuality, thrift, further differentiation between good and bad, the ability for "letting go" and "holding on," and the ability to control oneself are the psychological traits developed during this phase.

Doubt and ambivalence in the form of love and hate are more prevalent during this stage. The child subjects others and the self to harsh and unrelenting punishment at the time of transgression, reflecting the primitive aspects of the superego and the projective identification with parental prohibitions and disciplines.

According to Erikson, healthy development of the individual in the anal stage facilitates the establishment of the sense of autonomy. Pathological development results in an overwhelming sense of shame and doubt, which can plague the individual throughout life.

Erikson (1950), in his *Eight Ages of Man*, relates the development of the sense of shame, doubt, and guilt to Phase II, Muscular-Anal (ages 1½ to 3 years), and Phase III, Locomotor-Phallic

(ages 3 to 7 years), of childhood development. He stated:

> Shame is an emotion insufficiently studied, because in our civilization it is so early and easily absorbed by guilt. Shame supposes that one is completely exposed and conscious of being looked at: in one word, self-conscious.
>
> p. 252.

In another place, Erikson wrote:

> Visual shame precedes auditory guilt, which is a sense of badness to be had all by oneself when nobody watches and when everything is quiet—except the voice of the superego.
>
> ibid., p. 253.

Self-control is related to the development of the feeling of well-being and pride. Loss of control is the source of shame and doubt. Erikson lucidly discussed the origin of the superego and guilt, along with the remnant of the infantile parental imago, which remains throughout adult life:

> Naturally, the parental set is at first infantile in nature: the fact that human conscience remains partially infantile throughout life is the core of human tragedy. For the superego of the child can be primitive, cruel, and uncompromising, as may be observed in instances where children overcontrol and overconstrict themselves to the point of self-obliteration...
>
> ibid., p. 257.

Behaviors of the Anal Stage

Between ages 12 and 24 months, children begin to show curiosity about their bowel movements. They not only want to play with food and smear food around, but also may reach into their diapers and touch and feel their feces with their hands and may even eat it. They may smear their feces on their bodies, cribs, or on walls. It is important for parents to know that fascination with and interest in feces at this age is natural. Children do not differentiate between food and feces, or "clean" and "dirty." With patience and understanding, parents can help their children to become more discreet. Interest in feces is gradually displaced and sublimated to other more acceptable behavior, such as playing with mud, clay, Play-Doh, or coloring.

Between ages 16 and 25 months, in the period of rapprochement, the child becomes interested in the disappearing of feces down a flushing toilet. He is frightened and fascinated by the flushing toilet. He likes to play with the water in the toilet bowl and to drop objects into the bowl and retrieve them. He flushes the toilet over and over, perhaps repeating "all gone," but not really understanding where it has "all gone!"

Between ages 1½ and 2½ years, the child collects objects and hides them. Also, it is not uncommon for mother to discover that the child has gone to a corner of the house, has wiggled out of his diapers, and has had a bowel movement on the floor. These behaviors are related to two major developmental occurrences. One is the child's ability to separate himself physically from mother, and his acute awareness and apprehension concerning her comings and goings. The other is further cognitive awareness of body parts and functions, along with libidinal cathexis to the anal zone.

During the oral stage, and particularly the oral-aggressive phase, aggressive behavior, such as biting, occurred in an unpredictable and unorganized fashion. In the anal stage, the overt and object-directed expression of hostility and aggression occurs.

Temper Tantrums

Between ages one and 3 years, the child, when he is angry or frustrated, may throw temper tantrums. At this time, the child becomes extremely angry, screams, and cries. Sometimes he lies down on the floor and kicks his legs and moves his arms violently. He may cry so hard that he cannot inhale fast enough and he may become "blue in the face." Some children also may hold their breath, especially if they are having some difficulty with toilet training. In extreme situations, the child may bite, scratch, kick, hit, or throw objects at the mother. The child becomes obstinate, and the more one approaches him, the worse the tantrum becomes. The temper tantrum may end in a total panic reaction and physical exhaustion.

Management by the parents can intensify or decrease the intensity and frequency of temper tantrums. Loss of control by the parents frightens the child, who is just learning to control himself, and intensifies the temper tantrum behavior. Inconsistent management, such as at first frustrating the child, and then giving in to him, also encourages temper tantrums. Careful, sensitive, and "matter of fact" management on the part of the parents helps significantly in decreasing the frequency of temper tantrums.

Between the ages of one and 3 years, aggressive and hostile impulses find an effective mode of expression through newly acquired skills of body motility and through the emergence of anal behavior, such as withholding, expulsion, negativism, and oppositional behavior.

Toilet Training

Toilet training is accomplished when the child has gained control over defecation and urination. Some parents pride themselves in toilet training their child by the age of one to 1½ years. This could occur through a reflexive mechanism, but, from a developmental point of view, the ability to control the sphincter muscles occurs between 2 and 2½ years of age, following the mastery of body movement.

If the parents are sensitive to the temperament of the child, and allow him to go at his own pace, the painful and hair-raising "battle of the wills" over toilet training will not occur.

Children, from the ages of 1½ to 2 years, become curious and want to go to the bathroom like their parents and their older siblings. The "potty game" begins. The child's interest in the "potty game" waxes and wanes. The parents should respect and be sensitive to the child's interests, and not "coerce" or "bribe" the child for the ulterior motive of toilet training. The child should take the initiative and the parents should respond accordingly.

Between ages 2 and 2½ years, the child not only becomes more curious about toilet training, but also about mother's, father's, and siblings' sexual organs. The child's questions should be answered in simple language, without seduction or prohibition.

By the age of 2½ years, when the child has sufficiently mastered body motility and basic language and has passed through the troublesome phase of rapprochement and established some degree of object constancy, it is a naturally appropriate time to begin toilet training. At this age, the average child enthusiastically responds to mother's invitation to begin toilet training or will even ask to do so. Generally, if the parents' attitude is helpful and the timing is right, toilet training will take only a couple of weeks. The child will have occasional "accidents" at times of stress, illness, trauma, or in mother's absence. Parents need to be understanding and sympathetic when these "accidents" occur.

Critical Issues of the Anal Stage

If the relationship between mother and child is traumatized or based on frustration or intolerance, anal behavior, such as smearing, hoarding, and withholding, becomes reinforced and overly cathected with hostility and aggression. Obstinacy, passive resistive behavior, negativism, and oppositional syndrome, in the form of defying and opposing everthing parents—especially mother—

say, may occur. Normal and healthy oppositional behavior becomes exaggerated and pathological. Traumatic experiences in the anal phase may contribute to the arrest or fixation of some of the character traits in this phase, and to the development of personality disorders, such as oppositional disorder and passive-aggressive personality disorder.

Karl Abraham (1921) perceived overconcern with cleanliness, obsessional tendencies, compulsiveness, exaggerated parsimony, and overwhelming ambivalence as the major character traits of adult individuals with fixation in the anal stage.

INFANTILE NEUROSES

In precocious children, or in a family with overemphasis on cleanliness, orderliness, and avoidance of "dirty objects," the child may develop obsessional behavior and, at times, obsessional neuroses. The following behavior may frequently be observed: hand-washing, fear of germs, fear of the toilet, fear of holes, and approach and avoidance behavior. Fortunately, most of these developmental disturbances are temporary and transient. With parental counseling and minor changes in managing the child, these infantile neuroses subside. In severe situations, these symptoms may continue and become crystallized in the form of character traits and result in the development of obsessional-compulsive neurosis, compulsive personality disorders, or other forms of psychopathology. (see chapter 9)

SLEEP

Between the ages of one and 3 years, sleep becomes more regulated, and the child usually sleeps through the night.

Transient Sleep Disturbances

Transient sleep disturbances occur at the peak of the phase of rapprochement (16 to 25 months), especially when mother is absent or the child is under physical or psychological distress. The child may have difficulty in going to sleep, or may wake up panic-stricken, agitated, screaming, and crying, as though something horrible had happened. The child is terrified. Going to sleep, at this age, may be associated with the feeling of separation from mother and may provoke separation anxiety. Reassurance, singing a lullaby, or a story read to the child in his room by mother or

father, may help to decrease the child's fear of separation and insure proper sleep.

Some children insist on coming to the parental bed to sleep with the parents. Having a child share the parental bed may be frustrating for father or mother and deprive them of their privacy and intimacy. This will compound the ambivalent relationship between parents and child. The parents may perceive the child as an intruder or nuisance. The child may be sexually stimulated by sharing the parental bed. Overstimulation for the child, who is already burdened with numerous developmental tasks, contributes to further sleep disturbances, nightmares, night terrors, and possible future phobias. (Fraiberg, 1950; Anders and Weinstein, 1972)

Grandmother's Advice

In case of transient sleep disturbances, the grandmotherly advice of giving a warm bottle of milk, a cracker, a banana, or hot chocolate works well to induce sleep. Food not only symbolizes mother's affection and care for the child, but also we now know that there is a high level concentration of tryptophan in bread, milk, banana, and cocoa. Tryptophan in the body converts to serotonin, which has a tranquilizing, calming, and sedative effect on the agitated or anxious child.

The use of sedatives for inducing sleep in a healthy, normal child with a transient sleep disturbance should be avoided.

At the time of toilet training, transient sleep disturbance may reappear. At this time, the child is afraid that by going to sleep, or that when he is asleep, he will lose control and soil his bed. The fear of soiling and losing mother's approval can result in the child's refusal to go to sleep or in his waking up with nightmares. Premature efforts in toilet training, overstimulation, and separation from mother are three major factors in sleep disturbances in children between ages one and 3 years and older.

EEG and Sleep

The sleep EEG gradually resembles adult sleep, with the appearance of Stage IV sleep. The EEG of Stage IV sleep is comprised of high-voltage waves of 2 cycles per second or less. It is thought that during Stage IV sleep children and adults secrete somatotropin and growth hormones. The secretion of cortisol and other alerting hormones, which prepare the individual to deal with stress and also ready him for flight or fight, is related to the lighter phases of sleep—Stages I and

II. In older children and adults, Stage IV sleep occurs more frequently in the first few hours of sleep. Stages I and II, with the absence of Stage IV, occur more frequently in the last hours of sleep before wakefulness.

Onset of Dreaming in Childhood

According to Metcalf (1977), the onset of dreaming in children is at approximately age 18 months. The active sleep or REM sleep, which is prevalent during the first year of life, is frequently referred to as a predream or protodream state, because there is no symbolic representation attached. The onset of dreaming is associated with the development of symbolic thought representation, establishment of object permanency, and the development of language proper (ages 18 to 24 months). The child is able verbally to report his dreaming experiences.

EEG and Wakefulness

The major EEG changes during ages 1 to 3 years occur in wakefulness. The EEG becomes more organized with significant growth in the development of alpha rhythms. By age 3, there is evidence of EEG lateralization of alpha rhythms. In the right-handed child, the alpha rhythms over the left hemisphere are more organized and have a slightly higher amplitude compared with the alpha waves of the right hemisphere. This lateralization will continue to develop further throughout childhood and adolescence.

EATING

The child, by age 18 months, is able to feed himself with some spilling. He can eat almost anything, although it is advisable to avoid giving him (up to the age of 4 to 5 years) small, hard pieces of food, such as peanuts, because such food may be inhaled.

The question arises whether the child should continue bottle feeding at naptime or bedtime. This needs to be individualized. The use of a bottle or pacifier helps to satisfy the child's need for nonnutritive sucking, decrease tension, and may serve as a transitional object to alleviate worries of the child concerning separating from mother while going to sleep.

Transient Eating Disturbances

During the subphase of rapprochement (ages 16 to 25 months), the child may develop transient food fads to engage mother in further interaction. Also, at the time of separation from mother, the child may refuse to eat or may overindulge. Sensitive management usually alleviates these temporary disturbances.

At the time of toilet training, the child may also become a fussy eater. Smearing food, picky eating, and the concern about the "cleanliness" or "dirtiness" of the food may temporarily interfere with the child's healthy appetite. Sensitive management and allowing the child to eat when he wants, without forcing food, punishing, bribing, or saying, "Just eat another bite for mommy's sake," will alleviate the temporary problem.

It is important to have food available to eat if he is hungry, but if he is not hungry, or if for some reason does not want to eat, that is all right, too. If the child becomes hungry between meals at this age, it is perfectly all right to give him a healthy snack.

PLAY BEHAVIOR

Play enhances the sensory-motor development of intelligence, increases affective and emotional attachment between the child and parental figures, and becomes a major vehicle for socialization and the acquisition of skill in the second and third years of life.

Neonates' cooing and repeating playfully their own voices by the age of one month are precursors of play. Emergence of the social smile by the age of 3 months brings about the beginning of social play between the parents and the child. The recognition smile of 4 months reinforces the mother-child mutual play, in the form of rocking, babbling, touching, and making various noises. Between 8 and 10 months of age, the child begins to play pat-a-cake and peek-a-boo, which help him develop further eye-hand coordination and also help him in the mastery of separation anxiety. Repetition of behaviors is the essence of play. Affective expression and pleasurable discharges are also associated with play. From an ethological point of view, play is significant in the development of the social bond and in the grooming behavior between primates.

Problem solving is also an important ingredient of play. Freud (1920), in *Beyond the Pleasure Principle,* observed his 13-month-old grandson. He noticed that, when the child's mother left the room, the little boy found an object with a string attached to it. He would throw this object under furniture and out of sight, and then he would go and retrieve it. He engaged in this play activity over and over, with joy and relief, while vocalizing a monosyllabic word. Freud conceptualized this behavior as "compulsion to repeat." By making the object appear and disappear, the child re-created the mother's coming and going, and in this manner tried to master the anxieties of separation. The important point is the recognition and aware-ness that children do not follow the Puritan ethic of differentiating between "work" and "play." Work is play, and play is work. (Erikson, 1950)

Play enhances the child's mastery over the environment and his own impulses, and increases his adaptive behavior. Play is the mother of discovery, creativity, and invention.

Between ages 12 and 18 months, the child is usually engaged in play with adults or older siblings. He does not pay much attention to another child of the same age. He may grab a toy from a child or inadvertently touch or push the child. Between ages 18 and 24 months, parallel play begins between two children of the same age. At this time, the children play alongside each other, but really do not play with each other. They may grab things from each other, poke each other, and occasionally hit each other. They may play peek-a-boo, or the equivalent of hide and seek.

Between 2 and 3 years of age, after the establishment of relative object constancy, the child becomes ready to expand his dyadic relation-ship with mother to others, including children his own age. Then, real play with peers begins. (see chapter 4)

GENDER IDENTITY

The development of gender identity—the awareness of being a boy or a girl—occurs relatively early. Money and Ehrhardt's (1972) studies of children who were brought up as the opposite sex because of outward genital anomaly revealed that gender identity is not related to gonadal hormones or genetic endowments. It is directly related to the sex designation and sex assignment of the rearing environment.

Between the ages of 2 and 2½ years, the gender identity is firmly established in the child's mind. Serious psychological disturbances have occurred following surgical correction of genital anomalies, if one has not taken the gender identity and the sex assignment by the rearing environment (the parents) into consideration.

The development of gender identity precedes the emergence of the third psychosexual stage of human development—the phallic-oedipal phase (ages 2½ or 3 to 6 years).

REFERENCES

Abraham, K. (1921). Contributions to the theory of the anal character. In *On Character and Libido Development*. New York: Basic Books, 1966, pp. 165–187.

Anders, T., Weinstein, P. (1972). Sleep and its disorders in infants and children: A review. *Pediatrics, 50*, 312–324.

Chomsky, N. (1957). *Syntactic Structures*. The Hague: Mou-ton.

Chomsky, N. (1972). *Language and Mind*. New York: Har-court, Brace Jovanovich.

Erikson, E. (1950). *Childhood and Society*. Second Edition. New York: Norton, 1963.

Flavell, J.H. (1963). *The Developmental Psychology of Jean Piaget*. New York: D. Van Nostrand.

Fraiberg, S. (1950). On the sleep disturbances of early child-hood. *Psychoanal. Study Child, 5*, 285–309.

Fraiberg, S. (1969). Libidinal object constancy and mental representation. *Psychoanal. Study Child, 24*, 9–47.

Freud, A. (1935). Psychoanalysis and the training of the young child. *Psychoanal. Q., 4* 15–24.

Freud, A. (1936). *The Ego and the Mechanisms of Defense*. New York: International Universities Press.

Freud, A. (1945). Indications for child analysis. *Psychoanal. Study Child, 1*, 127–150.

Freud, A. (1949). Aggression in relation to emotional develop-ment. *Psychoanal. Study Child, 3–4*, 37–42.

Freud, A. (1951). Observations on child development. *Psycho-anal. Study Child, 6*, 18–30

Freud, A. (1965). *Normality and Pathology in Childhood: Assessments of Development*. New York: International Universities Press.

Freud, S. (1920). Beyond the pleasure principle. *Standard Edi-tion of the Complete Psychological Works of Sigmund Freud*, Vol. 18. pp. 1–64.

Freud, S. (1923). The ego and the id. *Standard Edition of the Complete Psychological Works of Sigmund Freud*, Vol. 19. pp. 3–66.

Harrison, S., McDermott, J.F. (Eds.) (1972). *Childhood Psychopathology: An Anthology of Basic Readings*. New York: International Universities Press.

Hartmann, H. (1949). *Ego Psychology and the Problem of Adaptation*. New York: International Universities Press.

Klein, M. (1931). A contribution to the theory of intellectual inhibition. *Int. J. Psychoanal., 12*, 206–218.

Klein, M. (1932). *The Psychoanalysis of Children*. London: Hogarth.

Klein, M. (1935). A contribution to the psychogenesis of manic-depressive states. In *Contributions to Psychoanaly-sis*. London: Hogarth, 1948.

Klein, M. (1940). Mourning and its relation to manic-depres-sive states. In *Contributions to Psychoanalysis*. London: Hogarth, 1948.

Lewis, M. (1977). Language, cognitive development, and per-sonality. *J. Am. Acad. Child Psychiatry, 16*, 646–661.

Levy, D.M. (1955). Oppositional syndromes and oppositional behavior. *Proc. Annu. Meet. Am. Psychopathol. Assoc., 44*, 98–111.

Mahler, M. (1967). On human symbiosis and the vicissitudes of individuation. *J. Am. Psychoanal. Assoc., 15*, 740–763.

Mahler, M. (1972). On the first three subphases of the separa-tion-individuation process. *Int. J. Psychoanal., 53*, 333–338.

Metcalf, D.R. (1977). Sleep and dreaming: Protodream and predream. In Wolman, B.B. (Ed.), *International Encyclo-pedia of Neurology, Psychiatry, Psychoanalysis, and Psy-chology*, Vol. 10. New York: Van Nostrand Reinhold, pp. 246–257.

Money, J., Ehrhardt, A.A. (1972). *Man and Woman, Boy and Girl*. Baltimore: Johns Hopkins University Press.

Mooré, B.E., Fine, B.D. (Eds.) (1968). *A Glossary of Psychoanalytic Terms and Concepts*. Second Edition. New York: The American Psychoanalytic Association.

Spitz, R. (1965). *The First Year of Life*. New York: International Universities Press.

Chapter 4

THE WORLD OF MAKE-BELIEVE: Three to Six Years of Age

The child between ages 3 and 6 years gains mastery of motor behavior—walking, running, jumping, and climbing. The child can comprehend and communicate through language and, by the end of this period, can create complete sentences with pronouns, prepositions, and adjectives. He gains the ability to differentiate on a symbolic thought level between big and small, tall and short, and strong and weak.

The 3- to 4-year-old child can leave mother fairly comfortably for a few hours to spend time with peers in nursery school. He can do so because of the development of object constancy and sufficient mastery of sphincter control. The child becomes acutely aware of the sexual differences between boys and girls and the various body parts. This cognitive awareness and emotional concern expresses itself in the form of "castration anxiety," an irrational fear about bodily injury.

The child's relationships become qualitatively different from when he was younger. Between ages 3 and 6 years, the child moves from a dyadic relationship with mother to a triangular relationship—now, not only mother, but father plays a significant role in the child's fantasy life, dreams, and daily activities.

The child becomes acutely aware of and concerned about what might be "going on" between mother and father sexually and in other ways. Competition with the parent of the same sex for the attention of the parent of the opposite sex emerges. These comparisons, concerns, and competitions pave the way for the child's peer interactions in nursery school and later in school. They also become the blueprints for the child's relationships in adolescence and in adulthood.

Due to the development of symbolic thought representation, object permanency, object constancy, and awareness of body size, control, and power, an active fantasy life emerges. The child is immersed in fantasy, play, and the world of make-believe. Every imaginable thing happens in this make-believe world. Alice in Wonderland, Jack in the Beanstalk, Wizard of Oz, Mickey Mouse, Little Red Riding Hood, Sleeping Beauty, and Hansel and Gretel, and other stories and fairy tales become alive and *real* in the child's mind. Fairy tales and stories give form and validity to the private, frightening, and lonely fantasies of the child at this age and help him master the frightening and enchanting fantasy world.

MOTOR BEHAVIOR

By age 3 years the child is walking and running well and can put on shoes and button and unbutton clothes. He begins to ride a tricycle. Imagine the joy of the child and the parents when he is able to do this! He can now zoom away from his parents and return to them at will. He can go visit neighbors on his tricycle and "show off" how well he can ride. This newly acquired skill gives the child freedom.

Between ages 3 and 4 years, the child is not only able to climb stairs, but uses alternate feet in doing so. He is able to "take turns," an important ingredient of cooperative play and for adaptation in nursery school. Walking and running become smoother. The child can run fast and stop at will without fear of falling.

By age 4 years, the child can stand for 2 seconds on one foot and can assume the posture of throwing. He is able to stack objects on top of each other more carefully and efficiently. The child at age 2 years could stack four blocks, but now the 4-year-old child can stack nine blocks or more. The conquest of space has begun. This achievement is the sign of further development of fine visual-motor coordination.

By age 5 years, the child can skip easily—a marvelous achievement! The child can now dress and undress himself, print letters of the alphabet, and compete in games. Most children have gained complete sphincter control of bowel movements and urination. They are dry at night and relatively free of accidents in the daytime. Some children continue to wet the bed at night. The issue of bedwetting is discussed in chapter 5.

DEVELOPMENT OF INTELLIGENCE
(Cognitive Development)

We have already discussed the beginnings (ages 1½ to 3 years) of Piaget's preoperational subperiod of intelligence, which spans ages 1½ to 7 years. (see chapter 3) As you recall, in this early subperiod, symbolic thought representation, language, fantasy, and play emerge.

Preoperational Thought

In the latter part of the subperiod of preoperational thought (ages 3 to 7 years), the child continues to improve and develop further cognitive ability for mental imagery, specifically for evoking and creating mental images independent of sensory-motor perception. (Flavell, 1963) The child, by now, has integrated the following cognitive abilities:

1. Establishment of object permanency
2. Deferred imitation
3. Symbolic play
4. Drawing images without relying on immediate sensory clues
5. Verbalization

Freeing the thought processes from immediate reliance on the sensory-motor field is an important step—perhaps as important as the child's ability to separate from mother. This freedom allows the child to construct the world in his mind without constant reliance on external objects. Now, if mother is not there, her mental image can be evoked. If an inanimate object is not there, the child can evoke its image and give it reality. The child, in the true sense, has become the owner of "Aladdin's Lamp." Anything he desires, by the magic of thought, appears.

The child still does not have the ability to differentiate between fantasy and reality or thoughts and actions. The thinking process is concrete and literal. The child believes that anything he thinks, dreams, sees, says, or hears

about is *real*. Thoughts and wishes mean action and occurrence.

Sometimes the child aged 4 to 6 years is able to say that something was "make-believe," or "pretend." But this discrimination or differentiation is shaky. Environment and events extensively influence the child's perceptions. Impulses and wishes find an important vehicle for expression in representational thoughts because everything is possible and nothing is impossible. In the world of "make-believe," everything is believable.

Piaget, in his earlier work, refers to the child's preoperational cognition and reliance on fantasy as "egocentric thought," because the child's idea of the world and events relies completely on his internal thought representation and perception. Logic, reasoning, and considering other people's opinions do not have a place in this type of thinking. Preoperational thought has an all or none quality.

If someone calls the child "stupid," he believes he is "stupid." If he hears someone in anger say to another, "I'll kill you," he thinks that it really will happen. The child has not developed the ability to take distance from perceptual inputs or internal thoughts in order to assess them in the light of reality.

The magic power and intensive fear and apprehension associated with this type of thinking is evident. One can easily imagine that when a child between the ages of 3 and 5 years sees on television, for example, two people fist-fighting or shooting at or killing each other, he believes that this is really happening. It is not uncommon for a 3-year-old child to become very upset, panic-stricken, and even cry when viewing such an episode. Unfortunately, many parents do not realize the overwhelming impact that television has on small children. They use television as a baby sitter, without regard to the programs' impact on the young child's mind. Cartoons and animated programs can be just as upsetting.

Absence of Reversibility

According to Piaget, "operation" is the essence of intelligence or thought processes. By operation, Piaget means the ability of a child to perceive reversibility in action and conservation of matter (transformation of reality). For instance, a child aged 5 to 6 years cannot comprehend that $2 + 1 = 4 - 1$. He knows that $2 + 1 = 3$, and he might even know that $4 - 1 = 3$, but he is not able to see that the outcome of these two are the same. He has not developed "reversibility in operation or action." This ability occurs by age 7 years.

Conservation of Matter

The 5- to 6-year-old child's perception of matter is related to one criteria of that object, for example, its length or height, rather than on considering all aspects. Piaget conducted a simple experiment. He poured the same amount of water from a short, wide glass container into a tall, thin one. The child in the preoperational subperiod (ages 2 to 7 years) perceived the amount of water in the tall, thin container as more. Piaget concluded that the child had not developed the understanding of conservation, i.e., matter of the same volume or weight can take various forms. The child does not develop this ability until he is 7 years old.

Summary of Thought Process: Age Three to Six

The predominant features of the child's thought processes between ages 3 and 6 years are as follows:

1. Magical thinking—what you wish will happen

2. Lack of differentiation between thoughts, actions, and reality—dreams, fantasies, and realities are one

3. Active symbolic and representational thoughts, particularly visual and verbal

4. Absence of causality and logical deductions

5. Concreteness

6. Lack of ability to consider more than one alternative or possibility

7. Thinking, seeing, hearing, or feeling is believing

8. Fluidity of identity—animate or inanimate objects can change places. Men and women, animals, and people can easily change identity

9. Belief in magical powers of the self and everything else

10. Timelessness and spacelessness

11. Primary process thinking predominates and the child feels comfortable moving back and forth from fantasies to reality

12. Fantasy, play, and dreams are the major components of thoughts and preoccupy a significant part of the child's life

PSYCHOANALYTIC CONCEPTS OF HUMAN DEVELOPMENT: Three to Six Years of Age

Phallic-Oedipal Stage: Ages 2½ or 3 to 6 or 7 Years

Between ages 2½ and 3 years, a qualitative change occurs in the child's emotional investment (cathexis) to various parts of the body, particularly the genital organs. After the child gains relative mastery in the anal phase, the libidinal drive then becomes highly cathected to the genital area.

Genital Behavior

Infant boys have erections soon after birth. Boys and girls both manifest some masturbatory behavior in the oral and anal stages in the form of rubbing themselves against mother or father or rubbing their legs together. At times, after these stimulations, they become flushed and show some form of relief in what appears to be the equivalent of an orgasm. It is not until ages 2½ to 3 years or older that one sees an intense preoccupation with sexual organs. The child between ages 3 and 4 years openly "plays" with himself and touches his genitals.

Children at this age become very curious about the differences between boys, girls, men, and women. Children become excited, giggle, blush, and touch their genitals while talking or asking questions about these differences. They ask why girls do not have a penis. They need to be reassured that girls have a special opening called a vagina so that they can have babies. These cognitive assurances may help temporarily, but the anxieties and concerns about bodily injury, particularly injury and damage to genitals, predominate.

In the psychoanalytic theory of psychosexual development, ages 3 to 6 years are referred to as the *phallic-oedipal stage:* phallic, because of the child's new awareness and intensive libidinal investment in the genital area, particularly the phallus; and oedipal, because of the child's competition and rivalry with the parent of the same sex and the wish for sexual closeness and union with the parent of the opposite sex (usually occurs in the latter phallic phase—ages 4 to 7 years).

Regarding phallic behavior, boys and girls both, between ages 2½ and 4 years, become very interested in sharp and protruding objects. They like to build high towers. They like to poke their fingers or long objects, such as nails or pencils, into any hole they see, such as electrical sockets, drains, and even parts of their own bodies.

Penis Envy

Girls, between ages 2½ and 3½ years, become acutely aware that boys have something they do not have. Sensitive parents' assurances that "When you grow up you can have babies like mommy," may temporarily alleviate the little girl's concern about not having a penis. But the child still has not developed the cognitive ability to perceive future events and possibilities. She is in the concrete and preoperational subperiod of cognition. Because of the upsurge of active fantasies and deep involvement in the world of make-believe, she may imagine that "bad" things have happened to her, and because of these things she has lost her penis.

The wish for having a penis finds expression in the child's behavior. For example, a 3-year-old, bright, articulate girl had become very curious about why her daddy had a bump in his pants. The parents explained the difference between daddy and mommy. They also used a book that tastefully pictured these differences. The little girl was satisfied with this explanation and went around repeating "Boys have a penis and girls have a vagina." A few hours later, she pointed excitedly to her wrinkled training pants and said, "Daddy, daddy, see—I have a penis!"

Parents need to be sensitive to the developmental stages of the child, the cognitive functioning, and underlying concerns and anxieties. The child may hear the parents' explanation and repeat it, but still not be able totally to understand or internalize it.

Masturbatory Behaviors

In the early phallic phase, "mounting behavior" also emerges. Children want to "play horsey" with mommy and daddy. They will also sit on the parents' or adults' laps and press themselves against adult bodies. Sometimes they go through a wiggling or back and forth motion. It is evident that the child not only enjoys the physical contact, but also is engaged in some form of sexually stimulating behavior.

Parents need not reject or encourage such behavior. They may respond by recognizing that the child at this stage has an upsurge of sexual urges and curiosity, but has not as yet developed enough inhibitions to contain these urges. Laughing at, encouraging, pushing away, or punishing the child will reinforce or inhibit the child's phallic behavior and increase anxieties. Encouragement can be an invitation for seduction and may lead to sexual abuse. Overreaction, rejection, or punishment may cause bewilderment, reinforce and intensify castration anxiety or separation anxiety, and may result in regression to the behavior of the anal or oral phases.

Reacting to the emerging sexuality of a young child is a difficult task. Parents unknowingly may respond automatically to the child's sexual behavior in the same way their parents related to them. This response could be healthy and appropriate or may be unhealthy and contribute to traumatic experiences. Some parents cannot tolerate the masturbatory behavior in children, particularly girls. They react vehemently, threaten the child physically, or shame the child. Masturbatory behavior in this phase is developmentally appropriate and is similar to the smearing of food in a year-old child or the smearing of feces in a 1½- to 2-year-old child. Phallic-oedipal behavior helps the child become more aware of his bodily strengths and limitations and begin learning to control his sexual and aggressive impulses.

Myth of Oedipus

According to Greek mythology, an oracle predicted that the King would have a son and that the son would grow up and kill his father (the King) in a battle and then marry his own mother (the Queen). This prediction frightened the King. When his baby son was born, the father rejected him and ordered his death. However, the baby son was not killed, but instead was taken far away to be raised by a shepherd who did not know his origins. He was called Oedipus because he was flat-footed.

When Oedipus grew older, he was recruited in the service of another King. Eventually, in a battle, as the oracle had predicted, he unknowingly killed his father and then married his own mother. Oedipus, after discovering what had occurred became despondent, gave up everything, and blinded himself.

Freud (1900, 1905), inspired by this Greek tragedy, and through self-analysis and clinical observation, proposed the existence of infantile sexuality. He hypothesized that the child progresses through three stages of psychosexual development: the oral stage (ages birth to 1½ or 2 years), the anal stage (ages 1½ or 2 to 2½ or 3 years), and the phallic-oedipal stage (ages 2½ or 3 to 6 or 7 years).

Children between ages 2½ and 3 years progress from a dyadic relationship with mother to a triangular relationship with mother and father. This triangular relationship peaks during the ages 4 to 6 years.

Boys in the Phallic-Oedipal Stage

In the phallic-oedipal stage, the boy and girl take relatively different tracks. The resolution of the oedipal stage for the boy appears to be less complicated. The boy continues to have attachment and longing toward mother. But now, this longing, instead of being related to the fear of separation, is changed to sexual attraction toward mother. The boy at this stage has active fantasies of pushing daddy out of the scene and marrying mommy. It is not uncommon to hear from a boy aged 4 to 6 years, especially when daddy is away, "Mommy, don't worry, I can look after you better than Daddy."

Children at this stage develop an intense awareness of and concern about different parts of their bodies and compare their body sizes with others, particularly grown-ups. The boy, for instance, in fantasy and play pretends that he is Superman. He thinks that he has "lots of muscles" and is "very strong." During encounters with daddy, especially when the father sets limits for him or is angry with him, he becomes aware of the reality of his smallness and vulnerability. At the same time, when he is sexually excited, he has masturbatory fantasies of sexual relationships with mother. These sexual and aggressive urges express themselves in the form of wishing to kill father and become "the big man of the house." These exciting and frightening wishes are experienced by the ego through the prohibitions of the primitive superego in the form of intense anxiety. The anxiety of this age is referred to as "castration anxiety," or "oedipal anxiety." Castration anxiety manifests itself in children of this age by irrational fear of bodily injury, fear of large animals, the dark, nightmares, and night terrors.

From a psychodynamic point of view, the hostile, aggressive wishes toward father are repressed. These wishes are now projected and displaced outward. For instance, the wish to hurt father is projected outward to "Father will hurt me." The idea of being hurt by father is very frightening and unacceptable to the child's mind, so this frightening idea is repressed and displaced outwardly in the form of irrational fears of bodily injury, large animals, and the dark.

In the latter part of the oedipal phase, the boy (ages 5 to 7 years) gives up outward competition with father. He begins to identify with him. He becomes proud of his father and does not verbalize openly his wish to replace him, as he did when he was aged 3 to 4 years.

By the end of the oedipal stage, competition with father is displaced outwardly to siblings and peers. He compares himself with his peers. He claims that he can "run faster," is "stronger," or is "smarter" than they are.

Sex Play

Between ages 4 and 6 years, mutual exploration games begin. Children go to the bathroom together or behind the garage and visually check or feel each other's genitals. Boys play the urination game (who can "pee" the farthest). They become interested in sex play with girls of the same age or younger. These games are transient and have a stimulating quality. Sex play contributes to the child's sense of discovery and realization of sexual differences between boys and girls. In these games, children sometimes imitate parental sexual behavior.

In situations where children have witnessed sexual relations between parents (the primal scene), or have shared the bed with the parents, the child may become overly stimulated. There are generally two ways children react to and cope with sexually overstimulating and traumatic situations. Some children become overwhelmed by a multitude of sexual wishes and fantasies, resulting in massive repression, overwhelming fear, anxieties, guilt, and phobias. Other children, by "identification with the aggressor," and through "repetition compulsion," will re-enact the stimulating and traumatic situation over and over, not only in play, but also in reality with their peers or, perhaps, with an adult.

Girls in the Phallic-Oedipal Stage

Working through the phallic-oedipal stage is more complicated for girls. The girl aged 3 years is aware of not having a penis, and usually has what is referred to as "penis envy." She also may have feelings of inferiority or of "being damaged."

Developmentally, the girl continues to have attachment and longing toward mother. Between ages 2½ and 4 years, this longing changes to sexual attachment toward mother. Soon afterward, between ages 4 and 6 years, the girl gives up sexual attachment to mother. She then identifies with mother and competes with her for father's affection.

Between ages 4 and 6 years, girls become "young ladies." They dress, act, and behave like mommy. They wear mommy's shoes, clothes, and even occasionally sneak mommy's lipstick to paint their faces. At the same time, they become seductive and coquettish toward daddy. They like to sit between mommy and daddy, separating them. One might hear, "Oh, Daddy, I really would like to marry you." In games and play, girls are constantly preoccupied with playing the roles of mother, wife, and girlfriend.

Bisexuality

Feminine and masculine sexual inclination is present in all human beings throughout life. Intrusiveness, assertiveness, receptivity, and caring are integral components of both feminine and masculine behavior. A predominance of a cluster of behaviors and attitudes gives shape to feminine or masculine identity. Each individual retains some characteristics and traits of the opposite sex. This is called bisexuality. Bisexuality is openly expressed in the phallic-oedipal phase. Girls sometimes act like boys, and boys sometimes act like girls. The expression, exploration, and sex play of the phallic-oedipal stage, along with meaningful relationships with the parents, help the child in the development of sexual identity.

Initiative Versus Guilt

Erikson (1950) calls the phallic-oedipal stage the locomotor-genital stage. According to Erikson, the child experiences guilt and internalizes guilt in the form of ethical and moral values. At the same time, sexual curiosities and interests become sublimated and channelized in the form of initiative. The healthy balance between initiative and guilt gives direction and purpose to the individual. (p. 274)

The concern about body parts, particularly the genitals, brings about intense fears and castration anxiety. These fears can help develop ethical values and the capacity to control sexual and aggressive impulses. Toward the end of the locomotor-genital stage, the superego becomes a consolidated and integrated part of the personality.

The abilities to take initiative and to be assertive evolve during this phase. According to Erikson:

I know that the very word "initiative" to many, has an American, and industrial connotation. Yet, initiative is a necessary part of every act, and man needs a sense of initiative for whatever he learns and does, from fruit-gathering to a system of enterprise.

Erikson, 1950, p. 255.

The experience of guilt by the ego, in the form of conflicts between the wishes of the id and the prohibitions of the superego, is the major and significant psychosocial development in this phase. Overwhelming guilt inhibits the individual's assertiveness and initiative and contributes to the development of a personality plagued by a multitude of phobias, anxieties, depressions, and neurotic inhibitions.

Galenson (1971, 1974, 1979) and Galenson and Roiphe (1976) observed the behavior of 70 children (35 boys and 35 girls) during the first 3 to 4 years of life. She discovered some "urinary awareness" (meaning selective attention to wet diaper, watching one's own urinary stream, and affective experiences, such as excitement, shame, embarrassment, and urinary self-exploration) in most children aged 11 to 14 months.

Soon after manifestation of "urinary awareness," almost all of these children became intensely curious about both parents' urinary behavior and sexual and anatomical differences. Galenson and Riophe postulated that the phallic-oedipal stage, with its awareness and concern about the genitals, occurs much earlier—between ages 1½ and 2 years, rather than at ages 2½ to 3 years. Further confirmation of these findings is necessary.

Children's Sexual Theories

Children between ages 3 and 6 years become very curious about everything in life and ask many questions. However, they also have their own explanations and theories. One area of intense curiosity is how babies are born. Pregnancy of mother, relatives, neighbors, and teachers fuels this curiosity.

Frequently, children believe that mommy got pregnant by eating something, such as peanuts, beans, watermelon seeds, and eggs, or by eating or drinking too much. Oral incorporative fantasies are the most predominant explanations for becoming pregnant. Some children think that the baby comes into the mother through the "navel." Some children have the fantasy that one can get pregnant by looking at something that one was not supposed to see.

Children between ages 3 and 6 years experiment with their theories! For example, they may swallow a seed to see whether they will become pregnant right away or overnight. They may drink a lot of fluid or eat a lot and go around with extended tummies saying that they are pregnant. These pregnancy fantasies occur in boys as well as in girls.

Children in the phallic-oedipal phase are still thinking concretely. One of their concrete experiences is having a bowel movement or occasionally vomiting. Because of this, children frequently think that birth occurs through the rectum or anal area. Fantasies of birth through the mouth, or by vomiting, are also prevalent. If a person can get pregnant through the mouth, then the baby can also come out the same way. Mother's morning sickness, or observing adult sexual relationships, in the form of oral-genital contact, give perceptual credence to these fantasies.

Parental Attitude

Parents need to be aware of the child's vulnerability. Modesty in attire and privacy during sexual intimacy is important. The child has an active imagination; seeing the sexual act or hearing "noises" from the parents' bedroom causes significant stimulation and concern. Young children perceive sexual relationships between adults as physical attacks, or as acts of aggression by the father toward the mother.

When children ask questions and are curious about sexual issues, parents should provide simple, direct explanations. This responsibility should not be left to someone else. Timing and readiness are important. When the child is curious and asks questions, he is ready to learn and wants the answer right away. While educating the child in regard to sexual issues, it is a good idea to ask the child his understanding, so that there will be a dialogue and exchange of information. This will help the parents communicate with the child on his level. Sexual education by the parents is important, but we should bear in mind that most knowledge children acquire about human sexuality is learned from their peers and through mutual exploration.

SLEEP

The child aged 3 to 6 years usually sleeps through the night and may take a brief nap in the afternoon or in nursery school. Sleep is regulated and synchronized with adult sleep. The child experiences all stages of sleep (Stage I through Stage IV). Approximately 20 to 25% of the sleep time is REM sleep.

Sleep Disorders

Sleep disorders in children and youth are divided into two types, based on EEG recordings and sleep polygrams: disorders of arousal and disorders of sleep. (Anders and Weinstein, 1972)

Disorders of arousal are nocturnal enuresis (night bedwetting); somnambulism (sleepwalking), somniloquy (sleep talking), and pavor nocturnis (night terror). These disorders occur when the child is emerging from deep sleep (Stages III to IV non-REM sleep). Because of this, they are referred to as disorders of arousal. Neurological imma-

turity contributes significantly to the development of these disorders. The various disorders of arousal frequently occur in the same family or the same person at different times.

It has been postulated that sleepwalking, talking, and night terrors may be associated with seizure activity, such as temporal lobe epilepsy, grand mal, or petite mal seizures. Careful laboratory observations have not confirmed this hypothesis. (Gastaut and Broughton, 1965; Kales *et al.,* 1968; Poussaint *et al.,* 1967; Yoss and Daly, 1960; Broughton, 1968)

Disorders of sleep include nocturnal enuresis, and narcolepsy (sleep paralysis—going to sleep suddenly while one is awake, talking, or walking). These disorders are associated with light sleep (Stage I REM sleep). Psychological stress plays a significant role in the development of these disorders.

Transient Sleep Disturbances

Transient sleep disturbances, in the form of having a difficult time going to sleep, nightmares, or night terrors, are common at this age. Overstimulation, fighting between parents, separation from parents, fear of bodily injury, and physical distress, such as high fever, overeating, sore throat, gastrointestinal distress, or urinary tract infection, contribute to these temporary and transient sleep disturbances.

Nightmares

In the oedipal stage, sexual and aggressive wishes, along with prohibitions against these wishes, find expression in the visual symbols of dreams. The child at the height of the oedipal phase usually wakes up with nightmares. The child willingly tells his parents about these nightmares. The theme of the nightmares is often related to fears of bodily injury: for instance, a big black bear, bad wolf, or a monster is attacking the child. Sometimes the oedipal fear is not disguised, and the child might say that he dreamt that daddy or mommy was going to "hurt" him. The child can be reassured by helping him talk about the nightmare, act it out in play, or draw a picture of it. Frightening television programs, overstimulation, overeating, or sharing the parental bed increase the frequency of these nightmares.

Night Terrors

Some children may wake up at night totally panic-stricken—screaming, crying, and confused.

They have amnesia and do not know where they are. They do not report dreams or nightmares. This overwhelming anxiety, confusion, and panic behavior is not only distressing to the child, but also to the parents. EEG studies have documented that night terrors in children are related to Stage IV non-REM deep sleep. This is why the children do not report dreams.

Nocturnal enuresis, sleepwalking and sleep-talking, and sleep paralysis will be discussed in chapter 5.

EATING BEHAVIOR

The child between ages 3 and 6 years can feed himself with little spilling. He eagerly identifies with mother and likes to serve others. Between ages 3 and 4 years, the child can pour water and milk from a pitcher. This newly acquired skill helps the child relate better at nursery school at "juice and cracker time." The child can take turns. He becomes more patient and understands the idea of waiting for lunch and supper, although he may need a little snack to tie him over. Between ages 4 and 6 years, the child likes to help set the table. Also he likes to experiment in the kitchen. Eating rituals and food preparation occupy a considerable part of the child's play.

Food Fads

Because of the active emergence of sexual fantasies, the child associates eating and food with his various sexual theories, such as oral impregnation, anal birth, and fatness or fullness of the tummy with pregnancy.

Fear of pregnancy or bodily injury may express itself in the child's refusal to eat or in developing food fads. The child may stop eating eggs, red meat, bananas, or other things. Usually there is some symbolic association to sexuality. The child may also want to eat a specific food all the time, such as peanut butter, tuna fish, or sweets, not only because he likes them, but also because of his private fantasies associated with these foods. Symbolic thought processes begin to emerge between ages 1½ and 2 years and come to fullest expression between ages 2 and 5 years. The child may associate power or growing taller and bigger than mommy or daddy with a particular food. "Spinach power" contributes to the reinforcement of these food fantasies. Parents often use the expression, "Eat your spinach or vegetables so that you will grow big and strong and have lots of muscles." The child at this stage is very concrete. As soon as he eats something, he checks his muscles and flexes them to see if they are stronger and bigger. Strength and size play important roles in the child's mind.

Parental reaction to the child's food fads can make a difference. If parents perceive food fads as a part of this stage and do not reinforce or discourage them, the child sooner or later overcomes these fads. If the parents become overly concerned about what the child eats, the battle over food begins. The more the parents insist, the more the child will become a picky eater. A relaxed and matter-of-fact attitude is the best way to deal with the issue. By the end of this stage, a healthy child gradually becomes free from intense preoccupation with the symbolic phallic-oedipal significance of food.

A traumatized child, or a child who has been exposed to sexual overstimulation, might become fixated and continue to have symbolic attachment to the food. Chronic feeding disturbances, such as anorexia, obesity, gorging oneself and then vomiting, periods of fasting and gorging, obsessional preoccupation with "clean" foods, avoidance of a particular food, or a driven tendency to prepare food for others, may occur.

PLAY

Schiller said, "Man is perfectly human only when he plays." (Erikson, 1950, p. 212) During this century, we have become aware of the significant role of play in human development. Throughout the ages, children were perceived as being idle, lazy, miniature grown-ups wasting their time in nonsense play. Children as young as ages 4 to 5 years were put to work. Many of them had to work 60 to 70 hours each week in the sweatshops or coal mines of Europe and America to fuel the Industrial Revolution. Only during the last 100 years, with emphasis on human rights, and the emancipation of slaves and women, have children gained the freedom to be children and to have the opportunity to play.

Because of this economical and societal change, clinicians' and educators' perceptions of children's play have also changed. Now, children's play is taken seriously. Play is perceived as the child's form of communication and creative expression and as being worthy of careful observation and scientific research. The role of play in psychomotor development, cognitive development, and the expression of internal feelings and fantasies has been recognized. Play therapy has become an effective mode of treating and healing the troubled child. (see chapter 21)

Play is the language of the child—the language of inner space, the unconscious, and the ego functions. Grown-ups talk; children play. The ability to immerse the self in play, which begins in childhood, continues to be a source of unbounded energy and rejuvenation throughout life. The happy adult is the one whose work is play and whose play is work. Children know this secret.

Meaning of Play

Piaget (1962), Spitz (1965), Axline (1964), Erikson (1950, 1972), Woltman (1964), Peller (1954), Lorenz (1972), Klein (1964), Anna Freud (1965), Gardner (1971), among others, have discussed the configuration, symbolic meaning, and developmental and therapeutic aspects of play.

Erikson (1950), in "Toys and Reasons," discussed the relationship of the child's play to adult work and the role of play in the development of the child's sense of mastery, reality, and reason. He divided children's play in the following way:

Autocosmic Play—the child uses the self and later the mother as a play object.

> The child's play begins with and centers on his own body....It...consists at first in the exploration by repetition of sensual perceptions, of kinesthetic sensations, of vocalizations, etc. Next, the child plays with available persons and things. He may playfully cry to see what wave length would serve best to make the mother reappear, or he may indulge in experimental excursions of her body and on the protrusions and orifices of her face. This is the child's first geography, and the basic maps acquired in such interplay with the mother no doubt remain guides for the ego's first orientation in the "world."
>
> p. 220.

Microsphere Play—at this time, the child begins to show interest in inanimate objects and small manageable toys. Playing in the world of small toys brings joy and fear to the child. He gradually masters this world and then ventures further to bigger and bigger objects.

Macrosphere Play—by the age of 3 years, the child begins to play with other children and can manage bigger toys, such as horses, tricycles, and the jungle gym. He discovers which fantasies can be shared with others and which ones should be kept quiet and private.

When the child is under stress or frightened, he may retreat to the microsphere or autocosmic play. The child between ages 3 and 6 years fluctuates between these 3 types of play.

Lili Peller (1954, pp. 178-198), in her classic paper, "Libidinal Phases, Ego Development and Play," divides normal play activities of children into 4 groups:

Group I—The central theme of play in this group is related to the child's body and the anxieties concerning the body. This play is basically solitary. This type of play is predominant in the first few months of life and, in an older child, in temporary or severe forms of ego regression.

Group II—The theme of play is based on the relationship with mother on a preoedipal level and on the fear of the loss of love object, i.e., mother. This type of play predominates from 6 months to 2½ or 3 years. Fantasies in this type of play are simple. The style of play is endless, monotonous repetition, with few variations and no real plot. The child plays with mother or alone. The child may also play with other children or pets, but not as a co-player. This is still a form of narcissistic play or egocentric play.

Group III—Spans ages 3 to 6 years. The theme of this play is the oedipal relationship and the defenses against oedipal wishes or fantasies. The child is not afraid of losing the love object, but is afraid of losing the love of the love object.

Fantasies are abundant. They are frequently compensatory in nature, in the form of "I am big," or "I can do as big people are doing." Not only fantasies about parents and siblings enrich the play, but also about doctors, nurses, firemen, policemen, astronauts, magicians, cartoon heros, and television personalities find an expression in the play.

Doll play predominates. The style of play is spontaneous, with a variety of emotional expressions, roles, settings, and plots. Drama and risk-taking, especially in the latter part of this stage are essential.

The child is engaged in cooperative play with peers and shares fantasies. He can play alone or with others. This play prepares the child for adult roles and skills and cooperation with others. It enhances initiative and encourages ventures into the unknown.

Group IV—The themes of this play, engaged in by children aged 6 years and older, will be discussed in the following chapter.

Erikson (1972) wrote that themes of play represent

> ...some repetitiveness, such as we recognize as the "working through" of a *traumatic* experience: but they also express a playful *renewal*. If they seem to be governed by some need to *communicate*, or even to *confess*, they certainly also seem to serve the joy of *self-expression*. If they seem dedicated to the *exercise* of growing faculties, they also seem to serve the *mastery* of a complex life situation.
>
> p. 131.

NURSERY SCHOOL

In most cultures, children aged 3 to 4 years are encouraged to venture away from home and the "apron strings" of mother. Association with children of the same age is encouraged. If there are no organized school activities, older siblings or some other person besides mother gathers a few children together for work or play.

The best time for a child to begin nursery school depends largely on the child's cognitive, emotional, and psychomotor development. For most children, age 3 is an optimal time because of the establishment of relative object constancy, the development of language, and the control of bowel and bladder functions.

By age 3 years, the child is able to separate from mother for a few hours without major trauma. Studies of children's reactions to separation from mother when beginning nursery school have shown that most children, during the first week, become quiet, unhappy, and have difficulty separating from mother. Some demand that mother stay with them at nursery school.

Children during the first week ignore the other children, only relating to them to take a toy or to hit or scream at them. They interact with the nursery school teacher in an ambivalent manner. At first they avoid the teacher, but soon displace their anger at mother to the teacher. Gradually, they "warm up" to the teacher, even on the first day.

For parents, especially the mother with her first, only, or last child, leaving their baby in nursery school is not an easy task. Mothers want the child to go to nursery school, but at the same time they are apprehensive. The parents' earlier childhood anxieties, particularly separation anxieties, may be reactivated in the form of irrational fear about their child's safety and well-being, concern about the child's soiling, or worries about how other children will treat him. Most parents are able to work through these feelings and to encourage their child to become involved in nursery school.

By the second week, most children become acclimatized to the nursery school and begin to recognize the presence and existence of other children. This recognition manifests itself in the form of mirroring other children's play, parallel play, and finally group play.

By age 4 to 5 years, cooperative play, extensive group fantasy play, and competitive play predominate. Daily traumatic events, such as parental illness, parental vacation, child's illness, grandparents' illness or visits, and even a peer's sickness or absence find creative expression in the child's play. The group as a whole intensively become involved for a short period of time in playing out these daily microtraumatic events. The dominant themes of play are related to developmental issues of the phallic-oedipal stage.

Children between ages 3 and 4 years can benefit from nursery school for 2 to 4 hours per day; children between ages 5 and 6, a full day.

Parental difficulty in separating from the child going to nursery school and giving ambivalent messages, i.e., pushing the child to go while simultaneously pulling the child to stay home, or keeping the child home for minor aches and pains, may contribute to the exacerbation of separation anxiety in the child and, later, to the possibility of school phobia. (see chapter 9)

REFERENCES

Anders, T., Weinstein, P. (1972). Sleep and its disorders in infants and children: A review. *Pediatrics, 50,* 312–324.

Axline, V. (1964). Accepting the child completely. In Haworth, M.R. (Ed.), *Child Psychotherapy, Practice, and Theory.* New York: Basic Books, pp. 239–242.

Broughton, R. (1968). Sleep disorders: Disorders of arousal? *Science, 159,* 1070–1078.

Erikson, E. (1950). *Childhood and Society.* Second Edition. New York: Norton, 1963.

Erikson, E.H. (1972). Play and actuality. In Piers, M.W. (Ed.), *Play and Development.* New York: Norton, pp. 127–167.

Flavell, J.H. (1963). *The Developmental Psychologies of Jean Piaget.* New York: D. Van Nostrand.

Freud, A. (1965). *Normality and Pathology in Childhood: Assessments of Development.* New York: International Universities Press.

Freud, S. (1900). The interpretation of dreams. *Standard Edition of the Complete Psychological Works of Sigmund Freud,* Vol. 4 and 5.

Freud, S. (1905). Three essays on the theory of sexuality. *Standard Edition of the Complete Psychological Works of Sigmund Freud,* Vol. 7, pp. 123–243.

Galenson, E. (1971). The impact of early sexual discovery on mood, defensive organization and symbolization. In Eissler, R.S., *et al.* (Eds.), *The Psychoanalytic Study of the Child,* Vol. 26. New York: International Universities Press, pp. 195–216.

Galenson, E. (1974). The emergence of genital awareness during the second year of life. In Friedman, R.C. (Ed.), *Sex Differences in Behavior.* New York: John Wiley, pp. 223–231.

Galenson, E. (1979). Development from one to two years: Object relations and psychosexual development. In Noshpitz, J. (Ed.), *Basic Handbook of Child Psychiatry,* Vol. 1. New York: Basic Books, pp. 144–156.

Galenson, E., Roiphe, H. (1976). Some suggested revisions concerning early female development. *J. Am. Psychoanal. Assoc., 24,* 29–57.

Gardner, R. (1971). *Therapeutic Communication with Children, The Mutual Storytelling Technique.* New York: Science House.

Gaustaut, H., Broughton, R. (1965). A clinical and polygraphic study of episodic phenomena during sleep. In Wortis, J. (Ed.), *Recent Advances in Biological Psychiatry,* Vol. 8. New York: Plenum, p. 197.

Kales, J.D., Jacobson, A., Kales, A. (1968). Sleep disorders in children. In Abt, L.E., Reiss, B.F. (Eds.), *Progress in Clinical Psychology*. New York: Grune and Stratton, p. 63.

Klein, M. (1964). The psychoanalytic play technique. In Haworth, M.R. (Ed.), *Child Psychotherapy, Practice, and Theory*. New York: Basic Books, pp. 277–286.

Lorenz, K. (1972). The emnity between generations and its probable ethological causes. In Piers, M.W. (Ed.), *Play and Development*. New York: Norton, pp. 64–118.

Peller, L. (1954). Libidinal phases, ego development and play. *Psychoanal. Study Child, 9,* 178–198.

Piaget, J. (1962). The stages of the intellectual development of the child. *Bull. Menninger Clin., 26,* 120–128.

Poussaint, A., Koegler, R., Riehl, J. (1967). Enuresis, epilepsy, and the EEG. *Am. J. Psychiatry, 123,* 1294–1295.

Spitz, R.A. (1965). *The First Year of Life*. New York: International Universities Press.

Woltmann, A. (1964). Concepts of play therapy techniques. In Haworth, M.R. (Ed.), *Child Psychotherapy, Practice, and Theory*. New York: Basic Books, pp. 20–32.

Yoss, R., Daly, D. (1960). Narcolepsy in children. *Pediatrics, 25,* 1025–1033.

Chapter 5

JOYS AND SORROWS OF FRIENDSHIP: Six to Twelve Years of Age

Children between ages 6 and 12 years develop secondary thought processes, reasoning, logical deduction, reality testing, and moral feelings. The child begins to acquire skills at school, at home, and in the community. The tumultuous psychosexual urges of the oedipal phase continue like a wild river that has left the steep and torrential course of the mountain and now quietly but swiftly gives life to the fertile ground of the plain.

Libidinal and aggressive energies are harnassed and channelized. They find effective expression in apprenticeship, whether it be in school, at home, or in the community. The child's horizon expands from the triangular relationship of the phallic-oedipal stage to multiple relationships with peers, teachers, and community members. The child begins to become a potentially productive member of the economic system.

Affection and attachment toward peers of the same sex and adults outside of the home emerge and become extremely important. Group affiliations and values influence the child's life. Friendships gain a new meaning. Some friends made at this age will be friends forever.

Girls continue to mature faster. By the end of this stage they will be 2 years ahead of boys of the same age—a striking difference!

MOTOR BEHAVIOR

Motor skills become more automatic, integrated, and efficient. By age 8 years, the child can ride a bicycle—another major accomplishment! Between ages 8 and 9 years, most children can dress and undress easily.

Regarding fine motor behavior, the child by age 8 years can draw a human form showing awareness of various body parts and sexual differentiation, along with awareness of depth and perspective. Between ages 8 and 10 years, reading and writing become smoother and more expressive.

Between ages 9 and 10 years, the child can function well in organized activities and sports. Parents need to be aware that undue emphasis on competitive sports at this stage might contribute to permanent physical injury and affect the development of joint and bone structures. Overprogramming impinges on the child's need for free and unstructured time.

By ages 9 to 10 years, the child shows preference for either verbal or motoric expression. Some children become interested in working with their hands. They may "tear down" and reassemble their bicycles, build things from wood, or put other things together. They become good at and enjoy manipulating objects. Others become more interested in reading, writing, and verbal expression. They show their agility in the use of words and language more than in the use of their hands. Some children are fortunate in having abilities in both areas.

DEVELOPMENT OF INTELLIGENCE
(Cognitive Development)

Stage of Concrete Operations
(Ages 7 to 11-12 Years)

According to Piaget (1962), there is a qualitative difference in the cognitive functioning of a child aged 6 to 7, as compared with a child aged 7 or older. The child aged '7 to 8 years is able to manipulate objects and to "...deal with logical classes and logical relations." (Harrison and McDermott, 1972, p. 163) The child now is also cognitive of the conservation of matter and reversibility. For instance, he now understands that $2 + 1 = 4 - 1$. He has reached the stage of "concrete operations."

The child from ages 7 to 11 or 12 years is able to classify, number, and serialize objects according to their similarities and differences. This process requires the ability for "inclusion"—in other words, including some objects according to specific criteria, and thereby creating general classes and subclasses or sets and subsets.

Piaget reported a simple experiment. He showed children in the preoperational stage (under age 7 years) a bouquet of flowers in which half were daisies and half were other flowers. He asked the children whether the bouquet had more daisies or more flowers. The children answered, "There are more daisies than flowers," or "...as many daisies as flowers." They had not developed the ability to understand that daisies are a subclass of flowers; they had not developed the ability for inclusion. When the same experiment was performed with children aged 7 to 8 years, they immediately said, "Daisies are flowers." These children were "...capable of solving a problem of inclusion." (ibid., p. 164)

Another form of operation of intelligence which develops between ages 7 and 8 years is the "operation of serialization." The child becomes able to organize and arrange objects progressively based on size or weight. Synthesis, classification, serialization, and construction of numbers also appear.

However, we must realize that the child is in the stage of concrete operation because he needs actual objects and the concrete presence of the objects for serialization, inclusion, or classification. The child is not able to create a hypothetical operation in his mind or do these operations abstractly without their concrete presence.

The child is not able to understand the meanings of metaphors or proverbs. He interprets them literally and concretely. For instance, if you ask a bright, articulate child between ages 9 and 10 years what the proverb, "The grass is greener on the other side of the fence" means, he might answer, "Those people water their grass more." Or, to the proverb, "People in glass houses should not throw stones," the child might answer, "Stones will break the glass."

Moral Feelings

According to Piaget, "moral feelings" appear in a child at age 8 years or older. The child between ages 6 and 7 years has some moral feelings, but their existence depends upon the existence of the parents: "...when the parents are gone, these rules or orders are not obeyed. There is no conservation of these orders when there is no material control." (ibid., p. 174) The child needs the concrete

presence of the parents to follow moral feelings and prohibitions, and he is not able to generalize these feelings to other situations.

Between ages 7 and 8 years, there is a qualitative difference in the child's actions. Now, he does not need the presence of parents to follow moral rules and is able to generalize the rules to other situations. Piaget refers to this development as "autonomous morality."

"Autonomous morality," or the "morality of reciprocity," means that the child has developed an internal sense of values and does not need to rely on the "morality of obedience," that is, obedience to the parents or other adults. (ibid., p. 175) As a result of this, between ages 8 and 10 years feelings of "fair play" and "justice" develop between peers.

PSYCHOSEXUAL DEVELOPMENT

Freud referred to the psychosexual development of children in this stage as "latency," meaning that the phallic-oedipal urges become relatively quiet and latent in the child. There has been considerable debate about the term "latency." Some feel that the term should be discarded and that this stage should be referred to as "elementary school age." Others feel there is still validity in using the term "latency," but with some modification.

Some authors, like Bornstein (1951), have divided latency into two phases—early latency (ages 5½ to 8 years), and late latency (ages 8 to 10 years). Some divide latency into the early school-age child (ages 6 to 8 years) and middle school-age child (ages 8 to 10 years).

We propose the following classification for more clearly describing the behavior and psychosexual development of children between the ages of 6 and 12 years:

1. Early latency (ages 6 to 8 years)
2. Middle latency (ages 8 to 10 years)
3. Late latency or prepubescence (ages 10 to 12 years)

Early Latency (Ages 6 to 8 Years)

During early latency, the child alternates between having active oedipal fantasies and experiencing the fear and guilt related to these fantasies. The ego's defense of repression is not consolidated.

The superego, like a newly appointed policeman, is inconsistent—at times unduly harsh and rigid and at other times clumsy and ineffective.

Because of this open struggle between lingering oedipal wishes and the clumsy superego, the child has frequent but temporary regressions to the oral or anal stages. For instance, transient separation anxieties appear when the child goes to kindergarten or school. Also, there is a tendency toward somatization of psychosexual conflicts. The child might have aches and pains or cling to mother. He might either refuse to go to school or find an excuse to come home early. Crystallization of these behaviors may result in an acute form of separation anxiety, such as school phobia. (see chapter 9)

Sphincter control, which was accomplished fairly well by the age of 4 to 5 years, may also be affected. Children might wet their pants in school or occasionally soil when returning home from school.

The child in this stage often complains, becomes cranky, and "projects" most troubles or unhappiness onto others, such as his teacher, the bus driver, and peers or siblings. By clinging, blaming, and aggressive behavior, the child invites parental punishment. Punishment by the parents appears to be more easily tolerated than the constant internal punishment of the rigid, clumsy policeman (superego).

Middle Latency (Ages 8 to 10 Years)

By ages 8 to 10 years, the child has come more to terms with the phallic-oedipal wishes. Frightening incestuous wishes have been repressed in the dungeon of the unconscious. Sexual and aggressive wishes find sublimation in school, work, and play. Masturbatory behavior continues in a more discreet manner.

Friends close to the same age and sex become the source of libidinal attachment. Children of this age horseplay with each other, grab each other's genitals, show each other their "private parts," and occasionally fondle each other in a "homosexual manner." Sexual jokes of oral, anal, or genital nature, especially between boys, permeate the conversation. Words such as "fart," "fuck," and "screw" take on new symbolic and affective meaning. Sexually colored jokes or talk gradually become more codified in the form of secret words or private language between a few friends. The child has become more discreet and does not easily reveal private thoughts and fantasies to adults, as he did between ages 4 and 6 years.

Obsessional defenses, such as isolation of affect from thought, rationalization, and intellectualization, help the child adapt to the environment and develop relative objectivity. Over-utilization of obsessional defenses, at the expense of experiencing the joy and pleasure of friendship and play, contributes to the development of obsessional neurosis and the emergence of a joyless, obsessive child. (Adams, 1974)

Late Latency (Ages 10 to 12 Years)

Boys and girls follow two separate developmental tracts in late latency. Girls—already with a developmental head start—now grow by leaps and bounds. Early signs of pubescence appear. Girls become taller and surpass boys of the same age in height. They lose baby fat from their face and acquire a rounding of the buttocks area. Breast buds begin to show. One of the earliest signs of pubescence is the appearance of hair in the genital area.

With the emergence of pubescence, girls become self-conscious, shy, and overly modest. They worry about whether peers, parents, or older siblings will find out about these changes. They become quiet, moody, withdrawn, and cry easily.

At first, girls often pretend nothing is happening. Some become more "tom-boyish," and deny the emergence of sexuality. Some feel that they are becoming "too fat" and begin to diet to lose weight, and thus outward physical changes become less obvious. In most situations, food fads and dieting are temporary. In some cases, because of extensive symbolization of food and disturbances in eating behavior in earlier years, children may develop symptoms of anorexia nervosa. (see chapter 12)

Girls, especially between ages 11 and 12 years, begin to show a surprising change in motor behavior and cognitive functioning. They become awkward, clumsy, and uncoordinated. They trip over or bump into things. This is probably due to the hormonal explosion (e.g., estrogen increases 40 to 50 times) and uneven and rapid body growth. They may also show some disorganization in thinking. They forget things easily and become "scatterbrained."

At this stage, girls are so sensitive and concerned about what is happening to their bodies that they do not even discuss these changes with their best friends. The mother, or another woman with whom the girl has a close relationship, can help the young person understand these tremendous body changes and provide proper information, guidance, and reassurance.

Height continues to increase between the ages of 12 and 13 years. The pelvic bony structure becomes wider. The buttocks become rounder, the uterus, vagina, labia, and clitoris become larger, and auxiliary hair begins to grow. In most girls, the menstrual period begins around 12½ years. At the same time, there is a significant decrease in skeletal growth.

Boys aged 10 to 12 years generally show only slight signs of pubescence or secondary sexual characteristics. Between ages 10 and 11 years, the penis and testicles increase slightly, with evidence of fuzzy pubic hair. Between ages 12 and 13 years, the activity of the prostate increases with evidence of gonadotropins in the urine. There is an increase in the size of the nipple and areolae of the breast. In boys, most pubescence growth activities occur between ages 12 and 15 years. (see chapter 6)

In late latency, boys continue to show similar behavior to that of middle latency, with emphasis on group activities with other boys and pride in muscle building and physical prowess. They become more involved in sports activities, camping, outdoor activities, or in having business enterprises, such as paper routes.

Boys feel threatened and frightened by the emerging sexuality of girls of the same age. Frequently, they act awkward, silly, and "childish" when relating to girls of the same age who are physically and emotionally more mature.

Early or delayed pubescence in both girls and boys may create apprehension, not only in the child, but also in the parents. The onset of pubescence is related to familial tendencies, nutrition, environmental stimulation, and the development of the central nervous system, especially the hypothalamus area.

Intense self-consciousness and embarrassment is a frequent psychological reaction to early or delayed pubescence. A young person with delayed pubescence may react with overwhelming self-doubt and concern about masculinity or femininity. He may feel that he is a "queer" or a "freak." When there is early or delayed pubescence, after a routine work-up the family physician or pediatrician can help significantly to alleviate the young person's and family's concern by openly explaining the situation.

INDUSTRY VERSUS INFERIORITY

Erikson (1950) perceived the latency stage as "entrance into life." This life "...must first be school life, whether school is field or jungle or classroom." (p. 258)

The child

...has experienced a sense of finality regarding the fact that there is no workable future within the womb of his family, and thus becomes ready to apply himself to given skills and tasks, which go far beyond the mere playful expression of his organ modes or the pleasure in the

function of his limbs. He develops a sense of industry—i.e., he adjusts himself to the inorganic laws of the tool world.

ibid., p. 259.

According to Erikson, in all cultures the child at this stage receives some form of *"systematic instruction."* The child learns *"the fundamentals of technology"* of that culture, whether it be hunting, farming, making things, or schooling.

The sense of industry versus inferiority predominates. The child experiences the feelings of accomplishment, achievement, and productivity. At the same time, when he compares himself with adults, he feels less productive and inferior. He realizes that he needs guidance. The healthy balance between the sense of industry versus inferiority helps the latency-age child to commit himself to hard work, to learn methods of productivity, and to gain competence. (ibid., p. 274)

FRIENDSHIP

Throughout the latency stage, boys as a rule avoid girls, and girls avoid boys. Friendship, closeness, and intimacy with persons of the same sex is the ethos of this stage. Cliques and group affiliations predominate. Scapegoating younger, weaker, smarter, or racially different children is common. Children up to ages 5 to 6 years are not aware of racial prejudice. Between ages 6 and 12 years, children acquire racial prejudicial tendencies from their parents, peers, and society.

The anxieties of prepubescence contribute to group "stickiness" and to the exclusion of those who are "different" from their group. Lack of affiliation at home increases the need for peer affiliation, sometimes to a pathological level. In troubled families, the child's anger and hostility toward parents are displaced onto authorities in the community. These children become more intolerant of others and overtly show racial prejudice.

On the other hand, overemphasis on family closeness, at the expense of a healthy balance between affiliation with peers and the family, creates conformity, obsequiousness, inhibitory tendencies, lack of adventurousness, and cultural and racial prejudice. A healthy balance between the joys and sorrows of friendship and the security of family life helps the latency-age child to unfold endowed potential, enrich the sense of industry in school or in the community, and become ready for the tumultuous stage of adolescence.

SUPEREGO DEVELOPMENT

In the middle and late latency, with the enhancement of autonomous ego functions and the relative neutralization of sexual and aggressive drives, the child begins to modify, change, and integrate parental and societal values. He becomes like a master chef who has acquired a multitude of new materials and now is creating his own dish.

The superego is now a relatively competent, efficient, and fair judge of the young person's wishes and actions. He does not punish himself mercilessly for "forbidden wishes." Words and wishes lose their overwhelming magical power. One hears children saying, "Sticks and stones might break my bones, but words will never hurt me." This is concrete representation of the beginning of differentiation between words and actions. There are times, during physical and emotional distress, when the child will regress. Then the primitive, harsh superego of the anal, phallic-oedipal, or early latency stages becomes operative.

Group affiliation enhances the development and integration of the superego. However, at times the group may contribute to "primitivization" of the superego, depending on the composition of the group and environmental situations. For instance, the peer group can become a harsh judge and merciless executioner toward a member who has broken the code of secrecy or who has betrayed the group. Expulsion from the group, bullying, and ostracizing are the most common forms of punishment. In severe situations, all inhibitions and values may be temporarily abandoned for the sake of compliance with the group.

The group and friends can help strengthen the child's ego ideal, enhance self-esteem, and give direction to the child's future choice of vocation. Participation in the group experiences of scouting, camping, and sports, along with involvement in various clubs at school, in the community, and at church expand the child's world view and develop abilities for group cooperation, problem solving, and leadership.

DISILLUSIONMENT WITH PARENTS

The child between ages 9 and 10 years begins to wonder whether or not he is adopted and whether his present parents are his "real" parents. In the phallic-oedipal stage, the child was actively involved with the "family romance fantasy," meaning that the child perceived his mother and father as the best, strongest, richest, and wisest people in the world: they could do no wrong!

By ages 9 to 10 years, with the integration of the superego, and by association with friends and their families, the child begins to realize the shortcomings and limitations of his parents. This realization is a blow to the child's inner world and self-esteem. So he fantasizes that he was adopted and that his "real" parents are "much better" than his present ones.

The "adoption fantasy" is a compensatory fantasy for softening the blow of the child's disillusionment with his parents. The child's adoption fantasy is a retreat to the world of make-believe. Some of these children become quiet, morose, and temporarily depressed. They may seriously ask their parents whether they have been adopted or if the parents really care for them. The parents' sensitivity to the child's concerns helps in alleviating doubts about his origin and decreases the intensity of the disillusionment.

LANGUAGE AND THOUGHT

Increased myelinization and dendritic development of the cortex enhance the child's memory, thinking, reasoning, and conceptualization. According to Piaget, the child between ages 7 and 8 years has developed the cognitive ability for perceiving conservation of matter, reversibility in action, serialization, and classification. These cognitive developments, along with the repression of primary process thinking and the ability for delayed gratification, facilitate the development of secondary process thinking. Secondary process thinking means having an ability for logical deduction, reasoning, and assessment of internal wishes in accordance with the principles of reality. It also refers to the ability of considering multiple possibilities and variations. The "all or none" thinking of the world of make-believe decreases.

Consensual validation through considering the opinions of others enhances reality testing. The child's thought processes move from concrete visual perception and symbolic representation to concrete logical representation and verbal expression. Although the primary process continues to play an important role in the child's dreams, daydreams, and creative work, secondary process thinking becomes the primary mode of communication.

The defense mechanism of isolation facilitates the development of objectivity. The defenses of rationalization and intellectualization contribute to the effective use of words and language for logical reasoning.

UNDERSTANDING THE FINALITY OF DEATH AND THE SENSE OF TIME

Young children do not understand the meaning of death. The child between ages 5 and 6 years may say that his dog is dead, but a few hours later will ask what the dog is going to have for supper, or what the dog is having for dinner in heaven.

It is generally agreed that children begin to recognize the finality and inevitability of death betwen ages 9 and 10 years. The child needs to develop the ability to understand conservation of matter and reversibility in operation before he will be able to understand the finality of death.

In the death of a dear one, it is important for parents to be open and honest with their children, no matter what age. Parents should not hide their emotions and should allow the child to see how they feel about the loss. Children express their feelings in various ways, depending on their age and developmental level. Under the age of 6 or 7 years, they may cry briefly but then seem to "forget about it!" Internally, children of this age may fantasize that the death occurred because of "something they did or thought." They need to be reassured that they did not "cause" the death. If children can be encouraged to talk about or "play out" their reactions and ideas about death, it might help them partially to master the loss. Some children refuse to acknowledge a death. They cover their ears and do not want to hear about or talk about it. Parents should respect the child's feelings and not force the issue. Usually, several months later, the child will be ready to communicate his feelings.

The middle and late latency-age child usually experiences the loss of a dear one intensely. Some become quiet and withdrawn and do not outwardly express emotion. In this situation, an adult can help the child verbalize thoughts and feelings about the deceased. Other children openly express their feelings. The more the family is able openly to express their emotions concerning the loss of the dear one without embarrassment or inhibition, the easier it will be for the children to do so. Open expression of feeling helps the family work through the mourning process and come to terms with the loss. This may take months, or even years.

Children should be given a choice whether or not they wish to attend the funeral home, funeral services, or burial. They should not be forced to attend or be kept from these mourning activities. They should not be made to feel guilty for not attending.

Development of the *sense of time* occurs between ages 9 and 10 years. Many children can tell time or read the clock between the ages of 5 and 7 years. But developing the internal sense of time and appreciating, for instance, the idea of next week, next month, or 2 years from now occurs with the ability for distancing thought from action, which is achieved between the ages of 9 and 10 years.

Younger children between ages 5 and 6 years may understand time within the context of sensory-motor and symbolic thought representation. But this is usually related to concrete experiences, such as mealtimes, birthdays, and holidays.

SLEEP

The latency-age child sleeps through the night. In early latency, or between ages 6 and 8 years, because of an upsurge of separation anxiety and oedipal wishes, the child may have transient sleep disturbances—especially on school nights. Throughout latency, children will experience dreams and sometimes nightmares, which are usually forgotten by the next morning. Repression does its work well in middle and late latency.

EEG Findings

EEG findings during latency are of utmost interest and reveal a number of deviations. The EEG, which had become fairly rhythmic and regular, "...now becomes discontinuous, and various transitory EEG discharges show numerous escapes from control." (Metcalf, 1979, p. 69) During latency, positive spikes of 6 and 14/second in the posterior part of the temporal lobe occur predominately in the right hemisphere while the child is in the stage of light sleep. Slowing of the waves in the posterior part of the right hemisphere and "...vertex spikes which appear to be distortions of combined vertex sleep spindles and k-complex activity..." occur. (ibid., p. 69)

General rhythmicity of the EEG shows disruption. It is postulated that this disruption and dysrhythmicity might be related to the maturational and interactional aspects of the child's psyche and central nervous system. These events "Periodically...give way to intermittent escape of cortical EEG from sub-cortical control. This takes the form of rhythmic and transient disturbances in the electroencephalogram, primarily during latency." (ibid., p. 69)

The EEG escape and dysrhythmicity is related to a temporary failure or decrease in the central nervous system's inhibitory functions in the course of shifting from an affective focus to a cognitive focus.

Sleep Disturbances

Major sleep disturbances during latency include difficulties in going to sleep, nightmares, night terrors, bedwetting, sleepwalking, sleep talking, and sleep paralysis. Difficulties in going to sleep, nightmares, and night terrors were discussed in chapter 4.

Bedwetting (Nocturnal Enuresis)

The earliest remedy for the treatment of enuresis, written on the Papyrus Ebers in Egypt in 1550 B.C., was a mixture of equal amounts of juniper berries, cyprus, and beer! (Garrison, 1923, p. 13; Glicklich, 1951, p. 859) For more than 3,500 years human beings have been concerned about the treatment of bedwetting!

Now, nocturnal enuresis is perceived as a form of sleep disturbance. According to Anders and Weinstein (1972), "Bedwetting past the age of three is the most prevalent childhood sleep disorder." In children ages 3 to 5, the prevalence of enuresis is 15%, at 6 years of age 10%, and at 14 years 5% (MacFarlane et al., 1954; Backwin, 1961; Simonds, 1977) Lovibond and Coote (1970) found the prevalence of enuresis to be 2% by age 14. Enuresis is more common in boys.

Enuresis is divided into two types—organic and nonorganic (idiopathic).

ORGANIC ENURESIS. Organic enuresis is referred to as incontinence and is less common than nonorganic enuresis. The demonstrable organic pathology, such as central nervous system defects (for example, spina bifida occulta), genitourinary tract abnormalities, frequent infections, diabetes, and epilepsy are causative factors. Only 3 to 10% of all bedwetting is organic. (Ritvo et al., 1969)

NONORANIC ENURESIS (IDIOPATHIC OR ESSENTIAL ENURESIS). Nonorganic enuresis comprises between 90 to 97% of all enuresis. (ibid., p. 115) There is no demonstrable organic etiology. Nonorganic enuresis is divided into two types—primary and secondary.

Primary Enuresis. The majority of children (70 to 80%) with nocturnal bedwetting have primary enuresis. Primary enuresis means that the child from infancy has never been totally dry at night. The occurrence of primary enuresis is familial. Usually there is a history of primary enuresis in one or both parents and in other siblings.

The child is generally well-adjusted and emotionally stable. There is no or little family disharmony. There is absence of impulsive behavior or academic problems. In most areas of psychosexual, cognitive, and physical development, the child is on the appropriate age level, or even ahead.

This type of enuresis represents a delay in the maturation of the autonomic nervous system related to bladder control during sleep. Studies by Ritvo et al. (1969), Anders and Weinstein (1972), and Anders and Freeman (1979) described this form of enuresis as sleep-related enuresis. Sleepwalking and sleep talking are also associated with this type of enuresis.

Careful sleep EEG studies of children with primary enuresis have shown that "... most enuretic events took place during the early part of the night," during deep, non-REM, Stages III to IV sleep. (Ritvo et al., 1969, p. 118)

Stages III and IV sleep occur more frequently in the first 2 to 3 hours of sleep. Primary enuresis or "arousal enuresis" is a disorder of sleep arousal. The child is in such deep sleep that the feedback mechanism between sphincter control of the bladder and the autonomous nervous system does not work effectively. Most of these children, by ages 10 to 12 years, with further maturation of the autonomous nervous system, stop bedwetting. Some of these children under physical or emotional stress, overstimulation, or excitement may have occasional bedwetting.

Secondary Enuresis (Regressive Enuresis). Secondary enuresis comprises approximately 20% of nonorganic enuresis. These children have a period of being dry at night after age 3 years. Sometime later, they again begin to wet the bed.

Secondary enuresis is associated with moderate to severe psychopathology, such as aggressive behavior, lack of impulse control, difficulty in school performance, fire-setting, cruelty to animals, phobia, depression, and overwhelming anxiety. There is often a history of parental disharmony and no familial history of bedwetting.

Sleep EEG studies of children with secondary enuresis show that the child usually wets the bed when he is awake or in Stage I or, particularly, Stage II sleep (light sleep). This enuresis occurs more in the early morning when Stages I and II sleep are prevalent.

A simple way to differentiate between primary and secondary enuresis is to determine whether there is a family history of enuresis or a multitude of psychological problems within the family unit. Also, it is important to find out whether enuresis occurs in the first part of the night or in the early morning hours.

Treatment

There have been a multitude of treatments for enuresis. Approximately in one-half of the cases of primary enuresis, imiprimine has been effective. The use of imiprimine for enuresis will be discussed in chapter 23 on pediatric psychopharmacology.

Mixed results are reported for psychological therapies, such as conditioning, positive reinforcement, and the use of an alarm-sounding device.

The authors suggest a supportive and relaxed attitude for the treatment of primary enuresis. Recognizing that this type of enuresis is related to delayed maturation of the autonomous nervous system and that almost all of these children between ages 10 and 12 years stop bedwetting, may help the parents and the child accept this developmental delay and alleviate undue concern.

Children are sensitive and self-conscious about bedwetting and wish more than anything to overcome it. Undue punishment or expecting the child to "make up for it" by, for instance, washing his own sheets or clothes, frequently compounds the problem. Shaming, punishing, or depriving the child may contribute to the secondary development of a psychological disturbance.

Parental attitudes of tolerance and acceptance reassure the child that this is a normal event for him and for 10 to 15% of all children. Explaining to the child that he will gradually stop wetting the bed as he grows older is helpful.

Enuretic children should not be deprived from going overnight to visit friends or from camping experiences. A small plastic sheet for the sleeping bag, or a couple of extra sheets will help solve the problem and reassure the child. It is also important to let the child know that you will need confidentially to share this bedwetting problem with the parents of the child he is going to visit or with the camp counselor. The parents' attitudes about bedwetting significantly influence the child's attitude and also the attitudes of friends and their parents.

In the *treatment of secondary enuresis*, imiprimine and a variety of conditioning methods are not usually effective. Psychotherapy with the child and the family helps work through internal and interactional conflicts. The family needs to realize that enuresis is a symptom of a cluster of psychological problems. Psychotherapeutic work should not be focused on bedwetting alone. In most situations, the family needs to become aware that because of their conflictual relationship with the child, the more they focus on the bedwetting issue the worse the situation will become. The child might stop wetting the bed for a few days or a few weeks with conditioning approaches, parental focus, punishment, or reward, but the symptoms will most probably reappear.

Other sleep disorders, i.e., narcolepsy and hypersomnia, will be discussed in chapter 6.

REFERENCES

Adams, P. (1974). *Primer of Child Psychotherapy.* Boston: Little Brown and Co.

Anders, T., Weinstein, P. (1972). Sleep and its disorders in children: A review. *Pediatrics, 50,* 312–324.

Anders, T.F., Freeman, E.D. (1979). Enuresis. In Noshpitz, J. (Ed.), *Basic Handbook of Child Psychiatry,* Vol. 2. New York: Basic Books, pp. 546–555.

Bakwin, H. (1961). Enuresis in childhood. *J. Pediatr., 58,* 806.

Bornstein, B. (1951). On latency. In Eissler, R.S., *et al.* (Eds.), *The Psychoanalytic Study of the Child,* Vol. 6. New York: International Universities Press, pp. 279–285.

Erikson, E. (1950). *Childhood and Society.* Second Edition. New York: Norton, 1963.

Garrison, F.H. (1923). In Abt, I.A. (Ed.), *Abt's Pediatrics,* Vol. I. Philadelphia: W.B. Saunder Co., p. 13.

Glicklich, M. (1951). An historical account of enuresis. *Pediatrics, 8,* 259–269.

Harrison, S., McDermott, J.F. (Eds.) (1972). *Childhood Psychopathology: An Anthology of Basic Readings.* New York: International Universities Press.

Lovibond, S.H., Coote, M.A. (1970). In Costello, C.G. (Ed.), *Symptoms of Psychopathology.* New York: John Wiley.

MacFarlane, J.W., Allen, L., Honzik, M.P. (1954). *A Developmental Study of Behavior Problems of Normal Children Between Twenty-One Months and Fourteen Years.* Berkeley: University of California Press.

Metcalf, D. (1979). Organizers of the psyche and EEG development: Birth through adolescence. In Noshpitz, J. (Ed.), *Basic Handbook of Child Psychiatry,* Vol. 1. New York: Basic Books, pp. 63–71.

Piaget, J. (1962). The stages of the intellectual development of the child. *Bull. Menninger Clin., 26,* 120–128.

Ritvo, E., Ornitz, E., Gottlieb, F., Poussaint, A., Maron, B., Ditman, K., Blinn, K. (1969). Arousal and nonarousal enuretic events. *Am. J. Psychiatry, 126,* 115–122.

Simonds, J. (1977). Psychiatric consultations for 112 pediatric inpatients. *South. Med. J., 70,* 980–984.

Chapter 6

THE WORLD OF ABSTRACTION, INDIVIDUATION, AND EMANCIPATION: Twelve to Eighteen Years of Age

Between the ages of 12 and 18 years, the adolescent experiences dramatic physical and psychological growth. At no other time in life, except during the first 3 years, does the individual go through so many changes.

Height, muscle mass, strength, and fatty distribution increase significantly. Throughout this stage, secondary sexual characteristics emerge. By age 16 years, most young women and men are capable of reproduction from a physiological point of view, but usually they are not ready to assume the psychological responsibilities of parenthood.

By age 12 years, a qualitative change occurs in cognitive development. The young person becomes capable of abstract thinking. By mid-adolescence, the individual has formed definite ethical, religious, and political values and ideals. Between ages 14 and 18 years, some adolescents will experience a relatively quiet evolution and others a revolutionary turmoil in establishing and integrating their sense of identity.

By late adolescence, ages 16 to 18 years, the integrative forces of individuation, along with the establishment of the sense of identity, facilitate the individual's psychological emancipation from the parents. Affective intimacy between young men and women begins to develop outside of the family in a new form of dyadic relationship.

The young person begins to think about the future and explore vocational possibilities. By the end of adolescence, the child of yesterday becomes the adult of tomorrow, ready to assume economic and social responsibilities and the joy of possibilities.

PUBERTY

Muscle and Body Mass

Body mass in both boys and girls increases twofold during puberty. (Barnes, 1975) In boys, muscle mass increases more in quality and quantity than in girls. This partially explains their greater increase in body strength.

Before puberty, nonlean body mass, principally fat, decreases in boys and in girls to some extent, but during puberty,

...there is a dramatic increase in the velocity of fat accumulation in the female and to a lesser degree in the male...By the time somatic maturation is complete, the average female has twice the amount of body fat as the male. The greater proportion of fat in the female may play a critical role in the onset and maintenance of menses.

ibid., p. 1306.

Frisch and McArthur's (1974) studies show that approximately 17% of body composition needs to be of fatty substance for the occurrence of menarche, and approximately 22% for the beginning and maintenance of regular ovulation.

Body Systems

During puberty, "...the size of the heart, lungs, liver, spleen, kidneys, pancreas, thyroid, adrenals, gonads, phallus, and uterus double" (Barnes, 1975, p. 1306) The central nervous system increases a small, but distinct, amount in size. On the other hand, tonsils, adenoids, and thymus decrease significantly.

Height

Growth spurts in girls can begin as young as age 9½ years, or as old as age 14½ years; in boys, these growth spurts may occur as young as age 10½ years, or as old as age 16 years.

Tanner (1962, 1968) and Tanner et al. (1966) conducted classical studies of growth in British adolescents; these studies documented that the "peak height velocity" in girls is at age 12.1 years, and in boys is at age 14.1 years. The same data may be applied to the adolescent population in the United States.

Usually, the growth spurt in girls begins by age 10 years and reaches its peak by the age of 12 years. Height growth continues with lesser speed up to the age of 15 years. In boys, the growth spurt begins by age 12 years and reaches its peak by age 14 years. Height growth continues at a lesser speed to age 17 years or older.

There is a wide range of variability in height, but, after considering genetic dispositions, if an adolescent falls below the third percentile of the normal range, or goes above the 97th percentile, careful medical evaluation should be completed.

Weight

Gain in body weight has greater variability than height. In females, the peak weight velocity at 12½ years is about 6 months later than the peak height velocity. In boys, the peaks of height and weight velocities are at approximately the same age—14 years. "As a general rule, the individual height percentile and weight percentile should not differ by more than 15 percentile points for the chronologic age." (Barnes, 1975, p. 1309)

Lack of weight gain or decrease in weight during puberty should be a matter of concern. It may be a manifestation of intestinal malabsorption, regional enteritis, endocrine imbalance (e.g., hyperthyroidism, diabetes mellitus), chronic infections (e.g., tuberculosis), collagen disease (e.g., systemic lupus erythematosus, rheumatoid arthritis), or liver and kidney disease. One of the most common causes of weight loss is voluntary starvation in the form of anorexia nervosa. (see chapter 12)

If an adolescent's weight is 20% or more above the ideal weight for his age and height, a careful medical examination should be performed to rule out the possibility of an endocrine abnormality. In most cases, the cause for obesity will be overeating.

Secondary Sexual Characteristics

Males

The earliest sign of puberty in boys is a change in the genital area. The testes enlarge from 1.6 cc. to 6 cc. The scrotum becomes redder, thinner, and larger, with minimal or no enlargement of the phallus. This occurs around age 11½ years, plus or minus 2 years.

Approximately one to 1½ years later, by age 13 years, the size of the scrotum more than doubles to 12½ cc., and there is greater thinning of the skin. The phallus increases in length.

In males, one the earliest signs of puberty is the growth of long, straight or curly, slightly pigmented, downy pubic hair at the base of the phallus and/or scrotum. This occurs around age 13 years, plus or minus 2 years. Between ages 14 and 15 years, the size of the scrotum increases to about 20 cc., or to adult size. The color darkens and there is further enlargement. The phallus increases in length and circumference. The size of the glans increases.

By age 15 years, plus or minus 2 years, the male adolescent's genitals have all the characteristics of the adult's, with an increase of curl, coarseness, pigmentation, and spread of pubic hair to the entire genital area.

In adolescent boys, the size of the areola of the breast increases. Approximately 30% of adolescent males develop enlargement of the breasts (gynecomastia). Generally, this enlargement is bilateral and nontender. However, some have unilateral gynecomastia or tenderness. Gynecomastia occurs in mid-adolescence and lasts 6 to 18 months. If it continues more than 24 months, a medical consultation and possible surgical removal may be indicated for psychosocial implications.

Generally, facial and axillary hair appears between ages 15 and 16 years and reaches adult distribution between ages 16 and 17 years. At first, dark pigmented hair appears at the corners of the upper lip, then spreads over the whole upper lip, cheeks, and in the midline below the lower lip. Eventually, hair covers the chin.

Deepening of the voice, or "breaking of the voice," usually occurs in late adolescence, between ages 16 and 18 years, when the serum level of testosterone reaches adult level. (Barnes, 1975)

Axillary hair in boys develops approximately 2 years later than the development of pubic hair. Appearance of hair on the chest in boys is usually the final secondary sexual characteristic. It begins in late adolescence or in the early twenties.

Females

In the female, the earliest signs of puberty—the budding of the breasts or the growth of pubic hair—occur around age 11 years, plus or minus 2 years. We have discussed early signs of puberty in females in chapter 5. Any female who begins breast development or has pubic hair before age 9 years should have a careful medical examination for precocious puberty. On the other hand, any female who does not show breast budding by 13½ years or pubic hair by age 14 years should be examined for delayed puberty.

As the female grows during adolescence, the breasts become larger and more elevated. The areola widens further. Between ages 13 and 14 years, the areola and papilla form a mound projecting from the breast contour. By age 15½ years, plus or minus 3½ years, the female breast reaches adult size. Areola and breast are in the same plane, with no mound.

Pubic hair in females increases in curl, coarseness, and pigmentation by age 12½ years and by age 13 years covers almost the entire mons veneris. Axillary hair develops approximately 2 years later than pubic hair.

MENSTRUATION. Tanner's (1962, 1968) studies revealed that the mean age for the beginning of menarche (menstrual period) for British girls is 13.5 years of age. Zacharias *et al.* (1970) found that for American girls, the mean age is 12.7 years. For both groups, there is a one year plus or minus deviation.

Approximately 5% of girls begin the menarche between ages 11 and 11½ years; 25% between ages 12 and 12½ years; 60% at age 13 years; and the final 10% between ages 14 and 16 years. "About 99 percent of normal females have the onset of menses within 5 years of beginning breast development." (Barnes, 1975, p. 1315) If an adolescent girl has demonstrated peak height and weight velocity and has developed secondary sexual characteristics, but has not begun to menstruate by age 15½ years, she should have a complete medical work-up to rule out primary amenorrhea. Also, if a girl begins to menstruate before age 10 or 10½ years, she should be carefully examined for precocious puberty.

In the first 2 years of menarche, the menstrual periods may be irregular. If periods continue to be irregular after 2 years, a gynecological examination is necessary.

HEALTH

In late adolescence, between ages 16 and 18 years, young people frequently have a number of physical symptoms, often related to vision, respiration, skin problems, headaches, and emotional difficulties. Some girls develop anemia. There is also evidence of increased alcohol and drug use. Studies by Shafii *et al.* (1981) have revealed that the highest incidence of suicide in children and youth is between ages 17 and 18 years. (see chapter 14)

Young people during adolescence have a tendency to deny or minimize physical and emotional symptoms. Parents, educators, and clinicians need to be cognizant of the young person's health, take his complaints and symptoms seriously, and attend to them immediately.

COGNITIVE DEVELOPMENT

Stage of Formal Operations
(Ages 12 to 15 Years)

Inhelder and Piaget (1958), in *The Growth of Logical Thinking from Childhood to Adolescence,* explored the development of intelligence. According to Piaget (1962):

> The last stage of development of intelligence is the stage of formal operations or propositional operations. At about eleven to twelve years of age we see great progress; the child becomes capable of reasoning not only on the basis of objects, but also on the basis of hypotheses, or of propositions.
>
> Harrison and McDermott, 1972, p. 164.

Piaget found that a qualitative difference develops in the thinking of young people aged 11 to 12 years. A 12-year-old begins to develop logical reasoning based on verbal propositions, rather than on concrete objects. If one asks, "Whose hair is the darkest if Joan's hair is lighter than Ann's, but darker than Mary's?" the child under age 12 years will not be able to answer. A young person 12 years or older usually will be able to answer this question, because by this age he has developed the ability to make comparisons on an abstract level, rather than having to rely on the concrete presence of the object.

Another qualitative change is the appearance of

> ...two reversibilities: reversibility by inversion, which consists of annulling or canceling; and reversibility which we call reciprocity, leading not to cancellation, but to another combination.
>
> ibid., p. 165.

For instance, if A = B, by reciprocity B = A. If A is smaller than B, through reciprocity B is larger than A. The young person by age 12 years is able to recognize this reciprocal relationship and use two systems or more for reasoning.

At age 12 years and older, the young person begins to develop abstract thinking and can understand proverbs and metaphors. Now, he realizes that the proverb, "The grass is greener on the other side of the fence," has two "systems of reference" or meaning—one, concrete and the other, abstract. Adult form of thinking, or "formal intelligence," has begun.

Piaget observed that "ideological beliefs" develop in this stage.

These feelings are not attached to particular persons or only to material realities but attached to social realities and to essentially ideal realities, such as feelings about one's country, about humanitarianism or social ideals, and religious feelings.

ibid., p. 175.

The idealogical beliefs and commitment begin to develop in middle adolescence and become more definite in late adolescence or young adulthood.

A number of studies have been done to determine whether people generally reach Piaget's final stage of intelligence (formal operations). Dulit (1972) tested the following groups to determine the percentage reaching the stage of formal operations:

1. Average adolescents, age 14 years—10% reached formal operations
2. Average adolescents, ages 16 to 17 years—35% reached formal operations
3. Gifted adolescents, ages 16 to 17 years—60% reached formal operations
4. Average adults—25 to 33% reached formal operations

From these studies, it appears that approximately one-third of the adult population of average intelligence, and two-thirds of gifted adolescents reach the stage of formal operations. In all groups, males were two to four times more likely to function on this level than females. The ability for formal operations increases through practice, experience, and training.

Intelligence Quotient

Intelligence quotient (IQ) reaches its peak in late adolescence between ages 16 and 19 years. Findings demonstrate that intellectual ability continues to develop throughout life, if the mind is stimulated on a highly intellectual and abstract

level. (Rosenthal and Jacobson, 1968; Eichorn, 1973)

Ability for Self-Observation

In late adolescence, the young person is able to take distance from feeling and action and thus perceive the outcome of his behavior or ideas. This ability is related to the cognitive development of the sense of time, concern for the future, and the ability to construct a multitude of hypothetical situations and possible outcomes in his mind—a significant development for choosing life's future course.

This cognitive development facilitates adults' communication with the young person in guidance, counseling, and in psychotherapeutic situations. From a psychodynamic point of view, the young person has begun to develop the ability for self-observation.

PSYCHOSEXUAL DEVELOPMENT

Adolescence is generally divided into three stages: early adolescence/pubescence from ages 12 to 14 years; middle adolescence, from ages 14 to 16 years; and late adolescence, from ages 16 to 18 years. These chronological divisions are approximations.

Early Adolescence—Pubescence (Ages 12 to 14 Years)

Males

With the hormonal explosion and massive growth spurt, the early adolescent male experiences temporary psychosexual confusion and disorganization. This rapid growth strains the cognitive and emotional equilibrium. Behaviorally, the early adolescent appears disjointed, disorganized, clumsy, and gangly.

Body growth is uneven. The head, hands, and feet grow first, then the upper and lower extremities, and finally the chest and shoulders. It takes time to internalize these massive changes into a new *body image* (mental perception of the body).

SELF-ESTEEM. The internal perception and value of the self fluctuates. One moment the adolescent feels exuberant, elated, and "on top of the world," and the next moment he feels "down in the dumps," "blue," and worthless.

Psychosexually, with the manifold increase of gonadotropin, estrogen, and testosterone, libidinal and aggressive urges burst into the mind like flowers in the desert following spring showers. Sexual fantasies of a phallic-oedipal, anal, or oral nature overwhelm the conscious, preconscious, and unconscious life of the mind. Repression and obsessional defenses of the latency stage no longer work effectively under the continuous surge of libidinal and aggressive drives.

Incestuous and seduction fantasies are predominant. Every object the young person looks at and everyone he sees has sexual meaning. For instance, a long object is immediately associated with the phallus or the growth of the phallus. A round object is associated with breasts or buttocks, and a hole with oral, anal, or vaginal orifices.

The young man feels sexually attracted to both parents, particularly the mother—a reactivation of earlier bisexual longings. These attractions are expressed in very thinly disguised or obvious sexual dreams.

Sexual attractions and incestuous wishes are frequently associated with feelings of guilt and anxiety—reactivation of phallic-oedipal or castration anxieties. These feelings may be expressed in the form of overconcern about body parts, hypochondriasis, aches, pains, and fear of venereal disease.

MASTURBATION. Masturbation and masturbation fantasies increase significantly at this time. Some adolescents may masturbate two or three times each day, or more. Masturbatory behavior is related to the discharge of sexual urges, the temporary alleviation of castration anxieties, the exploration and examination of the genitals, and the need for reassurance.

Guilt and anxiety related to masturbatory fantasies and practices contribute to irrational fears and concerns about venereal disease, "going blind," becoming "queer," losing strength, losing one's mind, or stunting growth. Temporary sleep disturbances, in the form of wakefulness, might occur because of erotic, incestuous, or wet dreams.

SEDUCTION FANTASIES. The young adolescent at times projects the intensity of sexual wishes outwardly and feels that other people, particularly adults, have the same sexual thoughts toward him. He feels that they are there to "seduce" him, or to "take advantage" of him. Seduction fantasies actively intermingle with the fantasies of seducing others.

Adults, parents, and other meaningful persons in the young person's life, such as teachers and coaches, need to be aware of the vulnerability of adolescents at this stage. Sexual jokes, innuendoes, and suggestive remarks from adults are often perceived as invitations to seduction. Adolescents may react by withdrawal, fear, apprehension, lack of trust, or sexual acting out behavior.

Females

Menarche occurs in most girls between ages 12 and 14 years, with age 13 being the most likely (60%). With the change of parental attitudes and emphasis on sexual education, the young female's overwhelming fear about the beginning of menses has decreased to some extent. However, even with all of the cognitive and educational approaches, the adolescent shows appropriate development anxieties with the beginning of menses—surprise, excitement, concern, apprehension, fear of bodily injury, and denial are some of the most common responses. After the initial reaction, most well-prepared young women experience the feelings of excitement and accomplishment—the girl now feels like a woman. Mother's perceptiveness, receptivity, and guidance at this stage, and father's quiet acceptance help the young person adapt to this new development.

Some young women, because of electrolyte imbalance and retention of water, become moody, irritable, impatient, hypersensitive, or argumentative a few days before the monthly period. Recognition of this biological and rhythmical fluctuation of mood may help the young person and the family.

Adolescent females discuss with each other their concerns, fears, hopes, wishes, and fantasies about menarche. Rarely do they share these feelings with adults. This need for privacy should be respected. If the adolescent wishes, she will share these thoughts with adults.

Phallic-oedipal, anal, and oral fantasies of the earlier psychosexual stages become intensively reactivated. Incestuous fantasies predominate. Competition with mother for the attention of father or undue closeness to mother to avoid heterosexual feelings occurs frequently.

With the emergence of the menses and the deceleration of the growth rate, there is more organization in the mind and integration of behavior. The young woman has an upsurge of interest in academics, sports, and household activities.

Between ages 12 and 14 years, the adolescent female, on the whole, devalues males of the same age and becomes interested in older boys or men. Crushes on male teachers and coaches are a common and transient phenomenon. These crushes often represent displacement of affective and libidinal attachment from father to a person outside the family.

Crushes on idealized figures in the sports and entertainment fields are common. Group influence reinforces these crushes. The mass hysteria of young adolescent girls after seeing or hearing nationally or internationally known musical performers or celebrities are manifest phenomena of the process of displacement.

Parental Attitudes and Dating

The parents' attitudes regarding emerging sexuality in males and females is important. In early adolescence, both young men and young women need a period of moratorium to handle their internal revolution. Developmentally, young adolescents prefer association with peers of the same sex. Psychologically, the period of latency continues regarding friendships, with changes and modifications. Some friendships of latency become more intensified and deepen, and also new friends of the same sex are made.

Undue pressure by peers or parents for dating and premature heterosexual interaction contributes to the development of feelings of insecurity and doubt about the self, shallowness in human relationships, decrease in sublimative tendencies, and possible sexual acting out. Adolescents at this stage need their psychic energy to cope with and master internal physical and psychological upheaval. Premature involvement with dating puts added stress on an already overtaxed system.

Parental inconsistencies or giving double messages to the young adolescent concerning sexual behavior will add to the confusion, increase reliance on peers, and contribute to sexual acting out. The parents' openness, clarity, direction, and limit-setting are important in helping the young person handle sexual and aggressive wishes.

Middle Adolescence (Ages 14 to 16 Years)

During this stage, males and females both continue to grow, but the males at an accelerated pace. By the end of this stage, males will have caught up with females in regard to physical, cognitive, and psychosexual development.

Appearance

During middle adolescence, the "ugly duckling girl," and the "gangly boy" become graceful, coordinated, and attractive young people.

The adolescents begin to put great emphasis on appearance. They follow fashions avidly—especially the fashions of peers and close friends. Both males and females become particularly concerned about hair styles—long hair versus short hair and curly hair versus straight hair. Most girls begin to wear make-up. It is not uncommon for an adolescent girl to spend hours in front of the mirror to "fix" her hair or put on make-up.

Minor changes in the way the hair curls or the emergence of a pimple can plummet the adolescent's self-esteem to the depths of despair. The adolescent reacts by becoming unhappy, temporarily depressed, and wanting "to be alone." Soon after, however, the adolescent again feels elated, happy, and "on top of the world."

Self-Esteem and Mood

The adolescent's self-esteem is mercurial. It rises and falls with any slight internal or external change. There is an intensive cathexis of libidinal energy to the self (reactivation of earlier narcissism). Moods are at the mercy of mercurial self-esteem.

Moodiness—the ebb and flow of feelings—of adolescents in this stage is developmentally appropriate. Parental and adult understanding of these mood changes is helpful. Parental overreaction to the adolescent's mood swings may contribute to explosive behavior, pouting, withdrawal, and serious disagreements between parents and the young person. Frequently, the young person does not know why he is unhappy or moody. Undue prodding by parents or adults will reinforce this behavior.

Parents' remembrance of their own adolescence will help them establish a healthy respect for their children's mood swings. At the same time, being receptive and available to the young person when he wants to relate will help the parents enjoy their role of parenthood.

Relationship with Parents

In middle adolescence, the young person consciously and unconsciously re-examines the parents' attitudes, appearance, behavior, and values. A devaluation of the parents may occur. For instance, adolescents now are not only concerned with their appearance, but begin to criticize the parents about the way they dress, eat, look, and behave. Everything that parents do can become sources of "embarrassment" and agony. Adolescents worry about being embarrassed in front of their peers by their parents' behavior. They agonize over minute and trivial issues. Sometimes, adolescent criticism of the parents' attitudes or behavior is valid. The parents' honesty and receptivity to genuine criticism can help increase the adolescent's assessment of reality, effectiveness, and self-esteem. Parents' phony acquiescence or defensive denial and overreaction to these criticisms contribute to the adolescent's feeling of isolation and lack of communication.

Children—particularly adolescents—are good

teachers. They like to teach the parents as they have been taught by them—a mutual reciprocity. Adolescents' acute perceptiveness and sensitivity can open new vistas of perceptual, intellectual, and affective experiences to the receptive parents. Parents and adolescents can learn and grow together.

Peer Relationships

Peer relationships, which began in the early phallic-oedipal phase and gained further impetus in latency, now reach peak importance in adolescence. Friends and small groups of peers become the essence of psychosocial existence. Adolescents confide in peers and share their mutual thoughts and intimate fantasies. Intense affective experiences, such as love and loyalty, along with anger and disappointment, permeate these relationships. Small group relationships that began in latency are intensified. The group provides a feeling of cohesiveness and security, as well as a sense of identity.

During adolescence, peer influence outweighs parental influence. For the first time in a young person's life, the pendulum swings toward the direction of peers and away from the parents.

Late Adolescence (16 to 18 Years)

In late adolescence, the young person has passed through puberty. He has found a way to cope with intense libidinal and aggressive urges. There is more organization in thought, action, and behavior. There is less narcissistic emphasis on appearance. The late adolescent begins to care for others based on their attributes and needs rather than the needs of the self.

Relationship with Adults

Now, the young person is cognitively able to take distance from his feelings and actions and carefully consider the opinion of parents and other adults. The young person no longer finds it necessary to negate either inwardly or outwardly everything parents say and do. This is the beginning of introspection.

The young person begins to develop the ability to observe the self internally. Cognitive development of the sense of time, caring for other people's feelings and ideas, and anticipating future possibilities strengthen the emerging observing ego.

Relationship with Peers

Peers continue to be important, but their opinions are not perceived as the "whole truth." The young person more seriously compares his opinions with those of peers and respected adults. Then, with relative objectivity, the adolescent makes thoughtful decisions. Behaviorally, the urge for impulsive action is curbed by reflective pauses.

Dating

Libidinal attachments become more channelized to the opposite sex outside of the family constellation. The occasional "polymorph-perverse" sexual experiences of latency and early and middle adolescence give way to a blossoming interest in a dyadic heterosexual relationship. In late adolescence, the young person generally becomes ready to date.

Dating is associated with many rituals and guidelines, depending on the family's socioeconomic level and religious and cultural values.

The young person's sexual and aggressive urges are integrated in the form of an intense longing for a relationship with another human being, generally of the opposite sex. This relationship is usually emotional and psychological rather than physical.

Intense love and romantic feelings of youth through the ages in various cultures have given life to creative expression in art, music, and poetry. The love for another human being becomes a catalyst for sublimation of sexual and aggressive urges, which have enriched human culture from Stone Age communities to post-industrial societies.

The narcissism (self-love) of early and middle adolescence is transformed in part to feelings of love and caring for another human being. The healthy balance between self-love and love for others at this stage helps shape the individuals' relationships toward others and the self throughout life.

Sexual Behavior

There are many misconceptions concerning the sexual behavior of adolescents. Adults and some clinicians think that during the last few decades adolescents have "gone wild" in their sexual behavior and have broken the taboos and prohibitions of past generations.

Offer and Offer (1971) reported an 8-year longitudinal study of a group of white middle-class adolescents in the Chicago area, whom they followed from ages 12 to 21 years. The study was conducted during the 1960s, one of the most tumultuous decades in American history. In structured and semistructured interviews, they followed 73 males and 30 females.

In reporting sexual behavior, Offer and Offer found that most adolescent males aged 15 to 16 years "... rarely spoke about sexual incidents" (p. 31) By ages 16 to 17 years, they would blush when answering the interviewer's questions about sex.

The cardinal findings are that there was a discrepancy of several years between the time our adolescent subject was biologically able to produce children and the time that the adolescent engaged in intensive heterosexual activities.... Ten percent of our study population had sexual intercourse by the end of high school (18 years). The rate rises to 30 percent by the end of the first post-high-school year (19 years), and 50 percent by the end of the third post-high-school year (21 years).

p. 31.

They observed that the adolescent male was more worried about controlling aggressive impulses than sexual behavior. On the contrary, the adolescent female was more concerned and preoccupied with sexual issues. They confirmed that "... the girl who does act out is likely to utilize the sexual route." (ibid., p. 32)

Offer and Offer concluded:

Recent empirical studies on adolescents and young adults do not support claims of increased sexual experiences for today's adolescents as compared to past generations.

ibid., p. 32.

A survey questionnaire of 800 boys and 400 girls by the same researchers have confirmed these findings.

It is true that teenage pregnancies are on the rise. This rise appears to be related to socioeconomic background and family relationships. Sexual acting out behavior, particularly in girls, is directly related to the family's instability. Disharmonious families, one-parent families, poor families, racially segregated families, and economically dislocated families have a much higher incidence of adolescent sexual acting out and teenage pregnancies.

Masturbation

In late adolescence, the compulsive need for masturbation decreases. The individual continues to masturbate frequently, but with less intensity and less driven quality. Masturbation fantasies change their focus from immediate family members to the love object or idealized love object outside the family.

Repression and sublimation help in providing neutralized energy for expansion of autonomous ego functions. Aggressive energies become channelized in competitive sports, enhancement of physical endurance and strength, development of skill, and further academic progress.

IDENTITY AND INDIVIDUATION

Peter Blos (1962) perceived adolescence as the second stage of individuation, similar to Mahler's phase of separation-individuation—the first 3 years of life. (see chapters 2 and 3)

Separation-individuation in adolescence is a culmination of the following developments for eventual psychological emancipation from parents:

1. Physical growth, strength, and attractiveness signify youth. This often occurs when parents are reaching middle age and are experiencing a gradual decline of physical strength and appearance.
2. Sexuality—now the young person is capable of physiological productivity at the time of the relative decline in the physiological productivity of parents.
3. Cognitive processes—the adolescent has integrated all stages of cognitive development and has reached the final stage of formal operation and abstract thinking, similar to the parents. In some areas, the adolescent may be surpassing the parents.
4. Cumulative knowledge and skill—in industrial and postindustrial societies, parental knowledge and skill rapidly become outdated. In the past, parents transmitted their knowledge and technical skill to their children. Frequently, the young person followed the parents' vocational path, and looked up to his parents as teachers, supervisors, and vocational guides. Now, because of fast-paced technological changes, parents are not needed in most cases to provide technical skills and know-how to the young person. This transgenerational dissonance brings possibilities of wide-ranging opportunities for the young person, but, at the same time, may contribute to the disruption of family relationships and force premature closure in the development of the sense of identity and individuation.
5. Wisdom of life—explosion of knowledge in human development, health, and medicine and transmission of this knowledge through the

schools and media have, to a great extent, replaced the cumulative wisdom of parents and grandparents. In a technological society, there is less emphasis on the wisdom of life. In the past, parents, grandparents, and the elders of the family were respected as sources of wisdom. The lack of emphasis on the wisdom of life contributes to further separation of children from parents.

6. Ideology—during late adolescence, the exaggerated psychological investment in the self transfers to some extent to involvement in social, political, religious, and cultural causes.

7. Occasional experimentation with drugs and alcohol—in spite of parental prohibitions, most adolescents experiment with cigarettes and alcohol. Some will also experiment with marijuana and/or varieties of drugs.

8. Interest in alternate life styles—such as communal living, vegetarianism, change in religious affiliation, and changes in attire and appearance.

These are the forces that facilitate the process of individuation and the development of the sense of identity.

Sense of Identity

Erickson (1950), regarding the stage of adolescence and ego identity wrote:

The integration now taking place in the form of ego identity is...more than the sum of the childhood identifications. It is the accrued experience of the ego's ability to integrate all identification with the vicissitudes of the libido, with the aptitudes developed out of endowment, and with the opportunities offered in social roles. The sense of ego identity, then, is the accrued confidence that the inner sameness and continuity prepared in the past are matched by the sameness and continuity of one's meaning for others, as evidenced in the tangible promise of a "career."

pp. 261–261.

According to Erikson, the opposite pole of identity is role confusion—confusion in sexual identity, in values, in competence, and in relationships with peers, parents, and others. The normal adolescent simultaneously experiences a sense of identity along with role confusion.

Premature closure of identity contributes to arrest in development, immaturity, or pseudomaturity. Delayed sense of identity reinforces doubt, insecurity, confusion, and can result in ego disintegration.

The balance between identity versus role confusion helps the adolescent consolidate and integrate forces within.

The healthy outcome of the crisis of identity versus role confusion is the emergence of devotion and fidelity—a new sense of commitment which begins by late adolescence and early young adulthood. (ibid., p. 274)

NARCISSISM

The term "narcissism" is used in psychoanalysis and dynamic psychotherapy to describe an individual's love and attachment to the self. The word narcissism originates from Narcissus. In Greek mythology, Narcissus was a beautiful young man who fell in love with his own image reflected in the water. Because of this self-love, he pined away and changed into the narcissus flower.

Primary Narcissism

In the psychoanalytic concept of human development, the first few months of life are referred to as the stage of primary narcissism. Mahler's stages of normal autism (first month of life) and normal symbiosis (second through fourth months of life), Spitz's stage of objectlessness (birth through third month of life), and Anna Freud's concept of egocentricity can also be referred to as primary narcissism.

In primary narcissism, everyone and everything exists to satisfy the needs of the self. Self-love and lack of feeling for others are the essence of primary narcissism.

Secondary Narcissism

With the development of the recognition smile (at age 4 months) and the beginning of separation-individuation phases (ages 4 to 36 months), feelings begin to develop for a love object (mother) outside of the self. This is the beginning of secondary narcissism. Secondary narcissism means that the infant begins to recognize that there is a *reciprocity* in his relationship to mother (someone outside the self) in order to fulfill the needs of the self. In secondary narcissism, there is a *quid pro quo* relationship: I do this to get that.

By age 36 months, with the relative establishment of object constancy, the child begins to consider other people's feelings, needs, and reactions independently from the needs of the self.

The narcissistic concern about the self waxes and wanes throughout childhood and adolescence. Fear of bodily injury in the phallic-oedipal stage, concern about puberty in early adolescence, and extreme preoccupation with appearance in middle adolescence are some of the manifestations of primary narcissism. Creative productivity in children and adults represents symbolic projections of the self into the environment, which is sublimated expression of secondary narcissism.

Self-esteem and ego ideal are the healthy representations of narcissism. Unrealistic omnipotent fantasies are overcompensations for feelings of helplessness, impotence, and narcissistic injury. By late adolescence and early young adulthood, the mature individual develops a healthy balance between the love of the self and the love of others.

Overconcern for others, at the expense of the self, or overpreoccupation with the self, at the expense of others, can result in the development of serious psychopathology, such as depression, narcissistic personality disorders, borderline psychosis, and psychosis. (Kohut, 1971; Kernberg, 1975)

ADOLESCENT TURMOIL AND REBELLION

During the last few decades, the adolescent stage has been associated with turmoil, rebellion, and instability. Anna Freud, for instance, perceived adolescence as a "psychopathological stage." Irrationality, raw expression of sexual and aggressive impulses, and intense and constant battles with parents and those in authority were seen as the essence of this stage.

The professional community and the parents both "expected" the adolescent to be unstable, troubled, and a "rebel without a cause." This distorted perception and expectation probably originated from the clinicians' exposure to troubled youth and the patient population, which they encountered in daily clinical practice. This viewpoint did not take into consideration the whole adolescent population.

Offer and Offer (1971), Offer and Howard (1972), Offer and Sabshin (1974), and Offer and Simon, (1975) followed a group of nonpatient adolescents in the Chicago area for more than 8 years. Some of their findings concerning the adolescents' sexual behavior have been discussed earlier. Regarding adolescent turmoil and rebellion against parental values, they found that, although adolescents need emotionally and intellectually to separate from parents and "disengage" from them, this

...independence could be achieved without a total devaluation of parents. The adolescents studied in our normal population rarely rejected important parental values. Similarly, studies of student protesters and civil rights workers have shown a congruence of parent-adolescent values.

Offer and Offer, 1971, p. 35.

According to Offer, emotional disengagement between adolescents and parents occurs over numerous trivial issues. Adolescent rebellion is usually a form of "negation." The adolescent does something the parents do not want him to do. For example, the parents might ask the adolescent to turn off the television set while he is studying; the adolescent argues that he cannot study unless the television is on. If the parents insist, a battle ensues. The more the parents insist, the more oppositional the adolescent becomes—similar to the 2-year old child's oppositional behavior.

The adolescent at this stage wants to emancipate himself from his parents, but has a passive longing for them. The negation of parents is a form of "negative dependence." (Peterson and Offer, 1979)

Adolescent oppositional behavior and negative assertiveness need not become catastrophic battles of wills. "Adolescent rebellion," like the "terrible twos," is overly exaggerated and can become a self-fulfilling prophecy.

Offer and Offer's (1971) studies convincingly show that many adolescents, with the help of sensitive and receptive parents, can disengage themselves from parents

...without total renunciation of parental values, but rather through conflicts on minor issues which have been endowed with major importance for the adolescent's own growth and development.

p. 37.

Peterson and Offer (1979) found in their longitudinal studies that adolescents usually take one of 4 possible tracts:

1. Continuous Growth. Twenty-three percent of the 61 male subjects, whom the researchers followed from ages 12 to 21 years, demonstrated "continuous growth." Continuous growth means that these young people were able to cope with internal and external changes with a balance between reasonableness and emotional expressions. There was a continuity in their acceptance and adaptation to the norms of family and society. Parents in this group

respected and encouraged the young person's independence. The parents grew and matured along with their adolescents. "Throughout the eight years of the study there was basic mutual respect, trust, and affection between the generations." (p. 225)

Adolescents in this group continued to develop their own value systems, which were similar to or complemented the values of the parents. The nuclear family was stable, and there was no death, separation, or serious illness. Most of this group by the end of adolescence began to develop intimacy with someone of the opposite sex. They had an an active fantasy life, but at the same time were able to fulfill some of these fantasies through hard work and determination, such as by being good academically or in sports. They were able to delay gratification for attainment of future goals. They were able to deal effectively with their sexual and aggressive impulses. Any feelings of anxiety or depression were transient. On the whole, these adolescents were content, happy, and had "…many of the qualities attributed to ideal mental health."(ibid., p. 226)

2. Surgent Growth. This group, which comprised 35% of the adolescents studied, went through developmental spurts. They experienced cycles of progression and regression instead of continuous growth. There were more problems in the family in the form of severe illness, death, or separation.

Sometimes these adolescents related to developmental tasks and events smoothly, but at other times they stubbornly resisted changes. They reacted to the environment with anger and used projection more frequently than the first group. They were less action oriented than the first group and because of that were more prone to temporary depression or anxiety. Their self-esteem fluctuated more profoundly and relied more on the approval and encouragement of peers or parents. Parents had open conflicts with each other concerning the adolescent, and the adolescent had open conflicts with the parents.

Most adolescents in this group began heterosexual relationships later than the first group. A few, through counterphobic defenses, began transient heterosexual relationships earlier.

On the whole, this group adapted successfully, similar to the first group. The only difference was that they were slightly more inhibited, suppressed emotion easily, and were less introspective than the first and third groups.

3. Tumultuous Growth. This group comprised 21% of the total group. Their development was quite similar to the description of the adolescent rebellion and turmoil reflected in psychoanalytic and psychological literature. These adolescents had considerable internal turmoil and difficulty at home and in school. They were preoccupied with self-doubts and omnipotent fantasies. They had considerable conflicts with parents and showed inconsistencies in responding to social and academic demands. For them, adolescence was a period of discord. The family environment was disharmonious, with overt parental marital conflicts or mental illness. A larger number in this group was from the lower class. A higher percentage of this group displayed overt clinical problems and had received psychotherapy. (ibid., p. 227)

There were considerable difficulties in communication between the parents and adolescents. The parents gave contradictory messages concerning values to the young person. At the same time, a strong family bond existed within this group. Reality testing was very good compared with the adolescent patient population. These adolescents were more prone to anxiety and depression. The individuation process was accompanied by considerable emotional turmoil, with wide mood swings. They were more dependent on the peer group for modulation of their self-esteem. They were more prone to depression when they experienced the loss of friends or a meaningful person. Depressions were rarely accompanied by self-destructive impulses or feelings. This group was very sensitive and introspective. These adolescents, in spite of experiencing intense pain, suffering, and turmoil, did attain success academically and socially, although they were less happy with themselves and more critical of the social environment. (ibid., p. 228)

4. The Remaining Group. This group comprised 21% of the total group. It resembled the first two groups, but could not be classified.

EMANCIPATION

In late adolescence the young person usually becomes psychologically emancipated from the parents. The process of individuation, with the establishment of the sense of identity, is the prerequisite for psychological emancipation. The concept of psychological emancipation does not necessarily include physical separation or economic independence from parents. The young person could be physically away from home or economically self-sufficient, but continue to be embroiled in the conflict of dependence versus independence from parents.

Emancipation is a state of psychological freedom in which the individual recognizes the mutual interdependence of human beings on each other. This interdependence is based on mutual respect for one another's individuality, and on the need for reliance on each other.

REFERENCES

Barnes, H.V. (1975). Physical growth and development during puberty. *Med Clin. North Am., 59.* 1305–1317.

Blos, P. (1962). The ego in adolescence. In *On Adolescence: A Psychoanalytic Interpretation.* New York: The Free Press of Glencoe, pp. 170–197.

Dulit, E. (1972). Adolescent thinking à la Piaget: The formal stage. *J. Youth Adolesc., 4,* 281–301.

Eichorn, D. (1973). The Institute of Human Development Studies, Berkeley and Oakland. In Jarvick, L.F., Eisdorfer, L., Blum, J.E. (Eds.), *Intellectual Functioning in Adults.* New York: Springer.

Erikson, E. (1950). *Childhood and Society.* Second Edition. New York: Norton, 1963.

Frisch, R.E., McArthur, J.W. (1974). Menstrual cycles: Fatness as a determinant of minimum weight for height necessary for their maintenance or onset. *Science, 185,* 949.

Harrison, S.I., McDermott, J.F. (Eds.) (1972). *Childhood Psychopathology: An Anthology of Basic Readings.* New York: International Universities Press.

Inhelder, B. Piaget, J. (1958). *The Growth of Logical Thinking from Childhood to Adolescence.* New York: Basic Books.

Kernberg, O. (1975). *Borderline Conditions and Pathological Narcissism.* New York: Aronson.

Kohut, H. (1971). *The Analysis of the Self.* New York: International Universities Press.

Offer, D., Howard, K. (1972). An empirical analysis of the Offer self-image questionnaire for adolescents. *Arch. Gen. Psychiatry, 27,* 529–537.

Offer, D., Offer, J. (1971). Four issues in the developmental psychology of adolescents. In Howells, J.G. (Ed.), *Modern Perspectives in Adolescent Psychiatry.* New York: Brunner/Mazel, pp. 28–44.

Offer, D., Sabshin, M. (1974). *Normality: Theoretical and Clinical Concepts of Mental Health.* Revised Edition. New York: Basic Books.

Offer, D., Simon, W. (1975). Stages of sexual development. In Freedman, A., Kaplan, H., Sadock, B. (Eds.), *Comprehensive Textbook of Psychiatry.* Second Edition. Baltimore: Williams and Wilkins, pp. 1392–1400.

Petersen, A.C., Offer, D. (1979). Adolescent development: Sixteen to nineteen years. In Noshpitz, J. (Ed.), *Basic Handbook of Child Psychiatry,* Vol. 1. New York: Basic Books, pp. 213–233.

Piaget, J. (1962). The stages of the intellectual development of the child. *Bull. Menninger Clin., 26,* 129–137.

Rosenthal, R., Jacobson, L. (1968). *Pygmalion in the Classroom.* New York: Holt, Rinehart, and Winston.

Shafii, M., Whittinghill, R., Gilliam, P., Pearson, V. (1981). Risk factors in childhood and adolescent suicide: Psychological autopsies. In progress.

Tanner, J.M. (1962). *Growth at Adolescence.* Second Edition. Oxford: Blackwell Scientific Publishers.

Tanner, J.M. (1968). Growth of bone, muscle, and fat during childhood and adolescence. In Lodge, M.E. (Ed.), *Growth and Development of Mammals.* London: Butterworths.

Tanner, J.M., Whitehouse, R.H., Takaishi, M. (1966). Standards from birth to maturity for height, weight, height velocity, and weight velocity: British children, 1965. Part I. *Arch. Dis. Child., 41,* 454–471.

Zacharias, L., *et. al.* (1970). Sexual maturation in contemporary American girls. *Am. J. Obstet. Gynecol., 108,* 833.

Part II

EMOTIONAL DISORDERS

Chapter 7

DEPRESSION IN INFANCY, CHILDHOOD, AND ADOLESCENCE: Failure in Human Contact, Sadness, and Withdrawal

At the time of distress or danger, a living organism responds in the form of fight-flight or withdrawal. In mammals, primates, and particularly human beings, the fight-flight response is called anxiety, and the withdrawal response is called depression. In human beings, anxiety and depression are the two primary affects in response to distress or danger. Both are essential for survival and development. The experience of anxiety is a signal to the organism of approaching distress or danger, and depression is a frequent reaction to this experience.

As an affect, depression, or the feeling of dysphoria, sadness, low mood, and loss of interest and pleasure, is one of the most common human experiences in health and disease. Depression as an emotional disorder is now referred to as an affective disorder.

In this chapter, depression will initially be discussed as an affect in normal development, and later as a psychopathological disorder, such as major depression (unipolar disorder) and dysthymic disorder (classical depressive neurosis). In chapter 8, Feinstein *et al.* will discuss bipolar disorder (manic-depressive disorder) and cyclothymic disorder.

ADAPTIVE ASPECTS OF DEPRESSION

Depression as an affect is expressed behaviorally as a decrease in body movement, slowing down of body functions, sad facial expression, and partial or total temporary withdrawal.

When the organism experiences failure in a distressful situation, it generally withdraws. This withdrawal serves to *conserve* energy and to facilitate survival. Engel *et al.* (1956) studied a 15-month-old girl, Monica, who had a gastric fistula. Monica experienced depression and withdrawal whenever she felt in acute distress, such as when

someone she loved or was attached to left her. Engel *et al.* noticed that, along with depression and withdrawal, Monica's gastric secretions also decreased significantly. They postulated that Monica's depression and withdrawal had survival value and helped her to conserve energy and resources. According to the researchers, withdrawal-conservation in human beings has an adaptive significance that is similar to withdrawal and hibernation in animals.

Before these studies, withdrawal and depression were perceived as severe psychopathological disturbances or as pathological defensive reactions to anxiety. Now, it is understood that withdrawal and depression are primary affective responses that help the individual conserve emotional and physiological resources for further adaptation. Only following frequent and multiple failures or a single, massive, and overwhelming failure—particularly in the areas of human contact and loss of love object—will an individual manifest pathological depression in the form of a depressive disorder.

DISENGAGEMENT AND WITHDRAWAL IN INFANCY

Until recently, it was thought that children began to manifest depression as a primary affect between ages 1 and 2 years, following the development of object relationship and symbolic thought processes. (Dorpat, 1977; Mahler, 1966) Studies by Tronick *et al.* (1978) have thrown a new light on the possible existence of depression as a primary affect soon after birth. They videotaped face-to-face interactions between seven mothers and their infants from age 2 through 20 weeks. There were two types of experimental situations, each lasting 3 minutes. In the first, the mother had a natural face-to-face interaction with her baby. In the second, she sat face-to-face with her baby while "...remaining unresponsive and maintaining an expressionless face." (p. 2)

In order to emphasize the infants' sensitivity, responsiveness, and affective reaction in reciprocal communications with their mothers, we have used extensive, direct quotations from Tronick *et al.*'s fascinating observations. A 2-month-old baby sits quietly alone in an infant seat, "...face serious, cheeks droopy, mouth half open, corners down, but there is an expectant look in his eyes as if he were waiting." (p. 5) As soon as his mother comes into the room and says "hello," his face and hands reach out in her direction. He follows his mother with his head and eyes as she comes toward him.

His body builds up with tension, his face and eyes open up with a real greeting which ends with a smile. His mouth opens wide and his whole body orients toward her. He subsides, mouths his tongue twice, his smile dies, and he looks down briefly, while she continues to talk in an increasingly eliciting voice.

ibid., p. 5.

His mother begins to touch him and gently move his hips and legs.

He looks up again, smiles widely, narrows his eyes, brings one hand up to his mouth, grunting, vocalizing, and begins to cycle his legs and arms out toward her. With this increasing activity, she begins to grin more widely, to talk more loudly and with higher-pitched accents, accentuating his vocalizations with hers and his activity with her movement of his legs.

ibid., p. 5.

The mother continues to accentuate the interaction, and after 40 seconds,

He looks down again, gets sober...makes a pouting face. She looks down at his feet at this point, then comes back to look into his face and he returns to look up at her. She lets go of his legs, and they draw up into his body. He bursts out with a broad smile and a staccato-like vocalization for three repetitions.

ibid., pp. 5–6.

Whenever the baby's face "broadens and opens wide," and his arms and legs move toward the mother, she

...seems to get caught up in his bursts, and smiles broadly, her voice also getting brighter. After each burst, he subsides to a serious face, limbs quiet, and her quieting response follows his.

At 70 seconds, he subsides completely, and looks down at his feet with a darkly serious face. She gets very still, her face becomes serious, her voice slows down and almost stops, the pitch becomes low. Her mouth is drawn down, reflecting his serious mouth. After 3 seconds, he begins to brighten again into a wide, tonguing smile.

ibid., p. 6.

The mother immediately responds coyly with a gentle smile and gentle voice. The baby responds with staccatolike vocalization and the cycling of his legs toward her. At 90 seconds, "His movements subside and his face becomes serious. She also is quite serious. (ibid., p. 6)

This interaction continues with intermittent encouraging smiles, serious looks, and quiescence in harmony between mother and infant. The mother becomes quiet when the baby becomes quiet. Then the baby entices mother toward interaction. When the baby becomes very excited, the mother gently holds the baby's hips and legs to contain the peak of his excitement.

This observation clearly documents the emotional and affective exchanges and reciprocal interactions between the infant and his mother. When the interaction reaches a crescendo of excitement, the infant actively begins disengagement by looking serious or sober, or by looking away, thereby modulating and decreasing mother's input. When the infant wants more contact with his mother, he invites renewed involvement by a look, smile, gesture of hands, cycling of the legs, and change in the shape of his mouth or in the pitch of his voice. Mother's sensitivity and receptivity to her infant's affective communication reinforce his behavior and facilitate his sense of effectiveness and competency.

In the second experimental situation with the same infant, the mother remains expressionless for 3 minutes. The infant is sitting alone in an infant seat, looking down at his hands

...fingering the fingers of one hand with the other. As the mother enters, his hand movements stop. He looks up at her, makes eye-to-eye contact and smiles. Her masklike face does not change. He looks away quickly to one side and remains quiet, his facial expression serious. He remains this way for 20 seconds. Then he looks back at her face, his eyebrows and lids raised, his hands and arms startling slightly out toward her. He quickly looks down at his hands, stills for 8 seconds, and then checks her face once more. This look is cut short by a yawn, with his eyes and face turning upward.

ibid., p. 7.

He begins to pull at the fingers of the other hand while his whole body is motionless. After the yawn, which lasts 5 seconds, he looks at mother's face briefly. When mother does not respond, his arm movements become jerky,

...his mouth curves downward, his eyes narrow and partially lid. He turns his face to the side, but he keeps his mother in peripheral vision. He fingers his hand again, his legs stretch toward her and rapidly jerk back again. He arches forward, slumps over, tucks his chin down on one shoulder, but he looks up at her face from under his lowered eyebrows. This position lasts for over a minute, with brief checking looks at the mother occurring almost every 10 seconds. He grimaces briefly and his facial expression becomes more serious, his eyebrows furrowing. Finally, he completely withdraws, his body curled over, his head down. He does not look again at his mother. He begins to finger his mouth, sucking on one finger and rocking his head, looking at his feet. He looks wary, helpless, and withdrawn. As the mother exits at the end of the 3 minutes, he looks halfway up in her direction, but his sober facial expression and his curled body position do not change.

ibid., pp. 7–8.

According to Tronick *et al.,* this is a typical pattern of the infant's reaction to the mother's expressionless face. Initially, the infant responds to the mother and greets her. When she does not respond, the infant becomes sober and wary. He tries to engage her with brief smiles. When he does not receive any response, he looks away. He continues to persist. When consistent persistence for contact meets failure, he

...eventually withdraws, orients his face and body away from his mother with hopeless expression, and stays turned away from her. None of the infants cried, however.

ibid., p. 8.

The mothers felt that it was extremely taxing and difficult to remain emotionally unresponsive to their babies for 3 minutes. When they returned after this experiment, it took at least 30 seconds for the babies to warm-up to their mothers again. Initially, the baby showed "wary monitoring" of the mother. On occasion, the baby "...would arch away from the mother as if he had not forgiven her the previous insult." (ibid., p. 10)

MICRODEPRESSION OR ADAPTIVE DEPRESSION

Infants have an innate ability to respond discriminately to other human beings even in the first day of life. The studies conducted by Tronick *et al.* demonstrated the infant's rich affective and emotional responses to other human beings. They convincingly demonstrated that failure in human contact, even in a 3-minute time period, creates sadness, soberness, withdrawal, helplessness, and hopelessness in the infant. We propose that these signs in toto could be called a *microdepression,* or *adaptive depression.*

Microdepression is a mild to moderate transient form of depression, which usually lasts a short period of time—a few minutes to a few days. It is experienced on a sensory-motor, proprioceptive, and visceral level. This experience is not retrievable through memories, recall, or free associations. Microdepression is related to a disturbance in the biological rhythm of engagement and disengagement in human contact. Disengagement, withdrawal, and microdepression modulate and "tone down" mood and affective responses, facilitate the conservation of energy and resources, and stimulate more effective ways of adaptation. Microdepression activates attachment behavior in the mothering person, modulates affective responses, and stimulates initiation of new contacts.

Melanie Klein's observation of the depressive position in normal infants between the ages of 3 and 6 months and Margaret Mahler's description of "mini anaclitic" depression in children in the subphase of rapprochement (ages 15 to 24 months) reveal behavioral manifestations of cumulative microdepressions.

A certain amount of microdepressive experiences are inevitable and promote further growth and development. Temporary, but adaptive, depression during adolescence, midlife crisis, retirement, and aging, and the experience of loss and grief, are manifestations of cumulative microdepressions. Disengagement and withdrawal for the sake of new engagement, commitment, and integration are essential features of human development from birth to death.

We hypothesize that an overwhelming number of microdepressive experiences gradually erodes the individual's feeling of well-being, effectiveness, and self-esteem. These cumulative traumas contribute to the development of affective disorders, particularly the spectrum of depressive disorders.

DEPRESSIVE DISORDERS

Types of Affective Disorders

Affective or mood disorders are divided into four types.

Major Depression, or Unipolar Disorder

The patient experiences single or recurrent episodes of depression without the experience of mood elevation, elation, or mania. Because the patient experiences only depression, this disorder is sometimes referred to as unipolar.

Bipolar Disorder or Classic Manic-Depressive Disorder

The patient experiences manic episodes in the form of predominate elevation of mood, expansiveness, irritability, hyperactivity, pressure of speech, flight of ideas, and inflated self-esteem. Later, the patient may experience a period or periods of depression. Because of mood fluctuation between two opposite poles, elation-depression, this is called bipolar disorder.

Other Specific Affective Disorders

This includes affective disorders of less intensity.

CYCLOTHYMIC DISORDER. This condition "...is a chronic mood disturbance of at least two years' duration, involving numerous periods of depression and hypomania, but not of sufficient severity and duration to meet the criteria for a major depressive or a manic episode." (*DSM-III,* 1980, p. 218)

DYSTHYMIC DISORDER, OR CLASSICAL DEPRESSIVE NEUROSIS. "The essential feature is a chronic disturbance of mood involving either depressed mood or loss of interest or pleasure in all, or almost all usual activities and pastimes." (ibid., pp. 220–221) The severity and duration of this disorder is less than in major depressive episodes—usually 2 years' duration for adults and one year for children and adolescents.

Atypical Affective Disorders

These patients have experienced a variety of affective disorders which do not follow the criteria of the earlier types.

Evidence of Depression in Infancy, Childhood, and Adolescence

The spectrum of depressive disorders, such as major depression (unipolar disorder), dysthymic disorder (classic depressive neurosis), depressive equivalent, and masked depression, will all be discussed as a group under depressive disorders. Following a discussion of general clinical features, age-specific clinical features will be discussed.

The existence of depression as an emotional disorder in infancy and childhood has been a matter of controversy. Some psychoanalysts and dynamic psychiatrists feel that infants and children cannot experience depressive neurosis because they have not, as yet, internalized the superego and therefore are unable to experience guilt. (Rochlin, 1959; Rie, 1966) In classical psychoanalytic theory, internalization of the superego and the experience of guilt are prerequisites for depressive disorders. (Abraham, 1911, 1916; Freud, 1917, 1923, 1938)

In Europe, most clinicians apply adult criteria of depression to children, without regard to developmental stages and issues.

Careful observation of infants during the first year of life by Spitz (1945, 1946, 1965) and Spitz and Wolf (1946) convincingly document the presence of severe depression following maternal deprivation. Bowlby (1946, 1951, 1960) related the loss of maternal attachment in childhood and the accompanying pathological grief, mourning, and depression to the occurrence of juvenile delinquency. Harlow (1958, 1959, 1960) studied the effect of maternal deprivation on infant monkeys. He found that maternal deprivation and disturbance in attachment behavior lead to the development of severe psychopathology, including profound depression, delay of development, and the possibility of psychosis.

Anthony and Scott (1960) and Anthony (1970, 1976, 1978) documented the existence of depression in children and adolescents. Sandler and Joffe (1965) related the existence of depression and depressive affect in children to the loss of feeling of well-being, rather than to the loss of self-esteem or guilt.

During the last decade, there has been extensive interest in the study of depression in childhood and adolescence. Glaser (1967) described masked depression in childhood and adolescence. Poznanski and Zrull (1970), Malmquist (1971), Annell (1972), Cytryn (1972), and Cytryn and McKnew (1974, 1979), Weinberg *et al.* (1973), Brumback and Weinberg (1977), Dorpat (1977), Cantwell and Carlson (1979), Puig-Antich and Chambers (1978), and Phillips (1979) have contributed significantly to the study, documentation, classification, and development of behavioral scales for the measurement of depression in children and adolescents.

Incidence and Prevalence

The incidence of depressive disorders in infancy, childhood, and adolescence is not known.

Adults

The prevalence of high risk for depression in individuals aged 17 years and older, in Alachua

County, Florida, was reported by Schwab *et al.* (1979) to be 14.5%. National Institute of Mental Health Studies report that the prevalence of depressive disorders in adults is approximately 15%. (Gallant and Simpson, 1976)

An extensive epidemiological study of affective disorders in 1975–1976, in the New Haven, Connecticut, area, by Weissman and Myers (1978) found the prevalence of definite cases of adult depressive disorders to be 5.7%, using Research Diagnostic Criteria (R.D.C.)

Nonpatient Population

Albert and Beck (1975) in 63 nonpatient seventh and eighth graders, using a modified Beck Depression Inventory, found that 23% showed signs of moderate to severe depression.

Kashani and Simonds (1979) and Kashani *et al.* (1981) found that if they applied strict *DSM-III* criteria to 103 nonpatients, ages 7 to 12 years, only 1.9% had depressive disorders. However, 17.4% showed distinct sadness, along with "...more somatic complaints, overactivity and restlessness, fighting, low self-esteem, and refusal to go to school." (Kashani and Simonds, 1979, p. 1204) It was their opinion that these children had a "subclinical form of depression" or "an early manifestation of child or adult depression." (ibid., p. 1204)

Patient Population

Annell (1972), in a study of 1,200 children in a psychiatric clinic, ages 1 to 19 years, reported that 2.3% were diagnosed as having depression. (p. 467) On the other hand, Bauersfeld, in a study of 2,200 children in a psychiatric clinic, ages 8 to 13, found that 13.7% were diagnosed as having depression. Using *DSM-III* criteria, of 788 children and adolescents who were evaluated in the Child Psychiatric Services, University of Louisville School of Medicine, from July 1980 through June 1981, 23% were diagnosed as suffering from affective disorders (major depressions and dysthymic disorders).

Regarding prevalence of depression in an inpatient psychiatric setting, Petti (1978), applying the Bellevue Index of Depression, diagnosed depression in 59% of 73 children aged 6 to 12 years.

General Clinical Features

Cytryn, *et al.* (1980) have made a "point by point comparison between the diagnostic criteria" of their own work, Weinberg's criteria, Kovacs'

Children's Diagnostic Inventory (CDI), and *DSM-III* criteria for depression. They found that "...childhood and adult diagnostic criteria for affective disorders are very similar, and DSM-III is a valid instrument for diagnosing childhood affective disorder." (p. 22)

According to *DSM-III,* the following clinical features or diagnostic criteria of major depressive episodes apply to infants older than age 8 months, children, adolescents, and adults.

Dysphoric Mood

Dysphoric mood includes the following symptoms: depression, sadness, loss of interest, loss of pleasure or joy in activities or pastimes, hopelessness, irritability, feeling blue, low, or down in the dumps.

This mood disturbance is prominent and persistent. Children under age 6 years usually cannot verbalize their dysphoric mood, but clinicians can infer it from a persistently sad facial expression.

Symptom Clusters

Four or more of the following symptoms are present consistently for at least 2 weeks:

1. Poor appetite, significant weight loss, failure to gain weight in children under the age of 6 years, or increase in appetite and significant weight gain
2. Insomnia or hypersomnia
3. Psychomotor retardation; agitation; or hypoactivity in children under 6 years of age
4. Loss of interest and pleasure, or apathy under age 6 years
5. Fatigue and loss of energy
6. Feelings of worthlessness, self-reproach, or excessive or inappropriate guilt
7. Complaints or evidence of diminished ability in thinking or concentrating
8. Recurrent thoughts of death, suicidal ideation, wishes to be dead, or suicide attempts
   (Adapted from *DSM-III,* 1980, pp. 213–214)

In children under age 6 years, three of the first four criteria will suffice for diagnosis of depressive disorder.

Regression

Depression in children, in addition to the general clinical features of depression, expresses itself by regression. The child loses some acquired age-specific developmental skills and functions on an earlier level.

The clinician needs to be familiar with the developmental tasks of each stage, so that absence, delay, or regression of any behavior will be readily apparent and serve as a signal of possible disturbance.

DEPRESSION IN THE FIRST YEAR OF LIFE

Depressive disorders in infancy are closely related to the disorders of attachment and mothering, child neglect, maternal deprivation, and placement of infants in institutions. Anaclitic depression, hospitalism, failure to thrive, and sensory-motor depression will be discussed.

Anaclitic Depression—Partial Emotional Deprivation

Anaclitic depression is a term used by Spitz (1946) to describe partial emotional deprivation of infants. Spitz and Wolf observed 123 infants, the total population of an institution. Each infant was observed for 12 to 18 months or longer, Males and females were almost evenly distributed.

The infants were in a "nursery" of a penal institution for delinquent girls who were pregnant at the time of incarceration. The infants' mothers were mostly young adolescents with a multitude of psychological problems, such as delinquency, mental retardation, or immaturity.

The infants were totally cared for by their mothers with some supervision from a small nursing staff. Spitz (1965) noticed that the infants, during the first 6 months, had a good relationship with their mothers and showed appropriate developmental progress.

However, in the second half of the first year, some [19] of them developed a weepy behavior which was in marked contrast to their previous happy outgoing behavior. After a time, this weepiness gave way to withdrawal. They would lie prone in their cots, face averted, refusing to take part in the life of their surroundings.
pp. 268–269.

Most of these troubled infants ignored adults, and a few of them watched adults with "a searching expression." If the observers were insistent on interaction, "...weeping would ensue, and in some cases screaming." (ibid., p. 269)

The troubled infants demonstrated the following symptoms, beginning at approximately 6 months of age:

1. Weeping and withdrawing behavior, lasting 2 to 3 months

2. Loss of weight instead of expected weight gain
3. Insomnia in some cases
4. Increased susceptibility to recurrent colds and infections
5. Retardation in the rate of psychological and intellectual growth, followed by actual decline
6. Frozen rigidity of expression replaced weepy behavior after 3 months. "Now these children would lie or sit with wide-open expressionless eyes, frozen immobile face, and a faraway look, as if in a daze, apparently not seeing what went on around them." (ibid., p. 269)
7. Human contact became "...increasingly difficult and finally impossible." (ibid., p. 269)

Spitz referred to these phenomena as *anaclitic depression,* anaclitic meaning "leaning up against." In the first year, the infant "leans up against" the mother for physical and emotional growth. The infants' symptoms and facial expressions strongly reminded the investigators of depressed adults. Spitz discovered that all of the infants with anaclitic depression had

...one experience in common: at some point between the sixth and eighth month of life all of them were deprived of the mother for a practically unbroken period of three months. This separation took place for unavoidable external administrative reasons.
ibid., p. 271.

Spitz noticed that the infants developed this syndrome after separation from mother. "No child developed this syndrome whose mother had not been removed." (ibid., p. 271) Concerning intellectual development, these maternally deprived infants were brighter (Developmental Quotient mean 130) than the control group (mean 116 to 120).

After separation from mother, the infant's intellectual development declined significantly. If the separation continued for more than one year, the infant's intelligence deteriorated to the moderate-severe retarded range (Developmental Quotient 40 to 50), as compared with the control group (Developmental Quotient 110).

Spitz observed that if the infant's deprivation from mother lasted not more than 3 to 5 months, most of the infants recovered, although not completely. However, if the deprivation exceeded 5 months "...the whole symptomatology changes radically and appears to merge into the prognostically poor syndrome of what I have described as 'Hospitalism'." (ibid., p. 272)

Hospitalism—Total Emotional Deprivation

According to Spitz, if emotional deprivation continues for more than 5 months, the infant will show "...the symptoms of increasingly serious deterioration, which appears to be, in part at least, irreversible." (ibid., p. 277)

In another study, Spitz observed 91 infants in a Foundling Home. These infants were breast-fed for the first 3 months by their mothers or by someone else. They grew normally. At age 3 months, the infants were separated from their mothers. The medical care, food, and hygiene provided for these infants were as good as or superior to any other institution, but one nurse had to care for 8 to 12 infants.

After separation from their mothers, these children went through the stages of progressive deterioration.... The symptoms of anaclitic depression followed one another in rapid succession and soon, after the relatively brief period of three months, a new clinical picture appeared.

ibid., p. 278.

In addition to all of the signs and symptoms of anaclitic depression, the observers now saw the following symptoms:

1. Significant motor retardation
2. Complete passivity—the infants would lie supine on their cots and would not turn around or assume a prone position
3. Vacuous facial expression
4. Defect in eye coordination
5. Spasticity in body movement after extensive rehabilitation
6. Bizarre finger movements similar to decerebrate or athetoid movements
7. Progressive decline in developmental quotient—by the end of the second year, the average Developmental Quotient was in the moderate to severe retarded range
8. Mortality rate was extremely high—29.6% died in the first year
9. The authors followed some of these children up to age 4 years. Most of them, even by this age, could not sit, stand, walk, or talk

Anaclitic depression and hospitalism are manifestations of infantile depression and maternal deprivation in its most severe form. A number of studies have documented that disorders in mothering, such as maternal depression, parental immaturity, family disharmony, drug and alcohol abuse, child abuse, and emotional neglect can also contribute to the development of depression in infancy, delayed development, and growth failure.

Failure to thrive in infancy is one of the most frequent results of disorders of attachment.

Failure to Thrive

Failure to thrive is a clinical syndrome quite common in pediatric practice. It usually does not come to the attention of child psychiatrists or psychiatrists because of the child's age.

Incidence

The incidence is unknown, but this is "...one of the most common reasons for admission of infants to the hospital." (Reinhart, 1979, p. 594) Failure to thrive frequently occurs in multiple problem families, families prone to child abuse and neglect, and lower socioeconomic families, although clinicians also need to be aware of the possibility of failure to thrive in middle or upper class families.

Etiology

Approximately 50% of the infants suffering from failure to thrive do not show any organic or physical cause of growth failure. The other half may suffer from growth failure because of kidney, heart, gastrointestinal, metabolic, or central nervous system abnormalities, malnutrition, or chronic infection.

Clinical Features

Failure to thrive, which is also referred to as reactive attachment disorder of infancy (*DSM-III*, pp. 57–60), has the following features.

ONSET BEFORE EIGHT MONTHS OF AGE. If the child is older than 8 months, but has the following symptoms, the diagnosis of affective disorder—major depression is most appropriate.

EVIDENCE OF LACK OF CARE. Gross emotional neglect, institutionalization, or disorders in the development of attachment behavior and human bonding is evident.

DELAY IN DEVELOPMENT. The infant is behind in many areas of development, such as affective response, cognitive development, and physical development.

Failure to thrive should be considered one of the major diagnostic possibilities if the infant has not developed or has significant delay in the following psychosocial behaviors:

1. Visual tracking of eyes and human face by age 2 months

2. Social smile at human face by age 2 months
3. Visual reciprocity by age 2 months
4. Alerting and turning to the caretaker's verbal communication by age 4 months
5. Vocal reciprocity by age 5 months
6. Spontaneous reaching to mother by age 4 months
7. Anticipatory response when the infant is approached to be picked up by age 5 months
8. Involvement and participation in playful games with mother or caretaker by age 5 months

WEIGHT. Most of these infants have gained very little weight or have lost weight. Usually, the weight is below the third percentile at the time of evaluation. The infant gains weight rapidly after hospital admission or environmental changes in maternal care.

HEIGHT. Height is usually affected, but not as severely as weight. If the child suffers from failure to thrive for a long period of time, a significant decrease in height will result.

HEAD SIZE. Head size is normal.

ABSENCE OF PHYSICAL DISORDER, MENTAL RETARDATION, OR INFANTILE AUTISM. The mother or primary care giver of a great majority of infants suffering from failure to thrive is "...depressed, angry, helpless, and desperate and with poor self-esteem." (Reinhart, 1979, p. 596) One of the most striking clinical features of children suffering from failure to thrive, besides weight loss, is apathy. These infants appear totally joyless and lifeless. Evidence of sadness or depression, instead of overwhelming apathy, indicates that the infant is still experiencing and communicating internal feeling. This is a favorable sign.

ADDITIONAL SIGNS. Some of the following signs may also be present:

1. Weak cry
2. Hypersomnia (excessive sleep)
3. Apathy (lack of interest in the environment)
4. Hypotonia of the muscles due to lack of stimulation and movement
5. Hypomotility
6. Weak rooting and grasping reflexes when feeding

Sensory-Motor Depression

In infancy, anaclitic depression, hospitalism, and failure to thrive represent severe and prolonged forms of depression and deprivation with dire consequences. However, other clinical symptomatologies have been observed in infants, which do not follow these syndromes, but which do have significant features of depression. For example, Robertson (1965) reported on the presence of depression in a 2-month-old infant, who improved significantly when the mother became more involved with her infant. Wisdom (1977) reported on an acute form of depression in a 6-month-old boy from an intact family. This depression lasted 3 to 4 days following the loss of a "nanny." Fraiberg and Freedman (1964) and Fraiberg (1968, 1977) found that parental depression and withdrawal contributed to sadness, withdrawal, autoerotic, and autisticlike behavior and developmental retardation in blind infants.

Brazelton et al. (1971) described an infant girl who manifested soberness, sadness, withdrawal, and unresponsiveness beginning 10 days following birth. The research team had observed that, at birth and during the ensuing week, this infant "...was an alert, wide-eyed newborn who looked vigorous and mature. She was entirely normal in all neurological and behavioral responses." (p. 303)

The research team, on a home visit 3 days later, reported that the mother appeared "quiet and unresponsive." The baby "...was curled in fetal position...and moved very little as we handled her." (p. 304) She was, to some extent, responsive to auditory and visual stimuli. By age 3 weeks, the infant was subdued, in a semialert state, and preoccupied most of the time with sucking her fist. Observations at 10 weeks and 3, 4, 7, and 8 months revealed that the infant continued to deteriorate cognitively and emotionally, was significantly behind in developmental milestones, and had very little facial animation. However, there was no report of weight loss or failure to gain weight—a prerequisite of failure to thrive.

At 8 months the infant was seen by a neurologist. The neurologist told the mother that her infant was retarded and that her brain was "...not normal and that her prognosis for ultimate development was probably poor." (p. 306)

When the research team made a home visit 2 weeks later, they noticed a profound change in the mother's attitude. She had mobilized her resources to overcome her own depression and apathy and had begun active involvement with her baby by an increase in body contact, talking, and playing. The observers noticed that the infant was already more active, rolled around in the play pen, tried to creep, and sat without support. The infant continued to improve dramatically. By age 12 months, her motor coordination was age appropriate, by 18 months she walked alone, and by 21 months she played with dolls. At age 2 years, this child was warm, expressive, affectionate, and functioning close to chronological age.

This infant, who at one time was diagnosed brain-damaged and retarded by a neurologist, and "possibly autistic" by the research team, dramatically improved after her mother's sensory-motor and affective contact increased. This case illustrates a severe form of depression which does not follow the criteria for failure to thrive, anaclitic depression, or hospitalism. Disturbance in human contact and mothering contributed to the development of withdrawal behavior, soberness, apathy, and significant delay in sensory-motor and affective development.

Definition of Sensory-Motor Depression

We feel there is a cluster of behaviors in infants related to depression which do not follow the classic descriptions of anaclitic depression and hospitalism, or the criteria for failure to thrive. Because of the infant's cognitive stage and the affective nature of the disturbance, we have chosen the term sensory-motor depression to describe this affective disorder in infancy. The term "sensory-motor depression" emphasizes the two major components of this disturbance—cognitive and affective.

The use of the term "sensory-motor" refers to the sensory-motor stage of intelligence—the first stage of human cognition—from birth to age 18 months. (Piaget 1962; see chapter 2) Human intelligence and cognition originate from environmental and bodily stimuli and the motoric responses to these stimuli. Decrease, disturbance, or failure in human contact and stimulation have an immediate effect on the infant's cognitive and affective development.

The use of the term "depression" describes the affective and emotional component of the infant's response of soberness, sadness, and withdrawal following disturbance or failure in human contact.

Onset

Onset of sensory-motor depression can occur immediately after birth, but usually becomes noticeable in the second to third week of life or later. The infant cannot verbally express feelings of sadness and dysphoria, but the informed and sensitive clinician can detect the infant's emotional state through observation of facial expression and behavior.

Duration

In acute form, sensory-motor depression is of short duration, lasting a few hours to a few days. If the mothering person does not alleviate the depression through human contact, it can become rhythmical and eventually chronic.

Clinical Features

FACIAL EXPRESSION. The infant persistently has a sober, sad, and joyless facial expression. This sadness and lack of joy are contagious. Sensitive parents, observers, and clinicians, when seeing the infant's face, often feel profound sadness within. This empathic feeling of sadness in the clinician has diagnostic value and facilitates in the differentiation of depression from other forms of withdrawal behavior, such as in physical illness, childhood autism, or severe mental retardation.

The sad face of the infant reactivates maternal and care-giving behavior in the observer. The observer may spontaneously feel like picking up and hugging the infant in order to comfort him.

CRYING. Initially, the crying of the depressed infant has the quality of a "pain" cry, but it gradually loses forcefulness and becomes a cranky, irritable cry or whimper.

When an adult approaches, the infant gazes at the adult's eyes, with a long, wary, and deeply sad look, and then bursts into a pain cry. As the infant's depression becomes more prolonged, the pain cry may disappear and only a cranky, irritable cry or whimper remains. After a while, the infant may stop any crying. Insensitive parents might then feel that the infant is doing much better and is becoming a "good baby." Significant decrease in crying or absence of crying in a depressed infant is an ominous sign.

EYE CONTACT. The eye contact of normal infants has a bright-eyed quality, which usually creates a feeling of joy in the observer. The depressed infant, especially in the early phases of depression, has prolonged eye contact, but without "brightness" and emanating wariness and sadness, as though communicating internal misery.

As the depression progresses, the infant continues to have eye contact but it is usually brief. However, in profound depression, the infant might gaze at the observer in an empty and apathetic manner or avoid eye contact. Facial expression and eye contact are the two major clues in helping the clinician become aware of the possibility of sensory-motor depression and disorders in mothering.

LANGUAGE. In a depressed infant, cooing and babbling will not occur between ages 1 and 2 months. The infant will continue to be fussy. It appears that the infant has not been able to learn new schemata for expression of internal states, such as cooing, babbling, and vocally responding to maternal stimulation. In the older infant, the imitative behavior and acquired language skills decline and the child regresses to more fussiness and crying behavior.

SMILE. When the infant becomes depressed, one of the first behaviors to disappear is the social and recognition smiles. The infant may have an anemic proto-smile or grimace, but this connotes internal sadness rather than joy and pleasure.

MOTOR BEHAVIOR. The depressed infant has hypomotility and motor retardation, particularly in the first 6 months of life. In the second 6 months of life, with the emergence of separation anxiety and stranger anxiety, the acutely depressed infant may have restlessness, agitation, and fidgetiness, along with hypomotility.

The motor skills acquired last will be the first to disappear. Also, there will be a delay in the development of new skills. The more prolonged the depression, the more profound motor retardation.

EATING BEHAVIOR. The depressed infant does not suck at the breast or bottle vigorously. He does not appear to experience pleasure and relief following eating and becomes a fussy eater. Vomiting, spitting up food, rumination, and occasionally overeating may develop if depression continues. Lack of expected weight gain or weight loss might signal early sign of failure to thrive.

SLEEP. Sleep becomes dysrhythmic. Depressed infants sleep significantly more (hypersomnia) than normal infants. This sleep is restless, with frequent whimpering. Older infants may wake up agitated and crying or regress to dysrhythmic sleep.

LACK OF ASSERTIVENESS AND CURIOUSITY. Depressed infants, because of frequently experiencing failure in human contact, lose their assertiveness and their curiosity for new experiences. They become withdrawn and resigned. This resignation, however, is different from passivity, because there is an underlying tone of sadness, depression, and apathy.

APATHY. As the depression progresses, the sober and sad facial expression might be replaced with an unresponsive and vacuous expression. Apathy signals the child's profound feeling of hopelessness and helplessness, as though he has given up communicating his inner state. The presence of apathy is an ominous sign and might lead to anaclitic depression or failure to thrive.

MOTHER-CHILD INTERACTION. If the depression occurs in the first 6 months of life, the development of the mother-child interaction suffers profoundly. There will be a significant fracture in the attachment behavior between the infant and mother; for instance, lack or delay in recognition smile at 4 months and stranger-separation anxiety at age 8 to 10 months.

The older infant (age 10 to 12 months) may regress and show intensified and overwhelming stranger-separation anxiety and become clingy to the mother. If the depression continues, the older infant will regress further and become apathetic and unresponsive to either mother's presence or absence.

COGNITIVE DEVELOPMENT. Depending on what age the infant becomes depressed, there will be significant delay or regression in cognitive development, e.g., reciprocity, imitative behavior, and object permanency, because of a lack of stimulation and motivation. In no area of human development is the tragic impact of prolonged infantile depression more profound than in the area of cognitive development.

HEALTH. The depressed infant suffers from a variety of physical illnesses, such as frequent respiratory infections, vomiting, diarrhea, and weight loss. Psychophysiological disorders, such as infantile eczema, dermatitis, asthma, and a variety of food or milk allergies are more prevalent. If the depression continues and becomes prolonged, failure to thrive with significant weight loss, and, in severe cases, hospitalism will follow.

DEPRESSION: AGES ONE TO THREE YEARS

Clinical Features of Depression

Depression in ages one to 3 years initially interferes with newly acquired developmental skills. Because a number of clinicians do not consider the possibility of depression at this age, it goes unrecognized. The clinical features of depression in the first year of life, along with the following age-related symptoms, are prevalent.

Motor Behavior

Delay or regression occurs in standing, walking, and running.

Eating Behavior

The child stops feeding himself and becomes a fussy eater with a poor appetite. Indiscriminate mouthing, pica (eating everything indiscriminately), and frequent coprophagy (eating feces) occur and are closely associated with depression or maternal deprivation or neglect.

Sleep

The child experiences disturbances in sleep, increase in the amount of sleep, frequent wakefulness, increase of nightmares and night terrors, and occasional insomnia.

Cognitive Development

There is delay in the development of symbolic thought representation and object permanency.

Language

Delay or regression in language development is profound. The child is not motivated to use language and might lose some language skills already acquired temporarily until depression is over.

Autoerotic Behavior

Self-stimulating behaviors, such as masturbation, rocking, head-banging, scratching the self, and self-biting, become predominant.

Transitional Object

In the early phase, clinging to the transitional object greatly increases, whereas in severe depression the child may lose interest in the favorite object—a serious sign.

Negativism and Oppositional Behavior

In the early phase, a feeling of distrust, or even paranoid behavior becomes manifest, but decreases as depression continues or becomes more severe.

Toilet Training

Delay or loss of recently acquired bowel or bladder functions occur.

Play Behavior

Interest in playing with adults or parallel play with peers decreases, and there is a loss of interest in manipulating objects and making discoveries.

Developmental Considerations

Depression in the subphase of rapprochement (ages 15 to 25 months) significantly interferes with the development of separation-individuation, object constancy, and psychological birth of the self. In the early stages of depression, the child may become much more clinging and manifest intensified forms of separation and stranger anxiety, similar to that manifested by an infant between ages 8 and 10 months. These behaviors are frequently associated with intense ambivalence toward mother, such as, crying outbursts, hitting, kicking, and biting, along with constant clinging and dread of separation.

The depressed child between ages 2 and 3 years may verbalize overwhelming fear of being killed or of being "eaten up" by humans or animals (intensified oral-incorporative fantasies). Nightmares often have these themes.

Etiology

Depression during early childhood is closely related to the loss of love object because the child has not totally internalized the maternal imago—object constancy. The child mourns and grieves over this loss in a pathological way. The child's grief and mourning resemble the chronic unresolved mourning of adults, which usually manifests itself in the form of clinical depression. (Abraham, 1927; Freud, 1917; Bowlby, 1960)

According to Bowlby (1960), in both children and adults, grief and mourning include protest, despair, and detachment. Protest is expressed through crying and expression of anger and hostility. Despair is affective sadness and temporary regression and depression. Detachment is the withdrawal of the affection and love invested in the lost love object. These processes occur concomitantly and help the individual work through and come to terms with the loss. According to Bowlby, children, particularly under age 6 years, are not able to work through a loss effectively. The mourning process in children becomes lifelong and chronic, similar to unresolved and pathological mourning in adulthood.

Depression in children and adults is often related to loss of the love object, loss of self-esteem, or loss of the feeling of well-being. Unresolved and untreated depression in childhood, along with lack of at least partial replacement of the love object, may result in the development of lack of empathy, resulting in cruelty to animals and other children. Later, in adolescence and adulthood, sadistic, destructive, and occasionally homicidal behavior may be the outcome.

According to Lorenz, human beings do not have innate inhibition against intraspecies destructive behavior. Only the establishment of attachment to another human being, usually the mothering person, can contain destructive tendencies. (see chapter 1) Through the establishment of the human bond, the child will learn to love other human beings and to respect life. (Fraiberg, 1967)

Depression in the first 3 years of life may contribute to the development of a multitude of psychopathologies in later childhood, adolescence, and adulthood, such as major depression, narcissistic personality disorders, borderline psychosis, delinquency, alcohol and drug abuse, psychophysiological disorders, and even psychosis.

DEPRESSION: AGES THREE TO SIX YEARS

Clinical Features

Depression in ages 3 to 6 years has the greatest impact initially on the developmental tasks and newly acquired skills of the phallic-oedipal phase. Following are the age-specific manifestations of depression.

Affect and Fantasies

Overwhelming sadness, helplessness, lack of joy, and preoccupation with punishment fill the child's world. Themes of failure, hurt, destruction, and death permeate fantasy play and the world of make-believe. In the early phase of depression, omnipotent and magical fantasies may alleviate the pain of despair temporarily. As depression continues, omnipotent fantasies disappear and "no one wins and everyone loses."

In prolonged and severe forms of depression, the forest of fantasies becomes an empty desert of loneliness and detachment. Usually, it is so painful for these children to share their morbid fantasies with others that they keep them within; however, some may act out with aggressive and destructive behavior. When the child begins to share fantasies with a caring listener, he is already on the road to recovery.

Motor Behavior

Loss of interest in newly acquired skills, such as running, climbing, buttoning clothes, putting on shoes, and riding a bicycle may occur. One of the first activities to decline is involvement in group games and play with peers.

Sphincter Control

The child between the ages of 5 and 6 years, who had been dry at night for some time, may become enuretic or encopretic.

Cognitive Development

A decline in cognitive functions, such as interest in reading, writing, or drawing occurs. The cognitive ability for drawing images without relying on immediate sensory input (deferred imitation) may decrease or disappear. Language ability declines. The more depressed the child becomes, the more he will lose cognitive schemata of the preoperational stage of intelligence and rely on sensory-motor intelligence. Because of the decline in cognitive ability, the child may feel that he is "dumb" or "stupid."

Play Behavior

Play with peers decreases significantly; daydreaming and isolation increase. When parents ask the child why he is not playing with others, he might burst into tears and say, "Nobody likes me," "Everybody hates me," or "Everyone says I'm stupid."

Eating Behavior

There is overemphasis on food fads and loss of pleasure in eating. The fantasies of prowess from eating certain foods are replaced by apprehension about the dangers of food. Extreme weight loss may result in anorexia. Occasionally the child may gorge himself.

Sleep

Sleep is disturbed with frequent nightmares, night terrors, difficulties going to sleep, or awakening during the night. Nightmares may have overwhelming themes of death, destruction, threats, and danger, without any hope of rescue. On occasion, dreams of denial prevail; for instance, the child dreams that he is happy and without any worries or concerns.

Nursery School

The joy of going to nursery school or kindergarten decreases or disappears. The child may cling to mother, express fear of leaving her, and manifest signs of school phobia. (see chapter 9)

Psychophysiological Symptoms

Frequent complaints of headaches, stomach-aches, or upset stomach are common. Weight loss, anorexia, ulcerative colitis, asthma, dermatitis, and other allergies are prevalent. (see chapter 12)

Suicidal Behavior

Until recently, it was thought that depressed preschool or latency-age children did not manifest suicidal behavior. We have seen a number of children between ages 3 and 6 years who have openly verbalized suicidal ideas, death wishes, and, at times, have even attempted suicide. They have tried to hang themselves, or deliberately run in front of a car, or tried to jump out of a window. (see chapter 14)

Some children do not openly verbalize suicidal ideas, but demonstrate self-destructive behavior, in the form of severe head-banging, biting, scratching themselves severely enough to bleed, swallowing sharp objects, or becoming accident prone. Most of these children have been physically abused or neglected or have witnessed frequent physical violence at home.

Developmental Considerations

During the phallic-oedipal phase, the emerging castration anxiety may become fused with depressive affect. In the early phase of depression, the irrational dread of bodily injury and autoerotic behavior significantly intensify. As the depression increases in intensity and duration, the child regresses further, giving up phallic-oedipal strivings of triangular relationships and retreating to the earlier dyadic relationship. Anal and oral behavior become more predominant.

DEPRESSION: AGES SIX TO TWELVE YEARS

Most studies of childhood depression are reports on the latency-age child or adolescents; this is probably because mental health clinicians have more contact with these age groups.

The child of this age is more verbal and can share his depressive feelings with others. Also, he attends school. Frequently, the teachers are the first to notice the child's persistent sadness, poor performance, withdrawal, and daydreaming. Parents often are unable to recognize their child's depression or tend to minimize or deny it.

Clinical Features

Depression occurring in children between ages 6 and 12 years expresses itself in a somewhat similar fashion to adult depression. Age-specific clinical features are as follows.

Affect and Fantasies

Dysphoric mood and depressive affects express themselves in morbid fantasies. Depressive themes, such as "...mistreatment, thwarting, blame or criticism, loss and abandonment, personal injury, death, and suicide," predominate in the child's play, dreams, and daydreams. (Cytryn and McKnew, 1979, p. 330)

These depressive themes play a significant role in the development and sustenance of depression. In some children, they are the only evidence of depression, as outward appearance and behavior may not be affected.

Cognitive Development and School Performance

Disturbance in academic performance and peer relationships in school are some of the earliest signs of depression in the latency-age child. Loss of interest, lack of motivation, and decline in cognitive functioning all directly affect school performance. The academic area that is newly acquired or the weakest is the most vulnerable; for instance, reading disturbances in an average or below average child or overwhelming apprehension and fear of failure in a bright child might be a sign of depression. Obsessive preoccupation about school work and undue concern about performance and lack of pleasure in achievement may be early signs of depression.

Decline of school performance in a bright child who had previously been performing well should be taken very seriously. Also, a change in behavior, such as clowning in a formerly quiet child, or withdrawal in a previously outgoing child, may also be a sign of depression.

Motor Behavior

In most depressed children, hypomotility, fidgetiness, agitation, clumsiness, and accident proneness are common. Some children, because of their temperament, show hyperactive behavior or aggressive and disruptive behavior in school. Symptoms of hyperactivity along with a decline in cognitive function are often misdiagnosed as hyperkinetic syndrome. (see chapter 10) Careful attention to the presence of dysphoric mood, depressive affect, and low self-esteem will help in the accurate diagnosis of depression.

Guilt

With the further development of the super-ego, and the cognitive development of morality, the depressed child becomes extremely self-critical. The child feels guilty about everything that he has said, done, or thought about. He may apologize over and over without relief. The child might become oversolicitous, ingratiating, and "too kind" to others (defense of reaction formation). Because of low self-esteem and overwhelming guilt, depressed children seek constant reassurance and praise. But, at the same time, undue reassurance and praise reinforce their guilt feelings and become ineffective. Judicious support and praise, with proper timing, can be effective.

Expression of Hostility and Aggression

Because of overt inhibition, overcontrol, and hypomotility, aggressive impulses and hostile feelings are repressed. The depressed child unconsciously turns these aggressive and destructive feelings against the self. Overwhelming guilt feelings, self-depreciation, and self-destructive behavior are manifestations of this pathological process.

The more the child is able to express directly aggressive and hostile feelings verbally or through play, the better will be the hope for recovery. Encouragement of physical activity and body motility channelizes repressed aggressive tendencies in a sublimated and effective manner.

Suicidal Behavior

In recent years, we have seen an increase in the prevalence of suicidal behavior in younger children. From 1973 to 1978, 43% of 340 children and adolescents who were referred for suicidal behavior to the Child Psychiatric Services, University of Louisville School of Medicine, were aged 12 years and younger. (Shafii et al., 1979)

Active suicidal ideation and suicidal attempts have become prevalent. During the last 5 years in the Louisville, Kentucky, area, the youngest child who committed suicide was 10 years of age. Nationally, there have been more than 130 suicides in this age group annually. It is a tragedy that many clinicians still believe that suicidal behavior in the form of suicidal attempts or actual suicide is rare in this age group. Suicidal ideation, messages, behavior, and attempts of children and adolescents need to be taken seriously. (See chapter 14)

Developmental Considerations

The depressed latency-age child loses interest in friendships and associations. The child regresses to the early phallic-oedipal stage, with increased evidence of castration anxiety. If the depression continues, he may regress further to anal or oral behaviors.

The sense of industry and enthusiasm for the development of skills gives way to feelings of inferiority and self-doubt. Ambivalence (love and hate feelings) may predominate in the child's relationship with the parents. Because of the child's ability to experience guilt more intensely, ambivalence constantly torments him and interferes with his functioning.

DEPRESSION IN ADOLESCENCE: AGES TWELVE TO EIGHTEEN YEARS

Clinical Features

Developmentally, normal adolescents have a proclivity toward depression. It is important to differentiate clearly and carefully the normal depressive mood swings of adolescence from pathological depression. This differentiation taxes even the ability of experienced clinicians. The major age-specific clinical features are as follows.

Dysphoric Mood and Depressive Affect

The normal mood swings of adolescence are significantly intensified. The experience of sadness and dysphoric mood are more common. Volatile moods prevail, and the proclivity toward rage reactions increases. Adolescents have a vulnerability for depressive disorders. The symptoms of depression in late adolescence are similar to those of adult depression.

Puberty

The emergence of puberty may be delayed in a chronically depressed early adolescent, particularly if the depression is associated with weight loss and anorexia. The depressed adolescent may have great difficulty accepting or understanding the signs of puberty. Self-consciousness and self-doubt are intensified. A flood of hormonal secretions, along with a stressful environment, may plunge the adolescent to the depth of depression and possible suicidal behavior.

Wet dreams and incestuous dreams add an extra burden to the already guilt-ridden depressed adolescent. The menstrual period of depressed adolescent girls may be delayed, quite irregular, or associated with exaggerated pain and discomfort. Dysphoric moods are intensified during "premenstrual tension." Depressed adolescent girls may feel "blue," "down in the dumps," cry without provocation, become sulky, pouty, isolate themselves in their rooms, and sleep much longer.

Cognitive Development

Temporary disorganization of cognitive functioning in pubescence becomes significantly exaggerated in depressed adolescents. In younger adolescents, the development of abstract thinking is delayed. In older adolescents, this newly acquired ability decreases or disappears.

School performance is frequently affected. If an adolescent was doing well in school and suddenly performance declines, depression could be considered as one of the possible causes. Skipping school, procrastination in finishing assignments, irritable behavior in the classroom, and lack of concern about achievement and future vocation can also be early signs of depression in adolescents.

Concrete thinking, along with withdrawal, isolation, and low energy level, may give the impression of a schizoid personality or of an early form of schizophrenia. This misperception is one of the most common errors made in diagnosing depression in adolescents.

Self-Esteem

Low self-esteem is one of the significant contributors to depression throughout life. In adolescents, depression intensifies low self-esteem. The depressed adolescent internally feels that he has failed himself and others. Hopelessness and helplessness lower the self-esteem further and a vicious cycle ensues. At times, the depressed adolescent tries to defend against low self-esteem by denial, omnipotent fantasies, or by escaping from reality through the use of drugs and alcohol.

Antisocial Behavior

Skipping school, stealing, fighting, and frequent driving tickets or accidents, particularly in an adolescent with a former history of good behavior, may be indicators of depression.

Alcohol and Drug Abuse

A large number of depressed adolescents abuse alcohol and drugs. The use of marijuana,

"uppers," (amphetamine, mood-elevating drugs), "downers" (barbiturates, tranquilizers, and sleep-inducing agents), and, particularly, alcohol is common. Some may use cocaine, heroin, or other narcotic derivatives or hallucinogens.

Recent studies by Johnston (1981) of 17,000 high school seniors in the United States found that, although the daily use of marijuana has decreased by 12%, still nearly 10% of these seniors smoked marijuana daily. Alarmingly, 65% reported that they have used some type of illicit drug during their lifetime. There is some evidence of decline in the use of hallucinogens, "uppers," and "downers." The use of cocaine, however, has nearly doubled from 1976 to 1979. (ibid., p. 3)

Sexual Behavior

Generally, depressed adolescents do not show interest in dating or heterosexual interactions. However, some depressed adolescent girls become involved in sexual acting out or even promiscuity. Promiscuity in depressed adolescent girls frequently has a self-depreciating and self-destructive quality. Many do not take precautions to prevent pregnancy or venereal disease. Some wish to become pregnant to compensate for object loss or low self-esteem.

Depressed adolescents might marry early to escape family conflicts, compensating for object loss or low self-esteem. Frequently, these marriages do not work out and reinforce depression.

Health

Depressed adolescents appear pale, tired, and lack the vigor and joy of youth. Frequently, these adolescents have a multitude of physical complaints, such as headaches, stomachaches, lack of appetite, and weight loss without any organic cause. Because the depressed adolescent does not usually verbalize his feelings, physical symptoms often may be the only route of coming in contact with a clinician. The clinician's sensitivity in picking up clues of dysphoric mood or depression may prevent an adolescent suicide.

Weight

Decrease in the velocity of weight gain or weight loss could indicate depression. At the same time, low self-esteem and lack of care may contribute to overeating and obesity.

Suicidal Behavior

Most adolescents, because of dysphoric mood and mercurial self-esteem, occasionally have thoughts of committing suicide. Usually, these suicidal thoughts are fleeting, not well-organized, and without a definite plan. Depressed adolescents are highly vulnerable to suicides. In the Louisville area, Shafii *et al.* (1981) have found a significant increase in actual suicide in adolescents from 1975 to 1980: in early adolescents, there was a more than 80% increase, and in late adolescents, a more than 100% increase. (see chapter 14)

Suicide is the third major cause of death in adolescents, following accidents and cancer. Most adolescents commit suicide through violent means. In the Louisville study (60 child and adolescent suicides), 57% used firearms. Many of these adolescents showed signs of depression and an increase in drug and alcohol use. Almost all of them had verbalized suicidal ideas prior to committing suicide. Some had attempted suicide earlier. Unfortunately, 82% of this group had never received psychiatric help.

It is of utmost importance for the clinician to take the symptoms of depression, suicidal ideas, gestures, or attempts in children and adolescents seriously. The management of a suicidal adolescent is in some ways similar to the management of child abuse. The clinician should mobilize all resources to help the family and the adolescent. Consultation with a child psychiatrist or a psychiatrist who is qualified in working with adolescents is essential. Postponing, delaying, or waiting to "see what happens" may cost a young person's life. For further discussion on child and adolescent suicide, refer to chapters 13 and 14.

PSYCHOBIOLOGY OF DEPRESSION

During the 1950's clinicians observed that the use of reserpine as an anti-hypertensive agent led to depression in patients. It was also noted that the use of isoniazid in patients with tuberculosis brought about euphoria. These findings increased interest in searching for psychopharmacological agents for the treatment of depression. The discovery of mood elevators, such as imipramine and amitriptyline, increased research interest in the biochemistry of depression in adults. Unfortunately, little work has been done in the biochemistry of depression in children and adolescents.

One of the most widely held psychobiological theories of depression is the *catecholamines theory*. This theory is based on the function of biochemical agents in the brain which facilitate the transmission of impulses from one neuron to another. These biochemical agents are called neurotransmitters. Two major neurotransmitters that influence presynaptic or postsynaptic trans-

mission are norepinephrine and serotonin. It has been hypothesized that depressive symptoms are related to a decrease of norepinephrine in the brain. Mood elevating agents increase the amount of norepinephrine and/or serotonin in the brain, and this contributes to the patient's mood elevation and symptomatic improvement. The balance between norepinephrine and serotonin is important in modulating mood.

Regarding the psychobiology of depression in childhood, studies by Cytryn and McKnew (1974) of nine depressed children, ages 6 to 12 years, showed that in a chronically depressed child the amount of norepinephrine in the urine deviated from normal. However, in repeated experiments, the results were not consistent. The urine norepinephrine level of children who were suffering from acute or "masked" depression did not deviate significantly from normal.

MHPG (3-methoxy-4 hydroxyphenylethyl glycol) is a metabolite of norepinephrine, which primarily originates in the brain rather than in other tissues. The study of the level of MHPG in the urine might represent the level of norepinephrine in the brain. It is thought that some forms of depression might be related to the level of MHPG in the urine. Cytryn and McKnew found that the level of MHPG in the urine of some depressed children was significantly higher than in the control group. (1979, p. 334)

For many years, psychoendocrinologists have searched for biological markers of depression. Michael and Gibbons (1963) and Rubin and Mandell (1966) suggested an association between affective disorders, particularly depression, and disturbance of hypothalamo-pituitary-adrenal (HPA) functions, such as those found in Cushing's disease. If a dose of dexamethasone (a steroid) is given to patients with Cushing's disease and a control group between 11:00 P.M. and midnight, and a blood sample is taken the next morning between 8:00 and 9:00 A.M., the level of plasma cortisol will remain high in patients with Cushing's disease, whereas it will be significantly lower in the control group. This procedure is referred to as dexamethasone suppression test (DST).

Because blood studies have consistently shown that a subgroup of depressed patients have hypersecretion of cortisol, it has been hypothesized that this subgroup suffers from "...cortisol hypersecretion or pituitary-adrenal disinhibition." (Brown and Shuey, 1980, p. 747 and Sachar *et al.*, 1967, 1973)

Carroll *et al.* (1968, 1976) have found that 48% of depressed patients showed an "early escape" from dexamethasone suppression as opposed to a control group or other nondepressed psychiatric patients. "Early escape" means that if 2 mg. of dexamethasone are given orally at midnight and blood samples are taken the next day at 8:00 A.M., 4:00 P.M., and midnight, there will be a relative suppression of plasma cortisol at 8:00 A.M., but a gradual increase of the cortisol level by 12:00 midnight (24 hours later). In the control groups, the suppression usually lasted at least 24 to 48 hours.

Brown *et al.* (1979) and Brown and Shuey (1980) have repeated these studies and have confirmed "...the utility of the dexamethasone suppression test (DST) in identifying a clinically meaningful subtype of depression." (p. 747) According to the authors, 50% of the patients with primary depression (a depressed patient without any other psychiatric diagnosis) showed escape from dexamethasone suppression. This nonsuppressor group, although similar clinically to the suppressor group, responded significantly better to treatment as opposed to other depressive groups. Most of the nonsuppressor group was free from psychiatric symptomatology before the depressive episode and after treatment returned to their earlier psychosocial functioning.

Difficulty in going to sleep and particularly early morning awakening, anorexia, vasovegetative disturbances, and EEG findings, such as absence of Stages III and IV sleep, increase of REM sleep, and shorter REM latency may be related to the limbic system and hypothalamo-pituitary-adrenal disinhibition. Similar studies are needed in the depressive disorders of childhood and adolescence.

Biochemical studies are opening new vistas for understanding the psychobiology of depression, but, as yet, there is not general agreement on these findings. Also, the implications of these findings for clinical practice need further exploration.

TREATMENT OF DEPRESSION IN INFANCY, CHILDHOOD, AND ADOLESCENCE

Emotional disorders, particularly depression in infancy, childhood, and adolescence, are underdiagnosed and undertreated. Clinicians' constant awareness of the possibility of depression and the exploration of the signs and symptoms of depression in this age group help in careful assessment and treatment.

Family history of affective disorders or depressive spectrum disorders, such as alcohol and drug abuse, antisocial behavior, tendency toward violence, and child abuse, increases the young person's vulnerability to depression and suicide.

In the treatment of depressed young people, the following principles are helpful.

Human Contact

Providing consistent, predictable, and emotionally supportive human contact for the depressed patient and the family is the most effective therapeutic agent. The clinician needs to be available to the patient and the family for regularly scheduled visits and also available 24 hours a day for emergency or crisis. Human contact has a healing and growth-producing effect far beyond our present understanding.

Psychotherapy

Commonly, the young person is the recognized patient, but usually the whole family suffers and requires therapeutic help and guidance. The most effective way of treating depressed children and adolescents is by being flexible in using a variety of therapeutic modalities. Examining the indications and contraindications of various therapeutic approaches is essential for choosing the most effective one.

Individual supportive-exploratory psychotherapy and play therapy, along with regular therapeutic work with the family throughout as indicated, are essential for effective treatment of depression. (see chapter 21)

Hospitalization

Short-term hospitalization in a psychiatric setting may be indicated for moderate to severe forms of depression, especially if the young person has expressed active suicidal fantasies or behavior.

In the case of failure to thrive, hospitalization is highly recommended in order to remove the infant from the psychotoxic environment, to provide required medical and dietary care, and to begin extensive psychosocial assessment and treatment of the infant and family.

Medication

The use of antidepressant medication and mood elevators in the treatment of childhood or adolescent depression is a matter of controversy. We do not recommend medication in mild or moderate depression.

In severe forms of adolescent depression, while the patient is hospitalized, and after careful assessment, antidepressant agents, such as imipramine or amitriptyline, may be indicated. The use of medication is discussed in chapter 23. The use of lithium in the treatment of manic-depressive disorder in children and adolescents can be found in chapter 8.

PROGNOSIS

Therapeutic work with depressed children and adolescents, although emotionally draining, is rewarding. Usually, within a short period of time, 2 to 4 weeks after the initiation of psychotherapy, the patient's dysphoric mood begins to improve.

In dynamic psychotherapy and play therapy, the therapist provides regular, consistent, and predictable human contact. The therapist encourages open expression of feeling, particularly anger and hostility. When the patient begins to express anger toward the therapist, parents, peers, or others, the prognosis improves.

The period of outpatient treatment usually lasts between 6 months and 2 or 3 years or longer. During this time, the child may go through a number of cycles of depressive episodes. As the treatment progresses, the intensity and duration of depressive episodes decrease.

The child and the family gradually become aware of the factors that contribute to the development of depression. This awareness helps the patient and the family anticipate possible depression and find effective ways of preventing or decreasing the intensity and duration.

Open expression of feeling, realistic assessment of one's ability and shortcomings, and acceptance of failure help the depressed child overcome depression and find an effective way of "working through" a multitude of emotional conflicts, disappointments, and failures throughout life.

REFERENCES

Abraham, K. (1911). Notes on the psychoanalytic investigation and treatment of manic-depressive insanity and allied conditions. In *Selected Papers on Psychoanalysis*. New York: Basic Books, 1960, pp. 137–156.

Abraham, K. (1916). The first pregenital stage of the libido. In *Selected Papers on Psychoanalysis*. London: Hogarth, 1948.

Abraham, K. (1927). A short study of the development of the libido, viewed in the light of mental disorders. In *Selected Papers on Psychoanalysis*. London: Hogarth.

Albert, N., Beck, A.T. (1975). Incidence of depression in early adolescence: A preliminary study. *J. Youth Adolesc., 4,* 301–307.

American Psychiatric Association (1980). *Diagnostic and Statistical Manual of Mental Disorders.* Third Edition. Washington, D.C.: American Psychiatric Association.

Annell, A.L. (Ed.) (1972). *Depressive States in Children and Adolescence.* New York: Halstead Press.

Anthony, E. (1970). Two contrasting types of adolescent depression and their treatment. *J. Am. Psychoanal. Assoc., 18,* 841–859.

Anthony, E.J. (1976). On the genesis of childhood depression. In Anthony, E.J., Gilpin, D. (Eds.), *Three Clinical Faces of Childhood.* New York: Spectrum Publications.

Anthony, E.J. (1978). Affective disorders in children and adolescents with special emphasis on depression. In Cole, J., Schatzberg, A., Frazier, S. (Eds.), *Depression: Biology, Psychodynamics and Treatment.* New York: Plenum, pp. 173–184.

Anthony, E.J., Scott, P. (1960). Manic-depressive psychosis in childhood. *J. Child Psychol. Psychiatry, 1,* 53–72.

Bowlby, J. (1946). *Forty-Four Juvenile Thieves.* London: Bailliere, Tindall and Cox.

Bowlby, J. (1951). *Maternal Care and Mental Health.* Geneva: World Health Organization Monograph.

Bowlby, J. (1960). Grief and mourning in infancy and early childhood. *Psychoanal. Study Child, 15,* 9–52.

Brazelton, T.B., Young, G.C., Bullowa, M. (1971). Inception and resolution of early developmental pathology. In Rexford, E.N., Sander, .W., Shapiro, T. (Eds.), *Infant Psychiatry, A New Synthesis.* New Haven: Yale University Press, 1976, pp. 301–310.

Brown, W.A., Johnston, R., Mayfield, D. (1979). The 24-hour dexamethasone suppression test in a clinical setting: Relationship to diagnosis, symptoms, and response to treatment. *Am. J. Psychiatry, 136,* 543–547.

Brown, W.A., Shuey, I. (1980). Response to dexamethasone and subtype of depression. *Arch. Gen. Psychiatry, 37,* 747–751.

Brumback, R.A., Weinberg, W.A. (1977). Childhood depression: An exploration of a behavior disorder of children. *Percept. Mot. Skills, 44,* 911–916.

Cantwell, D., Carlson, G. (1979). Problems and prospects in the study of childhood depression. *J. Nerv. Ment. Dis., 167,* 522–529.

Carroll, B.J., Martin, F.I.R., Davies, B. (1968). Resistance to suppression by dexamethasone of plasma 11-OHCS levels in severe depressive illness. *Br. Med. J., 3,* 285–287.

Carroll, B.J., Curtis, G.C., Mendels, J. (1976). Neuroendocrine regulation in depression. *Arch. Gen. Psychiatry, 33,* 1039–1044.

Cytryn, L. (1972). Proposed classification of childhood depression. *Am. J. Psychiatry, 129,* 149–155.

Cytryn, L., McKnew, D. (1974). Factors influencing the changing clinical expression of the depressive process in children. *Am. J. Psychiatry, 131,* 879–881.

Cytryn, L., McKnew, D.H. (1979). Affective disorders. In Noshpitz, J. (Eds.), *Basic Handbook of Child Psychiatry,* Vol. 2. New York: Basic Books, pp. 321–341.

Cytryn, L., McKnew, D., Bunney, W., Jr. (1980). Diagnosis of depression in children: A reassessment. *Am. J. Psychiatry, 137,* 22–25.

Dorpat, T.L. (1977). Depressive affect. *Psychoanal. Study Child, 32,* 3–27.

Engel, G.L., Reichsmán, F., Segal, H.L. (1956). A study of an infant with a gastric fistula. *Psychosom. Med., 18,* 374–398.

Fraiberg, S. (1967). The origins of human bonds. *Commentary.* New York: American Jewish Committee.

Fraiberg, S. (1968). Parallel and divergent patterns in blind and sighted infants. *Psychoanal. Study Child, 23,* 264–300.

Fraiberg, S. (1977). *Every Child's Birthright: In Defense of Mothering.* New York: Basic Books.

Fraiberg, S., Freedman, D.A. (1964). Studies in ego development of the congenitally blind child. *Psychoanal. Study Child, 19,* 113–169.

Freud, S. (1917). Mourning and melancholia. *Standard Edition of the Complete Psychological Works of Sigmund Freud,* Vol. 14, pp. 239–258.

Freud, S. (1923). The ego and the id. *Standard Edition of the Complete Psychological Works of Sigmund Freud,* Vol. 19, pp. 3–66.

Freud, S. (1938). Splitting of the ego in the process of defense. *Standard Edition of the Complete Psychological Works of Sigmund Freud,* Vol. 23, pp. 271–278.

Gallant, D., Simpson, G. (1976). *Depression: Behavioral, Biochemical, Diagnostic and Treatment Concepts.* New York: Spectrum Publications.

Glaser, K. (1967). Masked depression in children and adolescents. *Am. J. Psychother., 21,* 565–574.

Harlow, H.F. (1958). The nature of love. *Am. Psychol., 13,* 673–685.

Harlow, H.F. (1959). Love in infant monkeys. *Sci. Am., 200,* 68–74.

Harlow, H.F. (1960. Primary affectional patterns in primates. *Am. J. Orthopsychiatry, 30,* 676–684.

Johnston, L. (1981). In *International Herald Tribune,* February 20, 1981, Number 30, 484, p. 3.

Kashani, J., Simonds, J.F. (1979). The incidence of depression in children. *Am. J. Psychiatry, 136,* 1203–1205.

Kashani, J.H., Husain, A., Shekim, W.O., Hodges, K.K., Cytryn L., McKnew, D.H. (1981). Current perspectives on childhood depression: An overview. *Am. J. Psychiatry, 138,* 143–153.

Mahler, M. (1966). Notes on the development of basic moods: The depressive affect in psychoanalysis. In Lowenstein, R. (Ed.), *Psychoanalysis—A General Psychology.* New York: International Universities Press.

Malmquist, C. (1971). Depressions in childhood and adolescence. (Part One). *N. Engl. J. Med., 284,* 887–893.

Michael, R.P., Gibbons, J.L. (1963). Interrelationships between the endocrine system and neuropsychiatry. In Pfeiffer, C., Smythies, G. (Eds.), *International Review of Neurology,* Vol. 5. New York: Academic Press, pp. 243–292.

Petti, T. (1978). Depression in hospitalized child psychiatry patients: Approaches to measuring depression. *J. Am. Acad. Child Psychiatry, 17,* 49–59.

Phillips, I. (1979). Childhood depression: Interpersonal interactions and depressive phenomena. *Am. J. Psychiatry, 136,* 511–515.

Piaget, J. (1962). The stages of the intellectual development of the child. *Bull. Menninger Clin., 26,* 120–128.

Poznanski, E., Zrull, J. (1970). Childhood depression, clinical characteristics of overtly depressed children. *Arch. Gen. Psychiatry, 23,* 8–15.

Puig-Antich, J., Chambers, W. (1978). Schedule for affective disorders and schizophrenia for school-age children. Unpublished manuscript.

Reinhart, J.B. (1979). Failure to thrive. In Noshpitz, J. (Ed.), *Basic Handbook of Child Psychiatry,* Vol. 2. New York: Basic Books, pp. 593–599.

Rie, H.E. (1966). Depression in childhood: A survey of some pertinent contributions. *J. Am. Acad. Child Psychiatry, 5,* 653–685.

Robertson, J. (1965). Mother-infant interaction from birth to twelve months: 2 case studies. In Foss, B.M. (Ed.), *Determinants of Infant Behaviour,* Vol. 3. London: Methuen, pp. 111–127.

Rochlin, G. (1959). The loss complex: A contribution to the etiology of depression. *J. Am. Psychoanal. Assoc., 7,* 299–316.

Rubin, R., Mandell, A. (1966). Adrenal cortical activity in pathological emotional states: A review. *Am. J. Psychiatry, 123,* 387–400.

Sachar, E.J., MacKenzie, J., Binstock, W., *et al.* (1967). Corticosteroid responses to psychotherapy of depressions: I. Evaluation during confrontation of loss. *Arch. Gen. Psychiatry, 16,* 461–470.

Sachar, E.J., Hellman, L., Roffwarg, H., *et al.* (1973). Disrupted 24-hour patterns of cortical secretion in psychotic depression. *Arch. Gen. Psychiatry, 28,* 19–24.

Sandler, J., Joffe, W. (1965). Notes on obsessional manifestations in children. *Psychoanal. Study Child, 20,* 425–438.

Schwab, J., Bell, R.A., Warheit, G., Schwab, R.B. (1979). *Social Order and Mental Health.* New York: Brunner/ Mazel.

Shafii, M., Whittinghill, R., Healy, M. (1979). The pediatric-psychiatric model for emergencies in child psychiatry: A study of 994 cases. *Am. J. Psychiatry, 136,* 1600–1601.

Shafii, M., Whittinghill, R., Gilliam, P., Pearson, V. (1981). Risk factors in childhood and adolescent suicides: Psychological autopsies. In progress.

Spitz, R.A. (1945). Hospitalism. *Psychoanal. Study Child, 1,* 53–74.

Spitz, R. (1946). Anaclitic depression: An inquiry into the genesis of psychiatric conditions in early childhood, II. *Psychoanal. Study Child, 2,* 313–342.

Spitz, R.A. (1965). *The First Year of Life.* New York: International Universities Press.

Spitz, R.A., Wolf, K. (1946). The smiling response: A contribution to the ontogenesis of social relations. *Genet. Psychol. Monogr., 34,* 57–125.

Tronick, E., Als, H., Adamson, L., Wise, S., Brazelton, T. (1978). The infant's response to entrapment between contradictory messages in face-to-face interaction. *J. Am. Acad. Child Psychiatry, 17,* 1–13.

Weinberg, W.A., Rutman, J., Sullivan, L., *et al.* (1973). Depression in children referred to an education diagnostic center: Diagnosis and treatment. *J. Pediatr., 83,* 1065–1072.

Weissman, M.M., Myers, J.K. (1978). Affective disorders in a U.S. urban community. *Arch. Gen Psychiatry, 35,* 1304–1311.

Wisdom, J.O. (1977). A phase of depression in a six-months-old boy. *Int. J. Psychoanal., 58,* 375–377.

Chapter 8

MANIC-DEPRESSIVE DISORDER IN CHILDREN AND ADOLESCENTS: Bipolar Affective Disorders

Sherman C. Feinstein, M.D.
Susan Feldman-Rotman, Ph.D.
Alice B. Woolsey, A.C.S.W.

In adults the essential feature of bipolar affective disorders is a disturbance of mood which may assume full or partial manic or depressive symptoms. *DSM-III* (1980) divides affective disorder into Major Affective Disorders, Other Specific Affective Disorders (Cyclothymic Disorder and Dysthymic Disorder), and Atypical Affective Disorders, a residual category for those reactions that do not fulfill the defined entities.

In children and adolescents bipolar affective disorder, manifesting a manic-depressive pattern, may show specific equivalent behaviors that are the precursors of the cyclothymic personality and manic-depressive disorders of adulthood. Recent findings (Feinstein, 1980; Kestenbaum, 1980; Youngerman and Canino, 1978) suggest that the affective system of patients with manic-depressive illness may have a basic vulnerability which, when overstimulated, begins a discharge pattern that does not respond easily to autonomous emotional control. Some biological variation (probably on a genetic basis) leaves the affective system with specific vulnerability to affective stress. The typical bipolar cyclic states of adulthood, therefore, may be considered illness patterns rather than minimal criteria for diagnosis. (Feinstein and Wolpert, 1973; Feinstein, 1973; Feinstein, 1980)

In Kraeplin's (1904, 1921) classical description of the disorder, manic-depressive insanity was classified a unitary form of mental illness distinct from schizophrenia with periodic and circular manifestations, including manic and depressive confusion and delirium. He also included mood changes, periodic or continuous, which seemed to stem from personal predisposition. Beyond common fundamental features, Kraeplin noted that the clinical picture frequently changed, the prognosis was generally good, and he believed the illness had hereditary roots.

DEVELOPMENTAL ASPECTS OF AFFECTIVE DISORDERS

Although the normal individual is generally aware that he is subject to variations in mood, he rarely perceives the fact that rhythmic changes affect his biological and emotional patterns daily and over a long period of time. (Feinstein, 1973) For the first 16 weeks of life, the infant's biological rhythms of sleep and other physiological functions normally deviate from the 24-hour circadian rhythm of the adult caretakers. The maternal care provides a stimulus barrier for the still vulnerable newborn, and slowly the infant begins to exhibit activity and feeding patterns consonant with his family and the world around him.

During early childhood, from ages 7 to 18 months, phenomena of mood are of great importance. Most children demonstrate major periods of exhilaration or relative elation alternating with "low-keyed" periods when they become aware that mother is absent from the room. (Mahler, 1972) (see chapters 2, 3, and 7) At these times gestural and performance motility are reduced, interest in their surroundings diminishes, and they seem inwardly preoccupied. This low-keyed state may be inferred when comfort from another person may cause the child to burst into tears and the state disappears with mother's return. Mahler compares this "dampened down" state to a miniature anaclitic depression and believes that during this period of quiescence the child is attempting to hold onto the memory of the mother by "imaging." (Rubenfine, 1961) This is an early phase of the subsequently developed stage of object constancy during which the introjected memory of the mother can easily be maintained.

Patients who eventually manifest manic-depressive illness may have a dyssynchronization in the area of affective development. The early histories of many manic-depressive patients clearly indicate an interference with the capacity to dampen down, a developmental milestone which should be accomplished by 2 years of age. This is the possible result of some genetic-physiological impairment in the switching mechanisms, as described by Bunney *et al.* (1968, 1972), in which rapid and reversible changes from mania to depression and vice versa involve a neurotransmitter (i.e., biogenic amine) function at the adrenergic nerve endings or some instability of the neuronal membrane. More recently, genetic marker studies have not confirmed linkage, but did find a history of subclinical affective disturbance in childhood. (Gershon, 1978)

CHILDHOOD AND MANIC-DEPRESSIVE ILLNESS

Cohen *et al.* (1954) and Arieti (1959) both described early childhood patterns of manic-depressive adults and saw them as repressed children dominated by strong but changeable parents. Anthony and Scott (1960) questioned whether manic-depressive illness ever occurred in a clinically recognizable form in the younger child but were "prepared to admit...that certain 'embryonic' features may make a transient appearance in the very early years." They believed that there was a "manic-depressive tendency" that was latent in the susceptible individual and existed in an internalized form.

Behavioral Profile

Our clinical observations of early development revealed a behavioral profile usually consisting of all or most of the following characteristics:

1. Early evidence of affective instability. As early as one year of age parents recognize a pattern of affective extremes.
2. Dysphoric reactions to early stages of separation-individuation. The child has little ability to dampen down or achieve a low-keyed state. Separations usually lead to exaggerated reactions to loss, frequently manifested as temper tantrums or periodic hyperactivity.
3. Dilation of the ego with persistence of grandiose and idealizing self-structures owing to failure of normal transformations of narcissism. This may manifest itself as an outgoing, dramatic quality with a theatrical flair. Many

histories reveal early interest in acting and an easy willingness to perform.
4. Infantile circadian patterns tend to persist with reactions governed by inner, affective impulses rather than shifting to the environmental patterns of the family. Bizarre eating and sleep patterns and impulsivity may continue in spite of all efforts to enforce normal daily rhythms.
5. There is very frequently a family history of affective disorder. In addition to the presence of bipolar and unipolar patterns, equivalent states, such as alcoholism or compulsive gambling, may be elicited.

Manic-Depressive Disorder in a Preschool Aged Child

Jody was first seen at age 3 because of hyperactivity, low frustration tolerance, impulsive and destructive behavior, and inability to concentrate. The second of three children, she was active at birth and her care was considered difficult. She slept in short spurts and ate poorly. Coordination was good, walking developed at 14 months, but she was seen as hyperactive, impulsive, and uncontainable.

Mother sought psychiatric evaluation at age 2 years because Jody changed moods very rapidly. While playing and without apparent reason, she would hit, bite, scratch, and become destructive. On one occasion, mother was reading her a story and Jody suddenly turned and bit her. During these occasional periods of irrational behavior, she responded to no one and was very destructive. When frustrated, she would roll around on the floor flailing her arms and legs and was difficult to reach verbally. Mother described several incidents when Jody would start crying and tell her she felt "bad inside" and wished she could die.

At other times, for long periods, she was likeable, warm, friendly, and outgoing. She had a difficult time in nursery school and kindergarten with separation and relating to other children. However, her relationships with teachers were positive and her work was capable and creative.

The parents were cooperative and well motivated. Mother insisted that there was something wrong with Jody even though assured by her pediatrician and a psychiatric evaluation that Jody was developing normally. Mother described herself as a rather cyclothymic individual with mood swings, accentuated when fatigued. A maternal aunt (mother's sister) manifests wide mood swings and has had some manic psychotic episodes. Both maternal grandparents suffer from severe emotional difficulties; grandfather is a depressive with years of treatment and grandmother is described as a classic manic-depressive.

Jody was receiving weekly psychotherapy from age 3 years with some overall improvement. At age 5 years, after an upsetting incident, she became agitated, hyperactive, and demanding and remained in this agitated state for several months. She regressed to provocative, destructive behavior and appeared dilated and hypomanic. In school she was destructive, fought with her peers, and insulted and physically attacked close friends. After several months of close consultation with the family and the use of tranquilizers, Jody calmed down and resumed her better integrated state. Several months later a similar episode was precipitated.

It was at this point that it occurred to the senior author that we might be dealing with a bipolar, alternating mood state which was rooted in biological vulnerabilities and triggered by depressive reactions. The affective crisis resembled the dilated, hypomanic state of the adult and had many characteristics of a periodic reaction unrelated to reality stress.

Therefore, at age 5½ years, a decision was made to attempt to treat these alternating affective states with lithium carbonate. An evaluation of her cardiac, renal, and thyroid systems was undertaken and proved normal except for the discovery that the patient had manifested a periodic "salt hunger" for many years and would eat large quantities of table salt. At the point Jody cycled into a state of manic behavior, lithium carbonate, 900 mg. daily, was started on an outpatient basis. Within 2 weeks with monitoring of the blood lithium level every 3 days and adjusting the lithium intake to assure a blood level of 0.8 to 1.2 mEq./L., a noticeable leveling off of the manic affective state occurred and the patient was able to resume her usual activities without destructive, agitated symptoms. In addition, the salt craving seemed to disappear.

Jody has remained on lithium carbonate, 900 mg. daily, for the past 12 years and has periodically received psychotherapy. There have been brief recurrences of the periodic cyclic manic episodes when she stopped her lithium impulsively. In general we see a child who continues to function marginally in school and at home. While there was a remarkable amount of immaturity present, there has been a gradual improvement in function. Underlying the alternating affective states, Jody manifested the features of borderline personality disorder with difficulties in object relationships and self-esteem.

We believe that Jody is an example of juvenile manic-depressive illness. The onset of the illness was recognized by age 2 by the mother, but distinct phasic disturbance was not seen until age 5 years. Prior to this, distinct, episodic moods with erratic, disintegrative behavior were seen to alternate with periods of highly integrated behavior. Intellectual functioning has always remained intact. The affective episodes seem to have been precipitated by loss reactions that overwhelmed the ego and resulted in a shift to affective solutions. (Feinstein, 1967)

Manic-Depressive Disorder in a Latency-Aged Child

Jan, the second of three children, was first seen at age 10 years after she had an emotional outburst that upset the school and her parents. She was described as being restless, provocative, constantly bickering, excessively curious, and functioning poorly in school, although always being bright and precocious. She was born 11 months after her older sister, and she seemed happy and alert for the first few years and related to her sister as though she was a twin, and parents treated them as such.

She began manifesting symptoms of excessive reactivity, hyperactivity, and irritability at age 3, following the birth of her younger brother. This was a difficult time for the family. Father failed in his business in California; mother was struggling with severe separation anxiety and insisted on a move back to Chicago, where they moved in with the maternal grandparents. Jan had a poor relationship with her grandmother and was irritable and negativistic, apparently suffering from the birth of the brother, the move, and her mother's depression.

Jan's symptomatic behaviors continued for several years and interfered with her early school adjustment, where she was described as hyperactive and isolated. A diagnostic evaluation at age 5 revealed an IQ of 144 with projective test results that described her as "unusual." She perceived her parents as "mad" and also was preoccupied with death. Psychiatric evaluation found her constricted, anxious, angry, but affectless on the surface. Psychotherapy was advised but not carried out.

Jan's school adjustment has continued to be difficult. Under stress she becomes "paranoid" and "glazed over" as she withdraws. She has a short attention span and does not concentrate.

Mother described her behavior as having a definite cyclic pattern. These phases last several months and the "bad cycle" is characterized by frenetic activity, an inability to stop talking, and increased difficulty with relationships.

The paternal grandmother died early, and the

paternal grandfather had a stroke and a severe depression before death. The maternal great-grandfather is reported to have had a senile depression before death, and the maternal grandmother is described as unstable and has had depressive episodes.

In psychiatric examination, Jan, a petite, attractive 10 year old, was precocious and dramatic. She was very feminine and seductive. She inspected the office in an uninhibited fashion, commenting on the furniture, the "original" paintings, and tiny details of the evaluator's clothing. She quoted television commercials, wisecracked about her teachers and school, and offered to share her chewing gum with the evaluator. She talked about feeling "high" and said she liked the sensation of feeling "drunk."

Jan's speech was rapid with loose associations and flight of ideas. Thought content was not distorted and sensorium was clear. She discussed her difficulty in controlling affects and reported that she frequently cannot stop laughing, but handles it by acting "gruffy." She described herself as an anxious person who did not bother others with her fears. "I'm just a chicken. I just sit in bed and worry half of the night."

A tentative diagnosis of manic-depressive illness was made and after a medical work-up, lithium carbonate, 900 mg. daily, was prescribed. The patient was seen in weekly psychotherapy. A gradual leveling off of expansive affect occurred. Jan was able to go to camp for 2 weeks and had no separation anxiety. She remained outgoing and vivacious, but there were no violent affective swings. Long-term follow-up has included a manic episode at age 16 after stopping medication. Independent evaluation confirmed the presence of manic-depressive disorder. The patient resumed lithium therapy and is continuing with her education but underlying personality characteristics are immature and unstable.

ADOLESCENCE AND MANIC-DEPRESSIVE ILLNESS

The longitudinal, observational approach has confirmed the etiological importance of early infantile development, the oedipal period, and latency to psychic growth. The developmental tasks of adolescence have the same importance to later development as those that came before. This developmental work, which has been described by Blos (1967) as a recapitulation of the separation-individuation tasks, makes the adolescent vulnerable not only to normal everyday stress but also to unresolved conflicts from infancy and childhood. Other descriptions of the developmental work during adolescence include a liquefaction of the ego (Eissler, 1958) and partial regression of the ego to the stage of undifferentiated object relationships at the service of ego mastery. (Freud, 1958; Geleerd, 1961) This major reworking of the ego defenses at the service of character synthesis renders the pubertal adolescent suspectible to a breakdown of defenses and an emergence of symptoms.

The emergence of symtomatic manic-depressive disorder during adolescence is more common than during childhood. The early manifestations of affective disorders in adolescence do not conform to the traditional descriptions, but rather reflect the developmental level and the particular vicissitudes with which an adolescent is dealing. The nature of bipolar affective instability is also dependent on the genetic configuration and the quality of early character development.

Clinical Features

Manic-depressive disorder during puberty and adolescence manifests some of the following symptoms:

1. Severe adolescent rebellion manifested by negativism, overconfidence, and an insistence on a feeling of well-being.
2. Exaggerated self-esteem with grandiose conceptions of physical, mental, and moral powers and overcommitment to adolescent tasks.
3. Heightened motor activity manifested by restlessness, hyperactivity, and compulsive overactivity. Several patients with anorexia nervosa were later discovered to have manic-depressive disorder. In cases of anorexia nervosa, this possibility should always be considered.
4. Exaggeration of libidinal impulses may surface as a sudden change from an inhibited child to an aggressive, sexually acting-out adolescent. Puberty, particularly in girls, may be seen as a great threat to the body image. In one case a period of amenorrhea after menarche resulted in a manic-depressive breakdown with delusions of being pregnant.
5. Gradual emergence of a cyclic, bipolar pattern of affect disorder but often manifesting itself as marked instability with short periods of depression and mania rather than the longer periods typical of adult manic-depression. Suicidal ideation is frequently noted.

Manic-Depressive Disorder in an Adolescent

Art is a 21-year-old white male. While preparing to transfer to a college away from home, his behavior became expansive and dilated, increasing in mood until he was in a classical manic frenzy with agitation, flight of ideas, pressure of speech, and an inability to control affects. At this point he was admitted to the hospital.

Known to our institution from age 14, Art has been under continuous psychiatric treatment in various hospitals, residential treatment centers, and outpatient facilities. In the 2 years prior to the current episode, he attended a junior college while remaining in treatment. Various diagnoses were made, ranging from schizophrenia to character and neurotic disorders. Some descriptions of hypomanic behavior were scattered through the descriptive material and once manic-depressive psychosis was mentioned as part of the differential diagnosis. There was no evidence of thought disorder.

Art's parents reported marked difficulty with affective controls from infancy. The second of five children, he had a difficult birth and initially had trouble with sucking. He was a voracious eater, requiring three to four bottles of milk during the night through his second year. Teething was an ordeal with continuous irritability. He reacted poorly to aspirin and barbiturates. He was a very active child, constantly in motion. He weaned with difficulty at age 2, crying continuously for nights. He used a pacifier until age 4 and sucked his thumb vigorously until adolescence.

Art had severe separation anxiety, which became agitated if his parents went on a vacation. After their return, he would take weeks to settle down, requiring mother to sit with him for hours while he fell asleep.

At age 4 his nursery school teacher described him as having "peculiar mood changes." He would alternate between being "the life and soul and leader of an activity and suddenly without apparent cause would withdraw, put on his jacket, and suck his thumb in a corner." This pattern persisted throughout early life until overt symptoms of severe anxiety, temper tantrums, and, retrospectively, manic states began at age 11, following the death of a close relative and prior to a move to the United States from another country.

The paternal grandfather was described as a depressive personality. The maternal grandfather at the age of 35 suddenly left his business and became a compulsive gambler and alcoholic.

Art was placed on lithium carbonate, requiring doses as high as 2,400 mg. daily until the manic state was controlled. This patient represents an example of manic-depressive disorder that was not recognized in adolescence but, retrospectively, seems to fulfill the criteria of juvenile manic-depressive disorder. Long-term follow-up has confirmed the diagnosis of manic-depressive disorder. After a stormy course, patient has accepted his illness, continues therapy, and is making a good adjustment, although he remains vulnerable to cyclic affective states.

DIAGNOSTIC ASPECTS OF MANIC-DEPRESSIVE DISORDER

The identification of manic-depressive disorder in childhood has been a matter of some controversy, subject to changes in diagnostic fashion. (Anthony and Scott, 1960) This ambiguity stems from a multiplicity of sources, both theoretical and practical in nature. Traditional analytic thinkers have been particularly reluctant to acknowledge the existence of childhood affective disorders because, by psychoanalytic definition, clinical depression presupposes the development of superego structures. Psychodynamic theorists, such as Klein, meanwhile, have postulated mania as an inherent infantile coping mechanism—not necessarily an aberrant state.

Resolution of this conflict has not been forthcoming, in part because of inconsistent diagnostic criteria for assessing affective illness and a concomitant lack of observational agreement. Failure to identify depressive equivalents in the behavior-disordered child is one such limitation. Flight of ideas and pressured speech, commonly associated with manic-depression, have been considered by others to be a pathognomic of schizophrenia. (Carlson, 1979) Similarly, such behavioral characteristics as distractibility, lability of affect, and irritability—which would seem to be definitional of manic-depressive disorder—are often interpreted as hyperactivity, clearly not a psychotic state.

The criteria usually employed for the diagnosis of manic-depressive illness reflect Kraeplin's (1921) early descriptive studies. By utilizing end states as criteria, such as a full-blown manic episode, this system overlooks important developmental changes in affect, and thus would seem to preclude the diagnosis of manic-depressive illness in children. The diagnostic requirement that there should be both a distinct and marked phasic disturbance of affect (Redlich and Freedman, 1966) and evidence of a state approximating the classical description (Anthony and Scott, 1960) frequently delays the diagnosis for many years.

Klein (1934) contends that the child in early development passes through a transient manic state, which she considered a defense against early infantile depression. The basis for this inference was her observation of the infant's feeling of omnipotence and control over objects. In normal children, however, this natural overreaction typically disappears by the age of 2, as they develop a sense of separateness from mother and a self-concept. The persistence of mood extremes, coupled with a family history of affective disorder, could be considered consistent with early indications of affective illness.

Davis (1979) described what he calls a specific manic-depressive variant syndrome of childhood which requires the presence of affective storms; a family history of affective disorder; mental, physical, or verbal overactivity; troubled interpersonal relationships; and no formal thought disorder in children who respond to lithium carbonate.

The frequency of breakdown in manic-depressive illness increases with the development of puberty and the onset of adolescence. Again, the affective reactions are age appropriate and emphasize those defenses that are critical at a particular stage of life.

The question of the timing of the breakdown is of great interest. The loss of a mother and the transition from childhood to adolescence are both considered major demands on the gradually emerging adolescent ego. Mourning and progression through transitional developmental states require the capacity to utilize ego defenses in the mastery of the loss of loved objects (mother, childhood). A fundamental defect in the affect system, probably genetically determined, overwhelms the ego defenses and the resultant affective reactions may be characterized as manic-depressive, essentially indicating exaggerated or blocked capacities to deal with the normal affective response to the perception of a loss. If the intensity of the stimulation is too great, or the environmental supports are sadomasochistic rather than accepting and supportive, an alteration of consciousness may result, manifested by psychotic thinking or behavior.

Schizophrenia in adolescents is frequently a difficult diagnosis to make and, as Masterson (1967) points out, only in 25% of seriously disturbed adolescents can the diagnosis be made at the onset; the long-term picture of the disease process emerges slowly during the diagnostic and therapeutic process. Stone (1971) discusses the dilemmas of making a definite diagnosis of manic-depressive illness and the present tendency to call a patient "schizophrenic till proven otherwise." The diagnosis of manic-depressive illness in adolescents is made by keeping in mind adolescent behavioral equivalents of the classical end results of a bipolar affective disorder.

Anthony and Scott (1960) believe that a genetic clock is operative in an individual who is genetically predisposed or environmentally handicapped. Gershon (1978) reviewed genetic markers used in studies of psychiatric illness and studied red-green color blindness, Xg blood group antigen, and histocompatability lymphocyte antigen (HLA). The evidence has been against close linkage for each of these markers. The most promising prediction of vulnerability in adult life is the presence of subclinical disturbance in childhood. (McKnew et al., in press)

TREATMENT OF JUVENILE MANIC-DEPRESSIVE ILLNESS

A major advance in the treatment of the manic-depressive disorders is the present extensive use of lithium carbonate. First described by Cade (1949), who noted that lithium salts seemed efficacious in treating acute affective disorders of the manic-depressive type, lithium now appears equally effective as a prophylactic agent in preventing or minimizing recurrences. (Baastrup and Schou, 1967) Lithium carbonate is considered a safe drug and functions without blunting of perception or intellect. (Schou, 1959, 1968; Schlangenhauf et al., 1966; Kline, 1969) The common toxic symptoms of the fine hand tremor, anorexia, nausea, and diarrhea rapidly disappear if the dosage is reduced. (Wolpert and Mueller, 1969)

Annell (1969) described the use of lithium in 12 children from the ages of 7 upward. Only two adolescent patients (ages 14 and 16) manifested typical signs of a manic state. All others demonstrated various symptom complexes (sleep disorders, night terrors, and vegetative disorders, e.g., stomachaches and headaches), but many had histories of manic-depressive illness in their families, which led to the idea of trying the medication on an empirical basis. The cases selected for that study were characterized by the sudden change between normalcy and depression, or between depression and hyperactivity that has been described as typical of the bipolar type of depression found in the manic-depressive psychosis. (Perris, 1969)

The use of lithium carbonate has been reported in young children and adolescents with promising results. (Feinstein and Wolpert, 1973; Youngerman and Canino, 1978; Carlson, 1979) Careful medical cooperation is necessary and the dosage and lithium blood level studies must be carefully monitored. Even though the use of lithium in cases of affective illness frequently leads to a rapid resolution of the manic attack, the importance of concomitant psychotherapy should not be overlooked.

Clinical Management

A thorough medical survey should be conducted in children and adolescents with careful attention to cardiac, renal, liver, and thyroid function. An electroencephalogram should be secured if there is any history of convulsive disorder, since lithium may lower the convulsive threshold. Continuous monitoring of thyroid function is necessary because of the thyroid-suppressing effects of lithium. None of our patients have been affected, but several adults being followed have developed hypothyroidism.

The average dosage of lithium ranges from 900 to 1,800 mg. (or higher), depending on the blood level. The general therapeutic range is 0.8 to 1.4 mEq./L. with the most comfortable range between 1.0 to 1.2 mEq./L. Patients in a manic phase usually require a higher dosage to maintain therapeutic levels, which can be reduced with symptom remission. (Carlson, 1979)

Lithium carbonate is now available as tablets, capsules, and in the liquid as lithium citrate. Well absorbed by the gastrointestinal tract, the blood level peaks in 2 hours after ingestion, and half-life in adolescents is 18 to 24 hours. Many children complain of gastric irritation and it is recommended that lithium be taken with food. Small more frequent doses may also minimize the distress. Weekly lithium levels should be obtained for the first month or until a stable therapeutic dose is achieved, then monthly or bimonthly.

Side effects are of a minor nature (nausea, fine tremor, polyuria, polydipsia, weight gain, and toxicity) and are usually controlled by slight dosage reduction. (Carlson, 1979) Uncontrolled symptoms of affective disorder or psychotic reaction may require additional use of tranquilizers and antidepressants with appropriate attention to the toxic effects of these drugs, especially haloperidol.

Psychotherapy

Our long-term experience with a group of childhood and adolescent manic-depressives had led us to recommend ongoing supportive psychotherapy to help accept the disorder as well as more intensive psychoanalytic psychotherapy in the presence of developmental defect. The affective lability of childhood may be considered a traumatic factor in early development and often results in developmental interferences resulting in border-line personality organization. Many of our study group demonstrated personality organization, as described by Kernberg (1978), Masterson (1978), and Schwartzberg (1978), manifesting broad interference with self-development and distortions in object relationships.

CONCLUSIONS

The examples presented described children and adolescents with periodic alternating affective disorders who can be considered cases of juvenile manic-depressive disorder. Manic-depressive disorder may appear in early childhood, manifesting itself as erratic, rapidly shifting mood behavior with a basic intactness of intellect. The apparent lack of precipitating trauma may be explained by the enormous sensitivity of these patients to loss or the fear of loss, which triggers a distinct, affective episode.

The literature describing genetic and biochemical research is discussed. The effectiveness of lithium carbonate makes the early diagnosis of manic-depressive disorder necessary. Lithium carbonate is a useful drug in the treatment of juvenile manic-depressive disorders and its use is described, along with the definite need for psychotherapy to facilitate acceptance of the disorder and to avoid characterological defect.

REFERENCES

American Psychiatric Association (1980). *Diagnostic and Statistical Manual of Mental Disorders*. Third Edition. Washington, D.C.: American Psychiatric Association.

Annell, A.L. (1969). Lithium in the treatment of children and adolescents. *Acta Psychiatr. Scand.* (Suppl.), *207*, 19–33.

Anthony, E.J., Scott, P. (1960). Manic-depressive psychosis in childhood. *J. Child Psychol. Psychiatry, 1*, 53–72.

Arieti, S. (1959). Manic-depressive psychosis. In *American Handbook of Psychiatry*. New York: Basic Books.

Baastrup, P.D., Schou, M. (1967). Lithium as a prophylactic agent: Its effect against recurrent depressions and manic-depressive psychosis. *Arch. Gen. Psychiatry, 17*, 162–172.

Blos, P. (1967). The second individuation process of adolescence. *Psychoanal. Study Child, 22*, 162–186.

Bunney, W.E., Jr., Goodwin, F.K., Davis, J.M., Fawcett, J.A. (1968). A behavioral-biochemical study of lithium treatment. *Am. J. Psychiatry, 125*, 499–512.

Bunney, W.E., Jr., Goodwin, F.K., Murphy, D.L. (1972). The "switch process": In manic-depressive illnesses, III. Theoretical implications. *Arch. Gen. Psychiatry, 27*, 312–317.

Cade, J.F., (1949). Lithium salts in the treatment of psychotic excitement. *Med. J. Aust., 36*, 349–352.

Carlson, G.A. (1979). Lithium use in adolescents: Clinical indications and management. *Adolesc. Psychiatry, 7*, 410–418.

Cohen, M.D., Baker, G., Cohen, R.A., Fromm-Reichmann, F., Weigert, E.V. (1954). An intensive study of twelve cases of manic-depressive psychosis. *Psychiatry, 17*, 103–137.

Davis, R.E. (1979). Manic-depressive variant syndrome of childhood. *Am. J. Psychiatry, 136*, 702–705.

Eissler, K.R. (1958). Notes on problems of technique in the psychoanalytic treatment of adolescents. *Psychoanal. Study Child, 13,* 223–254.

Feinstein, S.C. (1967). Aggression and adolescence. *Bull. Chicago Soc. Adolesc. Psychiatry, 1,* 1–8.

Feinstein, S.C. (1973). Diagnostic and therapeutic aspects of manic-depressive illness in early childhood. *Early Child Dev. Care, 3,* 1–12.

Feinstein, S.C. (1980). Why they were afraid of Virginia Woolf: Perspectives on juvenile manic-depressive illness. *Adolesc. Psychiatry, 8.*

Feinstein, S., Wolpert, E. (1973). Juvenile manic-depressive illness: Clinical and therapeutic considerations. *J. Am. Acad. Child Psychiatry, 12,* 123–136.

Freud, A. (1958). Adolescence. *Psychoanal. Study Child, 13,* 255–278.

Geleerd, E.R. (1961). Some aspects of ego vicissitudes in adolescence. *J. Am. Psychoanal. Assoc., 9,* 394–405.

Gershon, E.S. (1978). Genetic markers in affective illness. *Continuing Medical Education Syllabus and Scientific Proceedings.* Annual Meeting American Psychiatric Association. Abstract 223, p. 109.

Kernberg, O.F. (1978). The diagnosis of borderline conditions in adolescence. *Adolesc. Psychiatry, 6,* 298–319.

Kestenbaum, C.J. (1980). Adolescents at-risk for manic-depressive illness. *Adolesc. Psychiatry, 8,* 344–366.

Klein, M. (1934). The psychogenesis of manic-depressive states. In *Contributions to Psycho-Analysis.* London: Hogarth.

Kline, N.S. (1969). Lithium: The history of its use in psychiatry. In *Modern Problems in Pharmacology,* Vol. III. White Plains, N.Y.: Albert J. Phiebig.

Kraeplin, E. (1904). Lectures on clinical psychiatry. In Wolpert, E. (Ed.), *Manic-Depressive Illness.* New York: International Universities Press, 1977.

Kraeplin, E. (1921). Manic-depressive insanity and paranoia. In Wolpert, E. (Ed.), *Manic-Depressive Illness.* New York: International Universities Press, 1977.

Mahler, M. (1972). On the first three subphases of the separation-individuation process. *Int. J. Psychoanal., 53,* 333–338.

Masterson, J.F. (1967). *The Psychiatric Dilemma of Adolescence.* Boston: Little, Brown & Co.

Masterson, J.F. (1978). The borderline adolescent: An object relations view. *Adolesc. Psychiatry, 6,* 344–359.

Perris, C. (1969). The separation of bipolar (manic-depressive) from unipolar recurrent depressive psychosis. *Behav. Neuropsychiatry, 1,* 17–24.

Redlich, F., Freedman, D. (1966). *The Theory and Practice of Psychiatry.* New York: Basic Books.

Rubenfine, D.L. (1961). Perception, reality testing, and symbolism. *Psychoanal. Study Child, 16,* 73–89.

Schlangenhauf, J., Tipin, J., White, R.B. (1966). The use of lithium carbonate in the treatment of manic psychoses. *Am J. Psychiatry, 123,* 201–205.

Schou, M. (1959). Lithium in psychiatric therapy: Stocktaking after ten years. *Psychopharmacology, 1,* 65–78.

Schou, M. (1968). Special review: Lithium in psychiatric therapy and prophylaxis. *J. Psychiatr. Res., 6,* 67–95.

Schwartzberg, A.Z. (1978). Overview of the borderline syndrome of adolescence. *Adolesc. Psychiatry, 6,* 286–297.

Stone, M.H. (1971). Mania: A guide for the perplexed. *Psychother. Social Sci. Rev., 5,* 14–18.

Wolpert, E.A., Mueller, P. (1969). Lithium carbonate in the treatment of manic-depressive disorders. *Arch. Gen. Psychiatry, 21,* 155–159.

Youngerman, J., Canino, I. (1978). Lithium carbonate use in children and adolescents; A survey of the literature. *Arch. Gen. Psychiatry, 35,* 216–224.

Chapter 9

PSYCHONEUROSES IN INFANCY, CHILDHOOD, AND ADOLESCENCE: Stress, Arousal, Panic, and Symptom Formation

The older term "psychoneurosis" refers to the types of psychopathological disorders related to overcontrol and inhibition. (see chapter 19) The present trend de-emphasizes the use of the broad term "psychoneurosis," and, instead, refers to specific psychopathological disorders based on observable behavior and symptom clusters, such as anxiety, somatoform, dissociative, and affective disorders. (*DSM-III*, 1980, pp. 9–10)

ANXIETY

During this century, the conceptualization of a psychological phenomenon called anxiety has significantly helped in understanding normal human development and psychopathology. More than 100 years ago, Sören Kierkegaard (1812–1855), the Danish philosopher, theologian, and psychologist, used the German word *angst,* which translates into English as dread or anxiety. Kierkegaard examined anxiety from a theological point of view and related it to the experience of fear and dread. He felt;

...that learning to know dread is an adventure which every man has to affront if he would not go to perdition either by not having known dread or by sinking under it. He therefore who has learned rightly to be in dread has learned the most important thing.

Kierkegaard, 1944, p. 139.

William James (1980) conceptualized anxiety as a "...peculiar kind of horror." (Bowlby, 1973, p. 96) This horror is "...the result of a combination of simpler horrors...such as loneliness, darkness, inexplicable sounds." (ibid., p. 96)

Anxiety and Psychoanalysis

Freud perceived the experience of anxiety and the psychological defense against anxiety as the essential core of psychoanalytic theory. In the beginning, Freud (1895, 1905) related the development of anxiety neurosis to the transformation of undischarged sexual and libidinal excitation. Later, Freud (1926) in *Inhibitions, Symptoms and Anxiety* modified the transformation theory of libido and proposed that anxiety was a normal function of the ego which alerts the individual to potential danger. Freud called this *signal anxiety.* Signal anxiety is adaptive and alerts the individual to potential danger and prepares him for fight or flight. When anxiety becomes overwhelming and the person feels helpless in coping with the real or imagined danger, it is called *traumatic anxiety.* The memories and experiences associated with traumatic anxieties are repressed in the unconscious. According to psychoanalytic theory, neurotic symptoms are the result of partial failure of repression and comprised solutions to earlier traumatic anxieties and intrapsychic conflicts.

Physiological Manifestation of Anxiety

Neurophysiological exploration of emotions and reactions to stress and anxiety have been extensively studied in animals and human beings. The following classical studies paved the way toward the understanding of the psychophysiology of anxiety. Goltz (1892) demonstrated that an animal does not need to have a brain cortex to produce emotions and the arousal response. Cannon and de la Paz (1911) and Cannon (1929) discovered that epinephrine is responsible for arousal in cats. He postulated that epinephrine secretion from the medullary part of the adrenal gland creates emotional arousal and prepares the animal physiologically for "fight or flight." Hans Selye (1946, 1950) studied the physiological and pathological responses to stress. As a result of these studies, Selye proposed the theory of *General Adaptation Syndrome.*

Stress and General Adaptation Syndrome

Selye discovered that a stressful reaction contributes to activation of the reticular formation and the limbic system. This activation stimulates the hypothalamus, which secretes corticotrophin-releasing factor (CRF). CRF stimulates the anterior pituitary gland. The anterior pituitary gland releases corticotrophin (ACTH). ACTH stimulates the cortex of the adrenal gland, which synthesizes adrenocortical hormones, particularly cortisol. Cortisol comprises 80% of the total corticosteroids in the blood.

Also, stimulation of the hypothalamus increases the level of secretion of catecholamines, particularly epinephrine and norepinephrine from the medulla of the adrenal gland, and the cells of the sympathetic and central nervous system.

Epinephrine is an "emergency hormone" that prepares the organism for fight or flight. (Euler, 1958, 1966; Axelrod, 1965) Injection of norepinephrine creates an anger response in animals. Injection of both epinephrine and norepinephrine creates a fear response.

Behavioral manifestation of anxiety is related to stress-arousal in the General Adaptation Syndrome.

> In physiological terms...one of the effects of anxiety is the mobilization of the functionally associated adrenocortical and sympathomedullary hormones. This produces secondary and subsequent effects which can facilitate processes of physiological adaptation to the evoking stress.
>
> Bridges, 1974, p. 102.

Behavioral Manifestations of Anxiety

Stressful or fear-arousing stimuli contribute to the secretion of epinephrine (adrenalin) and norepinephrine (noradrenalin) in animals and human beings. Extreme reaction to stress is called severe anxiety or panic reaction.

Panic Reaction

Panic reaction is an intense and overwhelming anxiety in response to stress and fear.

ONSET. Onset is sudden, with intense apprehension, fear, and terror.

RESPIRATORY SYMPTOMS. There is a feeling of choking or smothering; rapid, shallow breathing and shortness of breath.

CARDIOVASCULAR SYMPTOMS. There is a feeling of tightness, discomfort, or pain in the chest; there is a significant increase in pulse rate and heart beat (tachycardia), and palpitations.

AUTONOMIC NERVOUS SYSTEM. There are feelings of restlessness, nervousness, and unsteadiness; paleness; dryness of the mouth; sweating, and hot flashes and chills; trembling, shaking; tingling in hands or feet (paresthesias); dizziness, vertigo, faintness; hyperactivity, vigilance; scanning, motor tension, and pupil dilation.

GASTROINTESTINAL. There is a loss of appetite, nausea, vomiting, and diarrhea.

GENITOURINARY SYSTEM. There is increased frequency of urination and possible loss of bladder control.

PSYCHOLOGICAL RESPONSE. There is fear of dying, going crazy, or loss of control; feelings of impending doom, overwhelming apprehension, and unreality (depersonalization or derealization).

These psychophysiological reactions are similar to reactions of life-threatening situations or to marked physical exertion. These reactions are adaptive and help the individual survive at the time of extreme danger.

Repeated panic reaction, without actual life-threatening danger, is pathological and is called panic disorder, anxiety states, or anxiety neurosis. (*DSM-III*, 1980, p. 230)

DEVELOPMENTAL ASPECTS OF ANXIETY

Stress and Anxiety in the Fetus and the Newborn

Developmental physiology and psychology are the basic sciences of human behavior and the cornerstone for the understanding of psychopathology. An awareness of the internal experience and outward expression of anxiety in infancy and childhood is essential for the understanding and clinical management of anxiety states and other forms of psychopathology in adults.

How do infants and children experience stress and anxiety? What are the somatic and psychological manifestations of anxiety in children? What are the expressions of anxiety in the various developmental phases?

Stress and Intrauterine Life

In studies on animals, physical stresses, such as exposure to cold, heat, immobilization, or increase in muscular activities "...have very little or no effect on conception, implantation or fetal development during early pregnancy." (Gemzel, 1977, p. 155) In contrast,

> ...anxiety and fear can increase myometrial activity and cause uterine contraction and an eventual

abortion. If the emotional problems are solved, the contractions disappear. It has been suggested that norepinephrine, in response to emotional stress, may cause these contractions.

ibid., p. 155.

Thompson and McElroy's (1962) and Keeley's (1962) classical studies of pregnant rats and mice documented that psychological and physiological stress, such as conditioned anxiety, crowding, and epinephrine injection, contributed significantly to the development of permanent changes in behavior of the litters. There was a decrease in open field activity, slowness in maze learning, increase in defecation, and a decrease in grooming behavior. These behaviors are indications of persistent stress and anxiety and were evident in offspring who were tested one month and 4 to 5 months following birth.

In a study by Morishima *et. al.* (1978) of the effect of psychological stress on pregnant rhesus monkeys, it was demonstrated that, "Fetal bradycardia and decreased arterial oxygenation were noted . . ." in all of the fetuses. (p. 290) The authors observed that, ". . . maternal pain or fear results in decreased uterine blood flow. It can be concluded, therefore, that maternal hyperexcitability represents hazard to the fetus." (ibid., p. 290)

Intrauterine Monitoring

Animal studies have helped significantly in developing psychophysiological techniques to assess the level of stress on the fetus in the last months of pregnancy and during labor. These exciting developments have opened new vistas in understanding the trauma of the birth process and in improving the health care of high-risk pregnancies.

Hon (1974) and others have contributed to the understanding of the stress of the birth process on the fetus through fetal heart rate monitoring. Hon stated:

With better understanding of the birth process has come the realization that labor is a stress test for the fetus in which it may be handicapped by maternal medical complications, drugs for analgesia, and anesthesia, and maternal hypotension as the direct result of placing the mother in the supine position or in association with conduction anesthesia.

p. 139.

During labor, monitoring fetal heart rate (FHR) concomitantly with contractions can facilitate identification of fetal stress. During contraction there is a significant decrease in blood flow from mother to child. ". . . with each contrac-

tion the fetus is subject to hypoxemia and in some circumstances hypoxia and asphyxia." (ibid., p. 139) Decrease of pH blood level or acidosis concomitant with FHR deceleration are ominous signs of uteroplacental insufficiency and signal the possibility that intrauterine asphyxia and death may occur unless immediate measures are taken. These developments bring into focus the importance of the mother's psychological state during pregnancy and the impact of intrauterine life, labor, and delivery of the newborn infant.

Otto Rank (1924) proposed that the birth trauma is the origin of all anxieties. This concept was controversial and was not accepted by many at that time. Recent studies, however, of the fetus' reaction to intrauterine stress and to the stressful birth process demonstrate the pathological impact of a stressful pregnancy and birth on the infant's proclivity toward psychophysiological distress and anxiety following birth.

Distress in the First Six Months of Life

During the first 6 months of life, the term "anxiety" is generally not used to describe the infant's emotional state. Bronson (1968) refers to the infant's reaction to pain, discomfort, and sudden loud sounds as "distress."

Until recently, it was thought that only pain, discomfort, or sudden loud sounds created distress in the infant. Studies by Bower *et al.* (1970) have demonstrated that vision, too, plays an important role in experiencing distress and that an infant even a few weeks old ". . . flinches and cries whenever he sees an object approaching close to him." (Bowlby, 1973, p. 100)

Sensory-Motor Distress

We have used the term "sensory-motor distress" to describe stressful reactions in the first 6 months of life. Crying, whimpering, rigid posture, restlessness, and disruptive sleep, along with vegetative signs, such as spitting up, vomiting, diarrhea, sweating, and flushing, are manifestations of sensory-motor distress.

Frequently, sensory-motor distress is temporary and lasts only a few minutes. It acts as an alerting signal to help the mother become aware of the infant's distress so that she can alleviate the contributing factors. Usually, mother's intervention terminates the distress, reduces tension, and results in comfort and quiescence. This process contributes to the enhancement of mother-child bonding.

Sensory-motor distress can be referred to as

adaptive distress or adaptive anxiety. Sensory-motor distress is usually alleviated by the infant's being held, rocked, or engaged in nonnutritive sucking. (Bowlby, 1973, p. 100)

Persecutory and Depressive Anxiety

Melanie Klein (1952) and her followers believe in the existence of anxiety shortly following birth. Klein postulated that infants in the first 3 to 4 months of life are in "paranoid-schizoid position." During this time, the infant experiences persecutory anxiety, which is related to the aggressive and destructive impulses and "Hatred... to the frustrating (bad) breast, and love and reassurance to the gratifying (good) breast." (p. 283)

"Depressive anxiety" is prevalent during 3 to 6 months of life when the infant is in the "depressive position." According to Klein, persecuting anxiety "...relates predominantly to the annihilation of the ego; depressive anxiety is predominantly related to the harm done to internal and external love objects by the subject's destructive impulses. (ibid., p. 282)

Klein's concept of persecutory anxiety and depressive anxiety during the first 6 months of life is controversial. A number of psychoanalysts and child psychiatrists, particularly in England and South America, who have been trained in the Kleinian school, are proponents of these concepts. However, most psychoanalysts and child psychiatrists in the United States and the followers of Anna Freud do not accept this conceptual framework.

Pathological Sensory-Motor Distress

Pathological sensory-motor distress in the first 6 months of life expresses itself in the form of frequent loud crying. The infant appears to be in acute distress or pain, is constantly fussy, and has irregularity and dysrhythmicity in the bodily functions of eating, sleeping, elimination, and wakefulness. Feeding disturbances are quite common. The infant "does not take the nipple," or is "never satisfied," or has "mild allergies." Spitting-up, vomiting, and diarrhea are common. The infant overreacts, sometimes with a panic response, to new stimuli. If pathological distress continues, the infant may show signs of withdrawal, sensory-motor depression, and eventually failure to thrive.

Pathological sensory-motor distress can easily become chronic with greater or lesser intensity. The mother of this "difficult child" feels helpless and is unable to relieve the infant's distress.

(Thomas and Chess, 1977) When the infant is picked up, rocked, or patted on the back, he is not comforted. The anxiety becomes reciprocal. The infant's distress increases mother's anxiety and tension. This creates a vicious cycle and a pathological feedback mechanism. A severely colicky baby is an example of pathological sensory-motor distress. Pathological sensory-motor distress impedes the infant's development and may contribute to disorders of attachment, such as child abuse or neglect and failure to thrive.

Retrospective histories of some children with attention deficit disorders (hyperkinetic impulse disorder), psychophysiological disturbances, childhood psychosis, and infantile autism reveal evidences of pathological sensory-motor distress in the first months of life. (see chapters 10, 12, and 16)

The pathologically distressed infant is basically hyperalert and hypersensitive. He responds intensely and, at times, overwhelmingly to stimuli. For example, there is exaggeration and continuation of the startle reflex past the age of 3 months. There is usually hyperreflexia and jerky response to physical stimuli, such as sound, touch, and light. Some infants react with pain and distress to normal caregiving activities, such as holding, rocking, talking, or feeding. Parents need to modify their activities to accomodate the child's hyperalertness, hypersensitivity, and overreaction.

Autoerotic behaviors, such as thumb-sucking and nonnutritive sucking, do not usually give the infant comfort. The infant may look at the mother warily, with apprehension and a wide gaze. By the age of 2 or 3 months, when seeing a human face, instead of turning to smile, the infant may burst into tears. Continuous hyperalertness and overreaction interfere with the development of attachment behavior and increase parental anxiety.

One of the most important evidences of pathological sensory-motor distress and anxiety in infancy is delay in the development of rhythmically and synchrony in eating, sleeping, and active and quiet wakefulness, and relative adaptation to circadian rhythm by the age of 3 months.

Early evidence of wariness toward strangers by age 4 months, which is the precursor of stranger anxiety, may be intensely exaggerated. The infant often bursts into tears and overtly reacts in a panic manner to strangers. The continuation of this intense anxiety contributes to the development of withdrawal, avoidance of human contact, depression, and, in severe situations, autisticlike behavior.

Mental health clinicians are beginning to recognize the need for assessment and treatment of psychopathology in early infancy. The multidisciplinary field of *infant psychiatry* is emerging for the assessment and treatment of emotional disorders in infants and therapeutic work with parents.

Infants' sensory-motor distress should be referred to mental health professionals who have an interest in early infancy. These infants do not outgrow pathological distress. Lack of intervention may contribute to the development of severe and pervasive psychopathologies.

Anxiety: Six to Twelve Months of Life

The adaptive anxieties of stranger anxiety and separation anxiety are the major developmental milestones between ages 6 and 12 months. (see chapter 2) The absence of these developmental anxieties is cause for concern.

Fear and Anxiety

During this century, the existence of innate fears in infancy and the relationship between fear and anxiety have been debated extensively.

Watson (1919), the proponent of the School of Behaviorism, believed that there were two primal fears—loud sound and loss of support. Freud and other psychoanalysts, on the other hand, perceived fear as reactive to external danger. Anxiety and phobia were conceptualized as an irrational reaction to internal danger without any base in reality. Bowlby (1973) questioned both of these assumptions. Based on observations of animal behavior, and Darwin's evolutionary concept for species survival, Bowlby perceived fear and anxiety as the same phenomenon.

Bronson (1968) documented the fact that infants soon after birth showed distress in reaction to discomfort, pain, sudden loud sound, and an approaching looming object. Bronson felt that it was not until age 6 months that infants showed the reaction that is called fear. Bronson and Bowlby felt that the following fears are innate in human beings and have significant adaptive and survival value: fear of strangers, strange objects, heights, pain, discomfort, loud sounds, and looming objects. For example, fear of strangers, strange objects, and looming objects keeps the crawling infant close to mother and protects against dangers, such as predatory animals. According to Bowlby, innate fears are genetically programmed in the human species for survival. They are not neurotic or pathological.

By the end of the first year, the infant also shows fear of an anticipated situation. For instance, the infant under age 11 months does not show fear of the physician, although the infant may have had an injection a few weeks earlier. But, between ages 11 and 12 months, the infant begins to show fear of physicians in anticipation of the possible injection. (Bowlby, 1973, p. 74)

Pathological Anxiety

Pathological anxiety during ages 6 to 12 months expresses itself in the following forms.

DISTURBANCE IN MOTOR BEHAVIOR. The infant is hyperactive and fidgety. He may not sit up at age 6 months but may move prematurely to crawling or walking. Continuous anxiety may also delay the development of motor behavior.

DISTURBANCE IN ATTACHMENT BEHAVIOR. Stranger anxiety and separation anxiety are intensified. These anxieties, instead of having an alerting and adaptive quality, become overwhelming. The infant responds with a panic reaction, including sensory-motor and psychophysiological distress.

Separation from mother even for a very short time or the approach of a stranger creates extreme anxiety and panic in the infant. This anxiety overwhelms the infant. Helplessness and psychic traumas ensue.

The anxious infant usually is not able to progress smoothly to the practicing subphase of separation-individuation. He continues intense clinging behavior toward mother.

COGNITIVE DEVELOPMENT. Impairment in cognitive functioning, such as delay in object permanency, overconcern with reciprocity, and delay in intentionality, may occur.

EATING DISTURBANCES. Anxiety at this age overwhelms the already precarious eating behavior. Some of the normal transient eating disturbances might become intensely exaggerated and chronic. Usually, eating disturbances are among the earliest signs of pathological anxiety. The normally transient fussy and picky eating or the experience of pain and discomfort following eating is intensified.

Undereating, nausea, vomiting, diarrhea, constipation, and uneven growth are common. Occasionally, overeating and gorging may occur.

SLEEP DISTURBANCES. Transient sleep disturbances are intensified and may become chronic. The infant has difficulty going to sleep. Sleep is restless and irregular sleep, with frequent periods of wakefulness.

SPEECH DISTURBANCES. In normal infants, motoric development and speech development are closely synchronized. In anxious infants, a dyssynchrony occurs and speech is delayed.

OPPOSITIONAL BEHAVIOR. Oppositional behavior may occur earlier and is often intensified. The child may react with panic or severe temper tantrums to frustration.

TEETHING. The infant reacts with severe psychophysiological distress to teething, such as severe eating disturbances, diarrhea, and vomiting.

AGGRESSIVE BEHAVIOR. By the end of the first year, the anxious infant may discharge psychophysiological distress in the form of overt aggressive motoric behavior, such as biting, temper tantrums, and hyperactivity, or by becoming quiet, withdrawn, and inhibited.

PSYCHOPHYSIOLOGICAL DISTUR-BANCES. The infant may manifest psychophysiological disturbances, such as asthma, varieties of food allergies, eczema, dermatitis, delay in growth, and possible early anorexia.

Characteristics of Pathological Anxiety—The First Year of Life

1. Alarming and traumatic type of anxiety
2. Anxiety is chronic in nature
3. Reciprocal—infant and mother reinforce each other's anxiety
4. Anxiety contributes to maternal overprotection or neglect
5. Anxiety impedes physical, emotional, and cognitive development
6. Anxiety may contribute to the development of child abuse, sensory-motor depression, anaclitic depression, failure to thrive, delay or arrest in language development and object relationship, development of psychophysiological disorders, and, in severe forms, to childhood autism or mental retardation

Anxiety: One to Three Years of Age

In healthy children, during this period, separation anxiety continues with less intensity. Stranger anxiety diminishes or disappears by the end of the third year. The developmental anxieties concerning loss of control of body functions, loss of autonomy, and loss of love object emerge. These developmental anxieties are transient and have the quality of an alerting signal. Sensitive response by parents and the environment diminishes the intensity of these anxieties. Usually, when the developmental tasks of this stage are achieved, the related anxieties are diminished and replaced with feelings of mastery, achievement, and accomplishment.

Pathological Anxiety

Intensive or chronic anxiety during ages 1 to 3 years has the following clinical features.

MOTOR BEHAVIOR DISTURBANCES. The anxious toddler has delay or acceleration in walking and running. He is fidgety, restless, and is not able to sit still. He is clumsy and has difficulty in integrating and coordinating body movement. The development of hand and eye coordination and fine motor movement is delayed. The anxious child often is not able to feed himself partially or scribble by age 18 months.

The toddler may become overly cautious, apprehensive, and concerned about danger. At the same time, in a counterphobic way, he may become more impulsive and accident prone.

OPPOSITIONAL SYNDROME. Normal negativistic and oppositional behavior is intensified. Passive-aggressive outbursts in the form of passive-resistive behavior, obstinacy, defiance, frequent poutiness, severe outbursts of temper tantrums and breath holding may ensue. These are manifestations of pathological oppositional syndrome.

DISTURBANCE IN COGNITIVE DEVEL-OPMENT. The anxious child has delay in the development of object permanency, deduction, and evocative memory. Overreliance on sensory-motor intelligence and the discharge of tension through somatosensory modalities may interfere with the development of symbolic thought processes and the development of the preoperational stage of intelligence.

DISTURBANCE IN LANGUAGE DEVEL-OPMENT. If pathological anxiety occurs between the ages of 1 and 2 years, language development is delayed. The child may not be able to talk. If the pathological anxiety occurs between ages 2 and 3 years, when the child has already gained some language skills, the child may use these newly acquired skills in a repetitive-compulsive manner partially to discharge internal tension. The tone and pitch of the voice has a whiny, squeaky quality.

Regression and delay of further development may ensue. Baby talk, constant chattering, speech impediment, difficulty in enunciation, lack of proper use of pronouns or complete sentences, stuttering, or elective mutism may appear.

DISTURBANCE IN SEPARATION-INDI-VIDUATION. Pathological anxiety during the second year of life exaggerates the phase of rapprochement (age 16 to 24 months). The child becomes extremely clinging to mother and manifests the intense separation anxieties of 8 to 10 months of life. The child does not venture away from mother to explore the environment. Separation from mother is experienced almost like organismic pain and intensive psychophysiological distress. Frequent panic reaction occurs at the time of mild to moderate stress or possible separation.

Between 2 and 3 years of age, pathological anxiety interferes with the development of object constancy and the psychological birth of the self. In anticipation of separation, a strong ambivalence occurs toward mother in the form of physically clinging to her, but, at the same time, hitting, biting, and scratching.

The child becomes apprehensive of other children and avoids parallel play. These symptoms are manifestations of pathological symbiotic behavior, and, if they continue, may contribute to the development of a defect in ego function, borderline personality disorders, and childhood psychosis.

TOILET TRAINING DISTURBANCES. Pathological anxiety interferes with toilet training. The child overreacts to and, at times, panics over parental expectations and demands. He may become afraid of going to the bathroom or of the toilet bowl, sink, or drain. Flushing the toilet may create panic. The anxious child may respond by overcontrolled behavior, such as withholding bowel movements for days, or by loss of control. Soiling, or encopresis, is common in an anxious child. Shame, fear, and loss of control reinforce the child's anxieties.

SLEEP DISTURBANCES. Transient sleep disturbances become intensified and may become sleep disorders. Frequent nightmares and awakening in panic from frightening dreams are common. Hypnagogic (before going to sleep) and hypnopompic (the time of waking up) frightening hallucinations occur.

Stages I and II sleep are increased at the expense of Stage IV Sleep. Sleepwalking and sleep talking in a family prone to this disorder occur more frequently.

EATING DISTURBANCES. Eating disturbances are similar to those of an earlier age, with exaggerated awareness of cleanliness and dirtiness or fear of eating. Often, frightening symbolic meanings are attached to various foods.

DISTURBANCES IN PLAY BEHAVIOR. The play of the anxious child is overwhelmed with fear, anxiety, and dread. The child repeats a particular play over and over again in a repetitious-compulsive manner. Frequently, the developmental tendency for compulsion to repeat reinforces his anxieties instead of helping him master traumatic experiences. Play is limited and has a driven and sameness quality. Parallel play and the beginning of play with peers is delayed.

Characteristics of Pathological Anxiety—Ages One to Three Years

1. Alarming and traumatic type of anxiety
2. Anxiety is chronic in nature
3. Reciprocal—anxiety intensifies ambivalence between mother and child
4. There is continuation or intensification of the developmental anxieties of an earlier phase, which now become pathological and impede the development of object constancy, autonomy, and relative independence
5. If pathological anxiety continues for some time, part-object relationship (splitting) rather than total and integrated object relationship (object constancy) occurs
6. Intense preoccupation with symbolic thought processes and fantasies
7. Extreme fluctuation of affective expression in the form of violent temper tantrums and self-destructive behavior
8. Severe and prolonged forms of anxiety may result in the arrest of ego development in the form of autosymbiotic psychosis, childhood schizophrenia, borderline psychosis, severe depression, narcissistic personality disorder, and drug and alcohol abuse in later life

Anxiety: Three to Six Years of Life

The developmental anxiety of this age—phallic-oedipal anxiety or castration anxiety—helps in the consolidation of the triadic relationship and in establishment of identity with the parent of the same sex. (see chapter 4)

Pathological Anxiety

Intensive or chronic anxiety during ages 3 to 6 years has the following clinical features.

MOTOR BEHAVIOR DISTURBANCES. The anxious child demonstrates internal anxieties by hyperactivity or hypoactivity, overcontrol, and inhibition. As a general rule, the younger child will be hyperactive and the older child overcontrolled and inhibited.

The anxious child is nervous, restless, fidgety, and "always on the go." Anxiety may interfere with the development of motoric skills, such as involvement in group games, and development of fine motoric movements, such as buttoning, printing letters of the alphabet, writing, and drawing.

Frequently, parents, teachers, and clinicians mistake the hyperactivity of the anxious or depressed child for genuine hyperkinetic or attention deficit disorders. For differential diagnosis, it will help if the clinician realizes that the anxiety of the anxious child is contagious and often makes the observer anxious. Anxious children usually do not have a history of hyperactivity intrauterinely, in infancy, or in early childhood. Generally, anxious children are not impulsive. They have many worries, fears, and concerns. They have a history of overreaction to separation and stranger anxiety and overwhelming concern about loss of control. Both the children and the parents often have a history of psychophysiological distress and anxious overreaction to stress.

DISTURBANCES IN COGNITIVE DEVELOPMENT.
Pathological anxiety exaggerates the intensity of castration anxiety. It finds clinical expression in the newly acquired cognitive skills for symbolic thought processes, magical thought, and make-believe. The inability to differentiate between fantasy and reality reinforces the child's pervasive anxiety. Concrete thought processes and the inability for reversibility and conservation increase the child's experience of sensory-motor distress and somatic anxiety.

The anxious child has multiple fears and phobias, such as the fear of being lost, being left alone, bodily injury, animals, and insects. Children's fears and phobias will be discussed later in the section on phobic disorders.

Pathological anxiety interferes with the child's learning ability and paves the way for failure in school and academic disability in latency and adolescence.

DISTURBANCES IN PSYCHOSEXUAL DEVELOPMENT.
The child becomes inhibited in competing with the parent of the same sex for the love and affection of the parent of the opposite sex. This might contribute to failure in future triadic or multiparty group relationships. The child might remain in one-to-one, safe dyadic relationships.

The child feels apprehensive and inhibited in competing with peers. The child becomes passive and loses aggressivity and assertiveness. Curiosity, sense of discovery, and ambitiousness decrease. These pathological behaviors interfere with the child's performance in nursery school and kindergarten and make him vulnerable for learning disabilities and work inhibition in school and throughout life.

SELF-STIMULATING BEHAVIORS.
Self-stimulating behaviors, such as nail-biting, thumb-sucking, rocking, hair-pulling, and genital masturbation, increase significantly. These behaviors contribute to partial tension discharge, but, at the same time, increase guilt and apprehension, especially when these activities are condemned by parents.

SLEEP DISTURBANCES.
Sleep is one of the earliest behaviors affected. Apprehension about going to sleep, being alone in the room, being in the dark, and waking up frequently with nightmares or night-terrors are common. There is a decrease in Stage IV sleep and more prevalence of Stages I or II sleep or wakefulness.

Bedwetting is common, especially secondary enuresis. Secondary enuresis may be one of the earliest signs of an emotional disorder, such as anxiety or depression.

EATING DISTURBANCES.
Food fads, picky eating, and fussiness prevail. The child asks for many things to eat, but eats a very small amount. He receives little pleasure from eating. In severe cases of anxiety, secondary anorexia and extreme weight loss may occur.

Anxiety Disorders: Latency and Adolescence

Pathological anxiety now becomes more crystallized and internalized and expresses itself in more specific clinical disorders rather than the relatively fluid and diffuse anxiety of the earlier years.

Anxiety disorder in latency and adolescence are divided into three major types: separation anxiety disorder (school phobia), avoidance disorder, and overanxious disorder. (*DSM-III*, 1980, pp. 50–56)

Separation Anxiety Disorder—School Phobia

Adelaide Johnson and her associates (1941) described a clinical syndrome called school phobia. Eisenberg (1958) discussed clinical manifestations, management, and treatment of school phobia.

School phobia is most prevalent in children from nursery school age to the third or fourth grade, although it can occur in late elementary school, high school, and college. Shafii (1974) reported clear evidence of school phobia in the college age population. These cases had a history of untreated childhood school phobia. Separation from home, going away to college, and, in some cases, moving from one country to another for the pursuit of college education reactivated an intense separation anxiety in the form of school phobia.

SEX AND PREVALENCE.
Although it was previously thought that school phobia occurred more in girls than in boys, it is now estimated to be equally distributed. However, there is no accurate information concerning the prevalence of school phobia. Generally, 5 to 10% of the

children referred to a child psychiatric setting showed signs of school phobia. (Coolidge, 1979, p. 455)

CLINICAL FEATURES.

1. Presence of physical symptoms, such as headache, upset stomach, sore throat, dizziness, and occasionally vomiting, or low-grade fever before going to school in the morning.
2. Physical symptoms usually disappear if the child is allowed to stay at home.
3. Excessive apprehension about leaving home often is not initially verbalized.
4. Absence of physical symptoms on weekends and holidays.
5. Physical examinations reveal no organic basis for the symptoms.
6. Difficulty in going to sleep, particularly on school nights, and nightmares are common.
7. Precipitating factors usually are minor physical illness in the family, moving to a new neighborhood, parental disharmony, or the death of a relative or a pet.
8. Experience of many phobias, such as being kidnapped, having a car accident, being mugged, and fear of animals.
9. Most of these children are inhibited, pseudomature, high achievers, and perfectionistic and have done well in school but are afraid of failure.
10. In the clinical interview, it becomes readily apparent that these children have great difficulty separating from mother. Frequently, these symptoms are reactivated in anticipation of separation from mother. The child is worried that something might happen to his mother or to him while he is away from her. The only way he can be certain that everything is all right is to stay with her. This is why school phobia is now classified as a separation anxiety disorder.
11. Some of these children are afraid of not doing well in school and are frightened of the teachers or their peers.
12. In the family, the parents place great value on educational achievement. Parental, especially maternal, overprotection is common.
13. If the child is forced to go to school, he may become hostile and throw a temper tantrum.
14. Frequent absence from school, overemphasis on physical symptoms, and unnecessary medical work-ups reinforce the child's tendency toward somatization, intensify anxieties, increase family tension, and may result in difficulty in academic achievement and psychological development.

TYPES OF SCHOOL PHOBIA. Melita Sperling (1961, 1967) divided school phobia into two types.

Common School Phobia. In this type of school phobia, the child has experienced a traumatic event, such as a death or separation in the family. The child reactivates the traumatic experience over and over again through school phobic behavior in an attempt to master this overwhelming anxiety. Unconsciously the child fears the death of the mother or the death of the self. This type of school phobia resembles traumatic neurosis.

Induced School Phobia. The development of this form of school phobia is gradual and insidious. The parents induce this pathology in the child by their behavior and attitudes. The parents use the child consciously and unconsciously for the expression of their own psychopathology.

Both types of school phobia can be either acute or chronic.

DIFFERENTIAL DIAGNOSIS. It is important to differentiate school phobia from school truancy, school refusal, learning difficulties, and realistic fears.

School Truancy. The patient is usually older, either preadolescent or adolescent, with chronic history of little interest in school and poor school performance. Some exhibit antisocial behavior. The patient does not have any difficulty in leaving home. He frequently leaves home with the pretense of going to school. Usually, there is no panic reaction or physical symptoms. Some truant adolescents may have had histories of earlier school phobia.

School Refusal. The child openly expresses refusal to go to school. This is usually related to a distress at home or in school. There is no evidence of separation anxiety or panic reaction. School refusal is usually short-term, and, with gentle firmness and alleviation of the contributing factors, it disappears.

Learning Difficulties. The child avoids school because of failure. A careful academic assessment may reveal that the child needs special tutoring or reassignment to help him with underlying difficulties so that he can experience success in academic performance.

Realistic Fears. The child is afraid of being attacked or ridiculed by peers and, at times, by a destructive teacher. If careful exploration reveals that the child's fear is based on reality, the clinician and the parents need to move immediately to help the child face his fear effectively. If it is not possible to change the frightening situation, an alternative school placement should be found.

TREATMENT. School phobia, because of the intensity of the panic reaction, is a child psychiatric emergency. It interferes with the child's psychological development and perpetuates academic difficulties.

There are many approaches to treatment. The combination of active dynamic psychotherapy, along with family therapy and behavior modification therapy, seems to be the most effective approach. The following guidelines are helpful:

1. The patient and the family are seen immediately.
2. After initial evaluation of the child and family together and separately, the dynamics of symptomatology and contributions of the child and the family to the problem are discussed openly with all concerned.
3. The child's physician and teachers are encouraged to be involved and to become allies in the treatment program.
4. The child is expected to attend school immediately. If anxiety is severe, the child is expected to attend school, for example, for 5 minutes the first day; then on the following day the time is doubled, and so on, so that by the end of one week the child is attending school for about 1½ hours. This approach continues during the second week. In most cases, by the end of the second week, the child is able to stay in school for the entire day.
5. Usually a neutral person, other than the mother, should take the child to school. If the child refuses to go, he is physically taken. No excuse is acceptable.
6. The parents and the child are usually seen in outpatient psychotherapy every day, or at least two to three times per week during the first 2 weeks.
7. In this initial phase of treatment, the child and parents are encouraged openly and freely to express their worries, fears, concerns, and underlying ambivalence and hostile, destructive feelings toward each other.
8. Parental inconsistencies and their ambivalent approach concerning school attendance are pointed out directly. Parents are expected to make a conscious effort to change their approach.
9. The parents are helped to become aware of their own internal conflicts concerning separating from the child and "letting go."
10. Frequently, it becomes clear while working with the family that either one or both parents have had similar difficulty in childhood or other disturbances in the separation-individuation process.
11. No decision about the child's leaving school or not attending school should be made under *any* circumstances without the approval of the therapist.
12. Some of these children will have minor fevers. A rule of thumb is that the child's temperature should be above 101 before he can stay home. The temperature of these children needs to be taken with an adult present, because sometimes the children will put thermometers in hot water or drink hot liquids or rub the thermometers to raise the temperature. If the parents are not reliable, someone else will have to take the child's temperature.
13. In therapeutic encounters it is necessary to emphasize to the parents and the child that school phobia is only a symptom and continuous therapeutic involvement of the child and the parents after initial improvement is essential.
14. In some cases, after alleviation of the symptom, the parents resist further therapeutic involvement. If the underlying conflicts are not sufficiently resolved, some of the children will return with recurrent school phobia. At that time, the parents often then become more involved and are able to develop a meaningful therapeutic alliance.
15. In severe cases of school phobia or with the failure of outpatient treatment, the child's removal from home and short-term psychiatric hospitalization or a day-treatment program may be indicated.

PROGNOSIS. Prognosis depends upon the age and developmental history of the child, the intensity and duration of the school phobia, and, particularly, upon the ability of the family to develop a therapeutic alliance. The younger the child and the more acute the school phobia, the better the prognosis. In older children and adolescents, unless decisive therapeutic measures are taken immediately, the prognosis is not favorable.

FOLLOW-UP. In acute cases, with an effective treatment program, the follow-up shows that most of these children have done very well, with no reoccurrence of school phobia. In chronic cases and resistive families, many of the children begin to have academic difficulties in adolescence, have difficulty in relating to peers, and develop work phobia in adulthood. Lack of ambition, marginal work habits, and a tendency toward mediocrity prevail.

Avoidance Disorder of Childhood and Adolescence

Children between ages 2½ and 3 years overcome their fears and anxieties concerning strangers. If the child continues to show excessive fear of strangers and overwhelming shyness, he may be suffering from an avoidance disorder.

CLINICAL FEATURES.

1. Excessive fear of strangers.
2. Overwhelming shyness.
3. Withdrawal and crying when coming in contact with strangers.
4. Interference in social and peer relationships.
5. The child clings to parents or other familiar adults when encountering strangers.
6. Avoidance of facial, physical, or verbal contact with strangers.
7. Stranger anxiety can become extensive and develop into social anxiety (performance in public, being in crowds).
8. The child blushes easily and feels embarassed and timid.
9. These children are usually passive, inhibited, and insecure.
10. If the stranger and social anxiety continue and become more intense, selective mutism may ensue. (The child is quite capable of verbal communication at home, but is mute in public or at school.)

ONSET. The onset is between ages 2½ and 3 years, after the usual disappearance of stranger anxiety.

DIFFERENTIAL DIAGNOSIS. Avoidance disorder is a new category proposed in *DSM-III* (1980). Avoidance disorder needs to be differentiated from more severe forms of psychopathology, such as schizoid personality, schizophrenia, or other forms of psychosis.

In avoidance disorder, children feel quite comfortable and seek human contact with parents, siblings, and familiar persons and close friends. Their affects are quite appropriate in familiar surroundings. Reality testing is intact. There are no thought disorders or defects in ego functions.

In the schizoid personality, schizophrenia, and other psychotic disorders, the child withdraws from everyone. There is a disturbance in affective expression, thought processes, ego functions, and object relationships.

PROGNOSIS. Some of these children gradually overcome their shyness, only manifesting it at times of severe stress. In other cases, avoidance disorder may become chronic, interfere with the child's social skill, and contribute to feelings of isolation and depression.

Overanxious Disorder

Overanxious disorder is a form of chronic low-grade anxiety that usually occurs in latency-age children and adolescents.

CLINICAL FEATURES.

1. Nervousness, restlessness.
2. Excessive worries about future events, for instance, examinations, meeting deadlines, fulfilling people's expectations, and irrational concern about danger.
3. Anxiety concerning competence and performance at school, in extracurricular activities, or at home. Overwhelming anxiety and panic at the time of examination.
4. Overconcern about approval and acceptance, apprehension and fear of not being accepted and constant need for reassurance. Undue concern about criticism from others, especially peers.
5. Irrational fear of embarrassment and marked self-consciousness.
6. Intermittent physical symptoms of headache, shortness of breath, dizziness, nausea, lump in throat, heart palpitations, nervous habits, such as nail-biting, hair-pulling, hair-eating, nose-picking, and simple tics.
7. Hypermaturity and precociousness.
8. Overwhelming preoccupation with conformity.
9. Perfectionistic and obsessional tendencies.
10. Significant self-doubt.
11. Difficulty going to sleep.

PROGNOSIS. Some children with psychotherapy, a decrease in parental overexpectation, and decrease of perfectionistic tendencies improve significantly.

In some cases, the symptoms of anxiety increase and decrease related to stress. This disorder may become chronic and express itself in adult life in the form of chronic anxiety or social phobia. In severe cases, the child may become incapacitated, resulting in a variety of somatic symptoms, poor academic achievement, isolation, and depression.

Phobic Disorders—Phobic Neurosis

The child or adolescent has a persistent and *irrational* fear or fears. The irrational fear results in overwhelming anxiety and active avoidance of the phobic object. The patient is apprehensive and frequently has *anticipatory anxiety* even when thinking about his phobia. Fear of animals, insects, public places, eating in public, performing in public, and, in older adolescents and adults, driving, flying, and use of public lavatories are common.

ONSET. Generally, children aged 3 to 6 years manifest a multitude of transient phobias. These phobias might become persistent and chronic.

Phobia, from psychophysiological and psychodynamic points of view, is a form of anxiety which focuses on a specific object, person, or situation. The phobic object is invested with unconscious symbolic meaning.

TYPES OF PHOBIAS Fear of animals, insects, food, being lost or in strange places, and social phobia are more prevalent in childhood and adolescence. Phobias are divided into three types.

Agoraphobia. Fear of open places is more common in late adolescence or adulthood.

Social Phobia. Discussed earlier as an avoidance disorder.

Simple Phobia. Discussion follows.

SIMPLE PHOBIA OR SPECIFIC PHOBIA. This type includes all forms of phobia except agoraphobia and social phobia. The most common type of simple phobia is related to irrational fear of animals, "...particularly dogs, snakes, insects, and mice." (*DSM-III,* 1980, p. 229) Claustrophobia (fear of closed spaces), and acrophobia (fear of heights) are also common.

When the individual is exposed to the phobic stimulus, he becomes overwhelmingly frightened and may experience a panic reaction. The person goes to considerable effort to *avoid* the phobic stimulus.

PSYCHODYNAMICS OF PHOBIA: THE CASE OF LITTLE HANS. One of the classical cases of childhood phobia is that of "Little Hans," reported by Freud in 1909(a).

Little Hans, between ages 4 and 5 years, began to show a phobic reaction to horses. After having a tonsilectomy at age 5, his phobia worsened, to the extent that he could not step out of his house because of his fear of horse-driven carriages. He thought that a horse would bite him or hurt him badly.

Freud treated Little Hans through continuous work with his father. Freud conceptualized that Little Hans' phobia was, in actuality, a *displacement* of his fear of his father onto horses. From a psychodynamic point of view, fear of his father and castration anxiety were the *projections* of Hans' own phallic destructive tendencies toward his father.

ONSET AND COURSE OF PHOBIA. The onset of simple phobias begins in childhood, usually between ages 3 and 6 years. Most simple phobias are transient and disappear without treatment. Phobias that continue into latency, adolescence, and adulthood are usually not alleviated without treatment. Some phobias do not require treatment as long as they do not interfere with performance and functioning.

TREATMENT. Dynamic psychotherapy and behavior therapy are the most common forms of treatment for phobia. (see chapter 21)

Obsessive-Compulsive Disorder—Obsessive-Compulsive Neurosis

Patients with obsessive-compulsive disorder have overwhelming *obsessional thoughts* and *compulsive behavior.*

CLINICAL FEATURES.

1. Obsessional thoughts are related to destructive impulses, such as worrying about doing or saying something that might hurt someone. The patient has overwhelming concern about cleanliness, contamination, and fear of touching anything because it might be "dirty." The patient is plagued by doubts.
2. Compulsive behaviors are associated with obsessional thoughts. Some of the more frequent compulsive behavior in children and adolescents are handwashing, avoiding stepping on cracks, pacing, opening and closing doors, checking things over and over, and doing something and then undoing it. Perfectionistic tendencies interfere with the child's performance and the joy of life.
3. Compulsive behavior variations—if the child is forced to resist compulsive behavior, he becomes anxious, panic-stricken, and frequently develops new compulsive behaviors, similar to the previous ones, with minor variations.
4. Magical thoughts—in the mind of the obsessional child and adolescent, fantasies and thoughts continue to have a magical power and are frequently equated with action, similar to the thought processes of a child age 3 to 6 years. (see chapter 4)
5. Rigidity, excessive orderliness, self-righteousness, and lack of joy and pleasure are underlying personality characteristics.
6. Precociousness—most obsessive-compulsive patients are precocious, especially in the areas of thought processes and language development. These intellectual skills are used for symptom expression.

*PSYCHODYNAMIC PERSPECTIVE—
THE CASE OF "RAT MAN."* Freud (1909b) reported on a case of a young man who was suffering from obsessional neurosis. This patient was preoccupied and obsessed with the idea that rats were gnawing into the anorectal area of his dead father and his young woman friend. He developed these obsessional thoughts when he was between ages 6 and 7 years.

In analysis, it became apparent that this patient was seduced by his governess at age 4 years. At about the same time, he experienced the death of a sibling, and shortly afterward was severely beaten by his father. He was a precocious child and was quite "naughty" between ages 3 and 4 years. After the beating by his father, he became quite timid.

Freud hypothesized that the patient's symptoms represented his phallic aggressive and destructive wishes toward his father. Because of phallic-oedipal anxieties and fears, the patient regressed to the anal stage of psychosexual development. The patient's homosexual tendencies were also expressed in this symptom formation. The most prevalent defenses utilized in obsessive-compulsive disorders are isolation of affect, rationalization, intellectualization, doing and undoing, and regression. There is usually relative failure of repression.

ONSET. From a developmental point of view, in the anal phase and early phallic-oedipal phase (ages 2 to 4 years), transient obsessive-compulsive tendencies are quite common. In most cases, these behaviors are developmentally appropriate, and the child, by repeating the experiences—"compulsion to repeat"—tries to overcome the traumatic experiences and gain a sense of mastery. In some cases, because of the child's temperament, family interaction, and the intensity and frequency of traumatic experiences, obsessive-compulsive disorder crystallizes in latency and adolescence.

PREVALENCE. There is no information concerning the prevalence of obsessive-compulsive disorder in children and adolescents. Adams (1973) reported on 49 cases of children and adolescents suffering from obsessional neurosis—1.2% of a child psychiatric clinic population. According to Anthony (1967), "About 20 percent of all cases of obsessional neurosis begin under the age of 15, and 50 to 60 percent earlier than the age of 20." (p. 1401)

COURSE. Obsessive-compulsive disorder is usually chronic with acute exacerbations. It occurs in both males and females. Most obssesive-compulsive children and adolescents are unhappy and miserable. They are prone to depression.

Obsessive-compulsive behaviors may be early symptoms of borderline personality disorder, schizophrenia, and organic mental disorder. These symptoms could also be the symptoms of underlying phobia or depression.

Somatoform Disorders—Conversion Neurosis

The term "somatoform" is now used instead of conversion or hysteria to describe

> ...physical symptoms suggesting physical disorder...for which there are no demonstrable organic findings or known physiological mechanisms and for which there is positive evidence, or a strong presumption, that the symptoms are linked to psychological factors or conflicts.
>
> *DSM-III*, 1980, p. 241.

HISTORICAL PERSPECTIVE. At the end of the nineteenth century, with the work of Charcot in Paris and Bernheim in Nancy, interest emerged in the clinical description and treatment of hysteria. The use of hypnosis and suggestion for the treatment of hysteria gave impetus to the discovery of new psychotherapeutic methods.

Freud (1895), influenced by the work of Charcot and Bernheim, collaborated with Joseph Breuer in writing *Studies on Hysteria*. Breuer discovered that *catharsis* or *abreaction* is the most effective form of treatment for hysteria. Freud, inspired by Breuer's work and "talking out treatment," developed techniques of free association and eventually psychoanalysis as a psychotherapeutic and theoretical model for psychological and psychopathological development in human beings.

CONVERSION. Freud coined the term "conversion" to describe a mechanism of transformation of anxiety to bodily dysfunction. Conversion neurosis refers specifically to dysfunction of the voluntary part of the central nervous system involving motor and sensory apparatus.

According to Freud, the purpose of this conversion process is to decrease anxiety and unconscious conflicts through the defense mechanisms of repression and displacement. The choice of symptoms in conversion neurosis has specific symbolic meaning related to intrapsychic conflicts and traumatic experiences. Usually, the patient derives secondary gain from these symptoms and this perpetuates the conversion neurosis.

The Case of Dora. Freud (1905) reported the now famous case of Dora. Dora was seen by Freud for aphonia (loss of voice), convulsion, and facial neuralgia at age 19 years. In psychoanalytic treatment, Freud discovered that Dora's family had a long history of psychiatric problems and physical illnesses. Dora herself, between ages 6 and 8 years, developed enuresis and masturbated frequently. At age 8 years, she was seduced by an older man. Later, her father had an affair with someone else that she knew about.

Following her seduction by the older man, Dora changed from being an active and "wild creature" into a "quiet child." Around age 12 years, she developed the symptoms of nervous cough, hoarseness, and migraine. Between ages 16 and 19 years, Dora's father became ill with paralysis, and she had the responsibility of caring for him.

Based on this case, Freud conceptualized that, in actuality, Dora's conversion neurosis began at age 8 years, following the traumatic experience of seduction. The symptoms of nervous cough, hoarseness, and migraine at approximately age 12 years, and aphonia, convulsion, and facial neuralgia were the reactivation of this earlier conversion neurosis.

Dora's resentment and anger concerning having to care for her paralyzed father, along with her phallic-oedipal longing toward him, found compromised neurotic expression in the conversion symptomatology.

Later, Freud modified his position and suggested that not only actual sexual traumatic experiences, but phallic-oedipal fantasies and conflicts related to these fantasies contribute to the development of infantile neurosis and adult neurosis. (see chapter 15)

PREVALENCE. In the last few decades, there has been a significant decrease in classical and dramatic forms of conversion hysteria in children, adolescents, and adults.

There are no clear data on the incidence and prevalence of somatoform disorders. Proctor (1958) and Loof (1970) described the relative frequency of conversion hysteria in rural areas in the United States, such as Appalachia, the South, and the Midwest.

TYPES OF SOMATOFORM DISORDERS.

Somatization Disorder. This disorder is more common, chronic, and polysymptomatic. Previously, it was referred to as hysteria or Briquet's syndrome.

Conversion Disorder. Conversion symptoms are predominant and not an expression of another disorder.

Psychogenic Pain Disorders. Chronic complaint of pain with the absence of physical findings.

Hypochondriasis. The predominant feature of this disorder is unrealistic exaggeration and overwhelming preoccupation with physical signs or sensations leading to constant worry and "belief of having a serious disease." (*DSM-III*, 1980, p. 249)

Atypical Somatoform Disorder. The patient has overwhelming concern about "...imagined defect in physical appearance that is out of proportion to any actual physical abnormality that may exist." (ibid., p. 252) This syndrome is also sometimes referred to as "dysmorphophobia."

In childhood and adolescence, somatization disorder (hysteria) and conversion disorder (hysterical neurosis conversion type) are the most common. Other types of somatoform disorders occur so infrequently in this age group that they will not be described.

Somatization Disorder—Hysteria

CLINICAL FEATURES.

1. The patient has multiple somatic complaints with no apparent physical disorder.
2. The physical complaints are dramatic, exaggerated, or vague.
3. Pseudoneurological symptoms, such as convulsion, paralysis, loss of sensation, blindness, and loss of voice are frequent.
4. Abdominal pain, back pain, and painful menstruation.
5. Cardiopulmonary symptoms, such as palpitation of the heart, dizziness, shortness of breath, chest pain, and hyperventilation.
6. Occasionally, the patient may have hallucinations without disturbance in reality testing.
7. In most cases, these symptoms are also associated with anxiety or depression.

ONSET. Onset is most frequent in adolescence, although the latency-age or pubescent child may manifest any of these symptoms, particularly seizures, headache, abdominal pain, hyperventilation, or chest pain. Both males and females have this disorder, but it is rarely diagnosed in males.

PREVALENCE. No data are available on prevalence in children. Approximately 1% of adult females have somatization disorder. Personal histories of these patients reveal that most of them have a tendency toward somatization and have manifested a number of these symptoms, with some changes and variations, from early childhood.

FAMILY CONSTELLATION. Often, there is a tendency toward somatization in the family. It is common for the child to be taken to several physicians, both at the same time and consecutively. A history of multiple hospitalizations and a variety of medical procedures without any conclusive results are common.

From a psychodynamic point of view, the child and the family derive considerable secondary gain from somatization.

Conversion Disorder—Hysterical Neurosis, Conversion Type

Conversion disorder is the new name for classical hysterical neurosis, or conversion neurosis.

CLINICAL FEATURES.

1. The symptom expression is usually dramatic.
2. Loss or alteration in physical functions, which suggest a physical disorder, particularly in motoric or sensory functions.
3. No organic basis for the disorder can be found.
4. Symptoms do not follow anatomical and physiological patterns. They usually follow the pattern of what the lay person perceives as the function of the organ. For example, paralysis or loss of sensation in the hand follows the glove pattern rather than the anatomical distribution of the nervous system.
5. Pseudoneurological symptoms, such as seizure, aphonia, paralysis, coordination disturbances, akinesia, dyskinesia, anesthesia, paresthesia, blindness, and tunnel vision are frequent.
6. Vomiting, pseudocyesis (false pregnancy) can occur in adolescent girls.
7. Generally, there is a single symptom at a given time, which might be replaced by another symptom.
8. Frequently, there is temporal proximity between emotional distress and symptom expression. For example, an adolescent, after an argument with her boyfriend in the evening, may wake up the next morning with paralysis of the hand. The paralysis may symbolize the girl's destructive wishes toward the boyfriend and the internal prohibition against such wishes.
9. The patient's family is usually quite distressed about the symptom, but the patient may show little concern. This apparent lack of concen is called *"La belle indifference."* However, a casual attitude toward a symptom should not be considered pathognomonic of conversion disorder.
10. Frequently, the symptom disappears suddenly and dramatically, although the underlying psychological conflicts associated with anxiety and depression continue.

CONTRIBUTING FACTORS.
A family history of frequent physical illnesses and a personal history of physical disorders, such as epilepsy, are common in patients with conversion disorder. Warfare and recent death in the family can be precipitating factors.

Children and adolescents from families with a tendency toward dramatization, nonverbal communication, seductive behavior, or actual sexual stimulation and abuse are especially vulnerable to conversion disorder.

Dissociative Disorders

Dissociative disorders are related to conversion disorders. Usually a dissociation occurs between past memories and present experiences.

CLINICAL FEATURES.

1. Children or adolescents with dissociative disorders have a sudden change or alteration in consciousness, identity, or motor behavior.
2. Amnesia—abrupt and massive loss of memory.
3. Depersonalization—loss of ability to remember one's name, identity, background, and place of residence.
4. In severe cases, multiple personality might be the outcome of dissociative disorders.

HISTORICAL PERSPECTIVE.
Pierre Janet (1907) used the concept of dissociation to describe the "splitting" of experiences that occurs in hysteria and dissociative disorders. There is a disturbance of synthetic and integrative functions of the personality. Consciousness and memory are restricted and functions and feelings are "split off" from conscious awareness: dissociation has occurred.

PREVALENCE.
Adams (1979) reported that approximately 5% of all childhood neuroses are dissociative disorders. Dissociative disorders are more common in children and adolescents from subcultures, such as those found in Appalachia, or among rural blacks and Mexican-Americans, or in children who have migrated from one country or region to a new area.

TYPES OF DISSOCIATIVE DISORDERS. Psychogenic Amnesia.
The patient is unable to remember significant personal information or events. There are three types of psychogenic amnesia.

Localized or circumscribed amnesia is the most common form of psychogenic amnesia. It usually occurs after a severe, traumatic experience, for example, following a car accident. The uninjured survivor does not remember anything for a short period of time; usually this lasts from a few days to 2 to 3 weeks.

In selective amnesia, the patient loses memory for selective events. For example, in the case of a car accident, the patient does not remember the events related to the accident, but does remember everything else.

In generalized amnesia, the person fails to recall the experience and memories of his entire life. This is the least frequent form of psychogenic amnesia, but the most disturbing and most likely to come to the attention of the clinician.

Generalized amnesia occurs in adolescence or young adulthood. The patient is disoriented, perplexed, and may wander aimlessly. The patient may become involved in antisocial or inappropriate behavior without awareness of possible implications or outcome.

There is no history or evidence of organic disorders, such as epilepsy or head injury. If the patient uses alcohol or drugs and has loss of memory or black-out spells, his condition is not diagnosed as psychogenic amnesia.

The onset of psychogenic amnesia occurs dramatically and suddenly following severe psychological stress. The stress may be related to extreme family disharmony, loss or threat of a loss of a meaningful relationship, or threat of injury or death. The duration of amnesia usually is for a few days to 2 to 3 weeks or longer. Termination of amnesia is abrupt.

Psychogenic Fugue.   The patient suddenly and unexpectedly "...travel[s] away from home or customary work locale with assumption of a new identity and an inability to recall...previous identity." (*DSM-III*, 1980, p. 255)

Psychogenic fugue is quite rare in children and adolescents. It may occur in middle or late adolescence, or in young adulthood, especially in the case of adolescents who run away from home.

Drug or alcohol abuse, psychological stress, parental disharmony, war, or natural disasters, such as earthquakes or floods, are usually the precipitating factors. The fugue state usually lasts a few hours to a few days. In rare circumstances it may last many months. During the fugue state, the individual may be disoriented and perplexed.

It is important to rule out any organic mental disorders, temporal lobe epilepsy, and malingering.

Multiple Personality.   The patient assumes two, three, or more separate personalities. At a given time, one of these is usually dominant. Transition from one personality to another is abrupt. Multiple personality is rarely diagnosed until late adolescence or early adulthood.

Depersonalization Disorder.   In depersonalization, there is a change and alteration in the individual's "...perception or experience of the self so that the usual sense of one's own reality is temporarily lost or changed." (*DSM-III*, 1980, p. 259)

Perceptual changes in the size of the body, such as head, extremities, or perceiving oneself as away from the self—similar to the experience of dreaming—occurs.

Mild forms of depersonalization and altered states of consciousness are quite a common phenomenon. It is estimated that "...30%-70% of young adults..." might experience a mild form of depersonalization without "significant impairment." (ibid., p. 259)

Meditative experiences in adolescence may contribute to temporary regression and mild depersonalization.

In pathological forms of depersonalization, the individual feels frightened, anxious, and not in complete control of thoughts and behavior. Reality testing is usually intact. Depersonalization occurs suddenly, but disappears gradually.

In some cases, the adolescent experiences the "loss" of the external world. "A perceived change in the size or shape of objects...is common. People may be perceived as dead or mechanical." (ibid., p. 259) Hyperventilation, panic and anxiety reaction, dizziness, fear of losing one's mind, obsessiveness, depression, and loss of the sense of time are associated with depersonalization.

The course of moderate to severe depersonalization is usually chronic, with long periods of remission. At the time of psychological distress, depersonalization may reappear. The degree of impairment usually is minimal, unless associated with severe anxiety or fear.

Depersonalization disorder should be differentiated from schizophrenia, organic mental disorders, particularly intoxication and withdrawal, affective disorders, epilepsy, and personality disorders. In these disorders, depersonalization is a symptom and secondary to the primary disorder.

Sleepwalking.   This at one time or another has been associated with dissociative disorders, but, in most cases, sleepwalking is related to Stage IV sleep and now is considered a disorder of arousal and a form of sleep disorder rather than a neurotic dissociative disorder.

TREATMENT OF PSYCHONEUROSES

The type of treatment for neurotic disorders of childhood and adolescence depends, to a great extent, on the clinician's educational background and theoretical orientation.

Psychotherapy

The most prevalent form of treatment is dynamic psychotherapy and play therapy with the child and psychotherapeutic work with the family. In special cases with circumscribed symptoms, such as in phobic disorders or specific habit disturbances, behavior therapy has been used.

Family therapy, group therapy, and supportive therapy also are utilized. (For a detailed discussion, see chapters 21 and 22)

Pharmacotherapy

Medications in the treatment of anxiety disorders, phobic, obsessive-compulsive, somatoform, and dissociative disorders should be used parsimoniously. Some family physicians and pediatricians prescribe hydroxyzine (Atarax, Vistaril) for these disturbances. In younger children, diphenhydramine (Benadryl) is used for alleviation of severe forms of anxieties. Diazepam (Valium) is used for latency-age children and adolescents.

We have found that in most cases of anxiety disorders, phobia, and obsessive-compulsive, somatoform, and dissociative disorders medication is not indicated.

In extreme and severe cases, for a short period of time (a few days to a couple of weeks), the tranquilizing agent producing the least side effects can be used, such as Benadryl for anxieties, or chloral hydrate for sleep disturbances. The use of chlordiazepoxide (Librium) and barbiturates, because of their potential disinhibiting effects in children and adolescents, should be avoided. (For further details, refer to chapter 23.)

REFERENCES

Adams, P.L. (1973). *Obsessive Children: A Sociopsychiatric Study.* New York: Brunner/Mazel.

Adams, P.L. (1979). Psychoneuroses. In Noshpitz, J. (Ed.), *Basic Handbook of Child Psychiatry,* Vol. 2. New York: Basic Books, pp. 194-235.

American Psychiatric Association (1980). *Diagnostic and Statistical Manual of Mental Disorders.* Third Edition. Washington, D.C.: American Psychiatric Association.

Anthony, E.J. (1967). Psychoneurotic disorders. In Freedman, A., Kaplan, H. (Eds.), *Comprehensive Textbook of Psychiatry.* Baltimore: Williams and Wilkins, pp. 1387-1414.

Axelrod, J. (1965). The metabolism, storage and release of catecholamines. *Recent Prog. Horm. Res., 21,* 597.

Bower, T.G.R., Broughton, J.M., Moore, M.K. (1970). Infant responses to approaching objects: An indicator of responses to distal variables. *Percept. Psychophysics, 9,* 193-196.

Bowlby, J. (1973). *Separation Anxiety and Anger.* New York: Basic Books.

Bridges, P.K. (1974). Recent physiological studies of stress and anxiety in man. *Biol. Psychiatry, 8,* 95-112.

Bronson, G.W. (1968). The development of fear in man and other animals. *Child Dev., 39,* 409-431.

Cannon, W.B., de la Paz, D. (1911). Emotional stimulation of adrenal secretion. *Am. J. Physiol., 28,* 64.

Cannon, W.B. (1929). *Bodily Changes in Pain, Hunger, Fear and Rage.* New York: Appleton.

Coolidge, J.C. (1979). School phobia. In Noshpitz, J. (Ed.), *Basic Handbook of Child Psychiatry,* Vol. 2. New York: Basic Books, pp. 453-463.

Eisenberg, L. (1958). School phobia: A study in the communication of anxiety. *Am. J. Psychiatry, 114,* 712-718.

Euler, U.S. von (1958). Some aspects of the role of noradrenaline and adrenaline in the circulation. *Am. Heart J., 56,* 469.

Euler, U.S. von (1966). Twenty years of noradrenaline. *Pharmacol. Rev., 18,* 29.

Freud, S. (1895). Anxiety neurosis. *Standard Edition of the Complete Psychological Works of Sigmund Freud,* Vol. 3, pp. 90-115.

Freud, S. (1905). Three essays on the theory of sexuality. *Standard Edition of the Complete Psychological Works of Sigmund Freud,* Vol. 7, pp. 135-243.

Freud, S. (1909a). Analysis of a phobia in a five-year-old boy. *Standard Edition of the Complete Psychological Works of Sigmund Freud,* Vol. 10, pp. 1-149.

Freud, S. (1909b). Notes upon a case of obsessional neurosis. *Standard Edition of the Complete Psychological Works of Sigmund Freud,* Vol. 10.

Freud, S. (1926). Inhibitions, symptoms and anxiety. *Standard Edition of the Complete Psychological Works of Sigmund Freud,* Vol. 20, pp. 77-175.

Freud, S., Breuer, J. (1895). Studies on hysteria. *Standard Edition of the Complete Psychological Works of Sigmund Freud,* Vol. 2, pp. 1-307.

Gemzell, C. (1977). Effect of stress on conception and early pregnancy. In Kaminetzky, H.A., Iffy, L. (Eds.), *Progress in Perinatology.* Philadelphia: George F. Stickley.

Goltz, F. (1892). Der Hund ohne groszhirn. *Pfluegers Arch. Ges. Physiol., 51,* 570.

Hon, E.H. (1974). Fetal heart rate monitoring. In Gluck, L. (Ed.), *Modern Perinatal Medicine.* Chicago: Year Book Medical Publishers, pp. 139-147.

James, W. (1890). *Principles of Psychology.* New York: Holt.

Janet, P. (1907). *The Major Symptoms of Hysteria.* Second Edition. New York: Macmillan, 1929.

Johnson, A., Falstein, E.I., Szurek, S.A., Suendsen, M. (1941). School phobia. *Am J. Orthopsychiatry, 11,* 702-711.

Keeley, K. (1962). Prenatal influence on behavior of offspring of crowded mice. *Science, 135,* 44-45.

Kierkegaard, S. (1944). *The Concept of Dread.* Translated by Lowrie, W. Princeton: Princeton University Press.

Klein, M. (1952). On the theory of anxiety and guilt. In Riviere, J. (Ed.), *Developments in Psycho-Analysis.* London: Hogarth, pp. 271-291.

Loof, D. (1970). Psychophysiologic and conversion reactions in children: Selective incidence in verbal and nonverbal families. *J. Am. Acad. Child Psychiatry, 9,* 318-331.

Morishima, H.O. Pedersen, H., Finster, M. (1978). The influence of maternal psychological stress on the fetus. *Am. J. Obstet. Gynecol., 131,* 286-290.

Proctor, J.T. (1958). Hysteria in childhood. *Am. J. Orthopsychiatry, 28,* 394-403.

Rank, O. (1924, Eng. trans. 1929). *The Trauma of Birth.* London: Kegan Paul.

Selye, H. (1946). The general adaptation syndrome and the diseases of adaptation. *J. Clin. Endocrinol., 6,* 117.

Selye, H. (1950). *The Physiology and Pathology of Exposure to Stress.* Montreal: Acta.

Shaffii, M. (1974). Short-term psychotherapy in adult school phobia: A transcultural perspective. *Int. J. Psychoanal. Psychother., 3,* 166–177.

Sperling, M. (1961). Analytic first aid in school phobics. *Psychoanal. Q., 30,* 504–518.

Sperling, M. (1967). School phobias: Classification, dynamics, and treatment. In Eissler, R.S., *et al.* (Eds.), *The Psychoanalytic Study of the Child,* Vol. 22. New York: International Universities Press, pp. 375–401.

Thomas, A., Chess, S. (1977). *Temperament and Development.* New York: Brunner/Mazel.

Thompson, W.R., McElroy, L.R. (1962). The effect of maternal presence on open-field behavior in young rats. *J. Comp. Physiol. Psychol., 55,* 827–830.

Watson, J.B. (1919). *Psychology from the Standpoint of a Behaviorist.* Philadelphia: Lippincott.

Chapter 10

ATTENTION-DEFICIT DISORDER AND HYPERACTIVITY

Over the last 40 to 50 years, attention-deficit disorder has been referred to by various names: hyperkinetic behavior syndrome, hyperkinetic impulse disorder, hyperactive child syndrome, minimal brain damage, and minimal brain dysfunction.

Attention-deficit disorder is defined as "... developmentally inappropriate inattention... [and] impulsivity..." (*DSM-III*, 1980, p. 41) Hyperactivity or excessive motor activity significantly decreases during adolescence, although "...difficulties in attention often persist."(ibid., p. 41) Because of the persistence of "difficulties in attention," this disorder is now referred to as attention-deficit disorder (ADD).

HISTORICAL PERSPECTIVE

Heinrich Hoffmann (1844), a German physician, in a poem entitled "Fidgety Phil," vividly described over a century ago a restless youngster who now might be considered hyperactive:

Fidgety Phil
He won't sit still
He wiggles
He giggles..."
and when told off:
The naughty restless child
Grows still more rude and wild.
Weiss and Hechtman, 1979, p. 1348.

Bond and Smith (1935), in a 10-year follow-up of children who had "flu encephalitis" during the epidemic following World War I, described "post-encephalitic behavioral disorders" in a number of these children. Kahn and Cohen (1934) referred to these behavioral disorders as "Organic Drivenness." Today these behavioral disorders would be called attention-deficit disorders with hyperactivity.

Bradley (1937) reported on the effectiveness of Benzedrine on children between ages 5 and 14 years who had a variety of behavioral disorders. One-half of these 30 children showed a significant decrease in aggressive and hyperactive behavior and improvement in school performance while on Benzedrine for one week. As a result of Bradley's pioneer work, clinicians began to recognize the calming effect of psychostimulant medication on hyperactive and inattentive behavior.

Laufer and Denhoff (1957) proposed the term "hyperkinetic impulse disorder" to describe the symptom cluster of hyperactivity, short attention span, poor concentration, variability and unpredictability in behavior, impulsiveness, inability to delay gratification, irritability, explosiveness, and poor school work. They proposed that "...anything which produces dysfunction of the diencephalon and the diencephalocortical interrelations before birth, during birth, or in the first five years of life may result in this syndrome." (ibid., p. 467)

Laufer and Denhoff emphasized the organic nature of this disorder. They adapted a test from Gastaut (1950), the well-known French encephalographer, to substantiate this hypothesis. This test consisted of injecting the patient with Metrazol intravenously, while at the same time stimulating with flashes of light the visual cortex during the EEG recordings. According to Laufer and Denhoff, the threshold for developing the EEG equivalent of convulsive type waves in hyperkinetic children is significantly lower than in normal children, or in children suffering from other types of behavioral disturbances. Based on this test, Laufer and Denhoff conceptualized that the "hyperkinetic syndrome" was due to organic causes. They postulated that "hyperkinetic syndrome" was related to "minimal brain dysfunction," although there was no clinical evidence of specific central nervous system disorder.

CLINICAL FEATURES

Extensive work by Eisenberg (1964, 1966, 1971, 1972, 1973, 1979), Stewart *et al.* (1966), and particularly Keith Conners (1969, 1970, 1971) and Conners *et al.* (1972) helped to develop specific criteria for the diagnosis of hyperkinetic disorder. Conners (1969) designed parent and teacher questionnaires to assess, by the use of factor analysis, the nature and extent of clusters of symptoms and behaviors characteristic of this disorder.

Parent Questionnaire

The parent questionnaire contains 48 symptoms and behaviors to be rated regarding occurrence and intensity, ranging from "0" (not at all) to "3" (very much). The following 10 items are specifically related to and measure hyperactivity:

1. Excitable, impulsive
2. Difficulty in learning
3. Restless in the "squirmy" sense
4. Restless, always up and on the go
5. Fails to finish things
6. Distractibility or attention span a problem
7. Denies mistakes or blames others
8. Childish and immature
9. Mood changes quickly and drastically
10. Easily frustrated in efforts

Teacher Questionnaire

Frequently, the child's hyperactivity causes a major problem in the classroom, and thus the teacher is often the first to notice hyperactive behaviors. Because of this, Conners also developed a questionnaire for teachers. The following 10 behavioral items out of 28 are specific to hyperactivity:

1. Restless in the "squirmy" sense
2. Demands must be met immediately
3. Distractibility or attention span a problem
4. Disturbs other children
5. Restless, always "up and on the go"
6. Excitable, impulsive
7. Fails to finish things that he starts
8. Childish and immature
9. Easily frustrated in efforts
10. Difficulty in learning

A number of follow-up studies, for instance those conducted by Stewart *et al.* (1966), Menkes *et al.* (1967), and Weiss and Hechtman (1979), showed that many hyperactive children decrease hyperactive behaviors as they grow older. Attention deficit, however, continues to be a major problem. Because of these studies, the term "attention-deficit disorder" now has replaced the terms "hyperactivity" or "hyperkinetic impulse disorder."

TYPES OF ATTENTION-DEFICIT DISORDERS

There are three types of attention-deficit disorders.

Attention-Deficit Disorder with Hyperactivity

The following symptoms are present.

Attention Deficit

The significant features of this type are "...developmentally inappropriate inattention, impulsivity, and hyperactivity." (*DSM-III,* p. 41) These children have difficulty organizing and completing school work. They seem to have either not heard the teacher's instructions or have not listened to them. Careless and impulsive errors abound. Omissions, insertions, and misinterpretations are prevalent in reading, writing, arithmetic, and other activities.

In a group setting, for example the classroom, inattention difficulties are significantly increased. However, in a one-to-one situation, they may not be as prominent.

At home, these children have difficulty following parental instructions and frequently move from one activity to another without sustained attention.

Impulsivity

These children frequently act before thinking and need extensive supervision. They have difficulty waiting for their turn.

Hyperactivity

They are often "on the go" and cannot sit still. They run, climb, and move around much more than other children of the same age. In adolescents, gross hyperactivity may decrease, but most remain fidgety and restless.

In a setting that requires sitting down and relative quiescence of body motor activity, for instance in the classroom or in church, hyperactivity is quite noticeable, whereas, in a playground setting, it might not be evident. Some of these children might have excessive movement in sleep. Hyperactive behavior is usually intermittent, increasing in times of stress and excitement.

It is necessary to differentiate overactive children with high energy from hyperactive children. A child with "...hyperactivity tends to be haphazard, poorly organized, and not goal-directed." (ibid., p. 41)

Other Behavioral Disturbances

Low frustration tolerance, temper tantrums, fluctuation in mood, oppositional behaviors, negativism, stubbornness, difficulty in responding to discipline, poor self-esteem, learning and reading disabilities, and school failure are common.

Soft Neurological Signs

A number of authors have discussed the presence of minimal, nonspecific neurological signs in hyperactive children. Laufer and Denhoff (1957) described the inconsistent occurrence of "...scattered reflex changes or cranial nerve abnormalities, such as internal strabismus or central facial weakness." (p. 467)

Waldrop *et al.* (1978) observed "minor anomalies" immediately following birth, such as:

...head circumference out of normal range, more than one hair whorl, fine electric hair, epicanthus, hypertelorism, malformed ears, low-set ears, asymmetrical ears, soft pliable ears, no ear lobes, high steepled palate, furrowed tongue, curved fifth finger, single palmar crease, wide gap between first and second toes, partial syndactalia of toes, and third toe longer than second.

p. 563.

These minor anomalies represent deviation in the development of the central nervous system in the first weeks of gestation. Waldrop *et al.* hypothesized that this deviation "...is responsible for the hyperactive behaviors" at age 3 years of life. (ibid., p. 563)

Nonspecific soft neurological signs that may be present in hyperactive children are: clumsiness, mixed dominance, confusion in right and left laterality, difficulty in rapidly alternating hand movements, difficulty in fine motor coordination, hyperreflexia in a mild form, strabismus or jerkiness in visual tracking, and speech impediments.

Extensive debate exists concerning the presence or absence of soft neurological signs in attention-deficit disorders, the rule of thumb being that the clinician needs to look for clusters of behavioral and neurological signs and symptoms, rather than rely on the presence of one or two signs or symptoms to make the diagnosis. Only 5% of hyperactive children have specific, distinguishable neurological disorders.

Attention-Deficit Disorder Without Hyperactivity

This type of attention-deficit disorder is quite similar to attention-deficit disorder with hyperactivity, the major difference being the absence of hyperactivity. Also, the level of academic disability and psychosocial impairment is milder. The patient has never had a history or signs of hyperactivity.

Attention-Deficit Disorder, Residual Type

The patient has all the signs and symptoms of attention-deficit disorder with hyperactivity, except that hyperactivity does not exist at the present time. Attentional deficits and impulsivity are prevalent without remission. This type of disorder usually is present in adolescents or adults with a history of attention-deficit disorder with hyperactivity.

Inattentiveness, difficulty in concentration, distractibility, disturbance in organizing or completing work, impulsive decisions without thinking, frequent moving from one job to another, and poor academic achievement may impair the individual's psychosocial development and occupational achievement.

ONSET

Commonly, these children come to the attention of clinicians while they are in the first to third grades. A smaller number are identified when they begin nursery school at age 3 years.

Careful developmental history usually reveals that some of these children manifested signs of hyperactivity soon after birth.

PREVALENCE

In the United States, the prevalence of attention-deficit disorders in the prepubertal child is estimated to be between 3 and 10% with the figure of 3 to 4% most commonly accepted. The male to female ratio ranges between 5:1 and 9:1.

This disorder exists all over the world but appears to be more prevalent in the United States. Rutter *et al.* (1970), in the Isle of Wight studies in England, reported a prevalence of 1 per 1,000 in children aged 12 years.

The prevalence varies depending on the criteria the clinician uses for diagnosis. For example, in the United States, most teachers and clinicians quickly label a child "hyperactive" who may have other disorders, such as conduct disorder, learning disabilities, depression, anxiety, psychomotor epilepsy, malnourishment, or hypoglycemia.

ETIOLOGY

Extensive effort has been made to find a specific central nervous system disorder as a cause of attention-deficit disorders.

Laufer *et al.* (1957) reported the presence of nonspecific, fast or slow activity, amplitude asymmetry, and paroxysmal seizure discharges in the EEG's of a large number of hyperactive children. Grunewald-Zuberier *et al.* (1975) "...reported a lower state of EEG arousal, slower development of amplitude reduction to tone, and shorter arousal responses to light stimulus, together with longer latencies of reaction time." (Eisenberg, 1979, p. 444)

Shetty (1971) noticed increase in alpha rhythm in hyperactive children after intravenous injection of psychostimulants. Shetty postulated a disturbance in the inhibitory mechanism of the central nervous system as the basis for hyperkinetic disorders in childhood. He hypothesized that these children cannot "filter-out" the irrelevant stimuli from the relevant stimuli. Their inattention is related to being bombarded by a number of stimuli at the same time. In these children, psychostimulants, such as amphetamines or methylphenidate, increase the inhibitory mechanism of the central nervous system.

Buchsbaum and Wender (1973) found that the EEG auditory-evoked responses of hyperkinetic children appeared much younger and more immature than in the control group. They proposed the theory of maturational lag in these patients.

Surwillo (1977), in developing the histogram of half wave analysis of the EEG recordings of hyperactive male children, found that the EEG histogram appeared much younger than the control group. Methylphenidate improved EEG asymmetry, dysrhythmia, and brought the EEG age closer to the chronological age.

However, according to Eisenberg (1979), who has done extensive work in this area, the EEG findings so far are nonspecific and do not help in the diagnostic assessment of attention deficit disorders.

A number of psychobiological hypotheses have been proposed. Weiss and Hechtman's (1979) comprehensive article entitled "The Hyperactive Child Syndrome" is a useful reference. The authors have summarized the psychobiological postulates of hyperactivity. For instance, Shaywitz *et al.* (1977) have noticed a decreased turnover of dopamine in the central nervous system evidenced by lower concentration of homovanillic acid (HVA) in the cerebrospinal fluid of hyperactive children as compared with normal children after oral ingestion of probenecid. Shekim *et al.* (1977) observed a decrease of norepinephrine and a decrease of MHPG (3-methoxy-4-hydroxyphenyl glycol) in hyperactive children.

Satterfield *et al.* (1974) suggested that hyperactivity in some children might be related to a lower central nervous system arousal level that would contribute to a lower level of inhibition. They believe that the disorganized and disruptive behavior of these children and their relative improvement following the use of psychostimulants is related to this mechanism.

On the other hand, according to Weiss and Hechtman (1979), "Despite the widespread belief that hyperactive children have a disorder in the catecholamine system, there is no conclusive evidence for it." (p. 1350)

FOOD SENSITIVITY

Extensive debate exists concerning whether or not attention deficit disorders and hyperactivity are the result of sensitivity to natural salicylates and artificial food coloring.

Feingold (1976), an allergist, discovered that a number of adult patients when placed on a salicylate-free diet, showed significant behavioral improvement. He applied the same approach to hyperactive children and reported that 50% of these children dramatically improved. Feingold's diet is very stringent. Some foods eliminated include: almonds, apples, berries, grapes, raisins, oranges, tomatoes, cucumbers, and all foods that have artificial coloring and flavoring. In most processed food, tartrazine is used for coloring as a yellow dye and some of the salicylates are used for flavoring. Also eliminated are all cereals with artificial color and flavors, manufactured baked goods, luncheon meats, barbecued meats, candies, chocolates, all soft drinks except 7-Up, butter, margarine, catsup, mustard, and cheese.

A double-blind study of 46 hyperactive boys by Harley *et al.* (1977) in a controlled clinical trial "...failed to confirm Feingold's claims." (Kolata, 1978, p. 516) On the other hand, Conners *et al.*

(1976) found a small group of "...hyperactive children might improve with the diet." (ibid., p. 516)

In clinical practice, we have found that a few parents strongly advocate salicylate, starch, and sugar-free diets for their hyperactive children. Reports from some parents, teachers, and children, along with clinical observations, demonstrate that some children do improve on Feingold's diet in conjunction with other therapeutic methods, such as medication and psychotherapeutic work with the child and the family.

The clinician needs to keep an open mind. Rigid advocacy or condemnation of the food-sensitivity theory will not help the child or the family. In a small number of cases, if the child and the family are interested in or willing to follow such a diet, a clinical trial may be indicated, as long as it does not interfere with physical or psychosocial development.

MANAGEMENT AND TREATMENT

There is a tendency to diagnose incorrectly many children with a variety of emotional problems and family difficulties as "hyperactive." Consequently, psychostimulants are prescribed for these children. First of all, it is essential to diagnose hyperactivity correctly. Psychoeducational management, psychotherapeutic work with the child and the family, and possible use of medication are all essential components of a comprehensive and effective treatment program.

Psychoeducational Management

In cases of attention deficit disorder, it is essential to work closely with the child, the family, and the school.

Careful psychoeducational assessment determines areas of academic strengths and shortcomings. Many of these children, because of a short attention span, cannot sit long enough to read or to solve a mathematical problem. But, if the principles of behavioral modification and positive reinforcement are employed in remedial education with a warm and caring teacher on a one-to-one basis or in a small group setting, these children can improve significantly. For example, an academic task can be divided into several sections, each with a built-in reward. A fail-proof system of learning helps the child, not only in the academic area, but also behaviorally and psychosocially.

Psychotherapeutic Work With the Child and the Parents

Psychotherapeutic work with the child and the parents is essential; medication should not be used as a substitute. The parents need to become aware of the child's assets and liabilities. The therapist works with the parents and helps them become aware of their tendency to blame the child, the school, or themselves.

Consistency, structure, warmth, and genuine reward for the child's accomplishments, however small, improve attention span and increase self-esteem. Hyperactive children need a "time out period to let off steam and energy." When these children are confined, they become more fidgety, restless, and unmanageable. Encouraging activities, such as physical exercise, running around the yard, going out for fresh air, chasing the dog, playing tag or hide and seek, roughhousing, and particularly swimming, helps constructively to channel hyperactive and inattentive behavior.

Frustration, disharmony at home, excitement, and stimulating activities, such as some television programs, increase hyperactivity.

Parents, teachers, and therapists can help hyperactive children observe themselves and recognize what makes them more active. This ability for self-observation, anticipation, and finding effective ways of responding to highly stimulating situations are important steps in helping the child improve inner attention and thinking before being driven to an impulsive act.

Medication

In the last few decades, psychostimulants, such as dextroamphetamines and methylphenidate have been used extensively in the treatment of attention deficit disorder. Approximately 70% of hyperactive children show symptomatic improvement with psychostimulants; 10% need other medication, such as phenothiazine (e.g., Thorazine), thioridazine (Mellaril), or haloperidol (Haldol); and a small number of hyperactive children may benefit from anticonvulsive medication, such as phenytoin (Dilantin).

The use of benzodiazepine and barbiturates, because of their potential disinhibiting effect, are contraindicated. For further discussion, please refer to chapter 23.

Follow-Up and Outcome

Cantwell (1978) found that a large number of impulsive and destructive or alcoholic adults had a history of mild to moderate hyperkinetic disorders in childhood.

Menkes *et al.* (1967), in a 25-year follow-up of 18 hyperkinetic children, found that eight were self-supporting, although four had spent some time in jail or in juvenile detention centers. Four were psychotic and institutionalized, and two were mentally retarded and dependent on their families.

Borland and Heckman (1976) traced 20 male subjects who had been diagnosed as hyperkinetic 20 to 25 years earlier. They compared these men with their brothers. Four manifested antisocial personality, but none of the siblings were antisocial nor did they have psychiatric problems. The hyperactive subjects changed jobs more frequently and were socioeconomically below their brothers or fathers.

Weiss and Hechtman (1979) reported on prospective 5-year follow-up of hyperactive children in the Montreal area.

Despite a decrease of ratings of hyperactivity over a period of five years, as adolescents they continued to be distractible, emotionally immature, and unable to maintain goals, and they had developed a poor self-image.

p. 1352.

These adolescents' school performance was far below grade level compared with a matched control group. They were impulsive, less reflective, and 25% of this 64 patient group manifested delinquent behavior far above the matched control.

In 10 to 12 year's follow-up study of 75 hyperactive subjects without treatment with psychostimulants and 45 controls, Weiss and Hechtman (1979) found the following:

The hyperactive subjects had a significantly more impulsive life-style, as suggested by a higher rate of geographic moves and car and motorcycle accidents, and inferior results on cognitive style tests.

ibid., p. 1352.

The hyperactive group was one year behind the controls in the area of completed education. However, there was no difference regarding drug abuse. There were more court referrals for the hyperactive subjects during the preceding 5 years. None of the subjects was psychotic; two of the hyperactive subjects were considered borderline psychotic, and also two had died in car accidents, as opposed to none of the control group.

REFERENCES

American Psychiatric Association (1980). *Diagnostic and Statistical Manual of Mental Disorders.* Third Edition. Washington, D.C.: American Psychiatric Association.

Bond, E.D., Smith, L.H. (1935). Post-encephalitic behavior disorders: A ten-year review of the Franklin School. *Am. J. Psychiatry, 92,* 17–31.

Borland, B.L., Heckman, H.I. (1976). Hyperactive boys and their brothers: A 25-year follow-up study. *Arch. Gen. Psychiatry, 33,* 669–675.

Bradley, C. (1937). The behavior of children receiving Benzedrine. *Am. J. Psychiatry, 94,* 577–585.

Buchsbaum, M., Wender, P. (1973). Average evoked responses in normal and minimal brain-dysfunctioned children treated with amphetamine. *Arch. Gen. Psychiatry, 29,* 764–770.

Cantwell, D.P. (1978). Hyperactivity and antisocial behavior, *J. Am. Acad. Child Psychiatry, 17,* 252–262.

Conners, C.K. (1969). A teacher rating scale for use in drug studies with children. *Am. J. Psychiatry, 126,* 884–888.

Conners, C.K. (1970). Symptom patterns in hyperkinetic, neurotic, and normal children. *Child Dev., 41,* 667–682.

Conners, C.K. (1971). Recent drug studies with hyperkinetic children. *J. Learning Disabilities, 4,* 476–483.

Conners, C.K., Taylor, E., Meo, G., *et al.* (1972). Magnesium pemoline and dextroamphetamine: A controlled study in children with minimal brain dysfunction. *Psychopharmacologia, 26,* 321–336.

Conners, C.K., Goyette, C.H., Southwick, D.A., Lees, J.M., Andrulonis, P.A. (1976). Food additives and hyperkinesis: A controlled double-blind experiment. *Pediatrics, 58,* 154–166.

Eisenberg, L. (1964). Behavioral manifestations of cerebral damage in childhood. In Birch, H.G. (Ed.), *Brain Damage in Children.* Baltimore: Williams and Wilkins, pp. 61–72.

Eisenberg, L. (1966). The management of the hyperkinetic child. *Dev. Med. Child Neurol., 8,* 593–598.

Eisenberg, L. (1971). Principles of drug therapy in child psychiatry with special reference to stimulant drugs. *Am. J. Orthopsychiatry, 41,* 371–379.

Eisenberg, L. (1972). The clinical use of stimulant drugs in children. *Pediatrics, 49,* 709–715.

Eisenberg, L. (1973). The overactive child. *Hosp. Pract., 8,* 151–160.

Eisenberg, L. (1979). Hyperkinetic reactions. In Noshpitz, J. (Ed.), *Basic Handbook of Child Psychiatry,* Vol. 2. New York: Basic Books, pp. 439–453.

Feingold, B.F. (1976). Hyperkinesis and learning disabilities linked to the ingestion of artificial food colors and flavors. *J. Learning Disorders, 9,* 19–27.

Gaustaut, H. (1950). Combined photic and Metrazol activation of the brain. *Electroencephalogr. Clin. Neurophysiol., 2,* 249.

Grunewald-Zuberier, E., Grunewald, G., Rasche, A. (1975). Hyperactive behavior and EEG arousal reactions in children. *Electroencephalogr. Clin. Neurophysiol., 38,* 149–159.

Harley, J.P., Tomasi, L., Ray, R.S., *et al.* (1977). *An Experimental Evaluation of Hyperactivity and Food Additives: Phase I.* Madison: Food Research Institute, University of Wisconsin.

Kahn, E., Cohen, L.H. (1934). Organic drivenness: A brain stem syndrome and an experience. *N. Engl. J. Med., 210,* 748–756.

Kolata, G.B. (1978). Childhood hyperactivity: A new look at treatments and causes. *Science, 199,* 515–517.

Laufer, M.W., Denhoff, E. (1957). Hyperkinetic behavior syndrome in children. *J. Pediatr., 50,* 463–474.

Menkes, M.M., Rowe, J.S., Menkes, J.H. (1967). A 25-year

follow-up study on the hyperkinetic child with minimal brain dysfunction. *Pediatrics, 39,* 393–399.

Rutter, M., Graham, P., Yule, W. (1970). *A Neuropsychiatric Study in Children.* London: Heinemann.

Satterfield, J.H., Cantwell, D.P., Satterfield, B.J. (1974). Pathophysiology of the hyperactive child syndrome. *Arch. Gen. Psychiatry, 31,* 839–844.

Shaywitz, B.A., Cohen, D.J., Bowers, M.B., Jr. (1977). CSF monoamine metabolites in children with minimal brain dysfunction: Evidence for alteration of brain dopamine. A preliminary report. *J. Pediatr., 90,* 67–71.

Shekim, W.O., Dekirmenjian, H., Chapel, J.L. (1977). Urinary catecholamine metabolites in hyperkinetic boys treated with d-amphetamine. *Am. J. Psychiatry, 134,* 1276–1279.

Shetty, T. (1971). Alpha rhythms in the hyperkinetic child. *Nature, 234,* 476.

Stewart, M.A., Pitts, F.N., Jr., Craig, A.G., *et al.* (1966). The hyperactive child syndrome. *Am. J. Orthopsychiatry, 36,* 861–867.

Surwillo, W.W. (1977). Changes in the electroencephalogram accompanying the use of stimulant drugs (methylphenidate and dextroamphetamine) in hyperactive children. *Biol. Psychiatry, 12,* 787–797.

Waldrop, M.F., Bell, R.Q., McLaughlin, B., Halverson, C.F. (1978). Newborn minor physical anomalies predict short attention span, peer aggression, and impulsivity at age 3. *Science, 199,* 563–565.

Weiss, G., Hechtman, L. (1979). The hyperactive child syndrome. *Science, 205,* 1348–1354.

Chapter 11

CONDUCT, PERSONALITY, AND BORDERLINE DISORDERS

CONDUCT DISORDERS

Conduct disorders, or behavioral disorders, in children and adolescents are referred to in *DSM-III* (1980) as:

> ...a repetitive and persistent pattern of conduct in which either the basic rights of others or major age-appropriate societal norms or rules are violated. The conduct is more serious than the ordinary mischief and pranks of children and adolescents.
>
> p. 45.

Historical Perspective

Conduct disorders, previously referred to as behavioral disorders, have been the major concern of clinicians, law enforcement officers, and reform and rehabilitation agencies for more than a century.

During the early nineteenth century, antisocial behavior of children and adolescents, such as minor stealing, was punished harshly and mercilessly. For instance, Meeks (1979) reported, "...in the early nineteenth century, a ten-year-old child was hanged in England for stealing a letter from a mail box." (p. 484)

In the United States, during the latter part of the nineteenth century, with mass immigration, industrialization, increased urbanization, and economic and family dislocation, there was an increased incidence of juvenile delinquency. By the end of the nineteenth century, the need for separate legal management and treatment of juvenile offenders, as opposed to adult offenders, led, in the 1890's, to the establishment of the first juvenile courts.

The child guidance clinic movement and the discipline of child psychiatry began in the early part of the twentieth century for the treatment and rehabilitation of juvenile delinquents. Healy and Bronner (1936) wrote their famous book on delinquency, and established the Institute for Juvenile Research in Chicago in 1909. Within a short time, Boston, Philadelphia, and Louisville followed suit, creating and developing child guidance clinics to provide guidance and counseling to delinquent and emotionally troubled youth.

Also, during this time, August Aichhorn integrated psychoanalytic concepts of human development and treatment and established a residential program for delinquents in Austria. The outcome was published in Aichhorn's now classic *Wayward Youth* (1925).

In the 1910's and 1920's, emphasis gradually shifted from severe, harsh punishment to psycho-educational assessment of troubled young persons and their families. Juvenile homes, training schools, and psychiatric programs were established.

Delinquency and antisocial behavior began to be conceptualized as forms of emotional disorder and severe psychopathology, stemming from a child's reaction to inconsistent and disorganized, or severely harsh family upbringing, as well as societal mismanagement.

Recently, with the increased incidence of severe, antisocial behavior, such as stealing, breaking and entering, assault, drug abuse, the use of firearms, and homicide, the juvenile court system and associated treatment and rehabilitation programs for youth have come under sharp and sustained attack from both youth advocacy and conservative law and order groups.

Conduct Disorders Versus Personality Disorders

The terms "behavioral" and "conduct" disorders, as applied to children and youth, imply that these conducts and behaviors are more or less temporary, and sooner or later will diminish. The term "personality disorder" refers, on the other hand, to maladaptive traits and enduring patterns

129

that are more or less fixed. Conduct disorders in youth, if continued, will result in personality disorders in adulthood. However, there are some disorders of personality which do begin to manifest in childhood or adolescence. Most clinicians working with children and youth are reluctant to use the term "personality disorder."

Aggression and Conduct Disorders

Aggression plays a significant role in the development, sustenance, and types of conduct disorders. Freud (1923), in *The Ego and the Id,* proposed the existence of two basic instincts in human beings: *eros,* libido, the life, love, and sexual instinct, and the opposite, *thanatos,* or death instinct. The concept of death instinct was modified by Hartmann, Anna Freud, and others, and eventually became conceptualized as the aggressive drive. Destructive behavior in childhood and adolescence, such as physically hurting others, destroying property, antisocial behavior, and homicidal behavior, are pathological expressions of the aggressive drive.

According to psychoanalytic theory and the work of ethologists, such as Lorenz, the aggressive drive is biologically essential for species survival. In human beings, the aggressive drive is tamed and constructively channeled—from a tendency toward intraspecies destruction to adaptive behavior—through the establishment of a solid human bond: mother-child attachment. (See chapter 1)

Fractures in the human bond, disorganization in the family, poor parenting, and disorders in mothering interfere with the development of caring attitudes and respect for other human beings and societal rules. This lack of care and respect may manifest itself in the form of delinquent and antisocial behavior.

Destructiveness as a Learned Behavior

Behaviorists and learning theorists question the instinctive nature of aggression. (Dollard and Miller, 1950) They suggest that aggression is a learned behavior in response to frustration. No doubt, economic dislocation, poverty, racial prejudism, movement from rural areas to urban ghettos, drug and alcohol abuse, child abuse and neglect, and parental violence contribute to the increased incidence of destructive and antisocial behavior in children and youth.

In recent years, there has been extensive debate concerning the effects of the portrayal of violence in the media—particularly on television and in movies—on perpetuating violent and antisocial behavior in children and youth. It is estimated that most children and adolescents in the United States, by ages 13 and 14 years, have witnessed approximately 14,000 episodes of murder on television. In many families, television has assumed the parental role of occupying children's time and keeping them quiet.

In a vulnerable child, or in an economically dislocated and violence-prone family, the violence seen on television may become an added reinforcement for the expression of destructive behavior. The easy availability of firearms further contributes to this alarming psychosocial problem.

Prevalence

Approximately 20% of all boys between the ages of 10 and 17 years appear in juvenile courts, and 2% of all children and adolescents are ruled legally delinquent. (Harrison and McDermott, 1972, p. 505)

Status Offenders Versus Criminal Offenders

The clinician needs to differentiate between status offenders and criminal offenders. A status offense refers to a behavior that is illegal for youth under the age of 18 years, who are legally minors; however, the same behavior would not be considered illegal if committed by an adult. Examples of status offenses would include running away from home, truancy from school, incorrigibility, and curfew violations (in some states, minors must be accompanied by adults after 11:00 P.M.).

A criminal offense, on the other hand, refers to an act of aggression or violence toward another person or property, such as stealing, vandalism, breaking and entering, shoplifting, physical assault, or injury, sexual abuse, rape, homicide, and drug or alcohol abuse.

At the present time, the juvenile justice system and juvenile courts are under considerable criticism. Some groups feel strongly that the juvenile court system is "too lenient" toward youth criminal offenders. These critics propose that youth criminal offenders be tried in adult courts and that the juvenile justice system be abolished.

On the other hand, a number of youth advocacy groups, which are concerned with the legal rights of children and youth, strongly insist that all children and youth have legal counsel in juvenile courts (following the United States Supreme Court ruling concerning Gault's Case). These youth advocates propose that status offenders be separated from criminal offenders. In their opinion, status offenders should not come to the attention of juvenile courts, nor should they be incarcerated in juvenile homes or training schools in close proximity with youth criminal offenders. Such an approach, it is felt, would decrease the case load of the already overburdened juvenile court system, and focus the courts' attention on assessment, disposition, and rehabilitation of youth criminal offenders.

Violence in Children and Youth

In the Child Psychiatric Services, University of Louisville School of Medicine, out of 994 cases of children and adolescents between the ages of 1 and 18 years, who were seen on an emergency basis from 1973 to 1978, 305, or approximately 31%, exhibited *harmful or destructive behavior toward others*. This means

> ...attempting to harm or actually harming others; threatening to kill or seriously harm others; violent destructive behavior; fire-setting; being beyond the control of parents, teachers, or other authority figures; and serious antisocial behavior, including sexual assault on others.
>
> Shafii *et al.*, 1979, p. 1600.

Age and sex distribution of these 305 cases are listed in Table 11–1.

TABLE 11–1   **Age and Sex of 305 Emergency Cases Exhibiting Destructive Behavior Toward Others**

Age, yr.	Male, %	Female, %
1–6	20	5
7–12	35	10
13–18	23	7
Total	78	22

It is clear that in all age groups the male ratio is significantly higher than the female ratio (p < 0.001). However, the apparent decrease in the 13- to 18-year age group is probably due to the fact that Child Psychiatric Services usually serves patients who are under age 16 years.

In 994 child and adolescent emergency cases, 34% were suicidal or self-destructive and 31% were harmful or destructive toward others. It is evident that 65%, or approximately two-thirds, of all cases seen on an emergency basis were related to aggressive and destructive behavior toward the self or others.

Types of Conduct Disorders

Undersocialized, Aggressive

Undersocialized means that the child or adolescent has not developed sufficient social bonds with other human beings and that there is a lack of affection and empathy toward others. Relationships with peers do not exist, or function only on a very superficial level. The child is egocentric and selfish. He does not care for others, nor does he extend himself to others, unless he sees "an immediate advantage" in doing so. The youth manipulates others to get anything he can from them without giving anything in return. There is either no or very little guilt or remorse. The individual has a tendency to blame others for everything.

Aggressiveness manifests itself in the form of physical violence toward other human beings or property. This violence is usually unprovoked. Vandalism, rape, breaking and entering, fire-setting, mugging, and assault are common behaviors. Theft of property outside of the family, in the form of armed robbery, purse-snatching, and extortion occur frequently.

If an individual shows some of these behaviors repetitively and persistently over a period of 6 months or longer, he would be diagnosed as conduct disorder, undersocialized, aggressive. (*DSM-III*, 1980)

Undersocialized, Nonaggressive

In this type of conduct disorder, the youth violates the basic rights of others, but not in a directly aggressive or destructive way. The youth has the same difficulty in establishing human and social bonds with others, along with antisocial behaviors, such as truancy from home or school, substance abuse, running away from home overnight, and persistent lying and stealing without confrontation with the victim.

Socialized, Aggressive

The child or adolescent has developed social attachments and bonds with others. He differentiates between his own group, friends, family, neighborhood, and gang, as opposed to "outsiders." The child or adolescent usually does not perform antisocial behaviors toward his own group, but justifies his delinquent behavior against "outsiders." He may be quite manipulative, callous, and lack guilt feelings when dealing with outsiders.

Physical violence and theft in this group is the same as in the undersocialized, aggressive group, but the difference is the evidence of social attachment. The youth extends himself toward others without expectation of immediate advantage and does experience guilt or remorse, especially toward persons with whom he has developed attachment. He is concerned about and cares for his friends and companions.

Socialized, Nonaggressive

This type of conduct disorder is quite similar to the socialized, aggressive type of disorder, except that the antisocial behavior is not related to direct acts of violence or aggression. Persistent truancy, substance abuse, chronic running away from home, and stealing without confrontation with the victim occur.

Differential Diagnosis of Conduct Disorders

The four categories just discussed are new classifications of behavioral disorders in *DSM-III*. Two major parameters help in the differentiation of conduct disorders:

1. Ability or failure to establish a human or social bond
2. Presence or absence of repeated and direct acts of violence or aggression

In conduct disorders, the following additional symptoms may be present: poor school performance, academic disability, tendency toward temper outbursts, low frustration tolerance, provocative behavior, mistrustful behavior, acting out behavior—in the form of precocious sexual activity and aggressivity—early smoking, and drinking or substance abuse. Some of these patients may also suffer from attention deficit disorders. (see chapter 10)

In the differential diagnosis of conduct disorders in childhood and adolescence, the clinician needs to be cognizant that antisocial and delinquent behaviors may be symptomatic expressions of the following psychopathological disorders: depressive disorders, psychotic or borderline personality, psychoneurotic disturbances, and organic central nervous system disorders, such as grand mal seizures or psychomotor epilepsy.

Careful assessment of the child and the family, and a history of anxiety, phobia and depression, thought disorders, or seizure disorder and insult to the central nervous system may help to clarify the diagnosis.

Delinquency and Psychomotor Epilepsy

Lewis (1976) found that 6% of 285 children and adolescents, who were referred for psychiatric evaluation within a juvenile court setting, demonstrated symptoms of psychomotor epilepsy. This prevalence is approximately 20 times higher than the prevalence in the general population for all forms of epilepsy. This group demonstrated a triad of delinquency, psychomotor epilepsy, and paranoid behavior. Eight of these children had committed an offense against other persons, and two had committed murder. Fourteen out of 18 children had a history of severely episodic aggressive behavior. The author felt that central nervous system disorders, particularly psychomotor epilepsy, may significantly contribute to the development of delinquency, antisocial behavior, and paranoid symptomatology, and result in severe destructive behavior toward other persons and property.

Follow-Up

Robbins (1966) reported on a 30-year follow-up study of 524 children who were seen in a child guidance clinic because of "sociopathic" or antisocial behavior. As these children grew up, 22% of them—compared with 2% of the control group—manifested sociopathic personalities in adulthood. Children with running away behavior continued to do poorly in adulthood, and approximately one-third of them manifested sociopathic personalities.

Jenkins (1980) reported on the tendency to overlook extensive psychopathological disturbance and potential antisocial behavior in children and adolescents who are status offenders, particularly the runaway group. For instance, he reported on a 10-year follow-up study of 236 runaway youth and 90 youth who had been arrested because they had committed felonies. Sixty-four percent of the runaway group returned to the training school for parole violation, as opposed to 24% of the felony group. Also, 61% of the runaways were convicted in adult courts for a variety of criminal offenses, as opposed to 40% of the felony group in adult life. Jenkins concluded that, as a whole, the "…felony group did much better than the runaway group." (p. 322)

Kashani *et al.* (1980) reported on the "patterns of delinquency" in girls and boys in 184 cases committed to the juvenile justice center in a midwestern state for a period of one year, 1977-1978. The age range was from 8 to 17 years. The male to female ratio was 3:2, the white male to female ratio was much closer, 8:6, as opposed to the black male to female ratio, which was 3:1. Kashani *et al.* concluded that delinquency "…was greater among black than white juveniles," taking into consideration the racial distribution in the community. (p. 307) They also noticed that there was a trend demonstrating that "...the number of white female delinquents is approaching that of white males..." as opposed to blacks. (ibid., p. 307) In the 1960s and 1970s, it was estimated that the ratio of male to female delinquency was 4 or 5:1.

Psychodynamics of Conduct Disorders

Adelaide Johnson (1949) discussed the concept of "superego lacunae," meaning that there are weaknesses and holes in the superegos of parents which are disguised through a variety of defensive maneuvers. Children and adolescents frequently perceive the subtle antisocial messages of their parents, and act out openly against the outward norm and moral code of the family.

Redl (1951, 1957) and Redl and Wineman (1951), in their classic works *Children Who Hate* and *The Aggressive Child,* wrote extensively about specific ego disturbances in delinquent youth, including deficiency in impulse control, defects in reality testing, low frustration tolerance, psychological intoxication in delinquent group settings, insecurity, fear, anxiety, and disorganization. They developed the technique of "life-space interview" to deal immediately and effectively with the acting-out behavior of delinquent youth, with firmness and empathy.

Eissler (1949) in *Searchlights on Delinquency* emphasized that delinquent behavior should be assessed based on the intrapsychic and the internal significance of the delinquent behavior to the youth, rather than on legal standards or definitions.

Finch (1962) related delinquency to psychosocial conflicts within the family. He emphasized effective total intervention, from an educational, family, and intrapsychic point of view, for treating delinquent youth.

PERSONALITY DISORDERS

Specific personality disorders begin clinical expression in childhood and adolescence, and include:

1. Oppositional disorder
2. Avoidance disorder
3. Schizoid disorder
4. Borderline personality disorder (borderline psychosis)

Oppositional and avoidance disorders have been discussed in chapter 9.

Schizoid Disorder

Schizoid disorder usually manifests itself between the ages of 4 and 5 years and becomes progressively worse as the child reaches adolescence. "The essential feature is a defect in the capacity to form social relationships..." (*DSM-III,* 1980, p. 60) in a child who is not psychotic, schizophrenic, suffering from conduct disorders, or pervasive developmental disorder, i.e., childhood autism.

Social Isolation and Aloneness

Children with schizoid disorder are loners. They do not have any close friends. They are socially isolated, and this does not distress them. They are awkward, clumsy, and quite inept in social situations, and generally are withdrawn and aloof. They are not active in group activities such as sports, extracurricular activities, and outdoor activities.

These children may also show aggressive outbursts or temper tantrums when they are forced to participate in group interactions. They are hypersensitive and are usually very critical of themselves and others. Because of their awkwardness and ineptness in social relationships, they are often scapegoated and become the "laughing-stock" of their peers. Frequently, they are preoccupied with daydreams. They may have special interests in mechanical objects, space sciences, supernatural, unusual, and out-of-the-ordinary issues, and these interests reinforce their sense of isolation and aloneness.

Reality Testing, Destructive Fantasies, and Outbursts

Reality testing is usually intact. There is no evidence of hallucinations, delusions, or illusions. Internally, many of these children have a feeling of a void or emptiness. Often they are preoccupied with violence or destructive fantasies. They usually do not show emotions or feelings, except on occasions in the form of volcanic, destructive explosions.

Generally, they do not appear depressed or sad. At times, they show some signs of anxiety or nervousness, in the form of nail-biting, hair-pulling, rocking, pacing, or chain-smoking. Many are not aware of feelings of anxiety. Some are acute observers, and in a detached manner can see minute things going on around them. This acute observational ability and hypersensitivity frequently are used to rationalize and reinforce social isolation.

Follow-Up

Schizoid disorder is more frequent in boys than in girls. The degree of impairment is related to intellectual ability and the family support system. Some finish high school and go on to college, often to pursue technical or scientific fields that do not require social interaction. They usually function fairly well in an isolated setting. The "absent-minded, mad scientist" epitomizes some of the more successful ones.

In many cases, because of lack of social and academic skill, failure in learning and occupation is prevalent. These young people function marginally and drift from one place to another, without roots or social attachment. Some, under stressful situations, may disintegrate and manifest signs of borderline personality disorder, schizophrenia, or act out their destructive fantasies in the form of homicide or suicide.

A smaller number of this group, in a supportive family environment, with long-term outpatient psychotherapeutic care, are able to overcome their tendency toward social isolation and in late adolescence and adulthood become relatively free of symptoms.

BORDERLINE PERSONALITY DISORDER
(Borderline Psychosis)

Definition

Numerous terms describe the clinical condition now referred to as borderline personality disorder. Oberndorf (1930) used "borderline cases" to define a clinical condition between severe neuroses and milder psychoses. Glover (1932) used "borderline states" for a patient who has "one foot in the psychoses and the other in the neuroses." (p. 841) Zilboorg (1941) used "ambulatory schizophrenias" to describe borderline cases, incipient schizophrenias, and schizoid personalities. Deutsch (1942) used "as-if" personality for a patient who is passive, suggestible, and mimics the identity of others in an "automaton-like" manner. Deutsch felt that such a patient should not be called psychotic because reality testing is intact. During the last 40 years, the terms "schizophreniform," "incipient schizophrenia," "pre-psychosis," "latent schizophrenia," "schizasthenia," "ambulatory schizophrenia," "pseudoneurotic schizophrenia," and "narcissistic personality disorder" have been used synonymously with borderline.

Ekstein (1966) perceived the borderline condition as a fluctuation in ego states. Kernberg (1967) conceptualized borderline as a stable form of pathological personality organization. Grinker

et al. (1968) viewed borderline as a syndrome. Masterson (1976) proposed that borderline was a personality disorder with roots in developmental disturbances during the second year of life (subphase of rapprochement of the separation-individuation process). Spitzer and Endicott (1979) attempted to develop criteria to differentiate borderline personality from schizotypal personality disorder.

Diagnostic Interview for Borderline

Gunderson and Singer (1975) and Gunderson and Kolb (1978) developed a semistructured Diagnostic Interview for Borderline (DIB) for adults, to differentiate the clinical entity of borderline personality disorder. Soloff and Ulrich (1981) duplicated Gunderson and Kolb's studies and through cluster analysis and analysis of variance found that 19 items of the DIB discriminated borderline patients from depressive disorders, schizophrenia, and other types of psychopathology. (p. 690)

Some of these items are:

INTERPERSONAL RELATIONS CHARACTERIZED BY:

1. Intense, unstable relationships
2. Devaluation, manipulation, hostility
3. Dependency, masochism
4. Conflict over giving or receiving

IMPULSE ACTION PATTERNS.

1. Manipulative suicide threat or effort
2. Drug abuse
3. Promiscuity, homosexuality, sexual deviance
4. Runaway, assaults, antisocial acts

AFFECTS.

1. Demanding
2. Chronic dysphoria, emptiness, loneliness
3. Angry, hot-tempered, sarcastic

PSYCHOSIS.

1. Experiences derealization, depersonalization
2. Brief psychotic or depressed experiences
3. Transient psychosis in psychotherapy
4. Psychotic experiences with the use of marijuana or alcohol

Studies of Borderline in Children and Adolescents

Geleerd (1946), in her classic paper "A Contribution to the Problem of Psychoses in

Childhood," referred to a type of psychotic behavior in children which is now called borderline personality disorder.

> Often, [these children] when they feel frustrated, they have serious temper tantrums which differ from those of the normal or neurotic child. Their aggressive behavior is more dangerous to both the child and his environment. The child is out of contact with reality and believes himself to be persecuted. He cannot control his aggressive behavior as the more normal child can if he wishes, nor does he react favorably to firm handling as the neurotic child does. This child, on the contrary, becomes more paranoid when treated with firmness. He considers it proof of his paranoid ideas. But a loving, soothing attitude of a familiar, affectionate adult will bring him back to normal behavior.
>
> p. 272.

According to Geleerd, these children show little interest in playing with other children. They are extremely interested in animals, such as dogs, cats, frogs, snakes, and turtles. At times, they are quite cruel to these animals. Frequently, they have intensive or excessive interest in inanimate objects, such as cars, trains, spaceships, rockets, washing machines, and heating plants. At times, they have extraordinary knowledge in a particular area of special interest.

Mahler *et al.* (1949) divided childhood psychosis into malignant and benign types. In malignant types, the personality disturbance and ego defect were severe. In the benign form, the psychotic manifestations were insidious and the ego functions, for the most part, remained intact. These children "...*could employ neurosislike defense mechanisms,* and therefore there was a greater chance for the arrest of, and for a partial recovery from, the disorganizing psychotic process." (p. 302)

Following the pioneer works of Geleerd and Mahler, interest in describing the clinical features and developmental conflicts of borderline psychosis in children and adolescents increased. Ekstein and Wallerstein (1954) observed borderline and psychotic children and made detailed and vivid clinical descriptions, conceptualized a psychodynamic formulation, and developed a psychotherapeutic approach for treating these children. Ekstein's contribution culminated in the publication of a book entitled *Children of Time and Space, of Action and Impulse* (1966). This book is essential reading for those who work with emotionally troubled children, particularly borderline or psychotic children.

Weil (1953, 1956), Geleerd (1958), Cain (1964), Rosenfeld and Sprince (1965), Chethik and Fast (1970), Chethik and Spindler (1971), Fast (1972), Pine (1974), and Masterson (1975, 1976) have also contributed significantly to the clinical description, treatment, and management of borderline disorder in children and youth.

Kernberg (1967) discussed the borderline condition as a stable type of pathological personality organization, with the significant feature being the instability of symptomatic constellations, such as diffuse anxiety, polysymptomatic neurosis, prepsychotic character pathology, and nonspecific ego weaknesses in the form of a shift toward primary process thinking on the one hand, and specific primitive defense mechanisms, such as splitting, primitive idealization, early forms of projection, denial, omnipotence, and a particular pathological form of internalized object relations on the other.

Clinical Features

The borderline child usually comes to the attention of the clinician during latency or adolescence, or occasionally when the child is in nursery school or kindergarten. The prevalence of borderline personality disorder is much more common than earlier believed and more frequent than childhood schizophrenia and childhood autism. The exact percentage of prevalence is not known.

Intense and Overwhelming Anxiety

Borderline children experience overwhelming internal anxiety, which expresses itself in the form of restlessness, hyperactivity, jitteriness, and panic reaction. At times, they show psychophysiological distress, such as loss of appetite, nausea, vomiting, diarrhea, and increase in heartbeat and respiration. Their anxiety is usually contagious and escalates. Parents frequently react with feelings of helplessness and become overly anxious. Minor events, such as lack of approval, discipline, frustration, paying attention to another child, and minor falls and scratches result in catastrophic reactions. The child cries intensely, becomes agitated, and parental reassurance usually does not have immediate effect.

These children do not seem to experience *signal anxiety,* and, therefore, they do not anticipate stress and automatically modulate their responses in relationship to the degree of stress. Each disappointing or stressful situation is a catastrophic event, and anxiety is experienced in the form of *traumatic anxiety* and panic reaction rather than adaptive signal anxiety.

Initially, anxiety is free-floating, but eventually leads to withdrawal to the world of fantasy or severe temper tantrums and hostile, destructive, impulsive behavior. These behaviors partially discharge the intense feelings of anxiety.

Impulsive Behavior

The borderline child frequently manifests destructive and hostile behavior in the form of biting, kicking, scratching, and spitting at others, especially parents, siblings, or peers; cruelty to animals, particularly to cherished pets, is common.

Self-destructive behavior, such as scratching, biting, or kicking oneself occurs concomitantly with destructive behavior toward others. Sometimes the borderline child is impervious to physical danger and, in a moment of impulse, actively manifests suicidal behavior.

Autoerotic behavior, such as thumb-sucking, rubbing one's skin, mouthing, genital masturbation, rocking, and rubbing the legs against each other or against someone else occurs frequently, with little inhibition. The borderline child may suddenly gorge himself in a frenzy of overeating beyond the need for satiation. Bodily orifices, such as the mouth, nose, ears, and anus become the foci for autoerotic stimulation.

Hostile, destructive, or overt sexual behaviors are often the symptoms that create concern, overreaction, anger, and dismay in parents and school authorities and result in referral to a child psychiatric setting.

Disturbance in Human Relationships

Although borderline children do not usually come to the attention of clinicians for disturbances in human relationships, the developmental history often reveals long-standing problems in this area.

In most cases, intense ambivalence exists between the borderline child and his parents, particularly the mother. The child clings to his mother, whines, cries, and pouts. Frequently, the parents may say that the child is

...usually demanding, unreasonable, and never satisfied. As long as you give in to him he is happy and content and acts like an angel—but, as soon as you say "no" to him, it is the end of the world. He throws temper tantrums, becomes pouty, or goes to his room and sulks there for a long time. If we punish him, he goes into a frenzy and thinks we are killing him.

These children often do not have any friends and are lonely and isolated. At times, because of parental pressure or extreme loneliness, they attempt to relate to other children, but do so in a clumsy manner. They try to "buy" friends by giving away their prized objects. They usually are the scapegoats of their peer groups, "laughing stock" of the neighborhood, or they "play crazy" to reinforce the image of the "crazy weirdo kid" on the block.

The older borderline child may associate with a much younger child. In this relationship, he treats the younger child like a pet or toy to be used or abused without feeling or empathy. Occasionally, the borderline child comes to the clinician's attention because of physical or sexual abuse of younger children.

In human relationships the borderline child may function in an autisticlike manner or as though no one else exists; at the same time, he may form pathologically dyadic relationships with adults and behave in a clinging, overly dependent manner. The borderline child acts in an omnipotent, demanding, controlling manner. The grown-up exists only to fulfill his needs. At times, the borderline child is loving and giving, but, with minor disappointment, he quickly becomes hostile, aggressive, demanding, and paranoid. Underlying a facade of omnipotence, the borderline child is often unhappy, lonely, insecure, and impotent. He feels rejected, badly hurt, or literally destroyed when an adult does not immediately agree to all of his demands.

Thought Process

The neurotic child is usually inhibited and represses troublesome fantasies, daydreams, and dreams. After a period of psychotherapy, the child may be gradually able to modify the repressive defense mechanisms and share his fantasies with the therapist. The psychotic child—depending on the intensity of psychosis—may show a poverty of ideas or frequently express and act out his primitive fantasies in a disorganized, autistic manner, without elaboration or rich symbolism.

The borderline child's fantasies are rich, elaborate, and full of metaphor and symbolism. Fantasy frequently is a source of pleasure and retreat from the frustration of daily reality, and, because of this, the child is often addicted to his fantasies. The fantasies are gratifying but, at times, frightening. The borderline child has an ability to translate his primitive fantasies into a relatively coherent form of communication thinly veneered with secondary process thinking. The fantasies have an *all or none quality*. They are like dreams in wakefulness, although the child usually does not have visual or auditory hallucinations, or an extensive delusional system. The themes of power, magic, omnipotence, omniscience, becoming invisible, space travel, control of others, destruction of the world, explosion, death, and rebirth prevail.

Fluidity of thought processes is characteristic of the borderline child. In one moment, he can be totally immersed in the most bizarre, psychoticlike fantasy, and, in the next, communicating on a fairly well-put-together, reasonable, and age-appropriate level. This quality of rapid fluctuation is pathognomic of the thought processes of the borderline child. These children claim that they can turn fantasies on and off at will. However, when they are alone or frustrated, they automatically withdraw to the world of fantasy and make-believe. Daydreaming and automatic withdrawal to the fantasy world results in inattentiveness in school and learning disturbances and behavioral problems.

In normal children between ages 3 and 6 years the prevalence of fantasy and make-believe is developmentally appropriate and adaptive for mastery of internal conflicts and preparation for social interaction. In the borderline child over-preoccupation with and withdrawal to the world of fantasy become forms of pathological retreat and psychological fixation, resulting in arrest of development.

Disorders of Identity

Gender identity—knowing whether one is a boy or a girl—is usually firmly established between ages 2 and 2½ years. Awareness of one's own name occurs even earlier. Identification with parents and family is consolidated between ages 3 and 6 years.

The borderline child clinically exhibits fluidity of identity. At one moment he is himself, and his family relationships are age-appropriate. At the next moment, he believes he is someone else and tries to act and behave in a totally different manner. The confusion in gender identity is frequently disturbing to parents. Occasionally, the child may dress as a member of the opposite sex. Cross-dressing or wearing parents' clothing is dissimilar to the "dressing up" of normal children. When the borderline child dresses differently or talks about having a different identity, he actually believes for that moment that he is someone else.

Borderline children sometimes identify with animals or inanimate objects. For instance, Adam, a 10-year-old boy, in the fourth session of therapy, blurted out, "I am a skunk, the biggest skunk in the world!" Then he "farted" and, giggling, said, "I have the biggest smell. Nobody can come around me. I am going to kill all of my enemies with my smell. I am going to kill the whole world with my smell. Nobody will be left but me."

Identity disorders—in the form of lack of identity, fluidity of identity, confusion in sexual identity, and bisexuality—are major psychopathological symptom clusters of borderline personality disorder in childhood and adolescence. Bisexual conflicts in the form of cross-dressing and the struggle between homosexuality and heterosexuality contribute further to the adolescent's feeling of isolation and alienation. At times, the borderline child or adolescent may impulsively plunge into the sexual act in a counterphobic manner. In some borderline youth, particularly girls, promiscuity becomes a form of pseudointimacy. Emptiness, loneliness, and isolation of feeling underlie outward sexual acting-out behavior.

Disturbances of Body Image and Self-Esteem

Frequently, the borderline child and adolescent is concerned about body image. He wishes he would look quite different from the way he does. For instance, Adam, although outwardly handsome and fairly well-proportioned, saw himself as ugly. He wanted to have surgery to change his eyes, ears, nose, and face so that he would be handsome. Mark, age 9 years, would "stuff" himself in order to become strong. He associated obesity and a "fat" stomach with power and strength. Joan, age 11 years, became panic-stricken while wading in knee-deep water, because when she could not see her legs she thought that they had disappeared.

Poor self-esteem, overvaluing the self, or undervaluing the self are common. The borderline child or adolescent believes at one moment that he is Superman or the most powerful person in the world, and, at the next moment, feels hopeless, powerless, and utterly impotent.

Pseudomaturity and Immaturity

Frequently, the borderline child in a particular and limited area behaves in an adultlike fashion (pseudomature) with peers and grown-ups. This is most obvious in his verbal communication by the use of complicated scientific, legalistic, or rationalistic vocabulary in a mechanical, non-feeling, and pedantic manner, while, at the same time, the child behaves in a whiny, clinging, demanding way. Temper tantrums, explosive behavior, name-calling, and withdrawal occur frequently. Intellectualization and rationalization, along with low frustration tolerance and impulsivity, reflect the child's underlying struggle in the conflict between immaturity and pseudomaturity.

Polysymptomatic Psychopathology

Borderline disorder, by its very nature, is polysymptomatic. Obsessional thoughts, compulsive rituals, and phobic behavior abound. The tendency toward somatization and conversion disorder, along with neurotic anxieties and panic reaction, are common. Narcissistic tendencies—with great emphasis on self-gratification, concern about self-injury, and mercurial self-esteem—are prevalent. Depressive symptoms manifest themselves in the form of self-destructive behavior, feelings of helplessness, hopelessness, and sadness. Affective expressions fluctuate between extremes. Intense anger and sadness, along with momentary and unrealistic, but fleeting elation, occur concomitantly.

Psychoticlike symptoms of isolation, withdrawal, failure in the development of meaningful human relationships, extensive preoccupation with fantasy, and primary process thinking—along with massive and sudden regression and fluctuation of ego states—occur frequently. Disturbance in body image and fluidity in reality testing with a relative intactness of reality span are common.

Reality Testing

The borderline child or adolescent shows extreme fluidity and fluctuation in reality testing. However, the sense of reality and reality span are relatively intact, as opposed to the psychotic child. The borderline child, in areas related to self-gratification, may have hypersensitivity and hyperalertness, but, at the same time, may be oblivious to areas of human relationships, such as care and concern for others or having empathy.

Developmental Considerations

Detailed developmental history of the borderline child frequently reveals that there was a problem before or during pregnancy, such as marital disharmony, unwanted pregnancy, depression, extensive apprehension of labor, preeclampsia or eclampsia, or abnormal weight gain. Prolonged or difficult labor, hypoxia or anoxia at birth, and disturbances in human bonding between mother and child after birth are common.

During the first year of life, the infant may be "colicky" or have difficulty sleeping through the night. Usually, the parents see the infant as being "different" from their other children, in that he is restless, agitated, "never satisfied," unhappy, and cranky. The infant usually reacts in an extreme and distressed manner in minor environmental changes.

Development is usually uneven, for example, the infant may begin to crawl or walk before sitting up. Social and recognition smile may be delayed, although the infant may show intense anxiety and panic when separated from mother. In some cases, the development of stranger and separation anxiety may be delayed. Clinging to or withdrawal from mother is common.

Frequently, during the second year of life, the parents become concerned about the child's behavior. Language development may be delayed or show early precocity and then arrest in further development. The child usually does not show the daredevil, adventuresome behavior of the practicing subphase of separation-individuation (10 to 15 months). The child continues to be clinging, demanding, and panic-stricken when mother leaves. Sleep and eating disturbances are common. Delay of motor development results in clumsiness and fearful or phobic attitude toward physical activities and animate and inanimate objects. Most parents feel overwhelmed by the child's intense anxiety and psychophysiological distress in the subphase of rapprochement of the separation-individuation process (ages 16 to 25 months).

Arrest in development, fixation, and regression to earlier developmental levels occur frequently. Multiple allergies, hypersensitivities, physical illness, and possible hospitalizations further add to the child's anxieties and pathological distress.

Oppositional behavior, along with intense clinging behavior or an extensive ambivalent attitude, portray the child's pathological adaptation in the second and third years of life. Difficulty in toilet training, along with eating and sleep disturbances and delay in fine motor coordination, prevail. Language development is often infantile, with occasional evidence of pseudomaturity. The borderline child avoids playing with peers. Temper tantrums along with destructive behavior prevail.

Between ages 3 and 6 years, with the emergence of an active fantasy life, the borderline child becomes immersed in the world of fantasy. Imaginary companions, omnipotent wishes about controlling and detroying others, and the desire to be extremely powerful, along with magical thoughts, fill the empty, panic-stricken world of the borderline child. At this time or in latency, the child comes to the attention of a mental health clinician.

From a psychodynamic perspective, the borderline child usually is fixated at or regresses to the stage of part-object relationship (ages 1 to 2 years) before the establishment of object constancy. The borderline child perceives parents, peers, and events in an all or none manner. As long as an object (person) satisfies the child's immediate needs, he feels loved. As soon as gratification is withdrawn or is frustrated, the child feels totally unloved. He perceives, for instance, the mother as "good" when all immediate needs are gratified and as "bad" when needs are not met. The splitting of objects to "all good," or "all bad," i.e., "all or none" is one of the major pathological defenses and distortions of perception in the world of the borderline child. The child has not developed to the level of object constancy and synthesized good and bad qualities in the same person.

Differential Diagnosis

It is not uncommon to see a borderline child misdiagnosed as hyperactive, obsessive-compulsive, neurotic, schizophrenic, phobic, hysteric, or character disorder. The clinician must not only look at the symptom manifestation at a given time, but must also explore the quality of human relationships, the nature of impulsive behavior, and, particularly, the patterns of thought processes and the fluidity of identity.

In clinical discussion about these children, often the members of the diagnostic assessment or treatment team will focus on specific symptomatic behaviors. Opinions will differ as to whether the child is normal, neurotic, psychotic, or manifests a personality disorder. Diversity of opinions can be a clue to the possibility of the diagnosis of borderline personality disorder.

Management and Treatment

Therapeutic management of the borderline child or adolescent depends on the following factors:

1. Intensity and duration of symptoms
2. Nature of the symptoms and behavior
3. Areas of ego strengths and special abilities
4. Level of cognitive functioning
5. Level of family support for the child, and the readiness and willingness for assisting the child's further growth
6. Level of psychopathology in the family
7. Availability of therapeutic facilities in the community
8. Availability of special psychoeducational programs
9. Coordination and integration of therapeutic work with the child, family, school, family physician, and community support programs

In the case of severely destructive or suicidal behavior and the presence of severe psychopathology at home, inpatient psychiatric hospitaliza-tion on a short-term or long-term basis may be indicated. In most cases, regular, consistent, long-term outpatient individual psychotherapy with the child and regular, continuous work with the family is the treatment of choice. In family therapy the child should be included as much as possible if clinically indicated.

Pharmacotherapy is usually not indicated except in severe cases of anxiety or disorganization. Time-limited use of antipsychotic agents, such as thioridazine, haloperidol, or phenothiazine derivatives may be useful. Antidepressive agents and psychostimulants for the treatment of manifest depression or hyperactivity increase the child's anxiety and disorganization of thought processes or psychoticlike behavior. This is one of the most common errors found in pharmacotherapy of the borderline child. Usually, when this happens, the physician has decided to treat the manifest symptoms of hyperactivity or depression, without being aware of the underlying borderline psychotic process. Antidepressives or psychostimulants increase the secretion and uptake of norepinephrine or dopamine derivatives in the central nervous system. Norepinephrine and dopamine contribute to increased anxiety, restlessness, agitation, disorganization of thought processes, and possible psychosis, similar to amphetamine-induced psychosis in the borderline child.

Individual Psychotherapy

In dynamically oriented individual psychotherapy with the borderline child there are basically two approaches. One approach puts emphasis on strengthening the child's healthy ego defenses, particularly repression, and modifying pathological defenses, such as denial and projection. The therapist makes a conscious attempt to become a source of reality for the patient and discourages, directly or indirectly, regression to the world of fantasy and primary process thinking. The premise of this approach is that the therapist needs to help contain and bind the child's psychotic fantasies and behavior and reinforce repression, in other words, help the child develop neurotic adaptation through the process of repression and inhibition. Later, the therapist helps the child modify unhealthy or maladaptive neurotic tendencies. (Rosenfeld and Sprince, 1965)

In the second approach, the therapist attempts to become familiar with the borderline child's narcissistic fantasy world. The therapist recognizes that the borderline child's retreat to the world of fantasy and primary process thinking is his main source of pleasure and gratification. By suspending critical judgment, accepting, and eventually participating in the child's fantasy world, a dyadic relationship develops. The premise is that by first becoming a participant and then an indispensable part of the borderline child's inner world, preoccupation with narcissistic and auto-centered fantasies give way to a healthier, reality-oriented, and age-appropriate relationship. This approach at times is referred to as "communication within the delusional system," or "communication within the metaphor." (Ekstein, 1966)

Shafii (1972) reported on the psychotherapeutic treatment of a young prince who manifested the symptoms of severe anorexia, and had the delusion of being a cow. Avicenna, a Persian physician more than 1,000 years ago, effectively communicated with this patient within his delusional system by relating to him as a "sick cow," rather than challenging or confronting his delusion. This approach facilitated the development of basic trust and a therapeutic alliance.

Lindner (1956) reported a similar approach in treating a mad scientist who had the firm belief that "... part of the time he [was] living in another world or another planet." (p. 156) Lindner traveled through time and space with the patient and became an important part of his delusional system. Gradually, the patient gave up his delusion. Lindner suggested "It is as if a delusion such as ... [this] ... has room in it only for only one person at one time. . . . When ... another person invades the delusion, the original occupant finds himself literally forced to give way." (pp. 193-194)

We concur with Chethik (1979) that extensive repression does not occur and the borderline child is not transformed into a neurotic child. "Essentially it has been our experience through therapy that improvement in functioning may be profound, but borderline children nonetheless remain borderline children." (p. 318)

The borderline child requires long-term individual psychotherapy. Patience and acceptance of the child's "crazy world" and development of a reciprocal relationship are essential for improvement. The presence of another accepting human being within the child's inner world acts like a catalyst, welding fragmented ego parts together. The therapeutic alliance provides a relative stability to the child's ego functions, contains impulsivity, modulates extreme affective expressions, enhances human relationships, and facilitates sublimation and creative expression of psychoticlike fantasies.

REFERENCES

Aichorn, A. (1925). *Wayward Youth.* New York: Viking Press.

American Psychiatric Association (1980). *Diagnostic and Statistical Manual of Mental Disorders.* Third Edition. Washington, D.C.: American Psychiatric Association.

Cain, A.C. (1964). On the meaning of "playing crazy" in borderline children. *Psychiatry, 27,* 278–289.

Chethik, M. (1979). The borderline child. In Noshpitz, J. (Ed.), *Basic Handbook of Child Psychiatry,* Vol. 2. New York: Basic Books, pp. 304–321.

Chethik, M., Fast, I. (1970). A function of fantasy in the borderline child. *Am. J. Orthopsychiatry, 40,* 756–765.

Chethik, M., Spindler, E. (1971). Techniques of treatment and management with the borderline child. In Mayer, M., Blum, A. (Eds.), *Healing through Living.* Springfield, Ill.: Charles C Thomas, pp. 176–189.

Deutsch, H. (1942). Some forms of emotional disturbances and their relationship to schizophrenia. *Psychoanal. Q., 11,* 301–321.

Dollard, J., Miller, N. (1950). *Personality and Psychotherapy.* New York: McGraw-Hill Book Co.

Eissler, K.R. (Ed.) (1949). *Searchlights on Delinquency.* New York: International Universities Press.

Ekstein, R. (1966). *Children of Time and Space, of Action and Impulse.* New York: Appleton-Century-Crofts.

Ekstein, R., Wallerstein, J. (1954). Observations on the psychology of borderline and psychotic children. *Psychoanal. Study Child, 9,* 344–369.

Fast, I. (1972). Some aspects of object relations in borderline children. *Int. J. Psychoanal., 53,* 479–484.

Finch, S.M. (1962). The psychiatrist and juvenile delinquency. *J. Am. Acad. Child Psychiatry, 1,* 619–635.

Freud, S. (1923). The ego and the id. *Standard Edition of the Complete Psychological Works of Sigmund Freud,* Vol. 19, pp. 3–66.

Geleerd, E.R. (1946). A contribution to the problem of psychoses in childhood. *Psychoanal. Study Child, 2,* 271–291.

Geleerd, E.R. (1958). Borderline states in childhood and adolescence. *Psychoanal. Study Child, 13,* 279–295.

Glover, E. (1932). A psycho-analytical approach to the classification of mental disorders. *J. Ment. Sci., 78,* 819–842.

Grinker, R.R., Werble, B., Drye, R.C. (1968). *The Borderline Syndrome: A Behavioral Study of Ego Functions.* New York: Basic Books.

Gunderson, J.G., Singer, M.T. (1975). Defining borderline patients: An overview. *Am. J. Psychiatry, 132,* 1–10.

Gunderson, J.G., Kolb, J.E. (1978). Discriminating features of borderline patients. *Am. J. Psychiatry, 135,* 792–796.

Harrison, S.I., McDermott, J.F. (Eds.) (1972). *Child Psychopathology: An Anthology of Basic Readings.* New York: International Universities Press.

Healy, W., Bronner, A.F. (1936). *New Light on Delinquency and Its Treatment.* New Haven: Yale University Press.

Jenkins, R.L. (1980). Child psychiatry perspectives: Status offenders. *J. Am. Acad. Child Psychiatry, 19,* 320–325.

Johnson, A.M. (1949). Sanctions for superego lacunae of adolescents. In Harrison, S.I., McDermott, J.F. (Eds.), *Childhood Psychopathology: An Anthology of Basic Readings.* New York: International Universities Press, 1972, pp. 522–531.

Kashani, J.H., Husain, A., Robins, A.J., Reid, J.C., Wooderson, P.C. (1980). Patterns of delinquency in girls and boys. *J. Am. Acad. Child Psychiatry, 19,* 300–310.

Kernberg, O. (1967). Borderline personality organization. *J. Am. Psychoanal. Assoc., 15,* 641–685.

Lewis, D.O. (1976). Delinquency, psychomotor epileptic symptoms, and paranoid ideation: A triad. *Am J. Psychiatry, 133,* 1395–1398.

Lindner, R. (1956). *The Fifty-Minute Hour.* New York: Bantam Books.

Mahler, M.S., Ross, J.R., DeFries, Z. (1949). Clinical studies in benign and malignant cases of childhood psychosis (schizophrenia-like). *Am. J. Orthopsychiatry, 19,* 295–305.

Masterson, J.F. (1975). Intensive psychotherapy of the borderline adolescent. *Ann. Adolesc. Psychiatry, 2,* 240–268.

Masterson, J.F. (1976). *Psychotherapy of the Borderline Adult.* New York: Brunner/Mazel.

Meeks, J.E. (1979). Behavioral and antisocial disorders. In Noshpitz, J. (Ed.), *Basic Handbook of Child Psychiatry,* Vol. 2. New York: Basic Books, pp. 482–530.

Obendorf, C.P. (1930). The psychoanalysis of borderline cases. *N.Y. State J. Med., 30,* 648–651.

Pine, F. (1974). On the concept "borderline" in children. *Psychoanal. Study Child, 29,* 341–368.

Redl, F. (1951). Ego disturbances. In Harrison, S.I., McDermott, J.F. (Eds.), *Childhood Psychopathology: An Anthology of Basic Readings.* New York: International Universities Press, 1972, pp. 532–539.

Redl, F. (1957). *The Aggressive Child.* New York: Free Press of Glencoe.

Redl, F., Wineman, D. (1951). *Children Who Hate.* New York: Free Press of Glencoe.

Robins, L.N. (1966). *Deviant Children Grown Up.* Baltimore: Williams and Wilkins.

Rosenfeld, S.K., Sprince, M.P. (1965). Some thoughts on the technical handling of borderline children. *Psychoanal. Study Child, 20,* 495–517.

Shafii, M. (1972). A precedent for modern psychotherapeutic techniques: One thousand years ago. *Am. J. Psychiatry, 128,* 1581–1584.

Shafii, M., Whittinghall, R., Healy, M.H. (1979). The pediatric-psychiatric model for emergencies in child psychiatry: A study of 994 cases. *Am. J. Psychiatry, 136,* 1600–1601.

Soloff, P.H., Ulrich, R.F. (1981). Diagnostic interview for borderline patients. *Arch. Gen. Psychiatry, 38,* 686–692.

Spitzer, R.L., Endicott, J. (1979). Justification for separating schizotypal and borderline personality disorders. *Schizophr. Bull., 5,* 95–104.

Weil, A.P. (1953). Certain severe disturbances of ego development in childhood. *Psychoanal. Study Child, 8,* 271–287.

Weil, A.P. (1956). Certain evidences of deviational development in infancy and early childhood. *Psychoanal. Study Child, 11,* 292–299.

Zilboorg, G. (1941). Ambulatory schizophrenias. *Psychiatry, 4,* 149–155.

Chapter 12

PSYCHOLOGICAL FACTORS AFFECTING PHYSICAL CONDITIONS: Psychosomatic or Psychophysiological Disorders

Beginning with the Renaissance in the sixteenth century and subsequent to the advances in the knowledge of anatomy by Vesalius, gross pathology by Morgagni, and improvement of the microscope by van Leeuwenhoek, great emphasis was placed on the natural sciences at the expense of psychological and behavioral factors.

During the nineteenth century, modern laboratory studies were incorporated into medical practice following the work of Pasteur on germs and Virchow on cellular pathology. Diseases were associated with structural changes of the cell. Psychological factors regarding the causation or treatment of disease were discarded. Clinicians tended to treat the disease rather than the person as a whole. This unbalanced emphasis has led to a dichotomy between mind and body which continues to plague Western medicine to this day.

In earlier times in Egypt, Mesopotamia, Greece, India, and China, the approach to the assessment and treatment of the patient was holistic. The priest or physician usually took all factors—physical, humoral (endocrine), emotional, dietary, and spiritual—into consideration. Emphasis was on finding effective ways of healing, rather than on diagnosis and causative factors.

Unfortunately, during the Middle Ages in Europe, from A.D. 500–1500, superstition and distorted religious beliefs dominated medical practices. "Sinning" and breaking religious taboos were thought to be the cause of physical and mental disorders. This period was the Dark Ages of Medicine. (Kaplan, 1975, p. 1625)

Although

This period might have been the Dark Ages of medicine and psychiatry in Europe...[the] study of the contributions of Islamic physicians, especially the Persians such as Razi, Avicenna, and Haly Abbas, reveals flourishing humanistic medical practices with emphasis on clinical observation, pharmacotherapy, and psychotherapy.

Shafii, 1973, p. 85.

In the West, it is only during the last few decades, following Freud's work on the effect of emotions on the development of hysteria, that others, such as Franz Alexander (1950), Dunbar (1954), Engel and Segal (1956), and Mirsky (1958), paved the way for clinical description, differentiation, and the impact of psychological factors on the etiology and treatment of psychosomatic disorders.

DEFINITION

In 1818, Heinroth, a German physician, coined the term "psychosomatic" to describe a disorder resulting from the effect of psyche and emotion on the soma, or body. He regarded insomnia as such a disorder. Later, the psychosomatic concept was expanded further to include disorders resulting from disturbances in the autonomic nervous system, such as peptic ulcer, ulcerative colitis, asthma, rheumatoid arthritis, and migraine headaches. Gradually, the term "psychophysiological" disorder (*DSM*, 1952) (*DSM-II*, 1968) replaced the term "psychosomatic."

Psychophysiological disorders refer to a

...group of disorders...characterized by physical symptoms that are caused by emotional factors and involve a single organ system, usually under autonomic nervous system innervation. The physiological changes involved are those that normally accompany certain emotional states, but in these disorders the changes are more intense and sustained.

DSM-II, 1968, p. 46.

In *DSM-III* (1980), psychophysiological disorders, for the most part, are grouped under "Psychological Factors Affecting Physical Condition," because it is believed that "...psychological factors contribute to the initiation or exacerbation of a physical condition." (p. 303) A temporal relationship exists between psychological factors, environmental stimuli, and the initiation or reactivation of physical conditions.

CLASSIFICATION

Disagreement exists on the classification of psychophysiological disorders. For the sake of consistency and acceptable clinical practice, the following disorders and symptoms are included here, although eating disorders and stereotyped movement disorders, for example, are classified independently in *DSM-III* (1980). (The disorders with asterisks will be discussed in this chapter.)

A. Eating disorders
  1. Anorexia nervosa*
  2. Bulimia
  3. Obesity
B. Gastrointestinal disorders
  1. Nausea, vomiting, and cyclic vomiting
  2. Pylorospasm
  3. Peptic ulcer (gastric or duodenal ulcer)*
  4. Regional enteritis*
  5. Ulcerative colitis*
  6. Functional encopresis*
C. Respiratory disorders
  1. Hyperventilation (see chapter 9)
  2. Bronchial asthma*
D. Central nervous system disorders
  1. Migraine headache
  2. Tension headache
  3. Sacroiliac pain
  4. Neurodermatitis
E. Cardiovascular symptoms
  1. Tachycardia (see chapter 9)
  2. Arrhythmia
  3. Angina pectoris
F. Genitourinary symptoms
  1. Dysmenorrhea (painful menstruation)
  2. Frequent micturition
  3. Functional enuresis (see chapter 5)
G. Autoimmune disorders
  1. Allergies
  2. Rheumatoid arthritis
H. Endocrine disorders
  1. Acne
  2. Diabetes mellitus
  3. Hyperthyroidism (Grave's disease)
I. Movement disorders
  1. Transient tic disorders*
  2. Chronic motor tic*
  3. Tourette's disorder*

ANOREXIA NERVOSA

Anorexia nervosa is a psychopathological disorder or syndrome characterized by refusal to eat, "...intense fear of becoming obese, disturbance of body image, significant weight loss, refusal to maintain a minimal normal body weight, and amenorrhea (in females)" without any known physical disorder. (*DSM-III*, 1980, p. 67)

Historical Perspective

Avicenna (A.D. 980–1037), a Persian physician, approximately 1,000 years ago effectively treated an adolescent prince with the symptoms of refusal to eat, weight loss, agitation, and distortion of body image. This symptom cluster is similar to the present-day description of anorexia nervosa. (Shafii, 1972)

Richard Morton (1689) described two patients with the symptoms of refusal to eat and severe weight loss. He referred to their condition as "nervous consumption," to differentiate it from "consumption" (tuberculosis).

E.C. Lasegue (1873) wrote a comprehensive psychological study of patients with loss of appetite, refusal to eat, loss of weight, amenorrhea, malnutrition, hyperactivity, and significant disturbances in human relationships. Lasegue called this clinical condition "anorexic hysterique."

Sir William Gull (1874) coined the term "anorexia nervosa." He described several female patients with symptoms of extreme weight loss, amenorrhea, and restlessness, without any organic lesions.

Onset

Anorexia nervosa most frequently occurs in early or late adolescence, although cases are reported in patients as young as age 4 years and as old as the early thirties. (Sylvester, 1945)

Sex and Prevalence

Anorexia nervosa is most common in adolescent females aged 12 to 18 years, with a prevalence of 1% in this age group. (Crisp *et al.,* 1976) The female to male ratio is approximately 7:1. (Bruch, 1973) Incidence in both males and females is increasing and reaching epidemic proportions. (Bruch, 1978, pp. VIII, X)

Clinical Features

Anorexia nervosa is a life-threatening disorder and a psychiatric emergency. In diagnosed cases, the mortality rate is 15 to 21%. (*DSM-III,* 1980, p. 68) This is one of the highest mortality rates within psychiatric disorders.

According to Feighner *et al.* (1972), Bruch (1973), Rollins and Piazza (1978), and Shafii (1981), the prominent clinical features and behavioral manifestations of anorexia nervosa are:

1. Intense fear of becoming obese, relentless pursuit of thinness, and preoccupation with dieting, even when significant weight loss has occurred.
2. Decrease in food intake or refusal to eat.
3. Weight loss of approximately 25% of body weight or a decrease of 20 to 25 pounds below normal weight for age and height. (Bliss and Branch, 1960, pp. 23–46)
4. Distortion of body image, denial of thinness, and preoccupation with the idea of "being fat" even when emaciated.
5. Development of unusual eating habits, such as avoiding eating meat, eating only fruit, or limiting food intake to a small amount of liquids. Hoarding, concealing, or throwing food away may also occur.
6. Amenorrhea in females, occurring in 50% of the cases before significant weight loss.
7. Intense preoccupation with preparing food for others or insistence that others eat.
8. High energy level even though emaciated.
9. Obsessional-compulsive or hysterical behavior, such as perfectionistic tendencies, wanting to be very "good" or "proper," concern about cleanliness, frequent hand-washing, doing and undoing, crying spells, and manipulative behavior.
10. Restlessness and agitation.
11. Preoccupation with a variety of exercises for losing more weight.
12. Fear of growing up and developing secondary sexual characteristics. Denial of sexual wishes and fantasies.
13. Fear of losing control or of being controlled by others.
14. Apathy and lack of emotional expression, especially the feelings of anger or hostility.
15. Disturbance in family relationships with difficulty in experiencing independence or expressing individuality—enmeshed family relationships.
16. Past history of feeding disturbances, mild to moderate obesity in approximately one-third of the cases, or undue emphasis on eating and dieting within the family.
17. Induced vomiting following eating in 50% of the cases, and the use of laxatives or enemas to lose weight in approximately 10 to 25% of the cases.
18. Bulimia (eating binges) followed by vomiting in some cases.
19. Abdominal pain with weight loss may give the false impression of acute surgical abdomen.
20. Physical symptoms in advanced cases, in addition to significant weight loss, include: hypothermia, hypotension, bradycardia, dependent edema, lanugo (downy hairs similar to those covering the body of the fetus), cyanosis, skin hyperkeratosis, breast atrophy, decrease of axillary and pubic hair, and associated metabolic changes.
21. Absence of any known physical illness.

Clinical Course

In most cases, a single episode of anorexia occurs, which usually, with treatment, results in full recovery. In some cases the clinical course is episodic with multiple episodes of anorexia and hospitalization. After these acute episodes, the patient may continue to be subclinically anorexic, especially in cases with underlying obsessive-compulsive features. Unfortunately, in 15 to 21% of the cases, the anorexic course will continue and result in profound starvation leading to death.

Some authors divide anorexia nervosa into primary and secondary: primary, referring to anorexia without any other disorder, and, secondary, to anorexia secondary to or resulting from other disorders, such as depression, schizophrenia, and organic disorders.

Psychobiological Considerations

Appetite for food is modulated by the hypothalamus. Stimulation of the ventral medial nucleus of the hypothalamus in some animals results in anorexia, and destruction of this nucleus creates hyperphagia and obesity. On the other hand, stimulation of the lateral nuclei results in hyperphagia and destruction results in anorexia. In human beings, the hypothalamic nuclei are under the control of the cerebral cortex, and thus affected by psychological stress, memories, fears, fantasies, and attitudes.

In most anorexic patients, the development of amenorrhea is attributed to emotional factors that reduce the secretion of gonadotrophins of the pituitary gland, resulting in the decrease of gonadal hormones and the subsequent absence of menses, often even before significant weight loss.

In advanced cases of anorexia nervosa, normocytic and normochromic anemia, along with leukopenia and lymphocytosis, may occur. "Hypoglycemia, hypercholesterolemia, hypoproteinemia, and hypercarotenemia have all been observed. All are probably a consequence of the malnutrition and abnormal diet." (Bliss, 1975, p. 1659)

The gonadotrophic functions of the anterior pituitary gland and the ovarian hormones are usually decreased, most likely due to psychological factors and malnutrition. Patients who induce vomiting may develop hypokalemia. Malnutrition lowers basal metabolism. Thyroid functions are usually normal.

Psychodynamic Perspective

The increased incidence of anorexia nervosa in the United States, Western Europe, and Japan may be related to increased affluence. Emphasis on dieting in the middle and upper classes has contributed to a significant increase in anorexia nervosa, particularly in pubescence and adolescence. Developmentally, many adolescents become concerned about their weight. Some may become vegetarians or follow a variety of food fads. A relatively small number become anorexic.

The pathological leap from dieting or transient food fads to the phobia of obesity, relentless pursuit of thinness, and self-starvation is related to psychosocial stresses, previous eating disturbances, and, particularly, to the family dynamics and intrapsychic conflicts.

In many cases of anorexia, the patients were brought up as "model" or "perfect" children or they had a "special" relationship with their parents, particularly their mothers. Expression of feelings, especially negative feelings, such as hostility and anger, were discouraged. Emphasis was placed on *denial* of feelings, behavior like "grown-ups," and *controlling* emotions, desires, and spontaneous behaviors.

Intrapsychically, fear of losing control is common. These patients are afraid of losing control and "eating like a pig." They fear losing their tempers, becoming "wild," and destroying objects or hurting people verbally or physically, particularly their parents. They fear sexuality and feel that they may give in to sexual impulses. Denial of thinness and distortion of body image reaches almost psychotic proportion, although other areas of reality testing are intact.

A number of anorexic patients come from "enmeshed families" in which there is an unusual pathological closeness and individual family members lack independence. (Minuchin *et al.*, 1975) Frequently, father is perfectionistic, authoritarian, and without warmth. Concern for the child is expressed by being intrusive and overattentive to the child's appearance, performance, behavior, and body functions. Mother may be quietly submissive but at the same time resentful toward her husband, and she may often feel oppressed. The child frequently identifies with the mother or the oppressed parent. Positive or negative identification with parental eating behavior is a major contributing factor to the development of anorexia.

Anorexia nervosa, to borrow a term from Erikson (1969), may be an expression of "militant nonviolent" aggression toward parents—a "... struggle for independence and liberation from the yoke of family suppression." (Shafii *et al.*, 1975, p. 631)

Management and Treatment

Dynamic psychotherapy, behavior therapy, psychotropic or antidepressant medications, hormone therapy, and hospitalization are the most common approaches to the management and treatment of anorexia nervosa. Some clinicians also prescribe isolation and bedrest. In the past, electroshock therapy, insulin coma, and even lobotomy were used.

Depending on the intensity of the symptoms, the amount of weight loss and the patient's psychophysiological distress, we recommend the following therapeutic measures.

1. Complete physical examination and laboratory studies, including a complete blood count (CBC), urinalysis, liver function and kidney studies, and serum electrolytes are indicated. Hormonal studies, CAT scan, EEG, and EKG are ordered if warranted.

2. After initial assessment, when the diagnosis of anorexia nervosa is established, the clinician needs to move decisively with firmness, conviction, and empathy. Findings and recommendations for treatment should be discussed openly with the patient and the family.

3. Ambivalence and indecisiveness in the treatment of anorexia depletes the resources of the patient and the family and contributes further to physical emaciation, psychological paralysis, and possible death.

4. In moderate to severe cases of anorexia, hospitalization is indicated.

5. We do not recommend any medication, unless the patient shows clinical evidence of depres-

sion or psychotic behavior. In such cases, antidepressant medications, such as imipramine, amitriptyline, or antipsychotic agents may be indicated. Supplemental vitamins should be prescribed for malnourishment.

6. Psychotherapy with the patient and the family is essential. In most cases, an integration of individual dynamic psychotherapy, family therapy, and behavior therapy is indicated.

7. Frequently, psychiatric hospitalization is required.

8. The patient should be weighed daily in severe cases, otherwise weekly.

9. In the hospital milieu, the patient is expected to come to meals but eating or not eating is left up to the patient.

10. If the patient continues to lose weight or fails to gain weight, the therapist should openly discuss this with the patient. The therapist should tell the patient that if he does not gain weight, for example 4 to 5 pounds per week, tube feedings will be necessary. This confrontation usually results in the patient's expression of anger and unhappiness toward the therapist. Some patients, although they protest, save face through this approach and begin to eat. Others will continue to resist either by not gaining weight or by losing more weight. In these cases, the pediatrician who is looking after the patient's physical needs should begin tube feedings. Amazingly, most anorexic patients accept the insertion of the nasal gastric tube and go to inpatient school and other activities with the tube in place. However, a few will induce vomiting or siphon off the tube feeding. After a few days or weeks of tube feeding, most patients gain weight. They gradually drink fluids and later begin to eat solid foods. If the patient continues to gain weight by voluntarily eating, the tube is removed after a few days. If the patient begins to lose weight, then the tube is immediately reinserted.

11. At the time of weighing, some patients will go through a variety of maneuvers to give the impression of weight gain, for instance, wearing heavy clothing, putting heavy objects in their pockets, and drinking large amounts of water or stuffing themselves with food. Some induce vomiting following weighing.

12. In psychotherapy, expression of feelings, especially anger, hostility, fear of imperfection, fear of pregnancy or sexuality, and fear of loss of control, is encouraged. The patient initially uses massive *denial*. Steady and gentle exploration and confrontation gradually "chip away" at the denial. Manipulative behavior, in the form of bargaining, complaining of being maltreated or abused by the staff or therapist, divisiveness, or insisting that parents come and rescue him from the "unjust" and "inhumane" hospital environment, is common.

13. The therapist needs to have regular therapeutic contact with the family, for example, in the form of family therapy. The patient and family members need to be helped to see that anorexia nervosa is a disorder of the family system as a whole. Each member of the family needs to become aware of the nature of his interactions with the other family members, and his contribution to this family disorder.

14. Countertransference reactions (irrational reactions of the therapist and the staff to the patient) are frequently intense. Anorexic patients often reactivate extreme feelings of ambivalence in the staff, such as overidentification or rejection, permissiveness, or overcontrolling, and indulgence or impatience. The therapist needs to be aware of these extreme feelings within himself and within the milieu in order to chart a moderate, reasonable, sensitive, but firm course in the management and treatment of these patients.

Outcome

Treatment outcome is reported to be favorable in 75% of anorexic patients. The other 25% continue to have recurrent anorexic symptoms. Fifteen to 21% of anorexic patients die. Three percent commit suicide.

In our experience of treatment or supervising treatment of 30 to 40 anorexic patients aged 5 to 18 years, with the methods discussed earlier, approximately 90% had a favorable outcome, 10% had recurrent anorexia symptoms, and, of these, one-half continued to be chronically subclinically anorexic. There were no deaths due to anorexia or suicide.

BRONCHIAL ASTHMA

The word "asthma" is thought to be related to the Greek word *aenai*, meaning to blow. "The Greeks confined the term to a difficulty of breathing, attended with sound, and more severe than the breath struggle called dyspnea." (Peshkin, 1963, p. 1)

Bronchial asthma is presently defined as "...a clinical state of heightened reactivity of the tracheobronchial tree to numerous stimuli. Characteristically, episodes of dyspnea and wheezing which are symptomatic of airway obstruction are features of the disorder." (Weiss, 1975, p. 3)

Historical Perspective

Asthma as a symptom, syndrome, and clinical disorder has been described throughout the ages. Hippocrates (460–357 B.C.), Aretaeus (A.D. 120), and Galen (A.D. 130–200) described the following symptoms of asthma: difficulty in breathing, coughing and expectoration. They thought that the humors from the head accumulated in the lungs and chest. Maimonides (born A.D. 1135), a well-known physician of the twelfth century, made significant contributions to the study of asthma. His acute clinical observations were "...a remarkable treatise in the light of our present knowledge." (Peshkin, 1963, p. 2)

Sir John Floyer (1649–1734) who, himself, suffered from asthma for most of his life, wrote a book entitled *A Treatise of the Asthma.* (1698) Floyer attributed the cause of asthma to mechanical pressure and contraction of the fibers of the bronchi. Benjamin Rush (1770) related asthma to spasm of the bronchi and wrote "Treatise on the Spasmodic Asthma of Children."

Salter (1860), who also suffered from asthma, carried out an exhaustive study of large numbers of asthmatic cases. He related asthma to the spasm of bronchial muscles and perceived it as a nervous disease related to the central nervous system. He emphasized the role of heredity in the development of asthma.

In recent years, immunological reactions to varieties of allergens and psychological factors were found to contribute to the development of asthma in a vulnerable child or adult.

Prevalence

It is estimated that 10% of all children under age 15 years in the United States suffer from some kind of allergic disorder that requires treatment. Bronchial asthma is believed to be "...the most common chronic physical illness in childhood with a prevalence of at least 2 percent." (Kavanaugh and Mattsson, 1979, p. 357)

Approximately 6 to 8 million Americans suffer from bronchial asthma, including 1½ to 2 million children and youth.

Onset

Asthma, particularly the type related to allergies, usually begins in infancy or early childhood. The onset may be abrupt or insidious.

Clinical Features

1. In sudden onset asthma, coughing spells occur precipitously. These spells "...may be associated with itching of the chin, anterior part of the neck or chest." (Nelson *et al.,* 1969, p. 503)
2. In insidious onset, asthmatic attacks often follow respiratory infection. Wheezing usually appears afterward.
3. Asthmatic paroxysm has the following characteristics: increased dyspnea, significant increase in the expiration period of respiration, wheezing, and fine musical or coarse bronchial rales on auscultation.
4. In severe asthmatic attack, pulmonary ventilation decreases greatly. Air hunger intensifies with manifestation of nasal flaring, use of accessory intercostal muscles, cyanosis and hypercapnia (significant increase of carbon dioxide in the blood).
5. Heart beat, respiration, and sweating increase.
4. Agitation, restlessness, and eventually physical exhaustion may occur.
7. Severe coughing may be associated with abdominal pain and vomiting.
8. Sputum in acute asthmatic attack is mucous and tenacious.
9. Frequent asthmatic attacks over a long period of time may result in emphysema.

Types of Bronchial Asthma

Bronchial asthma is divided into the following types.

Extrinsic Asthma or Allergic Asthma

External identifiable factors—allergens or antigens—such as pollens, molds, dusts, drugs, animal dander, and some foods, precipitate asthmatic attacks. Skin tests are usually positive to the allergens. This type of asthma is related to the body's hypersensitivity and immunological reaction to specific allergens.

Immunoglobulin E (IgE), which in normal serum concentration is about 0.03 mg.%, increases significantly in allergic disorders, particularly in asthma. IgE is a form of antibody "...synthesized by plasma cells in the mucosa of the nose, respiratory tract, and gastrointestinal tract, and in lymphoid tissues. It is found in various tissues, body fluids, and in nasal and bronchial secretions of allergic individuals." (Weiss, 1975, p. 24) Human IgE has a unique quality of "...antigenic determinants which lead to *specific tissue binding.*" (ibid., p. 24) The hypersensitivity of the skin or lung tissue of allergic patients may be related to increased IgE.

Extrinsic asthma usually begins in childhood or young adulthood. The asthmatic attacks are of sudden onset and brief duration. Between the paroxysms of bronchospasm, the patient is relatively free of the symptoms. Usually, these children have a history of other forms of allergies, such as eczema (atopy), hay fever, and allergic rhinitis. There is a family history of allergies. Patients respond favorably to hyposensitization.

Prognosis is usually favorable. Most asthmatic children become free of the asthmatic symptoms during adolescence or young adulthood. A small percentage have symptoms throughout life. Death occurs very rarely.

Intrinsic Asthma, Idiopathic, or Infective Asthma

Intrinsic asthma usually begins in adulthood, at age 35 years or older. There are no known allergies, no history of eczema in childhood, and usually no family history of allergies. Serum IgE is not elevated. The patient does not respond to hyposensitization. Skin tests are usually negative.

Asthmatic attacks are frequently related to infection, exercise, or psychological distress. The attacks are very severe. They may be associated with overwhelming anxiety, depression, or other psychopathological factors. Asthma may become chronic. Prognosis is poor and death may occur. In the United States, between 4,000 and 7,000 asthmatic patients die annually due to asthmatic complications, and, of these, approximately 200 are children. (Weiss, 1975, p. 72)

Mixed Asthma

Mixed asthma represents a combination of extrinsic and intrinsic asthma. Usually, the acute asthmatic episodes begin with respiratory infections, but the patient also has significant allergies.

Status Asthmaticus

Status asthmaticus is a medical emergency. The patient has severe wheezing, dyspnea, coughing, cyanosis, tachycardia, apprehension, and panic attack. The acute asthmatic attack is refractory to usual treatment. Prompt treatment and hospitalization are required. If the patient does not receive immediate and effective treatment, death may occur due to hypoxemia, hypercapnia, and respiratory acidosis.

Physiopathology

The smooth muscle of the bronchial airways plays a significant role in constriction and dilation of the airways. The tonicity of these smooth muscles is related to the balance between contraction by the vagus nerves (cholinergic) and dilation by the sympathetic nerves (β -adrenergic).

Recently, the theory of cholinergic dominance was postulated as a causative factor for asthma. It is thought that asthmatic patients hyperreact to a stimulus whether it be of allergic or nonallergic nature. Hyperreactivity may be related to decreased "...responsiveness of the beta adrenergic receptors in the patient's airways and other tissues." (Kavanaugh and Mattsson, 1979, p. 358) This decrease results in reduction of cyclic AMP, which plays an essential role in the relaxation of smooth muscles. The imbalance created affects the vagus nerve and its cholinergic-constrictive functions go unchecked. In asthmatic patients, allergic, psychological, physical, chemical, or infectious stimuli may contribute to this imbalance, resulting in bronchial constriction, increased airway resistance, and heightened airway reactivity.

Psychodynamic Perspective

During the last few decades, a number of clinicians have explored the developmental and psychodynamic considerations of bronchial asthma in children and adolescents. At one time, there was an extensive attempt to describe the "asthmatic personality," i.e., specific personality traits of an asthmatic patient. French and Alexander (1941) associated asthmatic attacks with the cry for mother's breast and the conflict between clinging to and separating from mother. They stressed that the child's inability to cry because of fear or rage was a significant factor in the development of asthma. Clinical studies of asthmatic children have not shown a tendency toward repression or suppression of crying. In fact, a number of these children have long histories of temper tantrums and aggressive behavior.

Separation anxiety and unusual close relationships between mother and child are thought to precipitate asthmatic attacks in many children. Sperling (1949, 1963) did extensive studies on the psychodynamics of psychophysiological disorders in children. She believed that the basic dynamics of bronchial asthma were similar to that of phobias.

Phobias are neurotic conditions based on unconscious conflicts in which the fantasy of omnipotence and magical thinking play a predominant role. Phobias respond to environmental manipulation, but such responses are only a surface adjustment. The phobic core remains, with severe crippling effects upon the personality of the child. The same is true for asthma.

Sperling, 1963, p. 162.

It is also postulated that asthmatic children are fixated in the anal or oral phases of psychosexual development. In addition, it is thought that the family, especially the mother, reinforces the child's dependence on her and the disease by paying exclusive attention to minor signs and symptoms of illness and rejecting the child when free from symptoms.

Knapp (1960) has explored the fantasies of asthmatic patients. The common themes were primitive fantasies of devouring, being filled with dangerous substances, retention, and expulsion, and, particularly, sadness, Knapp wrote:

Our clinical evidence suggests that both fantasy and affect, in many cases, represent aspects of a common struggle over urges toward intake and retention, in competition with powerful riddance impulses, being expressed in the previously sensitized pulmonary apparatus.

Knapp, 1963, p. 250.

Knapp hypothesized that symbolic stimuli and emotional experiences provoked asthma. Asthma "...can be regarded as a conversion process, using a predisposed organ system."(ibid., p. 252)

At the present time, it is not clear whether psychological factors create the asthmatic disorders or are a reaction to the severe life-threatening experience of wheezing, shortness of breath, and fear of death. No doubt, psychological factors, such as separation, disappointment, rage, anger, fear, and overprotection, play significant roles in the initiation and continuation of asthmatic attacks.

In some patients with chronic and intractable asthma, the home environment, itself, functions as a "psychological allergen." In this situation, the removal of the child from the home significantly decreases the frequency of the asthmatic attacks and the possibilities of secondary gains from these attacks.

Management and Treatment

This discussion will focus on the psychological and psychiatric management of asthma, rather than on pharmacological treatment. Prevention is the most effective form of treatment for asthma. Careful assessment and sensitivity studies help to find possible allergens. In the case of known allergies, it is important to balance avoidance of allergens with the child's psychological and developmental needs. Maintaining a relatively dust and mold free home or keeping favorite pets away from the living quarters may significantly decrease the frequency of asthmatic attacks without limiting the child's physical or social activities or food intake.

Calmness and patience will help to alleviate the child's and the family's anxiety. Extensive restriction of favorite foods, playing and staying overnight with friends, and attending camp increases the child's and the family's phobic behavior and reinforces the asthmatic attacks. Prudence in limiting age-appropriate activities and food intake, along with desensitization programs and helping the child to manage his own treatment program, decrease acute asthmatic episodes.

Relaxation therapies, yoga exercises, and biofeedback are helpful as adjunct therapeutic modalities for decreasing tension, fear, and anxieties, and possibly may result in decreased airway resistance and increased lung vital capacity.

Asthma is a chronic debilitating disorder that often requires multiple hospitalizations with extensive and intrusive tests, injections, and medical management. The asthmatic child reacts with apprehension, fear, and dread to asthmatic attacks and hospitalization. Hospitalization separates the child suddenly from his friends, family, and environment, including prized objects and pets. Regression to earlier psychosexual development and the sensory-motor level of cognitive functioning is common. The child becomes frightened, clinging, overdependent, passive, and, at times, helpless. Feelings of dislike, and aggressive or destructive wishes toward parents, physicians, and nurses, as well as the self, may predominate.

Reactive depression and possible chronic depression are the most common psychopathological findings associated with asthma. Depressive behavior may manifest itself in the form of withdrawal, chronic sad affect, and increased somatization. It may also express itself in a counterphobic manner in the form of hostile and belligerent behavior, daredevil or delinquent acts, and undue exposure to severe allergens and danger. Chronic use of corticosteroids in the treatment of asthma may contribute to the development of dysphoric mood, depression, or psychosis.

In these situations, psychiatric consultation and possible psychotherapy with the patient and the family is strongly indicated. In the treatment of asthmatic children, there is a tendency for over-treating physical symptoms and undertreating or avoiding psychiatric consultation and intervention.

GASTROINTESTINAL DISORDERS

Peptic Ulcer

The term "peptic ulcer" includes gastric and duodenal ulcers.

Onset

Gastric or duodenal ulcers can begin at any time from infancy to adulthood. The occurrence of duodenal ulcer is five times higher than gastic ulcer.

Prevalence

Sultz *et al.* (1970) reported on an epidemiological study of peptic ulcers in childhood. According to them, the incidence of peptic ulcer is increasing in this age group. During the years 1947 to 1949, the documented incidence was 0.5 per 100,000, and during 1956 to 1958, the incidence had increased to 3.9 per 100,000. The highest increase occurred in males aged 15 years.

Clinical Features

1. Gastric ulcer occurs more frequently in infancy, and duodenal ulcer occurs in childhood and adolescence. (Nelson *et al.,* 1969, p. 797)
2. Ulceration is acute rather than chronic. It may be secondary to other physical conditions, such as massive burns, central nervous system disorders (Cushing's ulcer), steroid therapy, infections, or marasmus.
3. Vomiting is the most common symptom in infancy.
4. Bleeding (hematemesis, melena) may occur.
5. Abdominal distention may be related to perforation of the ulcer.
6. Older children complain of epigastric pain, particularly before meals or at night, similar to adults. This pain is usually relieved by eating. In younger children, pain is erratic, frequently located around the umbilical area and may be intensified by eating. In infancy and early childhood, the major symptom is vomiting rather than pain.
7. Peptic ulcer is more frequent in children who have other symptoms of gastrointestinal dis-

orders, such as irritable colon syndrome and constipation.

Diagnosis

Diagnosis should be confirmed by radiography of the stomach and duodenum. Gastric ulcer is usually located in the anterior curvature of the stomach wall and rarely on the posterior wall. Duodenal ulcer is frequently located on the bulb of the duodenum, which shows a variety of deformities when filled with barium.

Psychobiological Factors

Alexander (1934) applied psychoanalytic concepts to the causative factors of peptic ulcer. He postulated that these patients had a strong oral dependent wish to be looked after, cared for, and, at the same time, felt overwhelmingly conflicted about these wishes and experienced shame, guilt, or parental rejection.

Tarboroff and Brown (1954) postulated that the most significant factors in the development of duodenal ulcer in children and adolescents were "... close relationship between onset of symptoms and the frustration of dependent love needs by the real or felt danger of losing the mother." (p. 609)

Chapman *et al.* (1956) found that beyond the patient's passive dependent facade was considerable hostility and aggression. These patients had difficulty expressing hostile and aggressive feelings openly. They experienced marked conflicts between dependent versus independent longings toward mother. The relationships with parents, particularly the mother, were marked by insecurity and anxiety.

Mirsky's (1958) classical studies showed that development of peptic ulcers was not only related to physical and psychological etiology, but to a combination of a number of factors, including:

1. A high rate of secretion of pepsinogen in the stomach with a significant increase of the level of pepsinogen in the serum or urine
2. Familial tendencies
3. Having blood group type O (higher incidence in this group)
4. Psychological factors, such as environmental stress, early developmental conflicts in the form of strong, overwhelming, oral dependent wishes, and immaturity and pseudomaturity—most of these children are perfectionistic, intense, driven, and performance-oriented youngsters, with evidence of significant interpersonal conflicts within the family

Engel and Segal (1956) and Engel (1975), in a study of a 15-month-old girl, Monica, with a gastric fistula, noticed that during times of affection, pleasure, or rage, the gastric secretion, particularly hydrochloric acid, increased significantly as opposed to times of withdrawal and disengagement, when it decreased or ceased.

Stein *et al.* (1962), in a study of adults with gastric fistula, also noticed that gastric secretions increased significantly during expressed or suppressed rage and fell during rejection and withdrawal.

It is now generally accepted that familial factors and genetic proclivity, along with psychological stress factors, such as extreme frustration in the mother-child relationship, loss, separation, passive dependency, pseudoindependency, tendency toward inhibition of aggressive and hostile feelings, and living in a setting of unpredictable feedback for success or avoidance, contribute significantly to the expression of peptic ulcer.

Ulcerative Colitis

Ulcerative colitis is a chronic intermittent inflammatory disorder of the large intestine. The mucosal membrane of the distal colon, and, in one-third of the cases, the ileum, becomes congested, edematous, and friable. Bleeding occurs easily. Gradual destruction of the mucous membrane results in ulceration, pseudopolyps, crypt abscesses, fibrosis, decrease in the internal diameter of the colon, and, at times, perforation.

Clinical Features

1. Ulcerative colitis is a serious disease.
2. Onset may be insidious or acute.
3. Diarrhea is the most common symptom.
4. Recurrent abdominal pain, rectal bleeding, weight loss, and anemia are frequent.
5. Arthritis, erythema nodosum, and growth failure may be associated with this disease.
6. Abdominal cramps, headache, fever, nausea, vomiting, anorexia, and enlargement of liver and spleen may occur.
7. Diagnosis depends upon the evidence of hyperemic, friable mucosa of the colon in sigmoidoscopy or evidence of ulceration, irritability, or spasm in radiography.

Psychobiological Factors

Familial and genetic factors play a significant role. It is hypothesized that external factors—including psychological stress—in a constitutionally or genetically prone individual, decrease the protective mechanisms and induce the disorder in the colon area.

Another theory emphasizes the role of hypersensitivity and allergic factors in the etiology of this disease. For instance, susceptible infants become hypersensitive to common gastrointestinal infections and to the antigens of bacteria which are usually present in the gastrointestinal tract. Recurrent allergy and infection results in the development of ulcerative colitis. Psychological stress frequently contributes to reactivation of the symptoms or may be the precipitating factor.

Children and adolescents with ulcerative colitis have many obsessive-compulsive features. They are usually inhibited in expression of feeling, overly conscientious, punctual, and orderly. They are extremely hypersensitive but hide their feelings behind the defenses of rationalization, isolation, intellectualization, and doing and undoing. Indecisiveness, doubt, ambivalence, mistrust, and a tendency toward messiness frequently underlie a facade of perfectionistic behaviors.

These children can be overbearing, demanding, pedantic, and joyless. Passivity, dependency, pessimism, and extreme ambivalence characterize their relationships with their parents, especially mothers, siblings, spouses, and associates.

McDermott and Finch (1967), in a study of 49 children with ulcerative colitis, reported that "Significant emotional illness was found to be associated with the occurrence of ulcerative colitis." (p. 524) Personality disorders, such as passive-aggressive or passive-dependent personality in boys, and compulsive personality in girls, were prevalent. None of the children was psychotic, although a number showed borderline psychotic features.

In children with ulcerative colitis, McDermott and Finch found that the basic underlying core of psychopathology was

...marked tendency toward depression and denial of the illness in all of these youngsters which posed a potentially dangerous problem both psychologically and physiologically; i.e., the tendency to withdraw at the time of exacerbation and to regress massively.

ibid., p. 518.

Regional Enteritis—Crohn's Disease

Crohn *et al.* (1932) described the clinical and pathological aspects of

...a disease of the terminal ileum, affecting mainly young adults, characterized by a subacute or chronic necrotizing and cicatrizing [healing by scar formation]

inflammation. The ulceration of the mucosa is accompanied by a disproportionate connective tissue reaction of the remaining walls of the involved intestine, a process which frequently leads to stenosis of the lumen of the intestine, associated with the formation of multiple fistulas.

p. 1323.

This disease is now referred to as regional enteritis, regional ileitis, granulomatous enterocolitis, or Crohn's disease. Inflammation of the intestine is usually limited to the terminal ileum but can be found in the jejunum or the colon. The lumen of the intestine is usually narrowed and has a "cobblestone" appearance. Inflammation occurs in all layers of the intestine, especially the submucosa. Mesenteric lymph nodes are enlarged. Giant cells and epithelioid cells abound in non-caseating granulomas.

Onset

The disease usually begins in preadolescence and early adulthood. The onset can be acute, resembling appendicitis, or insidious associated with low-grade infection.

Clinical Features

1. Periodic low-grade fever.
2. Recurrent abdominal pain, especially after eating.
3. Intermittent diarrhea and constipation.
4. Stools slightly loose, quite loose, or containing blood, mucus, or pus.
5. Weight loss.
6. Delayed pubescence.
7. Tenderness or mass may be present in the lower part of the abdomen.
8. Radiographic studies show a thickening and rigidity of segments of the bowel wall, irregularities of the mucosa, ulceration fistula or narrowing of the bowel, and a "cobblestone" pattern.
9. The colon may also be involved in some cases.
10. This disorder sometimes may be mistaken for anorexia nervosa, especially in the absence of gastrointestinal symptoms. However, in anorexia there is a distortion of body image, denial of thinness, refusal to eat, and relentless pursuit of thinness.

Psychobiological Factors

Bockus (1945) noticed that a significant number of patients suffering from regional enteri-tis were highly sensitive, excitable, or severely psychoneurotic. Stewart (1949) found that many patients had a variety of psychopathological disorders and that reactivation of the disease was closely related to emotional stress factors.

Whybrow *et al.* (1968), in a retrospective study of 59 patients, noticed that 62.5% had a history of psychiatric disorders, particularly depression. Temporal relationships existed in most of thse cases between psychological stress and exacerbation of the disease.

Latimer (1978) critically reviewed the literature pertaining to the psychological and social outcome of Crohn's disease. Patients suffering from Crohn's disease scored much higher on the scale of "neuroticism" as compared with the normal population and patients with other chronic medical illnesses, although their scores were similar to other psychosomatic or neurotic patients. In summary, approximately one-third of the patients with Crohn's disease have significant psychiatric disorders, such as anxiety or depression, and "...psychiatric morbidity increases with chronicity and severity of the Crohn's disease." (ibid., p. 653)

It is not clear whether the psychological traits or psychiatric disturbances associated with psychophysiological disorders are secondary to these chronic, debilitating diseases or exist before clinical manifestation. However, it is generally agreed that a combination of familial tendencies, hypersensitivity, proclivity to infection, and psychological stress contribute to the expression and exacerbation of psychophysiological disorders.

Functional Encopresis

Functional encopresis is voluntary or involuntary defecation in an inappropriate setting after age 4 years, which is not related to physical disorder. If soiling occurs because of organic factors, it is called fecal incontinence or fecal soiling.

Prevalence

Bellman (1966), in epidemiological studies of 9,591 7-year-old first graders in Sweden, found that the prevalence of encopresis was 1.5%. The male to female ratio was 3.4 to 1. Although encopresis is thought to be more common in lower socioeconomic groups in the United States, Bellman's studies showed that in Sweden it crossed all socioeconomic levels.

Clinical Features

1. Repeated voluntary or involuntary defecation in culturally inappropriate settings.
2. The stool is usually of normal or near normal consistency.
3. Occurs in a child or individual older than age 4 years, with a frequency of at least once per month.
4. Absence of organic pathology of physical disorder, such as aganglionic megacolon (Hirschsprung's disease) or anal fissure.
5. Functional encopresis may be related to constipation or fecal impaction with resulting overflow. In these cases, the child usually soils clothes after bathing due to reflex stimulation.
6. Encopresis is divided into primary and secondary types. In primary encopresis, the child has not had any fecal continence for a period of one year or longer after age 4 years. In secondary encopresis the child has had "...a period of fecal continence for at least one year." (*DSM-III*, 1980, p. 81)
7. Approximately 25% of encopretic children are enuretic.

Psychological Perspective

In most encopretic children, psychological factors play a significant role in the development and persistency of symptoms. The birth of siblings, separation from mother, hospitalization, surgical procedures, inadequate training, early, harsh, and punitive or inconsistent toilet training, intrusive methods, such as frequent enemas or use of laxatives, physical abuse, and lack of emotional support are significant contributing factors.

Continuous soiling may be related to the child's regressive tendencies, infantile wishes, or fixation in the early anal level of psychosexual development. Encopresis may be the expression of aggressive and destructive wishes and impulses. Shame, embarrassment, and guilt frequently are associated with this disorder. If children deliberately soil as opposed to involuntary soiling, the encopresis may be associated with antisocial and acting-out behavior. Frequently, encopretic children deny, hide, or cover up their soiling to avoid embarrassment or punishment.

Management and Treatment

In the management and treatment of functional encopresis, it is important to help the parents de-emphasize and "ignore" the symptom. The more the parents focus on the symptom, the more the behavior will be reinforced. Harsh punishment and coercive actions usually increase the child's feelings of shame, anger, ambivalence, and hostility toward the self and the parents. With support, encouragement, and emphasis on the child's positive behavior, 10 to 20% of encopretic children stop soiling soon after consultation with the clinician. In other cases, individual psychotherapy for the child and concomitant therapeutic work with the family are indicated. Play therapy, working with clay and paint, along with helping the child to express aggressive and hostile feelings through play or verbally, significantly decrease encopresis. It is important to help the child and the family realize that encopresis is just a symptom. This symptom is stubborn and takes, at times, a long period to disappear. Working with the patient's and family's underlying psychological problems through the psychotherapeutic process and shoring up the patient's self-esteem through support and encouragement or positive reinforcement is valuable.

Some authors, including Gavanski (1971), have used medication, such as imipramine (10 mg., tid), in nonretentive forms of encopresis, along with play therapy and therapeutic work with parents. Others, such as Connell (1972), associate encopresis with underlying depression and have found imipramine up to 75 mg. daily to be effective along with play therapy for the child and counseling for the family. Mild laxative and dietary management, along with psychotherapy, can also be helpful in cases of chronic constipation.

STEREOTYPED MOVEMENT DISORDERS

Tic and Tourette's Disorder

Stereotyped movement disorders that involve a variety of tics are quite common in childhood and adolescence.

Definition of Tic

Tics are involuntary movements or utterances involving contractions of functionally related groups of skeletal muscles in one or more parts of the body. These symptoms are brief, frequent, rapid, sudden, unexpected, repetitive, purposeless, inappropriate, stereotypic, sometimes irresistible, and of variable intensity.
Shapiro and Shapiro, 1980, p. 4.

Types of Tics

Tics are divided into three types, depending on the multiplicity, intensity, and chronicity of the tic: transient tic disorder, chronic motor tic disorder, and Tourette's disorder. (*DSM-III*, 1980, p. 73)

Transient Tic Disorder

Between 12 and 24% of children have some form of "nervous tic" or "habit tic." These tics are usually repetitive, rapid, involuntary, and recurrent movements. The individual is able to suppress the tic for a few moments to a few hours. The tic usually begins in early childhood or adolescence, from age 2 years onward. By definition, the duration of transient tic disorder is between one month and one year.

Eye blinking and facial grimaces are the most common tics. Head, neck, upper or lower extremity, or body tics—including vocal tics—may occur. Excitement, anticipation, and stress usually increase the frequency of the tic. Tics often decrease during self-absorbing activities and disappear during sleep.

The intensity and frequency of tics varies throughout the day, week, and month. At times, tics may disappear totally or decrease significantly, only to reappear in times of stress. In some cases, the transient tic disorder may become intensified, chronic, and may lead to Tourette's disorder.

As in other movement disorders, tics are three to four times more common in boys than in girls. The incidence of tics in family members is much higher than in the general population. In most cases of transient tic disorder, the tics are usually single, mild, and subside within one year. At times, the patient becomes quite self-conscious and avoids social interaction. However, in most cases, after careful evaluation, reassurance and support can help the child and the family to manage the tic effectively. Medication is usually not indicated. Follow-up and re-evaluation are important to study the course of the tic and to determine whether or not it will develop into Tourette's disorder.

Chronic Motor Tic Disorder

Chronic motor tic disorder is similar to transient tic disorder but has more than one year's duration. The tic usually involves one to three muscle groups at each given time. Vocal tics do not usually occur, but if they do occur they are of low intensity, are not noticeable, and have the quality of a grunt or contraction of the thorax, abdomen, or diaphragm. Chronic motor tic disorder appears in childhood or after age 40 years. Tics that appear after age 40 are usually single tics. The intensity of chronic motor tic disorder is constant.

Tourette's Disorder or Chronic Multiple Tic Disorder

Tourette's disorder is similar to transient tic disorder except that the duration is more than one year. Simple or multiple vocal tics are always present, such as grunting, complicated sounds, and coprolalia (involuntary verbal expression of obscene or vulgar words). Coprolalia occurs in 60% of the cases. Echolalia (involuntary repetition of words spoken by others), and palilalia (involuntary repetition of one's own last words) occur in less than one-fourth of the cases. (Abuzzahab and Anderson, 1973, p. 492; Lucas, 1979, p. 672)

Historical Perspective

Itard (1825) clearly described the clinical features of this disorder. His patient, Marquise de Dampierre, began by the age of 7 years to have jerking of the arms and various body parts. Later, she developed coprolalia. She continued to have these disturbing symptoms until her death at age 80.

George Gilles de la Tourette (1885) described nine cases of motor incoordination associated with echolalia and coprolalia. This disorder became known as "maladie des tics," or "Gilles de la Tourette syndrome," and now is called Tourette's disorder.

In recent years with the work of Mahler and Rangell (1943), Challas *et al.* (1967), Lucas (1970, 1973), Shapiro and Shapiro (1968) Shapiro *et al.* (1973, 1978), Shapiro and Shapiro (1980), Abuzzahab and Anderson (1973), Cohen *et al.* (1979), and careful clinical observations, developmental diagnostic criteria and effective therapeutic management have been established.

Prevalence

The true incidence and prevalence of Tourette's disorder is not known. The prevalence is estimated to be between 10 and 50 per 100,000 in the United States. Based on this prevalence, between 22,000 and 110,000 people suffer from this disorder. The male to female ratio is 3 to 1.

Diagnostic Criteria

Accurate diagnosis is important for effective management and treatment. Unfortunately, many patients with Tourette's disorder are undiagnosed. Frequently, they are misdiagnosed as hyperactive children, as exhibiting behavior disorders, or as suffering from severe forms of psychopathology, such as depressive disorders, obsessive-compulsive personality disorders, borderline personality disorder, or schizophrenia. A misdiagnosis contributes to mismanagement, additional distress, and cost to the family, as well as increases the possibility of secondary psychopathological reactions.

The diagnostic criteria of Tourette's disorder are as follows:

A. Essential diagnostic criteria
  1. Onset between ages 2 to 15 years
  2. Involuntary multiple tics—muscular and vocal
  3. Variations and changes in intensity and occurrence of symptoms
  4. Duration of more than one year
  5. Chronic and life-long
B. Confirmatory symptoms—not essential for diagnosis
  1. Coprolalia
  2. Copropraxia (making obscene gestures)
  3. Echolalia
  4. Echopraxia (repeating other's actions)
  5. Palilalia
C. Concomitant disorders—not essential for diagnosis
  1. Hyperactivity, perceptual problems, learning difficulties
  2. Nonspecific abnormal EEG
  3. Soft, abnormal neurological signs
  4. Evidence of subtle perceptual motor problems and minimal brain dysfunction in psychological testing. (Adapted from Shapiro and Shapiro, 1980, p. 6)

Multiple tics need to be differentiated from the following movement disorders:

1. Choreiform movements—these are irregular, nonrepetitive random, and dancing movements. The movements may vary in frequency and magnitude. They are frequently related to the trunk and extremities. Movements are usually away from the body.
2. Athetoid movements—these are irregular, nonrhythmic, slow, writhing movements, frequently in fingers and toes. The movements may be repeated, but do not have the stereotyped quality of Tourette's disorder.
3. Hemiballismus—these are intermittent, unilateral, coarse, jumping, and wild movements of the extremities. Amplitude and direction change continuously. These movements usually occur in older persons suffering from a vascular lesion of the contralateral subthalamic nucleus.
4. Myoclonic movements—these are often bilateral, brief, sudden, shocklike muscle contractions affecting part of or an entire muscle, but not the whole muscle group.
5. Dystonia—these are slow, twisting movements associated with prolonged muscle tension. Usually several muscle groups, such as extremities or the torso, are involved. The symptoms are stereotyped, but they are more variable than tics.
6. Dyskinesia—these lingual, oral, buccal, and masticatory movements are usually silent. They are associated with choreoathetoid movements of the extremities, such as in tardive dyskinesia.

Etiology

Tourette's disorder appears to be familial. The etilogy is not known, but seems to be of organic nature. It is thought that this disorder may be related to the basal ganglion of the midbrain area, particularly to the corpus striatum and globus pallidus.

At the present time, it is hypothesized that the dopaminergic system of the corpus striatum of patients with Tourette's disorder shows hyperactivity. The increase of dopaminergic activities contributes to the expression of multiple tics. L-dopa has produced facial and extremity ticlike movements in animals. Also, some children who have been on dextroamphetamine, methylphenidate, and pemoline have later manifested Tourette's disorder, perhaps because of increased stimulation of dopaminergic systems of the corpus striatum.

Management and Treatment of Tourette's Disorder

Seignot (1961) reported on the effective treatment of a case of Tourette's disorder with haloperidol. Since then, the use of haloperidol has become the treatment of choice. Approximately 90% of the patients respond favorably to haloperidol. Vocal tics usually disappear. The frequency and intensity of facial and body tics decrease significantly.

Haloperidol, 0.5 mg., is given initially, and increased every 5 days by 0.5 mg., until the desired effect is achieved. This medication is given twice daily. The usual daily maintenance dose is between 3 and 10 mg. Occasionally, a patient may require a much higher dose. The desired effect is symptom reduction by 50 to 70%. If symptom reduction does not occur, medication can be increased until side effects occur. After initial symptom reduction, medication should be adjusted to the lowest possible effective maintenance dose. Medication allows the patient to attend school or work and decreases psychosocial problems. Drug holidays (discontinuation of medications for a period of time) are essential for long-term management. (See chapter 23)

We have noticed that even with the use of haloperidol, the frequency and intensity of tics wax and wane, depending on psychosocial factors, such as the beginning of school, Christmas holidays, birthdays, involvement in sports, and watching exciting or aggressively loaded television programs. (Surwillo *et al.*, 1978) The patient's and parents' awareness of the variability of tics even while the patient is on medication helps them cope with these changes.

We have developed a form for the parents or older patients to record 3 to 4 times daily for a 15 minute period the types and frequency of tics. They are asked to record what the patient was doing at that time and what may have been precipitating factors. This record helps the parents carefully document the frequency, intensity, multiplicity, and variability of the tics. Also, it helps the patient and his family become aware of environmental factors that may contribute to precipitation of the tics.

For diagnostic assessment, the parents are asked to record observations for 2 weeks. Their observations are extremely helpful in diagnosing Tourette's disorder and in observing the patient's response to medication and therapeutic intervention.

Ross and Moldofsky (1977) have found pimozide (diphenylbutylpiperidine), which has a more specific antidopaminergic action than haloperidol (a butyrophenone), to be effective in the treatment of Tourette's disorder. They also found that patients on pimozide complained less of lethargy and showed less side effects. The dose of pimozide is usually 4 to 60 mg./day. The average dose is 8 mg./day.

Penfluridol, which is a more specific dopamine blocker and does not block norepinephrine or serotonin, is thought to be more effective than haloperidol. (Holomboe, 1977) This study was done in Norway. The patient received 60 mg. of penfluridol twice per week and showed an 85% symptom reduction. This medication is experimental and is under further study. For additional information concerning side effects of haloperidol, see chapter 23.

Patients (and families) suffering from Tou-

rette's disorder need long-term follow-up for adjustment of medication. At times, they need supportive psychotherapy, especially during adolescence and young adulthood to help them to cope with this chronic disorder and the associated psychosocially distressful symptoms.

Although some patients with Tourette's disorder manifest obsessive-compulsive features, it appears that the extent of psychopathology is not specific and frequently is a secondary reaction to poor medical management and lack of proper family support and a stressful educational and vocational environment. Unfortunately, only 5% of the patients with Tourette's disorder become totally symptom-free in adolescence or young adulthood.

REFERENCES

Abuzzahab, F.S., Anderson, R.D. (1973). Gilles de la Tourette syndrome. International registry. *Minn. Med., 56,* 492–496.

Alexander, F. (1934). The influence of psychologic factors upon gastro-intestinal disturbances. *Psychoanal. Q., 3,* 501–539.

Alexander, F. (1950). *Psychosomatic Medicine—Its Principles and Applications.* New York: Norton.

American Psychiatric Association (1952). *Diagnostic and Statistical Manual of Mental Disorders.* Washington, D.C.: American Psychiatric Association.

American Psychiatric Association (1968). *Diagnostic and Statistical Manual of Mental Disorders.* Second Edition. Washington, D.C.: American Psychiatric Association.

American Psychiatric Association (1980). *Diagnostic and Statistical Manual of Mental Disorders.* Third Edition. Washington, D.C.: American Psychiatric Association.

Bellman, M. (1966). Studies on encopresis. *Acta Paediatr. Scand., 170,* 1–151.

Bliss, E.L. (1975). Anorexia nervosa. In Freedman, A.M., Kaplan, H.I., Sadock, B.J. (Eds.), *Comprehensive Textbook of Psychiatry-II,* Vol. 2. Second Edition. Baltimore: Williams and Wilkins, pp. 1655–1660.

Bliss, E.L., Branch, C.H. (1960). *Anorexia Nervosa: Its History, Psychology, and Biology.* New York: Hoeber, pp. 23–46.

Bockus, H.L. (1945). Gastroenterology: Present status of chronic regional or cicatrizing enteritis. *J.A.M.A., 127,* 449.

Bruch, H. (1973). *Eating Disorders: Obesity, Anorexia Nervosa, and the Person Within.* New York: Basic Books.

Bruch, H. (1978). *The Golden Cage: The Enigma of Anorexia Nervosa.* Cambridge: Harvard University Press.

Challas, G., Chapel, J.L., Jenkins, R.L. (1967). Tourette's disease: Control of symptoms and its clinical course. *Int. J. Neuropsychiatry, 3* (Suppl. 1), 95–109.

Chapman, A.H., Loeb, D.G., Young, J.B. (1956). Psychologic aspects of pediatrics. A psychosomatic study of five children with duodenal ulcer. *J. Pediatr., 48,* 248–261.

Cohen, D.J., Shaywitz, B.A., Young, J.G. Carbonari, C.M., Nathanson, J.A., Lieberman, D., Bowers, M.B., Maas, J.W. (1979). Central biogenic amine metabolism in children with the syndrome of chronic multiple tics of Gilles de la Tourette: Norepinephrine, serotonin, and dopamine. *J. Am. Acad. Child Psychiatry, 18,* 320–341.

Connell, H.M. (1972). The practical management of encopresis. *Aust. Paediatr. J., 8,* 273–278.

Crisp, A.H., Palmer, R.L., Kalucy, R.S. (1976). How common is anorexia nervosa? A prevalence study. *Br. J. Psychiatry, 128,* 549–554.

Crohn, B.B., Ginzburg, L., Oppenheimer, G.D. (1932). Regional ileitis. A pathologic and clinical entity. *J.A.M.A., 99,* 1323–1329.

Dunbar, F. (1954). *Emotions and Bodily Changes.* New York: Columbia University Press.

Engel, G.L. (1975). Psychophysiological gastrointestinal disorders. I. Peptic ulcer. In Freedman, A.M., Kaplan, H.I., Sadock, B.J. (Eds.), *Comprehensive Textbook of Psychiatry-II,* Vol. 2. Baltimore: Williams and Wilkins. pp. 1638–1643.

Engel, G.L., Segal, H.L. (1956). A study of an infant with a gastric fistula. *Psychosom. Med., 18,* 374–398.

Erikson, E.H. (1969). *Gandhi's Truth: On the Origins of Militant Nonviolence.* New York: Norton.

Feighner, J.P., Robins, E., Guze, S.B., Woodruff, R.A., Jr., Winokur, G., Munoz, A. (1972). Diagnostic criteria for use in psychiatric research. *Arch. Gen. Psychiatry, 26,* 57–63.

Floyer, Sir J. (1698). *A Treatise of the Asthma.* London: Rich and Wilkin.

French, T.M., Alexander, F. (1941). Psychogenic factors in bronchial asthma. *Psychosom. Med. Monogr., 2, 4.*

Gavanski, M. (1971). Treatment of non-retentive secondary encopresis with imipramine and psychotherapy. *Can. Med. Assoc. J., 104,* 46–48.

Gilles de la Tourette, G. (1885). Étude sur une affection nerveuse caractérisée par de l'incoordination motorice accompagnée d'écholalie et de coprolalie (jumping, latah, myriachit). *Arch. Neurol., 9,* 19–42, 158–200.

Gull, W.W. (1874). Anorexia nervosa. *Trans. Clin. Soc., 7,* 22–28.

Holomboe (1977). Paper presented at VI World Congress of Psychiatry, Honolulu, Hawaii.

Itard, J.M.G. (1825). Mémoire sur quelques fonctions involontaires des appareils de la locomotion, de la.préhension et de la voix. *Arch. Gen. Med., 8,* 385–407.

Kaplan, H.I. (1975). History of psychophysiological medicine. In Freedman, A.M., Kaplan, H.I., Sadock, B.J. (Eds.), *Comprehensive Textbook of Psychiatry-II,* Vol. 2 Second Edition. Baltimore: Williams and Wilkins, pp. 1624–1631.

Kavanaugh, J.G., Mattsson, A. (1979). Psychophysiological disorders. In Noshpitz, J. (Ed.), *Basic Handbook of Child Psychiatry,* Vol. 2. New York: Basic Books, pp. 341–380.

Knapp, P.H. (1960). Acute bronchial asthma. Psychoanalytic observations on fantasy, emotional arousal, and partial discharge. *Psychosom. Med., 22,* 88–105.

Knapp, P.H. (1963). The asthmatic child and the psychosomatic problem of asthma: Toward a general theory. In Schneer, H.I. (Ed.), *The Asthmatic Child.* New York: Harper and Row, pp. 234–255.

Lasegue, E.C. (1873). De l'anorexie hystérique. *Arch. Gén. Med., 21,* 385–403. Translation: (1873), On hysterical anorexia. *Med. Times Gaz., 2,* 265–266, 367–369.

Latimer, P.R. (1978). Crohn's disease: A review of the psychological and social outcome. *Psychol. Med., 8,* 649–656.

Lucas, A.R. (1970). Gilles de la Tourette's disease: An overview. *N.Y. State J. Med., 70,* 2197–2200.

Lucas, A.R. (1973). Report of Gilles de la Tourette's disease in two succeeding generations. *Child Psychiatry Human Dev., 3,* 231–233.

Lucas, A.R., (1979). Tic: Gilles de la Tourette's syndrome. In Noshpitz, J. (Ed.), *Basic Handbook of Child Psychiatry,* Vol. 2. New York: Basic Books, pp. 667–684.

McDermott, J.F., Finch, S.M. (1967). Ulcerative colitis in children: Reassessment of a dilemma. *J. AM. Acad. Child Psychiatry, 6,* 512–525.

Mahler, M.S., Rangell, L. (1943). A psychosomatic study of maladie des tics (Gilles de la Tourette's disease). *Psychoanal.*

Q., 17, 579–603.

Minuchin, S., Baker, L., Rosman, B.L., Liebman, R., Milman, L., Todd, T.C. (1975). A conceptual model of psychosomatic illness in children: Family organization and family therapy. *Arch Gen. Psychiatry, 32,* 1031–1038.

Mirsky, I.A. (1958). Physiologic, psychologic, and social determinants in the etiology of duodenal ulcer. *Am. J. Dig. Dis., 3,* 285–314.

Morton, R. (1689). *Phthisiologia—Or A Treatise of Consumption.* London: Smith.

Nelson, W.E., Vaughan, V.C., McKay, R.J. (Eds.) (1969). *Textbook of Pediatrics.* Philadelphia: W.B. Saunders Company.

Peshkin, M.M. (1963). Diagnosis of asthma in children: Past and present. In Schneer, H.I. (Ed.), *The Asthmatic Child.* New York: Harper and Row, pp. 1–15.

Rollins, N., Piazza, E. (1978). Diagnosis of anorexia nervosa. A critical reappraisal. *J. Am. Acad. Child Psychiatry, 17,* 126–137.

Ross, M.S., Moldofsky, H. (1977). Comparison of pimozide with haloperidol in Gilles de la Tourette's syndrome. *Lancet, 1,* 103.

Rush, B. (1770). Treatise on the spasmodic asthma of children. In Schneer, H.I. (Ed.), *The Asthmatic Child.* New York: Harper and Row, p. 2.

Salter, H.H. (1860). *Asthma, Its Pathology and Treatment.* London: Churchill.

Seignot, J.N. (1961). Un cas de maladie des tics de Gilles de la Tourette guéri par le R. 1625. *Ann Soc. Medic-Psychologique, 119,* 578–579.

Shafii, M. (1972). A precedent for modern psychotherapeutic techniques: One thousand years ago. *Am. J. Psychiatry, 128,* 1581–1584.

Shafii, M. (1973). Psychotherapeutic treatment of rheumatoid arthritis. One thousand years ago. *Arch. Gen Psychiatry, 29,* 85–87.

Shafii, M., Salguero, C., Finch, S.M. (1975). Anorexia à deux. Psychopathology and treatment of anorexia nervosa in latency-age siblings. *J. Am. Acad. Child Psychiatry, 14,* 617–632.

Shafii, M. (1981). Pseudo-acute abdomen in anorexia nervosa. *Psychosomatics, 22,* 634–635.

Shapiro, A.K., Shapiro, E. (1968). Treatment of Gilles de la Tourette's syndrome with haloperidol. *Br. J. Psychiatry, 114,* 345–350.

Shapiro, A.K., Shapiro, E., Wayne, H.L. (1973). The symptomatology and diagnosis of Gilles de la Tourette's syndrome. *J. Am. Acad. Child Psychiatry, 12,* 702–723.

Shapiro, A.K., Shapiro, E.S., Bruun, R.D., Sweet, R.C. (1978). *Gilles de la Tourette Syndrome.* New York: Raven Press.

Shapiro, A.K., Shapiro, E.S. (1980). *Tics, Tourette Syndrome and other Movement Disorders.* New York: Tourette Syndrome Association.

Sperling, M. (1949). The role of the mother in psychosomatic disorders in children. *Psychosom. Med., 11,* 377.

Sperling, M. (1963). A psychoanalytic study of bronchial asthma in children. In Schneer, H.I. (Ed.), *The Asthmatic Child.* New York: Harper and Row, pp. 138–165.

Stein, A., Kaufman, M.R., Janowitz, H.D., Levy, M.H., Hollander, F., Winkelstein, A. (1962). Changes in hydrochloric acid secretion in a patient with a gastric fistula during intensive psychotherapy. *Psychosom. Med., 24,* 427.

Stewart, W. (1949). Psychosomatic aspects of regional ileitis. *N.Y. J. Med., 49,* 2820.

Sultz, H.A., Schlesinger, E.P., Feldman, J.G., et al. (1970). The epidemiology of peptic ulcer in childhood. *Am. J. Public Health, 60,* 492–498.

Surwillo, W.W., Shafii, M., Barrett, C.L. (1978). Single case study. Gilles de la Tourette syndrome. A 20-month study of the effects of stressful life events and haloperidol on symptom frequency. *J. Nerv. Ment. Dis., 166,* 812–816.

Sylvester, E. (1945). Analysis of psychogenic anorexia and vomiting in a four-year-old child. *Psychoanal. Study Child, 1,* 167–187.

Tarboroff, L.H., Brown, W.H. (1954). A study of the personality patterns of children and adolescents with the peptic ulcer syndrome. *Am. J. Orthopsychiatry, 24,* 602–610.

Weiss, E.B. (1975). Bronchial asthma. *Clin. Symp., 27* (1 and 2), 1–72.

Whybrow, P.C., Kane, F.J., Lipton, M.A. (1968). Regional ileitis and psychiatric disorder. *Psychosom. Med., 30,* 209–221.

Chapter 13

PSYCHIATRIC EMERGENCIES*

During the beginning of the Child Guidance Clinic Movement (1910's and 1920's), child psychiatry was a pioneer in creating community-based mental health services and providing emergency care for children and their parents. (Watson, 1975) During the last few decades, however, child psychiatric services have become less responsive and more reluctant to provide immediate, efficient, high quality emergency care. Visotsky (1975), regarding present mental health services for children, reported that these services tend "...to be oriented to the needs of professionals providing services rather than to the needs of children being served." (p. 14)

Placing children in crisis on waiting lists has become the usual procedure in child guidance clinics and in child psychiatric services within university training programs. It is not uncommon for a child to be on a waiting list for 3 to 4 months before initial psychiatric evaluation, and then to wait a few months longer before receiving needed psychiatric treatment.

In many parts of the United States, pediatricians, family physicians, school counselors, and other referral sources have "given up" expecting immediate response for psychiatric evaluation and treatment for children in crisis. The "ivory tower" image of child psychiatric facilities is further enhanced by the reluctance of the staff to respond to the emergency needs of the community. The staff often acts as "gate keepers" to "screen out" the most troubled patients and only accept the "best" patients for evaluation and treatment!

NEED FOR IMMEDIATE RESPONSE

Children and youth are experiencing various phases of growth and development. Any undue emotional stress and strain, if not attended to immediately, will not only complicate the emo-

tional problem but might contribute to an arrest in development. The sooner one takes care of an emergency situation, the more receptive the child, family, and community will be to therapeutic intervention, and the better the outcome.

Lindemann (1944), after studying the survivors' emotional reactions to the Coconut Grove fire in Boston, emphasized the need for immediate psychological and psychiatric intervention for helping to deal with grief, mourning, depression, and losses. Based on Lindemann's contribution and Gerald Caplan's (1961, 1964) work with war survivors in Israel, the community psychiatry movement in the United States for providing immediate emergency care for emotionally troubled adults on all socioeconomic levels became prevalent in the 1960's and 1970's.

Unfortunately, the development of emergency psychiatric services for children and adolescents has lagged far behind adult programs. For instance, in the United States in 1977, of 501 hospitals with psychiatric services, 43% provided emergency psychiatric care for adults, but very few provided such care for children and adolescents. (American Hospital Association, 1978)

Schowalter and Solnit (1966) reported on the development of a program for bringing child psychiatric trainees into the pediatric emergency rooms of general hospitals in order to provide the trainees with "...the opportunity to treat acute psychological problems in collaboration with the pediatrician and the community." (p. 534) They concluded that the availability of child psychiatrists for providing emergency care enhanced the relationship with the pediatrician and helped in

---

* An abbreviated version of this chapter, entitled "The Pediatric-Psychiatric Model for Emergencies in Child Psychiatry: A Study of 994 Cases," by Shafii, M., Whittinghill, R., and Healy, M.H., appeared in *Am. J. Psychiatry,* 136(12): 1600–1601, 1979.

integrating biological, intrapsychic, and environmental factors in the assessment and treatment of children and families in crisis.

STUDIES OF CHILD PSYCHIATRIC EMERGENCIES

Burks and Hoekstra (1964) studied 110 cases that were referred to Children's Psychiatric Hospital, Ann Arbor, Michigan, for emergency referral during a one-year period and compared them with 110 nonemergent, randomly selected children from the same Clinic.

Suicidal attempts, incipient psychosis, and school refusal were considered "bonafide emergency situations." Most of these children had had emotional problems for a long period of time, but "...it was an outsider who found a 'crisis' and instigated the emergency referral." (p. 137)

Mattson et al. (1967) reported on "...a retrospective and follow-up study of 170 child psychiatric emergencies [of children and adolescents under age 18] seen at the child psychiatry clinic [over a two-year period] at University Hospitals, Cleveland." (p. 584) The authors defined emergency as "...a condition of sufficient emotional distress in a child which he, his family, or the referral source feel incapable of handling for even a few hours." (ibid., p. 584)

Mattson et al. found that 83% of the emergency cases were from ages 12 to 18, and 60% of all emergency cases were girls. Almost one-half of the emergencies were self-referral.

The types of emergencies were:

1. Suicidal behavior—44%
2. Assaultive and destructive behavior—19%
3. Marked anxiety and fears frequently associated with physical complaints—13%
4. Bizarre and confused behavior—10%
5. School refusal—7%
6. Truancy and runaway—7%

Mattson et al. noticed that 62% of all referrals were related to changes of mood and behavior— for instance, depression (often with suicidal behavior), fears, and somatic complaints. Assaultive, aggressive, and unmanageable behavior only accounted for 38%. More than two-thirds of the emergency cases had a history of long-standing emotional disorder of more than one year. One-third of all emergencies were admitted to an inpatient setting.

Morrison (1969, 1975, 1979) related child psychiatric emergencies to "normal emotional dependence of the child." (1979, p. 522) He felt that

"...emotional disturbance in the family and in individual family members creates crisis for the child and leads to distortions or blocks in his emotional growth." (ibid., p. 522) He defined emergency as a "...situation in which the significant adults around the child can no longer help him master his anxiety and can no longer provide temporary ego support and control." (ibid., p. 522)

He conceptualized the child's symptomatology and "coping maneuvers" in the following way:

1. Withdrawal—suicide attempts, school phobia, conversion, dissociation
2. Projection—assaultive and delinquent behavior
3. Decompensation—panic and psychosis

PEDIATRIC-PSYCHIATRIC MODEL

During 1974 to 1975, in the Child Psychiatric Services, University of Louisville School of Medicine, we implemented a working model for responding to psychiatric emergencies, based on presenting symptoms and manifest behavior.

We have found that "...integration of the pediatric model of efficient, acute, short-term [outpatient or] inpatient care..." (Shafii et al., 1979a, p. 428) with "...the psychiatric model of developmental perspective, psychological sensitivity, and psychotherapeutic orientation..." is the most effective way of providing emergency care. (Shafii et al., 1979b, p. 1600) We call this approach the pediatric-psychiatric model. "The strength of this model is the immediate therapeutic response to the needs of the child and the family in crisis." (Shafii et al., 1979b, p. 1600)

Definition of Child and Adolescent Psychiatric Emergencies

In the Child Psychiatric Services of the University of Louisville, we have found the following working definition to be clinically and operationally useful. Psychiatric emergencies in infancy, childhood, and adolescence are defined "...as situations in which the life of the child or of someone else is in danger or the child is at high risk for a catastrophic trauma." (Shafii et al., 1979b, p. 1600) Generally, the situation is so severe that the family and community support systems cannot cope any longer without immediate intervention. These children and their families should be seen within 24 hours.

Trends in Emergency Service in Louisville

In 1972, before implementation of the pediatric-psychiatric model for emergency services, there were 20 emergency cases served. The model was implemented in 1974 and 1975. By 1977, the number of emergency cases served increased to 263 cases, an overall increase of 1,215% ($P<0.001$, $X^2 = 341.393$).

Between the years of 1972 and 1977, there was a 162% increase in the total number of outpatient diagnostic evaluations, and contacts increased from 358 to 938 cases, $P < 0.001$.

Looking at pediatric emergencies from 1972 to 1976, we found that emergency visits to Children's Hospital increased from 31,125 to 41,352—a 30% increase. From these data, it is evident that although there has been an increase in pediatric emergency case episodes, there has been a much more dramatic increase in child psychiatric emergencies.

We feel that this significant increase is related to the receptivity and availability of the staff in providing emergency services and reflects the great unmet need that exists for emergency child mental health services across the nation.

Types of Emergencies

From 1973 to 1977, 835 cases of children and adolescents under age 18 years were evaluated on an emergency basis. These cases were divided into the following categories, according to their most severe psycho-pathological behavior:

1. *Suicidal and self-destructive behavior*—includes suicide attempts, gestures, active suicidal thoughts, marked depression, severe withdrawal, and self-harming and self-destructive behaviors in younger children
2. *Harmful or destructive behavior toward others*—attempting or actually harming others, threatening to kill or seriously harm others, violent destructive behavior, fire-setting, being beyond the control of parents, teachers, or other authority figures, and serious antisocial behavior
3. *Abuse or neglect*—severe neglect, physical abuse, sexual abuse, molestation and incest
4. *Phobic or extremely anxious behavior*—severe school phobia, school refusal, panic reactions, other severe phobias, and severely anxious and agitated behavior
5. *Psychotic behavior*—acute psychotic episodes and other severe forms of psychotic confusion

6. *Runaways*—children or adolescents who have a high risk of running away from home (based on past history of runaway behavior)
7. *Medical-psychiatric emergencies*—severe anorexia nervosa, diabetic children who will not take insulin, and other serious physical conditions aggravated by emotional problems
8. *Drug and alcohol abuse*—including severe abuse of toxic agents, such as glue, paint, gasoline, alcohol, or drugs
9. *Others*—severe family crisis, war trauma, multiproblem crises, and extreme emotional fragility (Shafii *et al.,* 1979b, p. 1600)

From 1973 to and including 1977, 34% of the total cases seen were classified as suicidal or self-destructive and 26% of the cases as harmful or destructive behavior toward others.

We have observed a gradual increase in the number of cases of serious child abuse or neglect—from 3% in 1973 to 19% in 1977, or 13% of all cases.

Significantly, *73% of all emergency cases were directly related to severe destructive behavior toward the self or others or related to severe forms of child abuse and neglect.* The other 27% of the cases were distributed as follows: phobic behavior, 11%; psychotic behavior, 5%; runaways, 4%; medical-psychiatric emergencies, 3%; drug abuse, 2%; and others, 2%. *It is clearly evident that violence against young people and by young people against themselves and others is the most significant psychopathological factor in child psychiatric emergencies.*

Age Distribution

Data on age were available in 820 cases. Of the total number of emergencies, 43% were between ages 13 and 18 years; 39%, 7 to 12 years; 12%, 4 to 6 years; and 6% were one to 3 years.

Regarding the nine emergency categories and their relationships to age, 60% of the suicidal and self-harming behavior cases were between ages 13 and 18 years; 33%, ages 7 and 12 years; 5%, ages 4 and 6 years; and 2%, ages one and 3 years. In the one- to 3-year age group, severe head-banging and self-mutilating behavior were included.

In the group of those young people who exhibited harmful and destructive behavior toward others, 34% were between ages 13 and 18 years; 42%, ages 7 and 12 years; 20%, ages 4 and 6 years; and 4%, ages one and 3 years.

In the abuse and neglect population, 7% were between ages 13 and 18 years; 39%, ages 7 and 12 years; 34%, ages 4 and 6 years; and 18%, ages one and 3 years. Ninety-one percent of all the cases of child abuse and neglect were under age 12 years, with 52% under age 6. Preschoolers are not the only ones vulnerable for abuse. Abuse and neglect are found in all age groups.

Vulnerability and Age

What serious pathological behavior can one expect to see in the various age groups?

Under Age Three

Of the 43 emergency cases under age 3 years, 49% were referred for serious abuse and neglect, 21% for being harmful or destructive to others, and 14% for self-harming behavior. Altogether, 84% of the cases were related to abuse, neglect, and destructive behaviors against the self or others.

Ages Four to Six

In this category of 123 cases, 35% were harmful and destructive toward others, 32% abused or neglected, 14% had severe phobic behavior, and 12% were suicidal. Again, we notice that 79% were either abused or destructive toward themselves or others.

Ages Seven to Twelve

There were 300 cases in this category. Of these, 33% were suicidal, 30% were harmful and destructive toward others, 15% were abused or neglected, 14% were phobic, 3% psychotic, 3% runaways, and 2% medical-psychiatric emergencies. In total, 78% were either destructive toward themselves or others or were abused.

Ages Thirteen to Eighteen

In this group of 343 cases, 51% were suicidal, 21% harmful and destructive toward others, 3% were abused or neglected, 7% had phobic behavior, 7% psychotic behavior, 5% were runaways, and medical-psychiatric emergencies and drug abuse were each 3%. Again, 75% were destructive toward themselves or others or abused.

Sex and Race Distribution

Beginning in 1977, we expanded our data base to include information on the sex and race of emergency cases. In 1977 we saw 263 cases. Data on nine cases were incomplete so they were excluded. The following data are based on 254 cases.

Of these, 137 (54%) were male and 117 (46%) were female. Generally, the sex distribution in a child psychiatric setting is 66 to 75% male and 25 to 33% female. In the emergency population, the sex ratio was more evenly distributed.

The number of white males was 42%; white females, 35%; black males, 12%; black females, 9%; and others, 2%. Altogether, 77% were white and 21% were black. This closely matches the racial population in the community within this age group.

Regarding the nine emergency categories, 13% of white females were suicidal or self-destructive, 12% of white males, 3% of black females, and 2% of black males. Although the number of white females is less than the number of white males, the percentage of the suicidal behavior in them is higher.

Regarding harmful and destructive behavior toward others, 15% of white males, 6% of white females, 4% of black males, and 3% of black females were in this category.

Regarding child abuse and neglect, 8% of white females, 7% of white males, 3% of black males, and 1½% of black females were in this category. Although again the number of white females was lower than white males, the percentage of abuse of white females is higher than white males.

Management of Emergencies

The clinician must not only be flexible and ready for immediate diagnostic evaluation and intervention in emergency cases, but should also create a receptive and flexible system for the treatment and follow-up of such cases. Emergencies are highly demanding and require greater time and resources than regular cases.

For instance, in a case of severe child abuse or neglect, or an active suicidal youth, the clinician must work with the child, the distraught family, and also a multitude of social agencies—school, family physician, court, child protective agencies, and the support systems of relations, friends, neighborhood, and religious organizations. It is not uncommon to spend 12 to 18 hours on the initial phase of assessment and disposition, as oppsed to the 4- to 6-hour average for a nonemergent evaluation and disposition.

Many emergencies need immediate follow-up and treatment and cannot be placed on long-term waiting lists. Our experience shows that 65 to 70% of all emergencies referred to the Clinic become involved in treatment and follow-up. The rest are referred to other mental health and social support programs or private practitioners, as opposed to 50% of the regular and nonemergent cases.

Of the emergency cases referred, 40% need immediate short-term inpatient psychiatric hospitalization. Absence of an inpatient child psychiatric facility for providing immediate care for highly distressed children, youth, and their families decreases significantly the effectiveness of emergency care. The lack of an inpatient facility increases, in the long run, the cost of mental health care due to duplication of services, repetition in outpatient emergency contacts, and, above all, increases the mental health morbidity of children and families in distress.

Distribution of Resources

Approximately 25% of our case load during this time period were emergencies; however, 33% of the staffs' and trainees' time was devoted to inpatient and outpatient emergency care.

The Trend

The trend of emergency referrals has continued to increase at the Child Psychiatric Services, University of Louisville. In 1980, out of 883 new referrals, 365 were emergencies—slightly more than 40% of all referrals. Approximately 40% of these emergencies, or 16% of the total number of referrals, were for suicidal and self-destructive behavior in children and adolescents.

CONCLUSION

Emergency mental health care for children, youth, and their families is desperately needed. We have discussed the development of an emergency child psychiatric service based on a pediatric-psychiatric model. This service is totally integrated within the daily operation of a child guidance clinic.

All of the staff and trainees participate in providing emergency service. In our experience,

creation of a separate emergency service is not advisable. Total integration of such care within the daily routine of the program is most efficient. The establishment of a small, acute, short-term inpatient facility will significantly enhance the effectiveness of emergency care. (Shafii et al., 1979b)

The psychiatric education of primary care physicians, residents in psychiatry, child psychiatry fellows, and other mental health professionals must include their achieving competency in recognizing and managing child psychiatric emergencies.

REFERENCES

American Hospital Association (1978). *Hospital Statistics: Data from the American Hospital Association Annual Survey.* Chicago: American Hospital Association.

Burks, H.L., Hoekstra, M. (1964). Psychiatric emergencies in children. *Am. J. Orthopsychiatry, 34,* 134–137.

Caplan, G. (1961). *Prevention of Mental Disorders in Children.* New York: Basic Books.

Caplan, G. (1964). *Principles of Preventive Psychiatry.* New York: Basic Books.

Lindemann, E. (1944). Symptomology and management of acute grief. *Am. J. Psychiatry, 101,* 141–148.

Mattson, A., Hawkins, J.W., Seese, L.R. (1967). Child psychiatric emergencies. *Arch. Gen. Psychiatry, 17,* 584–592.

Morrison, G.C. (1969). Therapeutic intervention in a child psychiatry emergency service. *J. Am. Acad. Child Psychiatry, 8,* 542–558.

Morrison, G.C. (1975). *Emergencies in Child Psychiatry: Emotional Crises of Children, Youth, and their Families.* Springfield, Ill: Charles C Thomas.

Morrison, G.C. (1979). Emergency intervention. In Noshpitz, J. (Ed.), *Basic Handbook of Child Psychiatry,* Vol. 3. New York: Basic Books, pp. 519–536.

Schowalter, J.E., Solnit, A.J. (1966). Child psychiatry consultation in a general hospital emergency room. *J. Am. Acad. Child Psychiatry, 5,* 534–551.

Shafii, M., McCue, A., Ice, J.F., Schwab, J.J. (1979a). The development of an acute short-term inpatient child psychiatric setting: A pediatric-psychiatric model. *Am. J. Psychiatry, 136,* 427–429.

Shafii, M., Whittinghill, R., Healy, M.H. (1979b). The pediatric-psychiatric model for emergencies in child psychiatry: A study of 994 cases. *Am. J. Psychiatry, 136,* 1600–1601.

Visotsky, H.M. (1975). The joint commission on mental health of children: Progress report. *Psychiatr. Ann., 5,* 11–20.

Watson, A. (1975). Book review. *J. Am. Acad. Child Psychiatry, 14,* 178–180.

Chapter 14

SELF-DESTRUCTIVE, SUICIDAL BEHAVIOR, AND COMPLETED SUICIDE

The myth that children do not commit suicide still exists, even among psychiatrists and allied health professionals! We are reluctant to understand and take seriously our children's and youth's despair. This despair, more often than it is commonly realized, expresses itself in the form of either suicidal attempt or completed suicide.

The incidence and pattern of completed suicide in children and adolescents on a national level, along with a study conducted in the Jefferson County, Kentucky, area will be discussed.* The latter part of this chapter will focus on suicide attempts and other self-destructive behavior in children and adolescents and will include a discussion of management and treatment.

HISTORICAL PERSPECTIVE

Choron (1972) referred to "...the first known document dealing with suicide." (p. 12) This document, written in Egypt more than 4,000 years ago, is a dialogue between a despondent man and his soul, at the time he is actively contemplating suicide:

To whom can I speak today?
...
The friends of today do not love...
Hearts are rapacious;
Every man seizes his fellow's goods...
The gentle man has perished,
[But] the violent man has access to everybody...
There are no righteous;
The land is left to those who do wrong...
To whom can I speak today? I am laden with wretchedness
For lack of intimate friends...
...
Death is in my sight today...

ibid., pp. 12–13.

In the Old Testament, six references are made to self-killing; however, the term suicide is not used. The most well-known was the suicide of Saul (I Samuel 31:1–6), who killed himself during deep despondency with his own sword after defeat in a war. Samson (Judges 16:28–31) killed himself and his enemies by bringing the pillars of the temple down. One of the most often quoted incidents of mass suicide occurred in A.D. 74 in Massada, following the destruction of the second Temple by the Romans in Jerusalem. More than 600 Jewish Zealots, with their wives and children, were surrounded by the Roman army. They decided to commit suicide rather than to become enslaved by the Romans.

In Greek mythology, Homer dramatized the sucide of Jocasta, the mother of Oedipus, who hung herself after finding out that she had married her own son. Socrates, as dramatized by Plato in *Phaedo,* committed suicide by drinking hemlock.

During the Middle Ages, particularly in the fourteenth century when the "Black Death" (the plague) spread throughout Europe, many adults and children committed suicide out of fear. Also, during this time, and throughout the Renaissance, the Church and the community condemned suicide by refusing to bury the deceased in graveyards, confiscating their property, and by burying them at crossroads with crosses stuck through their hearts. Punishment and ostracism were severe for those who attempted suicide.

Gradually, in the eighteenth century, with the works of Voltaire in France and Hume in England—who emphasized freedom of individual choice—superstition, severe punishment, and ta-

---

*The study of the incidence and pattern of suicide in children and youth is in progress by Shafii, M., Whittinghill, R., Gilliam, P., and Pearson, V. The authors also acknowledge the contribution of R. Oliphant, M.D., and Kay Lutz, M.S., and the continuous support of Richard Greathouse, M.D., Coroner of Jefferson County, Kentucky.

boos against suicide were diminished. Also at this time, a number of writers began to connect emotional disorders, such as melancholy, with suicidal tendencies. Melancholy was frequently referred to as "English malady" because of its high prevalence in England.

Earliest Case of Adolescent Suicide

Thomas Chatterton was a 17-year-old poet who "... had failed in his brief attempt to make a living as a writer and was, literally, starving to death." (Alvarez, 1975, p. 32) In 1770, he committed suicide by taking arsenic. Soon after his death, he became "...the supreme symbol of the Romantic poet." (ibid., p. 32) Coleridge, Keats, Wordsworth, and Shelly wrote in exaltation of his talent and his act of suicide. Alfred de Vigny wrote "...a vastly successful and influential play..." about Chatterton. (ibid., p. 32)

Four years later, Goethe (1774) wrote the novel, *The Sorrows of Young Werther.* Werther was a young man who, after falling in love, dressed in a yellow waistcoat and a blue tailcoat, shot himself to death. Soon after publication of this book, and for decades after, an epidemic of suicide swept Germany, France, England, Holland, and Scandinavia. This was called the "Werther epidemic." Many aspiring adolescents and young men who experienced failure in love, art, or writing committed suicide dressed in yellow waistcoats and blue tailcoats.

Farberow (1975) hypothesized:

> ...that the rate of suicide has been high or low in particular eras in direct relationship with variations in social controls and different emphases on the value of the individual in comparison with the state, such as idealization of reason, rationality, individuality, and democratic processes. Where the controls were greatest the rate was lower; where the individual was more free, the rate was higher.
>
> p. 2.

COMPLETED SUICIDE IN CHILDREN AND ADOLESCENTS

Reporting of completed suicides in children and adolescents has been neglected throughout the ages. Violent or unnatural deaths of young people were often attributed to "accidents," rather than possible suicides. Even today, we minimize or ignore children's despair. This attitude is similar to our denial of child abuse. For centuries, children were abused and even killed but child abuse as a clinical entity was only "discovered" about 20 years ago. Our blindness to recognition of child abuse and childhood suicide reflects our insensitivity to the world of children and youth.

Suicide among American youth has become a massive health and social problem that is reaching epidemic proportions. Suicide is the second most common cause of death (after accidents) in young people between the ages of 15 and 24 years. Each year, in this age group, more than 4,000 young people kill themselves. Notwithstanding these alarming figures, most researchers agree that the number of adolescent suicides is underreported because of familial, religious, and social considerations. In addition, it is extremely difficult to estimate the number of presumably accidental deaths that are actually conscious or unconscious suicides.

Nationally, the annual rate of suicide among teenagers aged 15 to 19 years more than tripled from 1954 to 1972. Suicide is also becoming more prevalent in children aged 8 to 14 years.

JEFFERSON COUNTY STUDY

At Child Psychiatric Services, University of Louisville School of Medicine, during the last few years, we have seen an increasing number of children who are actively thinking about, threatening, or attempting suicide. These observations encouraged us to explore the incidence of completed suicide in children and youth under age 19 in Louisville and surrounding Jefferson County.

Methodological Problems

Although many articles have been published regarding suicide attempts and threats among youth, very few have reported the actual incidence of suicide among young people. Mulcock (1955), Toolan (1962), H. Bakwin (1957), R.M. Bakwin (1973), Seiden (1969), Holinger (1978), and Frederick (1978) base their reviews of incidence on national statistics rather than on careful examination of coroner's records.

We are in agreement with Shneidman (1970), Farberow *et al.* (1977), and Holinger (1978) that there are serious methodological problems in defining and reporting suicide which make interpretation of national statistics difficult. There are inconsistencies in reportng, lack of unified standards, and variance in the background and training of certifying officials, such as coroners, medical examiners, community physicians, sheriffs, and others.

Another important variable in assessing the incidence of suicide within a given population is the accuracy of population statistics. Rates must be adjusted for age, and it is vital to have accurate estimates of population shifts within the community in order to evaluate the seriousness of the suicide problem.

Trends in Suicide Among Youth

In a search of the literature on suicide among children and youth, we were unable to find a systematic study that carefully examined the coroner's records in a particular geographical area in the United States.

Shaffer (1974) studied 31 suicides among children aged 14 years and under in England and Wales. These suicides occurred over a 7-year period from 1962 through 1968. None of the children who committed suicide were under age 12 years. According to Shaffer, "...only one child out of every 800,000 alive in England and Wales and aged between 10 and 14 years, killed themselves each year." (p. 275) He stated that the rate of suicide among children under age 15 years in England has changed little during the last 100 years. Childhood suicide "...accounts for only 0.08 percent of all suicides in England and Wales." (ibid., p. 275) Based on these data, the incidence of suicide in children between ages 10 to 14 years was 0.125 per 100,000 population between 1962 and 1968. In the United States in 1965, according to Frederick (1978), the incidence of suicide in children between ages 10 to 14 years was 0.50 per 100,000, or four times higher.

Marek et al. (1976) reported 76 suicides in youth under age 18 years which occurred in Cracow, Poland, between 1960 and 1974. He also examined the documented suicide records in Cracow from 1881 to 1974. According to Marek et al., youthful suicides during 1960 to 1974 were less than 5% of the total number of suicides.

Marek et al. found that there was a "...permanent decrease in the lower age limit of the suicides. Thus in the years 1881–1919, the youngest suicide was 15 years of age; during the period of 1919–1939 it was 12 years, from 1945 to 1960, 10, and from 1960–1974, 8½ years of age." (p. 105) It is interesting that the population of Cracow in 1974 was 668,000, which is very close to the current population of Jefferson County, Kentucky. In Cracow, the months of March, May, and October had the highest rates of suicide.

Collection of Data

The Coroner's records of Jefferson County, Kentucky, were reviewed for the years 1975 through 1980. During these years, 657 suicides were recorded and documented. Sixty (9.1%) of these suicides were committed by children and youth under the age of 19 years, the youngest being 10 years old.

Setting

Jefferson County, Kentucky, encompasses the city of Louisville and its surrounding suburbs with an aggregate population in the 1980 census report of 684,793. Jefferson County, similar to most other mid-American counties, is both industrial and agricultural. The racial distribution is 83% white and 17% nonwhite, predominantly black. The 1978 per capita income was $8,496. In the census estimate percentage, there were 221,325 children and youth under age 19 years, which represented 32.3% of the population.

In Kentucky, the Coroner is an elected county official, who has the legal responsibility of deciding whether deaths are caused by suicide. The Coroner is not necessarily a physician. The present Coroner in Jefferson County, who is a pediatrician, began a systematic collection of statistical data on suicides in 1973. Our study is a review and analysis of the Coroner's records of all suicides of children and adolescents aged 19 years and younger in Jefferson County, during the years of 1975 through 1980.

Standard Procedure

Any person dying an unnatural death which is attended by a physician must be referred to the Coroner for investigation. Any death due to natural or unnatural causes, in which the deceased was not attended by a physician during the last 36 hours of life, must be referred to the Coroner's office. The criteria for natural and unnatural death are based upon the International Classification of Diseases and Causes of Death (ICDCD) (1968). Criteria for determination of suicides are as follows:

1. Presence of witness
2. Blatant act of suicide
3. Presence of suicide note
4. Autopsy
5. Police investigation and evidence
6. Medical Examiner's report

In Jefferson County, the Coroner rules the cause of death as suicide only when the evidence is beyond a reasonable doubt.

Incidence of Suicide in Childhood

National Incidence

In a comprehensive study, Frederick (1978) examined suicidal behavior in the United States from 1900 to 1975. The incidence of suicide for all ages in 1900 was 10.2 per 100,000 population, and in 1975 it was 12.7—a 22% increase.

According to Frederick, "Recently, there has been much justifiable concern among professionals about the increase in suicide among younger age groups." (1978, p. 177) In 1975, no suicide among children under age 10 years was reported. In the 3-year period, 1976, 1977, and 1978, however, there were a total of nine children in the 5- to 9-year age range who committed suicide in the United States. (National Center for Health Statistics, 1976, 1977, 1978)

In the 10 years from 1965 to 1975, there was an increase in suicide among children between ages 10 and 14 years, from 0.5 per 100,000 in 1965, to 0.8 per 100,000 in 1975. (Table 14–1) There were 103 children in 1965 aged 10 to 14 years who committed suicide and 170 in 1975—a 60% increase. In 1976, there were 158 children aged 10 to 14 years who committed suicide, and the incidence remained 0.8 per 100,000. However, in 1977 there were 188 children aged 10 to 14 years who committed suicide, and the rate rose to 1.0 per 100,000. In 1978, there were 151 children aged 10 to 14 years who committed suicide, and the rate declined to 0.8 per 100,000.

Among youth aged 15 to 19 years, the incidence increased from 4.0 per 100,000 in 1965 to 7.6 per 100,000 in 1975. There were 685 adolescents who committed suicide in 1965, and 1,594 in 1975—a 90% increase. In 1976, 1,556 adolescents committed suicide, and the incidence was 7.4 per 100,000. However, in 1977, 1,871 adolescents killed themselves, and the incidence rose to 8.9. In 1978, 1,686 adolescents killed themselves, and the incidence declined to 8.0.

Jefferson County Incidence

In Jefferson County, comparing 1965 with 1975, there was one recorded suicide for children aged 10 to 14 years in each year. The population during this time was stable and so the incidence remained the same, 1.5 per 100,000. (Table 14–2) In 1976, there was also one suicide in this age group, but because of a slight decline in popula-

tion, the incidence rate was 1.6. In 1977, four suicides occurred in children aged 10 to 14 years, and the incidence rate was 6.8 per 100,000. In 1978, two suicides occurred with the incidence of 3.4 per 100,000. In 1979, no suicides in this age group occurred, and in 1980, one suicide occurred, with the incidence of 1.9 per 100,000. (Table 14–3)

During the 5 years 1976 through 1980, the mean incidence among children aged 10 to 14 years was 2.74. This increase is more than 80% over the 1975 incidence in this area.

In 1965, the incidence of suicide in the 15- to 19-year age group in Jefferson County was 3.8, and in 1975 it increased to 7.1 per 100,000— slightly less than the national incidence of 7.6. (Table 14–2)

The incidence in Jefferson County within this age group was 11.5 in 1976, 17.8 in 1977, 8.6 in 1978, 19.1 in 1979, and 14.6 in 1980. (Table 14–3) During the 5 years 1976 through 1980, the mean incidence was 14.3 per 100,000.

Comparison with Suicide in Adults

During 1975 to 1980, there was a fluctuation in rates of suicide within all age groups. We have also noted a 10% decrease in the population of children and youth under age 19 years since 1975. Thus, we have population weighted the incidence of suicide within each age range, in order to determine whether there has been any trend toward younger ages in the occurrence of suicide.

The incidence of suicide in children aged 10 to 14 years has increased from 1.5 in 1975 to 2.7 for 1976 to 1980—a more than 80% increase. Among youth aged 15 to 19 years, again we see an increase of incidence, from 7.1 in 1975 to a 5-year incidence rate of 14.3—a more than 100% increase. During the same time, the incidence of suicide in adults aged 20 years and older declined from 25.8 to a 5-year mean incidence of 21.3—a 17% decrease.

Patterns of Suicide in Jefferson County, Kentucky

In analysis of 60 documented cases of suicide in Jefferson County from 1975 through 1980 in children and youth ages 19 years and younger, the following patterns emerge. (Table 14–4)

Age

Generally, it is believed that children under age 14 years do not commit suicide. Our data show that nine children, or slightly more than 15% of childhood and adolescent suicides, were committed by children aged 14 years and younger; the

TABLE 14-1 National Incidence of Suicide Among Children and Youth*

| Ages, yr. | 1965† | | 1975† | | 1976‡ | | 1977‡ | | 1978§ | |
	Cases	Incidence	Cases	Incidence	Cases	Incidence	Cases	Incidence	Cases	Incidence
10-14	103	.5	170	.8	158	.8	188	1.0	151	.8
15-19	685	4.0	1,594	7.6	1,556	7.4	1,871	8.9	1,686	8.0
Total (All Ages)	21,507	11.1	27,063	12.7	26,832	12.5	28,681	13.3	27,294	12.5

* Incidence is given per 100,000 population.
† Data from vital statistics, 1965, 1975.
‡ Data from National Center for Health Statistics, unpublished computer print-out, 1976, 1977.
§ Latest available date.

TABLE 14-2 A Comparison of Suicide Among Children and Youth in Jefferson County, 1965–1975

| Ages, yr. | 1965 | | | 1975 | | |
	Population	Cases	Incidence*	Population	Cases	Incidence*
0-9	150,101	0	0	112,414	0	0
10-14	66,516	1	1.5	66,632	1	1.5
15-19	53,073	2	3.8	70,701	5	7.1
20-Older	387,319	64	16.5	446,553	115	25.8
Total (All Ages)	657,009	67	10.2	696,300	121	17.4

* Incidence is given per 100,000 population.

TABLE 14-3 A Comparison of Suicide Among Children and Youth in Jefferson County, 1976–1980

| Ages, yr. | 1976 | | | 1977 | | | 1978 | | | 1979 | | | 1980 | | |
	P*	C*	I*	P	C	I	P	C	I	P	C	I	P	C	I
0-9	110,018	0	0	107,485	0	0	105,809	0	0	105,637	0	0	106,691	0	0
10-14	63,036	1	1.6	58,740	4	6.8	59,275	2	3.4	53,662	0	0	52,934	1	1.9
15-19	69,610	8	11.5	67,441	12	17.8	69,677	6	8.6	62,965	12	19.1	61,700	8	14.6
20-Older	449,036	93	20.7	447,334	114	25.5	454,587	104	22.9	452,188	93	20.6	463,468	78	16.8
Total	691,700	102	14.7	681,000	130	19.1	689,348	112	16.2	674,285	105	15.6	684,793	87	12.7

* P = population; C = cases; I = incidence per 100,000.

Table 14-4 Sex, Race, and Age Distribution of Suicides Among Children and Youth in Jefferson County, 1975–1980

| Age, yr. | Percentage | Male | | Female | |
		White	Black	White	Black
10	2%	1	0	0	0
12	5%	2	0	0	1
13	2%	1	0	0	0
14	7%	2	0	2	0
15	13%	6	1	0	1
16	10%	5	0	1	0
17	22%	9	1	›3	0
18	27%	12	2	1	1
19	13%	7	0	1	0
Totals:	100%	45	4	8	3
N=60)		75%	7%	13%	5%

youngest recorded suicide was committed by a boy 10 years old. During middle adolescence, ages 15 to 17 years, 45% of the suicides occurred, and in late adolescence, ages 18 and 19 years, 40% occurred.

More suicides occurred at ages 17 years (22%) and 18 years (27%) than at any other age. Ages 17 and 18 years are the most vulnerable ages for adolescent suicide in this community.

Sex and Race

Males comprise 82% of all suicides and females comprise 18%. In Jefferson County, the population within the 10- to 19-year age range has been almost evenly distributed during the years of 1975 to 1978. Thus, there are significantly more male suicides than female suicides ($p < 0.001$).

Regarding race, 88% of the suicide cases were white and 12% were black. The Jefferson County racial distribution within this age group is 77% white and 23% black. Therefore, the racial distribution of suicides is not significantly different from what would be expected within this population. Of the seven blacks who committed suicide, three were females, and four were males. The black females who committed suicide were much younger than the black males.

Time of Suicide

In 52 cases (approximately 87%), the time at which the suicide occurred was documented. Twenty-two (42%) of the suicides occurred during the evening hours (4:00 P.M. to midnight). Sixteen (31%) of the suicides occurred between midnight and 8:00 A.M. Fourteen of the suicides (27%) occurred during daytime hours (8:00 A.M. to 4:00 P.M.). Among the 10- to 14-year-olds, all of the suicides occurred between 3:00 P.M. and midnight. Suppertime and bedtime were the most vulnerable times for suicide among the younger children.

Season

By far, more suicides occurred in the month of March. Most of the suicides, 21 (35%), occurred in the spring (March, April, and May). During the summer, 14 (23%) occurred; in the fall, 14 (23%); and in the winter, 11 (19%). The occurrence of suicide in the spring was significantly more frequent than the other three seasons ($p < 0.05$)

Nine children between the ages of 10 and 14 years committed suicide. In this age group, four suicides occurred in March, two in April, and one each in June, July, and December. In all age groups, the likelihood of committing suicide was greater in spring. This was particularly true for children aged 10 to 14 years.

Methods of Committing Suicide

The use of firearms was the predominant method for committing suicide. Thirty-four (57%) of the suicides committed were the result of gunshot wounds to the head, chest or abdomen. Fourteen (23%) died of strangulation due to hanging. Chemical overdose accounted for only six (9%). Three youths (5%) committed suicide by carbon monoxide poisoning; one youth committed suicide by drowning, one by methane inhalation, and one by jumping in front of a truck. Males used firearms over 61% of the time, and hanging was the second most common means. Among females, gunshot wounds, hanging, and chemical overdose were equally distributed.

Previous Psychiatric Care

In the 60 cases of suicide, only 11 (18%) had previous psychiatric or mental health care; one had received pastoral counseling, and three were in the process of obtaining psychiatric help. More than 80% of the children and youth who committed suicide had never received any form of mental health or psychiatric care.

Summary of Jefferson County Study

Suicide among children and adolescents is a serious medicopsychiatric problem. During 1975 through 1980 in Jefferson County, Kentucky, 60 (9.1%) of the 657 suicides recorded occurred in the 10- to 19-year-old age group.

In the years 1976 to 1980, the mean incidence of suicide in children aged 10 to 14 years was 2.74 per 100,000—an increase of 83% over 1975. In ages 15 to 19, the mean incidence was 14.3 per 100,000 as opposed to 7.1 in 1975—a more than 100% increase. In 1965, the incidence of suicide in this age group was 3.8. Therefore, during the last 15 years, the incidence of suicide in youth aged 15 to 19 has tripled. In ages 20 years and older, the incidence of suicide in 1975 was 25.8 per 100,000, but the mean incidence from 1976 to 1980 decreased to 21.3—a 17% decrease. There appears to be a shift in the occurrence of suicide to the younger age groups.

Eighty-two percent were male, and 18% were female. Black and white were proportionately vulnerable. Suicide occurred more frequently in the spring, particularly in March. Eighty-two percent of the youth who committed suicide never received psychiatric help.

At the present time, we do not know why the suicide rate among children and adolescents in Jefferson County is increasing over the 1975 national and local incidence. We have wondered whether our findings represent only the "tip of the iceberg." Perhaps suicidal behavior and the incidence of suicide is greatly underreported in many communities. There is a lack of standardized data collection, as well as a tendency to minimize the possibility of suicide, especially in children and youth.

It is disturbing to note that more than 80% of the children and youth in Jefferson county who commited suicide never received psychiatric or mental health care. A need exists to educate parents, teachers, family practitioners, pediatricians, and clergymen to recognize early signs of suicidal behavior and take the messages of these troubled children and adolescents seriously.

We propose the creation of a uniform standard to be used on the local, state, and national levels of reporting and documenting, on a regular basis, suicidal behavior in children and youth. The creation of a National Registry on Child and Adolescent Suicide is essential for identifying the extent of this problem and in helping to find effective methods for prevention and treatment.

SELF-DESTRUCTIVE AND SUICIDAL BEHAVIOR

Suicidal behavior refers to active suicidal ideation or thoughts, suicidal gestures, and suicide attempts. Some clinicians define *suicidal gesture* as a suicidal act without the conscious intent of killing oneself, and a *suicide attempt* as a suicidal act with the intent of killing oneself.

We suggest that the use of the term "suicidal gesture" by clinicians can be misleading and minimizes the seriousness of potentially dangerous behavior. Frequently, the suicidal idea of yesterday is the suicidal gesture of today and could become the suicide attempt or completed suicide of tomorrow.

Relationship Between Suicide Attempt and Completed Suicide in Adults

Extensive debate exists among clinicians concerning whether or not the population who complete suicide are the same population who attempt suicide. Seiden (1969), for instance, believes that the individual who commits suicide is a different individual from the one who attempts suicide. Attempters generally use less violent means and in some way communicate their despair more openly.

In clinical contact with a patient who has attempted suicide, the following questions frequently arise: "Did the patient mean to kill himself?" "Is he going to try again?" "If he does try again, will he succeed?"

Dorpat and Ripley (1967) found that in adults the longer a group of suicide attempters was observed, the higher the incidence of completed suicide proved to be. Ettlinger (1964), in Sweden, observed 227 suicide attempters for a period of 12 years. Thirty, or 13.2%, committed suicide during this period. Moss and Hamilton (1956) followed 50 patients who were suicide attempters for a period of 2 to 20 years. Eleven of these patients, or 22%, committed suicide.

On the other hand, Ringel (1953) observed 2,879 suicide attempters for a period of 8 to 44 years and found that only one, or 0.03%, committed suicide.

Dorpat and Ripley (1967) concluded:

> ... the suicide rate was highest during the first 1 to 2 years after a suicide attempt. However, even after this initial 1- or 2-year period the suicide rate continued to be greater than the expected rate for the duration of the follow-up periods.... we would estimate the incidence of committed suicide among suicidal attempts to be between 10 and 20 per cent.
>
> p. 75.

What is the incidence of prior suicide attempts in a group who has committed suicide? Farberow and Shneidman (1955), in a retrospective study of 32 veterans who committed suicide following discharge from the hospital, found that 62.5% had previously attempted suicide. Dorpat and Ripley (1960), in a study of 114 consecutive and unselected cases of suicide in the Seattle area, found that 33.3% had a previous history of suicide attempt. On the other hand, Sainsbury (1955), in the London, England, area, in a study of 409 cases of suicide, found that only 8.6% had made prior suicide attempts.

Dorpat and Ripley (1967) stated: "... it seems reasonable to conclude that between 20 and 65 per cent of individuals who commit suicide have made prior suicide attempts." (p. 76)

Suicide Risk in Adult Attempters

Tuckman and Youngman (1963), in a one-year follow-up of 1,112 suicide attempters "... found the suicide rate among them to be 140 times greater than in the general population." (Dorpat and Ripley, 1967, p. 76) Motto (1965) calculated the suicide risk to be 80 to 100 times higher in suicide attempters than in the general population.

Relationship Between Suicide Attempt and Completed Suicide in Children and Adolescents

Long-term follow-up studies of child and adolescent suicide attempters are limited compared with studies of adults. Otto (1972) of Sweden has done the most extensive follow-up studies of suicidal behavior in children and adolescents. Between 1955 and 1959, there were 1,727 children and adolescents under age 21 years who came to the attention of the health authorities in Sweden for suicide attempts; 80% of these were females and 20% were males. The majority of the young people were between ages 15 and 20 years, less than 10% were under age 14 years, and the youngest was 10 years old. Otto chose a comparable control group from the general population.

Pattern of Suicide Attempts

In Otto's studies, the majority of suicide attempts occurred during the late afternoon or in the evening before midnight. The highest frequency was in November, February, and March. Regarding the method used to attempt suicide, almost 90% of the females and 76% of the males had used drugs, such as barbiturates. Sixteen percent had a history of previous suicide attempt.

In 13% of the cases, one or both parents were alcoholics. Nineteen percent of the parents "... had been declared mentally ill or disturbed." (p. 35) Thirty-four percent of the families had serious domestic disturbances.

Regarding precipitating factors, 37%, most commonly girls, indicated "love conflicts" and problems relating to the opposite sex, 32% family problems, 7% school problems, 18% mental illness, 4% pregnancy, and 2% military service.

In the 1969 follow-up 10 years later, Otto discovered that 84 (5.4%) of these suicide attempters had died. Eighty percent of these had committed suicide—32 males and 35 females.

In the control group, only 27, or 1.8%, had died. Otto (1972) concluded:

If the 1,727 individuals who attempted suicide during the five year period 1955-1959, are placed in relation to the known number of completed suicides it appears that there are about 11 attempts for every completed suicide amongst children and adolescents up to 21 years of age. Amongst the boys 3-4 suicide attempts are committed per completed suicide and amongst the girls 25-30.

p. 92.

Also, Otto observed that the greatest risk was during the first 2 years after a suicide attempt.

It is of the utmost importance that contact should be kept with the patient during this period. It need not be particularly intensive but it should be enough to ensure that the youngster has such faith in the therapy that he constantly takes advantage of it.

ibid., p. 107.

Psychological Morbidity

In regard to psychological and physical vulnerability and morbidity, Otto found that suicide attempters were "a risk group." They had a higher rate of divorce or a higher rate of being single as opposed to the control group. *Mental and social isolation was more prominent.* The attempters had more difficulty in compulsory military service, they had higher rates of emigration from Sweden, of antisocial behavior and involvement in reform schools or correctional institutions, of alcoholism, and of an increased frequency of "sick listing" for mental and physical reasons. (ibid., pp. 106–107)

Jacobziner (1965) estimated the ratio of attempted suicide to actual suicide in the United States in children and adolescents as 100:1.

Barter et al. (1968), in a follow-up of adolescent suicide attempts found that 42% continued to show suicidal behavior in the form of suicide attempts following hospitalization. They related suicide attempts to progressive family disorganization and social maladjustment.

Teicher and Jacobs (1966) and Teicher (1967, 1970, 1972, 1973, 1979), in the Los Angeles area, conducted a long-term longitudinal and descriptive study of suicidal behavior in adolescents aged 13 to 18. Seventy-five percent were females. Teicher described three progressive stages culminating in suicide attempts.

1. Long-standing History of Problems. In the majority (62%) of the adolescents' families, either both parents were working, or the families were one-parent units and this parent was working. Nearly 60% of the adolescents had a parent who was married more than once. More than 80% were living with an unwanted stepparent. More than 70% "... have one or both natural parents absent from the home (divorced, separated or deceased)." (Teicher, 1979, p. 689) Forty percent had a parent, close friend, or relative with a history of attempted suicide. In 20% of the cases, one parent had attempted suicide.

   Suicidal adolescents, from early childhood experienced enviromental changes, residential mobility, school changes, living with others rather than parents, and death or separation of parents two to three times more than the control group.

Teicher (1979) concluded, "The sum of these findings strongly suggests that the suicidal adolescent is far more subject to unexpected separations from meaningful social relationships in earlier life than are the controls." (p. 689)

2. Escalation of Problems. In this stage, the parents or parent had difficulty in relating to their developing adolescent. Approximately 50% of the adolescents' parents or members of their families suffered from physical or emotional disorders during this stage. There was lack of communication and discord between the parents and their children. Rebellion, sassiness, defiance, withdrawal, lying, gloominess, and running away from home occurred in almost 90% of the cases during the 5 years before the suicide attempt was made.

Most of the suicide attempters expressed their liking for school as a place for social contact rather than for academic reasons. Twenty-three percent of the suicide attempters, as opposed to none of the control group, felt that they did not have anyone they could talk to. Forty-six percent of the attempters, as opposed to 20% of the controls, felt their troubles were without solution.

The potential suicide attempter is intensely dependent on his peers. The intensity of this need threatens and frightens the peers, and directly and indirectly they reject these insatiable demands and expectations.

3. The Final Stage: The Romance. In this stage, parents are totally alienated, and friends are keeping their distance. "The adolescent yearns to reestablish the spontaneity, openness and intimacy that he feels characterized the earlier relationship with his parents." (ibid., p. 691) To achieve this idealized intimacy, the adolescent dives deeply into the world of romance. He begins frantically to pursue an intimate relationship with someone of the opposite sex. This intense relationship is at the expense of casual relationships with peers of the same sex, parents, and other social interests. It alienates the adolescent further from others, and others from him. Frequently, these romances end in failure. The adolescent then feels totally alone, isolated, and abandoned. The only thing left is to commit suicide!

Suicidal Thoughts and Ideas in Children and Adolescents

Almost everyone at one time or another has thoughts of committing suicide. Usually, these ideas are fleeting and do not include any organized plan or method. Having occasionally fleeting suicidal ideas is totally different from overwhelming and obsessional preoccupation with suicide. Teicher (1979) reported on a study of over 100 college freshmen regarding suicidal ideation. Seventy percent of these students had "...a recent suicidal thought or thoughts." (p. 687)

In comparison, Paykel (1974), in a survey of 720 adults, found that almost 9% had suicidal feelings during the year prior to the study, 2.8% wished to die, 1% had thought of actual suicide and 0.6% had attempted suicide. Depression, stressful life events, physical illness, and social isolation were associated with these suicidal feelings.

Psychodynamics of Suicide in Children

Bender and Schilder (1937) were pioneers in exploring suicidal preoccupation and suicide attempts in children. They observed intensive suicidal preoccupation in children as young as 6 years of age.

They felt that children manifested suicidal behavior in reaction to

...an unbearable situation with an attempt to escape. Mostly these unbearable situations consist of the deprivation of love.... The deprivation provokes aggressive tendencies which are primarily directed against those who deny love. Under the influences of feelings of guilt, these aggressive tendencies are turned against oneself.... The suicidal death represents also a reunion with the love object in love and peace. There may be also an identification with a dead love object.

pp. 233–234.

This insightful dynamic formulation is as valid today as it was more than 40 years ago.

Clinical Perspective

During the last 8 years, from 1973 to 1980, in the Child Psychiatric Services, University of Louisville, there has been a significant increase in the frequency and intensity of suicidal behavior in children and adolescents.

For instance, in 1973, 23 children and adolescents were seen on an emergency basis for suicidal and self-destructive behavior. In 1980, this number increased to 145—a more than 530% increase. In 1973, the total number of all new evaluations was 363, and in 1980 this number was 883—a 143% increase. Therefore, although the total number of new evaluations had increased by 143%, the number of new patients presenting with suicidal and self-destructive behavior increased by more than 530%.

During 1980, 40% of all emergency cases and 16% of the total number of cases seen were actively suicidal.

A Study of 340 Cases of Suicidal and Self-Destructive Behavior In Children and Adolescents Seen in the Child Psychiatric Services

From 1973 to 1978, 340 cases of children and adolescents were seen on an emergency basis for suicidal or severe self-destructive behavior. Age and sex distribution of these cases are given in Table 14–5.

Table 14–5   **Age and Sex Distribution of Suicidal Behavior Among Children and Youth**

Age, yr.	Male/Female Ratio (Significance)	Number of Cases	Percentage of Total Cases
1–3		10	3%
	2.1/1 (P < 0.05)		
4–6		25	7%
7–12	1.75/1 (P < 0.01)	112	33%
13–18	1/2.16 (P < 0.0001)	193	57%
	Total	340	100%

Until recently, it was thought that suicidal behavior was expressed primarily by adolescents and adults. In this study it is disturbing to notice that 43% of all the cases were children under age 12 years. Up to the age of 12 years, the male to female ratio was significantly higher. It was only in adolescents that the trend was reversed, and the female to male ratio became significantly higher. (Shafii *et al.,* 1979, p. 1601)

SELF-DESTRUCTIVE BEHAVIOR IN CHILDREN AGED ONE TO THREE YEARS. Approximately 3% of all suicidal and self-destructive patients seen on an emergency basis in the study just described were between ages one and 3 years. Self-destructive behaviors, such as severe head-banging, self-inflicted bites, self-mutilation, and intentionally running in front of cars, are symptomatic expressions of destructive behavior between ages one and 3 years. Because these children usually do not, or cannot, verbalize their intentions to kill themselves, the term "self-destructive behavior" is used rather than suicidal behavior.

SUICIDAL BEHAVIOR IN CHILDREN AGED FOUR TO SIX YEARS.   At this age, most suicidal children consciously and openly verbalize their intentions to kill themselves. These messages need to be taken seriously.

The Case of Patrick.   Patrick, a 3½-year-old white male, was referred by Protective Services because of accelerating self-destructive and suicidal behavior. Patrick's grandmother mentioned that during the prior 9 months Patrick had been clawing at his throat, hitting himself with various objects, such as chains and bottles, and saying "I want to die." A few months earlier, he had broken a window with a broomstick and had cut his wrist with the sharp edge of the glass, saying, "I want to bleed, I want to die."

Patrick had been physically abusive to his 5½-year-old sister and to his 19-month-old brother. He also had been hitting his head against the wall and frequently had run out in front of cars, saying, "I want to die."

Patrick petted and played with his dog, but also tried to hurt the dog physically. He threw objects at his grandmother and was very defiant and unmanageable.

At age one year, Patrick had been brought to the hospital for serious symptoms of malnourishment, severe weight loss, and a bloated stomach. Patrick had been physically abused and neglected by his natural mother and her boyfriend. Because of this, he had been placed with his maternal grandmother. His natural father had custody and saw Patrick weekly.

The maternal grandmother dated the beginning of Patrick's suicidal and destructive behavior to 9 months prior to his referral by Protective Services, when he had spent a few days with his nautral mother and her boyfriend.

In psychiatric evaluation, Patrick appeared to be spontaneous, friendly, and active. With great glee, he used crayons and paper to color. He separated easily from his grandmother and his father to go into the playroom. In the playroom, he was restless, moved around frequently, and had a short attention span. He "twisted the heads of the man, woman, and child dolls," and hit a whale puppet with a wooden board. The evaluator "...tried to elicit some sympathy from him by pretending the puppet had been hurt, but he continued to severely hit the puppet."

Patrick impressed the evaluator as being overanxious, characterized by self-destructive and suicidal behavior. Patrick was hospitalized for 3 to 4 weeks in an inpatient child psychiatric setting for complete physical and psychiatric assessment and treatment to help him rechannel his self-destructive and destructive behavior. At the same time, the grandmother and father were encouraged to become more involved with Patrick and to avoid using physical punishment. They were encouraged to develop a warm but firm relationship with him.

Patrick improved significantly during his short hospital stay, although he continued to be frightened of men. His self-destructive behavior subsided. He continued to be somewhat rambunctious and overactive. He was discharged to his grandmother and was followed in an outpatient clinic.

The Case of Charley. Charley, a 5-year-old white boy, ran into the street, screaming at the cars to hit him because he wanted to die. Three weeks prior to this attempt, Charley had tried to hang his 4-year-old brother with a rope. His grandmother had had to intervene. Charley had a history of setting at least one fire per week in his home. He lived with his mother and sibling—his parents were divorced. Charley was very oppositional to his mother and constantly fought with his peers and siblings. He wet his bed. He had a history of seizure disorder since age 2 years, and was, at the time of his evaluation, on phenobarbital and Dilantin.

Our experience shows that self-destructive and suicidal behavior in children between the ages of one and 6 years is usually related to severe physical abuse and neglect.

In a small number of cases, organic central nervous system disorders, such as epilepsy, may be contributing factors. Severely psychotic children, particularly autistic children, may show self-destructive behavior and lack of regard for danger, but they rarely verbalize suicidal intention.

SUICIDAL BEHAVIOR IN CHILDREN AGED SEVEN TO TWELVE YEARS. During latency, depression and loss play important roles in the expression of suicidal behavior.

The Case of Laura. Laura, a 7-year-old black female was brought to a psychiatric clinic because, on the previous night, she had tried to kill herself by putting two pillows over her face and pulling a sheet tightly over herself. Also, she had tried to choke herself. She had told her mother that she would either run away or try to kill herself again. The mother said that Laura just sat around at home, did not talk, seemed to feel tired, did not eat, cried frequently, and spent most of her time alone in her room.

Laura was considered a high-risk infant because of her mother's toxemic pregnancy. However, Laura developed normally. The mother began to toilet train Laura when she was 6 months old! Laura never crawled, but began to walk at 6½ months of age.

Laura was born out of wedlock; however, her father continued to pay child support. The factor that seemed to precipitate Laura's suicide attempt was that her father, who was living away from home, promised to come to see Laura and her siblings on Easter and buy them Easter clothes. They had waited patiently for their father, but he had never arrived. Apparently, similar instances occurred frequently.

The mother worked, and Laura had some responsibility for looking after her two younger siblings.

In the interview, Laura showed very little emotion and stared at the floor; however, she was able to answer questions. In regard to her suicide attempt, she said that she "...just wanted to block out the world for a little while and help me go to sleep for a little bit." She recounted that she enjoyed school a great deal and that she had some friends at the day care center who really tried to help her.

Laura's mother appeared to be very concerned and caring. Laura's mild depression was thought to be related to a feeling of anger and frequent disappointment toward her father. The mother appeared to be stable. Laura and her mother were referred to an outpatient community mental health center for individual and family therapy.

The Case of John. John was a 10-year-old black male who was referred because on the prior night he had packed his suitcase and disappeared from home for about 3 hours. He had told his mother earlier that he felt that he was not wanted and was in her way. A month earlier he had told his mother that he wished he was dead; later, on the same day, he had put a belt around his neck and was tying it to the top bunk when his mother found him.

John's parents were divorced. The precipitating factor was that the father frequently called the patient and his older brother and told them that he would come to pick them up—then he never came.

During the first 5 years of life, John was considered "...happy, social, and wanted to be the center of attention." At times he was stubborn. During the year prior to his referral, he had become disillusioned with his father.

John's mother had had 2 years of college education and worked as a secretary.

In the interview, John, a handsome, small boy, was quite anxious, with "a very broad smile." He occasionally sucked and chewed on his thumb. He did not appear depressed. He was preoccupied with "...a sense that his mother sometimes doesn't love him." He was very troubled by this feeling. He said that his mother frequently yelled at him and, at times, threw objects at him to get his attention and cooperation.

The patient had been reluctant and apprehensive about confronting his mother, because he was afraid that "She will get mad at me." In regard to his suicidal behavior, John said that he had known that his mother would find him with the belt, and that this had been his way of making her angry.

John and his mother were referred for outpatient psychotherapy.

The Case of JoAnn. JoAnn, an 11-year-old white girl, was found comatose and without respiration due to a Darvon overdose. This had occurred one week prior to Christmas. JoAnn said that she had attempted suicide because nobody at school liked her, her friends talked behind her back, and she had no privacy at home. She had to go to a friend's house to discuss her problems. It was also learned that the patient had been "grounded" until Christmas.

After stabilization of her vital signs, and after she had regained consciousness, JoAnn was transferred to an inpatient child psychiatric setting.

During latency, suicidal behavior may be a manifestation of anxiety, depression, or aggression turned against the self. Disappointment and loss often precipitate suicide in a vulnerable child. Suicidal behavior frequently is the last cry for help. If the message is taken seriously, and the child is able to develop a continuous and meaningful relationship with a therapist, and if the home situation is relatively improved, the therapeutic outcome is quite favorable.

SUICIDAL BEHAVIOR IN ADOLESCENTS.

Of the 340 cases of suicidal children and adolescents seen in the Child Psychiatric Services, University of Louisville, between the years 1973 and 1978, 194, or 57%, were between ages 13 and 18 years. The majority of these were aged 13 to 15. This is probably because, generally, adolescents up to age 16 years are seen in the Child Psychiatric Services, and those older than 16 years are referred to adult services.

Suicidal behavior and completed suicides in adolescents are major national health problems. Adolescents developmentally have a proclivity toward depression and a vulnerability for suicide.

Preoccupation with the self, disappointment with the parents, failure in academic performance, sports, friendship, and dissolution of romantic relationships reinforce the mercurial mood of adolescence. The troubled adolescent may carefully plan his suicide or plunge into it at a moment's notice.

In most cases, there is a history of isolation, a decrease in human contact, overexpectation by the self and the parents, alcohol and drug abuse, parental disharmony, and conflict between the adolescent and the parents.

Identification with the suicidal behavior of a friend, relative, or a national figure may also precipitate suicidal behavior in a vulnerable adolescent.

The Case of Adam. Adam, a 12½-year-old white male was referred by his pediatrician because he took 10 to 20 sleeping pills which belonged to his grandmother. He did not tell anyone about this, but he did tell the evaluator "...they suspected I had taken something or had been smoking pot when I became dizzy and was talking funny. I did not want to live and hoped the medication would kill me."

The precipitating factor was a fight Adam had had the day before with one of his older friends, who had accused him of stealing some money. Just prior to this, Adam's uncle's girlfriend had tried to kill herself by taking an overdose.

Adam described a volatile home life, which included much parental conflict and which had existed "...all of my life...Both of my parents have a drinking problem. They scream at each other and beat up on each other. Then my mom tells my dad to shoot her."

Adam's parents lived together, although they were divorced. Adam had to be a peacemaker between his parents to keep them "...from severely hurting each other during their drunken fights." Both parents worked in a factory.

Adam was hospitalized in a pediatric unit and was followed by a child psychiatric consultation team. After discharge from the hospital, outpatient therapy was recommended for Adam and his family.

The Case of Terry. Terry, a 13-year-old white female, was referred for "...running away from home, talking about committing suicide, and becoming increasingly withdrawn." Terry was in the eighth grade and was an "A" student.

The patient's mother had died 1½ years earlier of a "heart condition." After her mother's death, Terry went to live with her older brother; her withdrawing behavior began soon after. The natural father had custody, but did not show any interest in the patient.

In the initial interview, Terry was apprehensive and agitated. She was finally able to relate to the evaluator by saying, "My mother had a heart condition. She went to the shopping center with me. When she came back home, she died. Two months later, my brother blamed me for my mother's death, and said, 'If you had kept mother at home to rest, she wouldn't have died.'" Apparently, the patient's brother told her this several times.

Terry said she felt extremely angry with her brother, but could not say anything to him because she was dependent on him. She also was experiencing excessive guilt about her mother's death and had begun to have suicidal thoughts—however, she had no definite plan. Around Halloween of that same year, Terry had tried to have a "seance" to talk with her dead mother. Her aunt and uncle began to call her "crazy" and would not allow their children to play with her.

Terry was of high average intelligence, moderately depressed, and, at the same time, had some insight into the nature of her difficulty. She was quite apprehensive of criticism from her teacher, although she was an "A" student.

Terry was diagnosed as suffering from depressive disorder. She began individual outpatient psychotherapy on a one- to two-times-per-week basis with the evaluator.

Treatment continued for 8 to 9 months. Regular contact was maintained with Terry's older sister, with whom she had gone to live. Terry improved significantly and treatment was mutually terminated.

Six months after termination, Terry wrote the following letter to her therapist:

Mr. M. ...
Hello! How are ya? I hope your o-kay. I was just sitting here thinking about all of our talks and how much you helped me, and I remembered that I never thanked you. I don't really know how to thank you because if it wasn't for you I think, I might have gone crazy!!

I'm doing alot better in school now, and I'm trying to get along with my sister and her husband. Of course we still have a few problems, but I try to remember our talks and work them out. I guess what i'm trying to say is that I'll never forget you and, all you've taught me.

Did you have a nice Christmas? I had a really nice one, our whole family was together for the first time in two years, and we didn't even get in a fight.

Well I guess this letter is pretty boring by now, so I'll close for now but i'll write ya again sometime if you don't mind.

Love ya for a pal,
Terry
P.S. If you find time maybe you can write back, I'd love to hear from ya.
THANKS!!

This case demonstrates that effective intervention in a growing adolescent helped to prevent crystallization of pathological grief, severe depression, and possible suicide.

The Case of Claudia. Claudia was a 14-year-old white female who was brought to the pediatric emergency room for an overdose of Diabinese. This was her second suicide attempt. Claudia's mother had died a year earlier of cancer. Her father, suffering from a cerebral vascular accident, had been unable to care for his seven children. Claudia had been placed in a foster home. She had not liked the new home and had made her first suicide attempt. She was then placed in a second home and was being treated on an outpatient basis in a Comprehensive Care Center.

At the time of evaluation, Claudia was very depressed and complained of auditory and visual hallucinations. She would hear her mother telling her to "come home." Her affect was inappropriate, associations loose, and judgment impaired. She was a runaway and suicidal risk.

When she was younger, Claudia had been physically abused by her father. One of her brothers had been diagnosed as having schizophrenia, and her sister had been diagnosed as "having hysterical seizures."

In psychological assessment, Claudia's verbal WISC-R IQ verbal score was 74 and performance, 105, with full scale 87.

Claudia was admitted to a short-term inpatient child psychiatric service. Sleep EEG was moderately dysrhythmic with irritation focus in the left frontal region. She was placed on Dilantin and Thioridazine. At one time during her hospitalization, she escaped and tried to jump from the second floor.

In treatment, she was continuously preoccupied by guilt feelings concerning the death of her mother. She had been told by her relatives that her mother's death had been her fault.

Claudia had a few *café au lait* spots on her body, as had her mother. There was a possibility of von Recklinghausen's disease.

Although during the short hospitalization Claudia's hallucinations and delusions subsided, she continued to be disorganized and was a high suicidal risk. Claudia was transferred to a relatively long-term child and adolescent psychiatric setting.

The Case of Diana. Diana was a 15-year-old white female referred by a pediatric resident for taking 40 tablets of Donnatal. She was brought to the hospital in a comatose condition. Gradually, after 24 hours of intensive medical care, she regained consciousness.

According to her parents, the precipitating factor was receiving a failing grade in one of her high school courses. Six weeks earlier, she had received a failing grade in another course.

Diana had difficulty in getting along with her middle-class, successful parents. She had a boyfriend and she had been sexually active with him. Occasionally she had used marijuana, but she denied using drugs or alcohol.

Diana related in the initial interview that she had considered hurting herself in the past, especially on one occasion in particular when she had had an argument with her boyfriend.

Diana's mother stated that she had suspected that her daughter may have overdosed on a similar medication earlier that same year, but that her symptoms had not been nearly as severe. The parents had not pursued that episode and had not sought help.

When Diana had been in the sixth or seventh grade, she had received a few sessions of psychiatric care because she had been withdrawn and had stayed in her room for long periods of time.

In the interview, Diana appeared moderately depressed and she cried at intervals. The evaluator's opinion was that Diana was suffering from an acute life crisis regarding academic performance and that this crisis was most likely exacerbated by inadequate communication between family members.

The family was upwardly mobile, with high expectations. It was recommended that the patient and the family be followed in outpatient psychotherapy.

This case clearly demonstrates that the patient's depressive and suicidal tendencies had been operant for some time. She had made an earlier suicide attempt after a fight with her boyfriend. When her suicidal message had not been taken seriously, she made a more serious attempt and almost succeeded.

FIRST-AID FOR SUICIDAL CHILDREN AND ADOLESCENTS

Children and adolescents occasionally think about suicide, but when they begin to express these thoughts directly or indirectly or begin to show self-destructive behavior, it becomes an extremely serious situation.

The following first-aid guidelines are essential:

1. It is a myth that children and adolescents do not commit suicide
2. All suicidal messages and self-destructive behavior should be taken seriously
3. People working with children and adolescents need to examine their own internal feelings about suicide honestly in order to increase their receptivity and sensitivity toward subtle self-destructive clues
4. Clinicians need to be aware of their tendencies to deny, minimize, or not recognize suicidal clues
5. If there is any evidence or suspicion of suicidal behavior, a thorough *psychiatric examination* of the child and the family is essential
6. If the clinician does not have the time, knowledge, or interest in providing thorough psychiatric examination, immediate referral to a child psychiatrist, general psychiatrist, or qualified allied mental health professional is necessary
7. A potentially suicidal youth and his family should be seen *immediately*
8. Meanwhile, the parents or responsible adult should be instructed that one of them or a responsible person must be with the youth at *all* times and *never* out of his sight; someone must go to the bathroom with the suicidal youth
9. All potentially hazardous objects, drugs, or materials should be removed and kept away from the home or kept under lock and key, for instance, guns, prescribed or nonprescribed drugs, razors, knives, ropes, belts, shoelaces
10. Even with careful precautions, an actively suicidal youth is a high risk and needs to be attended continuously until psychiatric assessment is completed

PSYCHIATRIC ASSESSMENT

In assessing the potentially suicidal child or adolescent, the following guidelines are useful.

1. In a psychiatric assessment, the clinician should spend as much time as necessary to see the patient and other members of the family. Short cuts can be costly. It is not uncommon for skillful clinicians to spend 3 to 4 hours in the initial assessment.
2. In interviewing the young person and the family, it is important to be neutral but concerned. One must listen to all sides of the story, both on a one-to-one basis and with the family as a group. The clinician should avoid making value judgments or attaching blame.
3. Clinicians must remember that their first responsibility is to save the young person's life. Everything else is secondary; no consideration should compromise this responsibility.
4. At the time of crisis, frequently it is difficult to assess the intensity and lethality of suicidal behavior and ideas. When in doubt, it is prudent to admit the young person to the hospital, preferably a child or adolescent psychiatric setting.
5. In interviews with a child and his family, the suicidal ideas and behavior should be explored openly and thoroughly.
6. If the young person has planned the suicide carefully, left a note, or was discovered by accident, the suicidal behavior is more serious.
7. The use of violent means, such as a gun, rope, jumping, or taking a moderately large amount of drugs (10 to 12 tablets) is more serious.
8. Change of behavior, such as a quiet child becoming rambunctious and obnoxious, *or* an outgoing or assertive child becoming withdrawn and submissive or "too kind," can be important clues.
9. The giving away of prized objects by a child or adolescent may indicate suicidal preoccupation.

10. Verbalization of suicidal and death wishes, such as, "I wish I was not around," "Don't push me or you'll be sorry!" "Soon you won't have me around to bully or pick on," "I hope I sleep forever and never get up again," "Who gives a damn, there won't be a tomorrow!" or "Soon I'll be out of your way," should be taken very seriously.
11. Suicidal behavior does not know any age, race, or socioeconomic class.
12. Failure in human contact is the most significant contributing factor to the development of depression in childhood and adolescence; depression plays a crucial role in the development of suicidal behavior.
13. The risk of suicide is significantly increased when one or more of the following are present:
    a. A previous suicide attempt
    b. Death, particularly from suicide, of a relative, friend, teacher, acquaintance, or idol
    c. History of alcohol or drug abuse by the young person or by another family member
    d. Lack of emotional support in the family, alienation from friends, and isolation and withdrawal
    e. Perfectionistic tendencies, rigidity, over-expectation of the self or in the family; extreme overreaction and withdrawal at the time of failure
    f. Physical or sexual abuse
    g. Major loss during early childhood, such as of a parent or meaningful person
    h. Impulsive and destructive behavior, such as lack of regard for danger, cruelty to siblings, peers, and animals, fire-setting, and antisocial behavior.

MANAGEMENT AND TREATMENT

The *establishment of rapport* and expression of genuine concern for a suicidal youth and his family are essential. A meaningful relationship with a concerned clinician may be the last lifeline for a suicidal youth.

Availability to the suicidal young person and the family on a 24-hour basis is absolutely essential, particularly during the first 2 to 3 months following the suicide attempt or discharge from the hospital. It is important for the suicidal youth to be able to reach the therapist at any moment, day or night, when he feels in extreme distress and thinks he might do something to hurt himself.

A *therapeutic contract* with the young person is helpful in developing an effective therapeutic alliance. For instance, the therapist might say:

I am willing to work with you and the part inside of you that wants to live and to win this battle. Together

you and I can beat the other part of you that wants to kill yourself.

But, you have to promise me that you will never again attempt suicide or do anything to hurt yourself before you and I have had a chance to talk it over—even if that means calling me in the middle of the night.

Most children and adolescents will promise and shake hands on it. Often they will call once or twice on the weekend or in the middle of the night to test the therapist's concern and reliability.

Short-term psychiatric hospitalization is frequently indicated for suicide attempters. Hospitalization temporarily removes the youth from the psychotoxic environment. It concretely underlines to the young person and the family the seriousness of the behavior. Often, hospitalization mobilizes resources within the child and the family and makes them more receptive to therapeutic input and change.

Hospitalization can also provide relief for the distressed young person and the family. It is not uncommon for the family and the patient to resist hospitalization, particularly because of the fear of "stigma." The patient and the family should be directly confronted to make it clear that there might not be a next time.

Individual psychotherapy is recommended for almost all suicidal and self-destructive young people, whether it be on an inpatient or outpatient basis. The young person needs to re-establish and repair his fragile human contacts in the privacy of a dyadic relationship. The therapist can help the patient in expression of feeling and in the alleviation of guilt, shame, and embarrassment. It is essential for the patient to become aware of his assets and liabilities, so that he can shore up his shattered self-esteem and be able to accept failure without a catastrophic reaction. In inhibited and depressed young people, verbal expression of hostile and aggressive feelings is encouraged.

The most important part of the therapeutic process is the *establishment of human contact*. The suicidal youth might resist coming to treatment, storm out of the office, sit for hours in pouty silence, become belligerent, or call the therapist all names imaginable. Consistent presence of a caring human being, who is not intimidated by the patient's hostility or deluded by the patient's pleasantries, may not only save the patient's life, but may help him become relatively free from intrapsychic and interactional conflicts.

For most suicidal youth, we do not recommend the prescription of any *medication*. If the patient is psychotic, extremely disorganized, or overwhelmed by anxiety, the benefits of using a major tranquilizer should be weighed carefully against its potentially depressing effect. In these situations, major tranquilizers, such as Thioridazine or haloperidol, can be used while the patient is hospitalized.

Antidepressant agents and anxiolytic agents can be used by the patient for another suicide attempt, which might be lethal. This happens frequently.

Therapeutic work with the family is essential. Concomitant with individual therapy, if the youth is psychologically able, conjoint therapeutic work with the family might be useful. If the patient is not ready or not willing to join in family therapy, then the parents and perhaps other siblings need to be seen together to explore their own problems and their contributions to the patient's distress.

In many situations, the youth's suicidal behavior can be a turning point for reintegration of the family through utilization of psychotherapy for change and growth.

Following discharge from the hospital, continuous outpatient psychotherapeutic work for the young person and the family is of utmost importance. Inpatient hospitalization is the beginning of treatment rather than the end. At least one to 2 years of outpatient treatment and follow-up is recommended, based on Otto's studies, which confirmed that most completed suicides in children and adolescents occurred within 2 years of the previous suicide attempt. Treatment does not need to be intensive. For the first few months, the patient can be seen one to two times per week or more. If the patient continues to improve, the frequency can be decreased to once every 2 weeks or once a month for the next year or two. It is important for the patient and family to know that at the time of crisis they can call the therapist immediately.

Occasionally, *rehospitalization* is indicated. The youth and the family should be helped to see that rehospitalization does not necessarily mean failure; rather, it may be used as a preventive measure for helping the patient and family regroup their psychological resources to deal with a stressful situation.

For further exploration of the underlying psychopathology contributing to suicidal behavior, management, and treatment, refer to chapters 7, 8, 9, and 22.

REFERENCES

Alvarez, A. (1975). Literature. In Perlin, S. (Ed.) *A Handbook for the Study of Suicide.* New York: Oxford University Press, pp. 31–58.

Bakwin, H. (1957). Suicide in children and adolescents. *J. Pediatr., 50,* 749–769.

Bakwin, R.M. (1973). Suicide in children and adolescents. *J. Am. Med. Wom. Assoc., 28,* 643.

Barter, J.T., Swaback, D.O., Todd, D. (1968). Adolescent suicide attempts, a follow-up study of hospitalized patients. *Arch. Gen. Psychiatry, 19,* 523–527.

Bender, L., Schilder, P. (1937). Suicidal preoccupations and attempts in children. *Am. J. Orthopsychiatry, 7,* 225–234.

Choron, J. (1972). *Suicide.* New York: Charles Scribner's Sons.

Dorpat, T.L., Ripley, H.S. (1960). A study of suicide in the Seattle area. *Compr. Psychiatry, 1,* 349–359.

Dorpat, T.L., Ripley, H.S. (1967). The relationship between attempted suicide and committed suicide. *Compr. Psychiatry, 8,* 74–79.

Ettlinger, R.W. (1964). Suicides in a group of patients who had previously attempted suicide. *Acta Psychiatr. Scand., 40,* 363–378.

Farberow, N.L. (1975). *Suicide in Different Cultures.* Baltimore: University Park Press.

Farberow, N.L., MacKinnon, D.R., Nelson, F.L. (1977). Suicide: Who's counting? *Public Health Rep., 92,* 223–232.

Farberow, N.L., Shneidman, E.S. (1955). Attempted, threatened and completed suicide. *J. Abnorm. Psychol., 50,* 230.

Frederick, C.J. (1978). Current trends in suicidal behavior in the United States. *Am. J. Psychotherapy, 32,* 172–200.

Goethe (1774). *The Sorrows of Young Werther.* Leipig: Weygandschen Buchhandlung.

Holinger, P.C. (1978). Adolescent suicide: An epidemiological study of recent trends. *Am. J. Psychiatry, 135,* 754–756.

Jacobziner, H. (1965). Attempted suicides in adolescence. *J.A.M.A., 191,* 7.

Manual of the International Statistical Classification of Diseases, Injuries and Causes of Death (1968). Geneva: World Health Organization.

Marek, Z., Widacki, J., Zwarysiewicz, W. (1976). Suicides committed by minors. *Forensic Sci., 7,* 103–106.

Moss, L.M., Hamilton, D.M. (1956). The psychotherapy of the suicidal patient. *Am. J. Psychiatry, 112,* 814–820.

Motto, J.A. (1965). Suicide attempts. *Arch. Gen. Psychiatry, 13,* 516–520.

Mulcock, D. (1955). Juvenile suicide. A study of suicide and attempted suicide over a 16-year period. *Med. Officer, 94,* 155–160.

National Center for Health Statistics, Washington, D.C., Unpublished data for 1976, 1977, 1978.

Otto, U. (1972). Suicidal acts by children and adolescents. *Acta Psychiatr. Scand.* (Suppl.) *233,* 7–123.

Paykel, E.S., *et al.* (1974). Suicidal feelings in the general population. *Br. J. Psychiatry, 124,* 460–469.

Ringel, E. (1953). *Der Selbstmord.* Vienna: Maudrich.

Sainsbury, P. (1955). *Suicide in London.* New York: Basic Books.

Seiden, R.H. (1969). Suicide among youth: A review of the literature, 1900–1967. *A Supplement to the Bulletin of Suicidology.* National Clearinghouse for Mental Health Information. Washington, D.C.: U.S. Government Printing Office.

Shaffer, D. (1974). Suicide in childhood and early adolescence. *J. Child Psychol. Psychiatry, 15,* 275–291.

Shafii, M., Whittinghill, R., Healy, M.H. (1979). The pediatric-psychiatric model for emergencies in child psychiatry: A study of 994 cases. *Am. J. Psychiatry, 136,* 1600–1601.

Shneidman, E.S. (1970). Suggestions for revision of the death certificate. In Shneidman, E.S., Farberow, N.L., Litman, R.E., (Eds.), *The Psychology of Suicide.* New York: Science House, pp. 551–561.

Teicher, J.D. (1967). Treatment of the suicidal adolescent— the life line approach. *Excerpta Medica, International Congress Series, 1,* 747–751. Amsterdam: Excerpta Medica Foundation.

Teicher, J.D. (1970). Children and adolescents who attempt suicide. *Pediatr. Clin. North Am., 17,* 687–696.

Teicher, J.D. (1972). The enigma of predicting adolescent suicide attempts. *Feelings,4,* no. 4. Columbus: Ross Laboratories.

Teicher, J.D. (1973). A solution to the chronic problem of

living: Adolescent attempted suicide. In Schoolar, J.C. (Ed.), *Current Issues in Adolescent Psychiatry.* New York: Brunner/Mazel, pp. 129–147.

Teicher, J.D. (1979). Suicide and suicide attempts. In Noshpitz, J. (Ed.), *Basic Handbook of Child Psychiatry,* Vol. 2. New York: Basic Books, pp. 685–697.

Teicher, J.D., Jacobs, J. (1966). Adolescents who attempt suicide: Preliminary findings. *Am. J. Psychiatry, 122,* 1248–1257.

Toolan, J.M. (1962). Suicide and suicidal attempts in children and adolescents. *Am. J. Psychiatry, 118, 719–724.*

Tuckman, J., Youngman, W.F. (1963), Identifying suicide risk groups among attempted suicides. *Public Health Rep., 78,* 763–766.

Chapter 15

PHYSICAL AND SEXUAL ABUSE

An unknown author wrote, "The test of a society's civilization is its ability to care for its children." By this standard, most societies from antiquity to the present would miserably fail the test.

HISTORICAL PERSPECTIVE

Children from recorded times until the present have been battered, tortured, sexually abused, and frequently sold or killed for crying too much or too little, being deformed, or for being female. Lloyd deMause (1974), in *The History of Childhood,* wrote:

Children were thrown into rivers, flung into dung-heaps and cess trenches, "potted" in jars to starve to death, and exposed on every hill and roadside, "a prey for birds, food for wild beasts to rend."

p. 25.

Infanticide "...has been responsible for more child deaths than any other single cause in history, other than possibly bubonic plague." (Solomon, 1973, p. 773) Killing infants soon after birth by suffocation, a blow to the head, bodily trauma, or intentional neglect, and sacrificing older children for religious rituals and population control were common.

In Old Testament times, Abraham was prepared to sacrifice Isaac. Nimrod, the King of Babylon, killed all first-born males to preserve his throne. The Jewish ritual of passover commemorates the protection of first-born Israelite children from the plague of death suffered by all first-born Egyptian children. The New Testament recounts the slaughtering of all male children in Bethlehem under age 2 years by King Herod, who sought to kill the Christ child.

Aristotle, Plato, and Seneca sanctioned the killing of defective children. The American Indians, Egyptians, Australian Aborigines, Africans, and Europeans practiced the killing of legitimate and illegitimate children. In China and India, even in the nineteenth century, newborn infants, especially females, were cast into rivers.

Sealing children in walls, foundations of buildings, and bridges to strengthen the structure was also common from the building of the wall of Jericho [7,000 B.C.] to as late as 1843 in Germany. To this day, when children play "London Bridge is Falling Down," they are acting out a sacrifice to a river goddess when they catch the child at the end of the game.

deMause, 1974, p. 27.

As late as the 1890s, finding bodies of babies in the streets of London was common. During the same time in Eastern Europe, nursing nannies would kill babies they were in charge of for lack of payment or for having too many babies to care for.

During the Industrial Revolution, children provided cheap labor. They were often sold into servitude and slavery in both England and the United States. Charles Dickens' works epitomized such abuse and maltreatment. Children aged 5 years and older worked at least 16 hours per day and were kept in chains and irons to prevent their running away from work. According to Eisenberg (1975):

An "enlightened" law of 1833, passed over savage opposition, provided that children from 9 to 13 years of age were not to work more than 48 hours a week and those from 13 to 18 not more than 68 hours. Even these minimal regulations did not apply to children working in mines...

pp. 2042-2043.

Childhood and adolescence as distinct developmental stages differing from adulthood were not conceptualized until the last few decades. Throughout the ages, some children were loved and cared for by their parents, but often children were perceived as "miniature adults," "imperfect human beings," "wild beasts," and "ill-formed" or "incomplete adults."

Total obedience to adults was demanded. Children were "seen but not heard." In Puritan society, play was viewed as a "sinful act," and children were expected to work beginning before dawn and continuing until bedtime. "Idle hands do the work of the devil," and "Idle hands make idle minds."

The Case of Mary Ellen

In 1874, Mary Ellen, a young girl, was brought to the attention of the authorities by a group of church workers for being physically abused, maltreated, and chained to her bed by her parents. At that time, there were no laws or agencies for the protection and prevention of cruelty to children. Finally, the American Society for the Prevention of Cruelty to Animals, already organized, had to intervene and remove the child from her home. Soon after, in 1895, The Society for Prevention of Cruelty to Children was established in New York City.

MEDICAL RECOGNITION OF CHILD ABUSE

In 1888, West presented a paper on "Acute Periosteal Swelling in Infants." (Solomon, 1973, p. 774) This was the first medical recognition of child abuse. Sixty years later, Caffey (1946) reported on radiological findings of "Multiple Fractures in the Long Bones of Infants Suffering from Chronic Hematoma." There was no known medical etiology. This finding become known as Caffey's syndrome and was a source of puzzlement for clinicians. Eleven years later, Caffey (1957) associated these multiple fractures to traumatic lesions.

Less than 20 years ago, in 1962, Kempe *et al.* described and clearly connected bone fractures to physical battering of children by their parents. They referred to this phenomenon as the battered child syndrome. Kempe *et al.* based their report on a national survey of 749 severe cases of battered child syndrome and maltreatment. Seventy-eight of these children had died because of battering, and 114 were permanently brain damaged.

Also, around this time, DeFrancis (1963) reported a nationwide survey of not only the physical, but also the sexual abuse of children. Fontana (1963) referred to the battered child

syndrome as maltreatment syndrome and discussed clinical manifestations and the medical and legal responsibilities of physicians and juvenile authorities.

The Society for Prevention of Cruelty to Children, based on these findings, began a crusade to pass legislation in all 50 states, requiring by law that physicians, nurses, educators, social workers, and concerned citizens report cases of suspicion of child abuse without fear of legal liability. By 1969, all 50 states had passed laws for reporting child abuse to designated social agencies or protective services within the community and also to state authorities. Failure to report became a misdemeanor, punishable by imprisonment and fine.

PHYSICAL ABUSE

Definition

Kempe *et al.* (1962) defined the battered child syndrome as "…a clinical condition in young children who have received serious physical abuse," which frequently caused "…permanent injury or death."(p. 105) This definition was considered too restrictive because it was *post facto* and did not cover milder forms of child abuse. Fontana (1973) used the term "maltreatment syndrome," which not only included physical abuse, but also emotional abuse and nutritional deprivation and neglect. The problem with both of these definitions was that they did not take into account "accidental injuries."

Gil (1970) defined child abuse or neglect as

…intentional, non-accidental use of physical force, or intentional, non-accidental acts of omission, on the part of a parent or other caretaker, interacting with a child in his care, aimed at hurting, injuring or destroying that child.
National Center on Child Abuse and Neglect, 1978, p. 1.

Newberger expanded the concept of child abuse, defining it as "…an illness, with or without injury, stemming from situations in [the] home setting which threaten a child's survival."(ibid., p. 2)

Efforts toward defining, reporting, treating, and preventing child abuse resulted in the passage of the *Child Abuse Prevention and Treatment Act of 1974* (Public Law 93-247). According to this law, abuse and neglect are defined as:

…physical or mental injury, sexual abuse, negligent treatment, or mal-treatment of a child under the age of eighteen by a person who is responsible for the child's welfare under circumstances which indicate that the child's health or welfare is harmed or threatened thereby.

ibid., p. 2.

Incidence

The true incidence of physical abuse, sexual abuse, and child neglect is not known. Many cases do not come to the attention of clinicians or authorities. Frequently, when cases do come to the attention of the clinicians, they are misdiagnosed or unreported.

For instance, in Jefferson County, Kentucky, with a population in 1980 of approximately 680,000, about 200 cases of child abuse and neglect were reported monthly to Protective Services. Subsequent to a Grand Jury investigation in Jefferson County, concerning laxity, inefficiency, and inconsistency in reporting, management and follow-up of child abuse cases by clinicians and social agencies, the number of child abuse reports doubled to 400 per month. (Colwell, 1980, p. B1)

Kempe and Helfer (1972) estimated that the number of actual cases of physical abuse was "...60,000 incidents per year in the United States." (National Center on Child Abuse and Neglect, 1978, p. 7) Nagi "...estimated that 600,000 reports of child abuse and neglect came to the attention of protective agencies..." in the United States from October 1972 to September 1973. (ibid., p. 8) He also estimated that 325,000 cases were not reported.

Geles, in a sociopsychological survey of 2,143 families regarding the presence of violence, found that approximately 8 million people in the United States were stabbed, beaten-up, punched, kicked, or struck by members of their families at least once a year. He estimated that in 1975 "...between 1.4 and 1.9 million children were subjected to physical injury." (Durant, 1979, p. G-1)

Each year, according to the National Center on Child Abuse and Neglect, "...more than 300,000 instances of child maltreatment..." are reported in the United States, resulting in 2,000 deaths. (Fontana, 1980, p. 2734)

In summary, conservatively, approximately 300,000 children and adolescents are physically abused in the United States each year—an incidence of 1%. The frequency of child neglect is estimated at 6 to 10 times higher than child abuse.

Clinical Features

Physical abuse, although it occurs more frequently in children under the age of 3 years, also occurs throughout childhood and adolescence. Approximately 25% of physical abuse occurs in adolescence. At the Rochester Medical Center, New York, "...at least 15% of all children under age five who come into the emergency room fall into the battered category." (Kempe, 1969, p. 44) Ten percent of all traumas that occurred in childhood and adolescence and were seen in the emergency room resulted from physical abuse.

Usually, the child is brought to the emergency room or to the primary care physician's office with the chief complaint of physical injury which ostensibly occurred "by accident." In the interview, the parents are evasive and do not give a detailed or clear history of the injury. They are often anxious, defensive, and in a hurry. Their explanation does not correlate with the nature of the injury.

Physical Examination

Some of the following symptoms may be present:

1. Evidences of multiple, unexplained injuries, usually at different stages of the healing process—for example, evidence of black and blue marks, lashes, or belt marks, cigarette or other burns, skin lacerations, and repeated fractures or dislocations.
2. Evidence of poor care, poor hygiene, inappropriate dress, malnutrition, and dehydration without obvious cause.
3. The child is usually fearful and apprehensive of adults, whines and cries, or appears expressionless and remains quiet or mute during the examination.
4. There may be evidence of sexual abuse along with physical abuse.
5. Some children show signs of failure to thrive, but others look physically healthy and well cared for, except for physical injuries.
6. Behavioral observations reveal that these children are droopy, expressionless, without a smile, cautious, apprehensive, fearful, and anxious. Withdrawing from parents or clinging to them in a whiny, demanding manner is common. Some have a "watchful" look. Others appear listless, hyperactive, jittery, and nervous.

(Kempe and Helfer, 1972, p. 73;
Jones 1976, pp. 10–11)

Parental Attitude and Behavior

1. Parents may come from any socioeconomic group, race, religion, or educational level.

2. Parents may appear indifferent and unconcerned when reporting injuries or extremely apologetic, guilt-ridden or anxious. They give the impression of being afraid of revealing too much. Because of this, they often act in a defensive, hostile, or suspicious manner when questioned carefully.
3. Parents may change their story or blame the injury on the child, sibling, or someone else. Occasionally, parents will give an overly detailed explanation concerning the injury.
4. "Shopping" from one hospital to another or one doctor to another is common.
5. Parents often appear psychologically immature with a history of violent behavior, loss of control, or fear of losing control.
6. Marital disharmony, separation, divorce, spouse abuse, and history of the parents being abused as children by their own parents are common.
7. History of drug and alcohol abuse.
8. Parents give the impression of being lonely, isolated, and having no relatives or friends to turn to in times of distress.
9. Strong, ambivalent feelings exist toward the child (love and hate relationship). Overprotection, undue concern, overexpectation—frequently associated with impatience lack of tolerance, and loss of control toward the child resulting in physical injury are common.
10. The clinician may experience feelings of hostility and anger toward the parents.
11. The parents may be reluctant or refuse to give consent for hospitalization or further diagnostic assessment.
12. From a psychodynamic point of view, the parents frequently have unrealistic expectations of the child. Any deviation from "perfection" or misbehavior is perceived as an insult to them, a sign of their failure as parents and human beings. The resulting disappointment is experienced as a severe narcissistic injury, causing outbursts of anger, rage, and loss of control toward the child.

    Upon deeper psychiatric exploration, the clinician frequently finds that the parents, themselves, were abused, neglected, or maltreated as children. They treat their children as they were treated, but more severely, without any awareness of their physical strength at the moment of impulse. Some parents feel guilty and remorseful after physically injuring their child, but frequently repeat the abuse.
13. History of pregnancy at an early age, unwanted pregnancy, premature birth, serious psychopathology, antisocial behavior, lack of parenting skills, poor judgment, unstable

family relationships and work habits, and frequent moving increase the risk of child abuse and neglect.

Management and Treatment

Child abuse is a medical and psychiatric emergency. When there is a suspicion or evidence of child abuse, the clinician should move *immediately and decisively*. The prime concern is protection of the child's life. Lack of recognition of child abuse, minimizing the potential danger, overlooking clues, indecisive management, or returning the abused child to his home may be costly and result in repeated abuse or death.

Emergency Management and Treatment

The following guidelines may be helpful in emergency management.

1. At the initial stage, the clinician should avoid blaming the parents or confronting them with the suspicion of child abuse. Playing detective to find out who abused the child or trying to elicit a confession usually increases the parents' hostility, uncooperativeness, and refusal for further assessment and treatment.
2. All cases that involve suspicion of abuse or neglect should be immediately admitted to the hospital. Hospitalization of the child facilitates medical and psychosocial assessment of the child and the family, provides opportunities for observation of the child and the child-parent interactions on a 24-hour basis, underlines the seriousness of the situation, provides opportunity for immediate and effective therapeutic intervention, helps mobilize community resources on behalf of the child while he is in the hospital and following discharge, and, above all, provides a protective and secure physical and emotional environment for the child.
3. In assessment, careful documentation of physical or sexual traumas is essential for medicolegal purposes and for effectively discussing the final diagnostic impression with the parents. Color photographs of bruises and injuries are of immense value in documenting the nature and extent of injuries. Total body x-ray of younger children may show multiple fractures in various stages of the healing process. X-rays of the areas of contusion, injury, or trauma are necessary immediately and again after 2 weeks to facilitate detection of new bone fractures and calcification. Plotting the child's height and weight for evidence of growth retardation due to neglect or deprivation is also indicated.

4. Psychiatric assessment, in the form of detailed and accurate observations of the child's behavior and attitude, facial and emotional expressions, and direct quotations of the child's statements is important.

   In almost all cases of child abuse, children do not exaggerate, make up, or lie about being abused. If anything, they minimize the abuse to protect the abusers. With reassurance and support, most children age 2 years and older may verbalize some parts of the abusive experience. At times, it is easier for the children to play out the abusive incident through the use of a doll family, puppets, or stuffed animals. This is particularly true in the preschool-aged child.

5. When there is a suspicion of child abuse, the clinician should request consultation from the social work department. According to the law, child abuse cases should be reported immediately to the local child protective agency for psychosocial and possible legal investigation. In some states, the clinician must also report to the local and state police authorities or to the prosecuting attorney.

   It is recommended that all hospitals that serve children and adolescents have a child abuse team, in which case the team should be notified as soon as possible.

6. After the child's admission to the hospital and the collection of all relevant data, an experienced clinician should discuss the findings and the diagnosis of child abuse with the parents or caretaker in a supportive, concerned, and nonthreatening manner in the privacy of an office. The sensitive handling of the parents by the clinicians and nurses in the emergency room and the pediatric unit can contribute significantly to the success or failure of management and treatment.

   Parents frequently initially deny the abuse. Emphasis should be on helping them to see the potential danger that may result from abuse, such as severe, permanent physical or psychological damage to the child, or even death. Gentle, warm, empathic exploration and reassurance frequently help the frightened and defensive parents.

7. If the parents refuse permission for admission of the child to the hospital, the clinician can hold the patient in the hospital without parental consent for a period of up to 72 hours in most states. The protective services and juvenile authorities should be contacted immediately to assume temporary custody of the child until further therapeutic work can be done with the parents.

   Indecisiveness in this situation and allowing the child to return to his home may result in frightened parents leaving the area without a forwarding address, and, thereby, increase the possibility of recurrent abuse and possible death of the child. The need for immediate management of child abuse is comparable to the need for emergency management of a patient suffering from a life-threatening disease or a patient who has attempted suicide.

8. Awareness of the psychodynamic aspects of the abusing parents is essential for developing empathy for the family and for effective therapeutic intervention. Usually, the parents were abused themselves as children. They often felt unwanted. They are generally unhappy and troubled and have low self-esteem. They project their own inadequacies onto the child and have unrealistic expectations of him—as they have of themselves. Many of these parents care for their children, but in a pathological and distorted fashion. They perceive, for instance, the child's crying, colicky, oppositional behavior, temper tantrums, assertiveness, or defiance as rejection, a major insult to their self-esteem and the concrete evidence of their failure as parents and as human beings. Child abuse is a symptomatic expression of a disorder in parenting and dysfunction of the family. Isolation and loneliness are the most significant underlying dynamics in abusing parents.

9. Assessment of the whole family, particularly other siblings, for evidence of neglect, abuse, and physical or psychiatric disorders is of utmost importance. It is not uncommon for more than one child to be abused in the family or, following treatment or removal of the abused child from the family, for another child to become the scapegoat for abuse.

Mental Health Intervention

Child abuse is a psychosocial disorder that, after initial emergency management, requires careful psychosocial intervention. In some cases, psychiatric consultation and treatment of the parents for evidence of depression, psychosis, borderline psychosis, drug and alcohol abuse, and personality disorders is essential. In the absence of evidence of psychopathology, the following therapeutic measures may be helpful:

1. Regular home visits by the public health nurse or a visiting nurse, to provide basic parenting skills, support, and advice.
2. Involvement of the parents in a self-help group, such as Parents Anonymous. These groups are comprised of previously abusing parents.

3. Availability of a crisis nursery or a therapeutic nursery for children on a 24-hour basis, so that the parents can call the nursery anytime of the day, night, or weekend, when they feel over-whelmed by the child or by the responsibilities of parenthood and are afraid they may lose control and hurt the child. The establishment of crisis nurseries has been relatively inexpensive and most effective in many communities.

4. Establishment of a program for the lay public, particularly elderly women, who have been, themselves, successful mothers; such a program could provide continuous support, counseling, and role-modeling for abusing parents. Providing mothering to abusing mothers significantly helps to alleviate their feelings of loneliness, isolation, and maternal deprivation through support and encouragement.

5. According to Kempe (1969), 90% of abused children were reunited with their parents with active treatment and follow-up programs.

6. The permanent removal of the child from the family is indicated in cases of total family disorganization, severe alcohol and drug abuse, lack of parental commitment to the child, lack of parental interest in treatment and follow-up, and whenever there is the possibility of repeated abuse and neglect. Permanent removal is usually necessary in 10% of cases of physical abuse.

7. Throughout all legal proceedings, the child should have a legal advocate to protect his legal rights and physical and emotional well-being, especially in cases where there is the possibility of repeated abuse and lack of parental concern.

Prediction and Prevention

Criteria have been developed in the form of a questionnaire to be given to pregnant women to assess the potential for future child abuse. However, behavioral observations of mother-infant interactions by nurses and clinicians during delivery and the first few days following birth are found to be the most effective predictors of potential abuse.

Kempe observed that the parents' attitude toward the child immediately following birth has high predictive value. Mother's disappointment concerning the sex, size, color, or appearance of her infant, rejection of the infant, intolerance toward crying, expectations for a calm, quiet, and perfect baby, shouting at or physically punishing the baby, ignoring the baby, and undue concern about doing the "right" thing all significantly indicate the possibility of future abuse.

Helfer (1976) emphasized early identification and prevention of child abuse. He designed a 74-item questionnaire for exploring the mother's own childhood experiences, evidences of severe physical punishment by her parents, unrealistic expectations of her own children, and overwhelming concern about feeling lonely, isolated, or being criticized. The mother's behavior toward the child is also observed in the delivery room and on the maternity ward.

Gray et al. (1977) were able to identify 50 high-risk parents by using Helfer's approach. These high-risk mothers were randomly divided in half. One group received no intervention, while the other had assigned physicians, regular telephone contacts, and weekly visits by public health nurses to help the mothers increase mothering skills. In a 2-year follow-up, there was a 20% incidence of serious child abuse by the parents in the nonintervention group (Schmitt, 1980, p. 172) In the group that received intervention, none of the children were seriously abused, and 12% of the children were voluntarily given up for placement outside the home. Observation of the mother's attitude and behavior toward her infant in the delivery room and on the maternity ward had higher predictive value for detecting potential abuse and neglect than did a prenatal screening questionnaire and interview.

Altemeier et al. (1979) gave an interview questionnaire to 1,400 expectant mothers in a prenatal clinic to identify the high-risk abusers—273 high-risk mothers were found. The researchers randomly chose 225 mothers from those remaining as a control group. Child abuse, neglect, and failure to thrive were found to be significantly higher in the high-risk group as opposed to the control group.

By the time a child comes to the attention of protective services or clinicians for the symptoms of maltreatment, already significant physical and psychological damage has occurred to the child and the family. Silver et al. (1969) reported on a study "...covering three generations of families of abused children." They found that "...violence breeds violence and that a child who experiences violence as a child has the potential of becoming a violent member of society in the future." (p. 152)

Green (1978), in observing 59 abused children aged 5 to 13 years, noticed that more than 40% demonstrated self-destructive behavior—such as self-biting, self-burning, head-banging, and suicide threats or attempts—as opposed to 17% of neglected children and approximately 7% of normal controls.

Recognition of dysfunctional families with the potential for child abuse and neglect is a significant step toward primary prevention. An extensive body of knowledge exists concerning childhood development and the care of children. Special programs should be designed that include supervised practical experience in caring for infants and children, for high school and college students to prepare them for the task of parenting. Expectant parents need to learn much more about practical issues of child care and need opportunities to discuss their feelings about becoming parents openly, just as now efforts are being made to provide instruction and preparation for labor and delivery. Enhancement of human bonding in the delivery room, by encouraging physical and emotional contact between the mother and neonate immediately following birth and including other family members in this process, can significantly decrease the possibility of child abuse. Rooming-in of the neonate with mother, teaching parents in maternity wards how to care for their baby, frequent telephone contacts and office visits, and home visits by public health nurses to high-risk parents are helpful in increasing parenting skills, decreasing parenting disorders, and preventing child abuse and neglect.

Follow-Up

Recurrence of child abuse is, unfortunately, a common phenomenon in 20 to 60% of the families. Herrenkohl *et al.* (1979) reported on a 10-year follow-up of 328 families that were involved in physical abuse, emotional abuse, gross neglect, or sexual abuse.

The recurrence rate was 54% for physical abuse, 21% for emotional abuse, 44% for gross neglect, and 29% for sexual abuse. The most troublesome finding was that only 25% of the recurrent maltreatment was documented in official reports, although there were actually about 67% "verified incidences."

The authors concluded that the recurrence of child maltreatment is "…a more serious problem than has been generally recognized, highlighting the need to identify those factors which are predictive of repeated abuse." (p. 72)

SEXUAL ABUSE

Sexual abuse of children is tolerated or "quietly accepted" in many communities. Pretending that sexual abuse does not exist, or minimizing, denying, and rationalizing the abuse are common. DeFrancis (1969, 1971) contributed significantly in bringing the attention of clinicians,

legal authorities, and the community as a whole to the rampant problem of sexual abuse of children by adults, and the utter disregard for the protection of children against such abuses. Most clinicians, legal authorities, and "…communities have closed their eyes to the needs of these children. Their cry for help is unheeded—it is unheard or ignored." (DeFrancis, 1971, pp. 15-20)

According to DeFrancis, acknowledgment and recognition of the sexual abuse of children is unpalatable. "It is a reminder of society's failure to control destructive human behavior—of society's inability to protect its most defenseless from exposure to depraved, primitive, and emotionally sick cravings of a disoriented few." (ibid., pp. 15–20)

Exploration and recognition of the sexual abuse of children have been ignored much longer than physical abuse and neglect. From the early 1960s, there has been growing concern about the physical abuse of children, but only during the last few years has attention been focused on sexual abuse. The increasing concern over sexual assault on women, the Women's Rights Movement, and the Children's Rights Movement have probably contributed to this awareness.

Kempe (1978) referred to sexual abuse of children as "…another hidden pediatric problem." (p. 382) It is only during the last half of the 1970s that some of the states have included sexual abuse of children in their legislation related to physical abuse and child neglect. Still, some states do not have any legal mechanism to protect defenseless children against sexual violence.

Historical Perspective

According to deMause (1974), in antiquity children lived their earliest years "…in an atmosphere of sexual abuse." (p. 43) In Greece and Rome, the sexual use of children by older men was common. Girls and boys both were openly subjected to sexual exploitation. "Boy brothels flourished in every city, and one could even contract for the use of a rent-a-boy service in Athens." (ibid., p. 43) Most men slept with "slave boys" in the household, while their "free born children" witnessed their fathers' sexual abuse. This abuse was frequently in the form of anal intercourse; also, women in the household commonly "played" with the little boys' genitals to "hasten manhood." (ibid., p. 46) Plato and Aristotle both condoned sexual relationships with children, although Aristotle observed that homosexuality in adulthood was related to being sexually abused as a child.

Children frequently were castrated in order to be used as favorite sexual objects. "Intercourse with castrated children was often spoken of as being especially arousing, castrated boys were favorite 'voluptates' in imperial Rome..." (ibid., p. 46) Castration was performed frequently by physicians by placing the young child or infant in "...a vessel of hot water, and then when the parts are softened in the bath, the testicles are to be squeezed with the fingers until they disappear." (ibid., p. 46) Another method was to place the child on a bench, and cut off the testicles. Castration frequently was used as a method for treating children for various diseases. "...unscrupulous 'Gelders,' greedy to get children's testicles for magical purposes, persuaded parents to let them castrate their children." (ibid., p. 47)

In the Middle East, girls as young as the age of 9 years were forced to marry older men or were sold as concubines. Sexual exploitation of children continued throughout medieval times and the Renaissance. Boys were castrated so that they could play the roles of women in the theater, opera, and choruses.

The concept of "childhood innocence" in Christianity became an excuse for the sexual exploitation of children. It was rationalized that, because of innocence, children could not be corrupted and, therefore, were not harmed by sexual exploitation by adults!

In the sixteenth and seventeenth centuries, a campaign began against the sexual abuse of children. In the eighteenth and nineteenth centuries, parents, with the encouragement of clinicians, severely punished children for touching their own genitals. In the latter part of the nineteenth century and the early part of the twentieth century "masturbation phobia" swept Europe and America. Physicians connected the cause of many illnesses, particularly blindness, insanity, delinquent behavior, and a variety of physical sicknesses to the masturbation behavior of infants and children. Children were threatened with castration or the cutting off of fingers or ears if they continued to "play with" themselves. These types of threats are still prevalent today. Even though parents mercilessly oppressed childhood sexuality, they, relatives, and others continued to sexually abuse children. For example, until the 1900s, a treatment for venereal disease was sexual intercourse with a young child.

Freud and Breuer (1895) found in their studies of hysteria that actual sexual seduction in early childhood resulted in a traumatic psychological experience and contributed to the development of hysteria and other forms of psychoneurosis. In later analyses of patients, Freud found that many shared memories of earlier sexual abuse by parents, relatives, servants, or nursemaids. Freud, aghast at the frequency of incidents of sexual abuse, came to believe that most of these memories were probably fantasies rather than actual occurrences. Perhaps Freud and Breuer's earlier clinical observations regarding the rampant sexual abuse of children were closer to reality than Freud's revised position.

Incidence

Studies by Cagnon in reanalyzing the Kinsey research on 4,400 adult women, revealed that 24% of this group had "...at least one sexual contact or approach during childhood." (Sarafino, 1979, p. 131) Landis (1956), in a study of university students, reported that one-third had sexual contact with adults during childhood. Sarafino (1979), based on reported cases of sexual abuse, estimated that more than 330,000 sexual offenses are committed against boys and girls each year in the United States. Ninety percent of the victims are girls, and 10% are boys. The abuser is almost always an adult male. The incidence of reported sexual offenses against children is 122.5 per 100,000. It is now estimated that one out of every 4 girls becomes a victim of sexual violence, particularly child molestation and rape, between birth and age 18 years. (Adams, 1978)

In Jefferson County, Kentucky, during 1976 to 1977, of 950 reports of child abuse, 20% (N = 192) were sexually abused. (ibid., 1978)

DeFrancis (1969), in his New York study, reported that in 72% of the sexual abuse cases, parents or parent substitutes were involved by act of commission or omission. The father, mother's boyfriend, and male relatives were the most frequent abusers. Mother knowingly or unknowingly, through denial or passivity, did not provide effective protection of the child from the abuser.

Definition

Debate exists concerning the definition, types, and nature of sexual abuse. Generally, sexual abuse is perceived from a legal point of view as a sexual offense against a child or a youth aged 16 years or younger, based on the following categories:

1) forceable rape, in which physical force, threats or drugs are used to achieve sexual intercourse; 2) non-forceable rape, commonly called statutory rape, involving sexual intercourse between a legal adult and a child

who does not resist; 3) sodomy, referring to oral or anal intercourse; 4) incest, involving sexual intercourse with someone of close kinship; and 5) indecent liberties, including a wide variety of acts such as genital exhibition, rectal stimulation, masturbation, physical advances and the use of obscene language.

Sarafino, 1979, p. 128.

Brant and Tisza (1977) expanded the legal definition of sexual abuse and applied the terms "sexual misuse" to describe the "...exposure of a child to sexual stimulation inappropriate for the child's age level of psychosexual development, and role in the family." (p. 81) The presence of physical or behavioral symptoms and clinical evidence of dysfunction in the family are important in determining the "inappropriateness of the stimulation," taking into consideration the sociocultural, familial, and ethnic background.

Clinical Features

The following are some of the clinical manifestations of sexual abuse: complaint about the possibility of sexual abuse by the child, parents, or others; unexplained genital trauma; vaginal bleeding in a premenstrual child; venereal disease; recurrent vaginitis; behavioral symptoms of promiscuity, runaway, and precocious sexual interest; and pregnancy in a young adolescent. In all of these, the clinician should immediately consider the possibility of sexual abuse. Failure to consider this possibility can lead to misdiagnosis and, more seriously, may perpetuate further abuse.

In a case involving suspicion of sexual abuse, the clinician needs to be particularly sensitive, empathic, and supportive. The development of a warm rapport, in spite of internal feelings of outrage, is essential in helping the victim and the family. Not only should the child be interviewed individually, but also each member of the family should be seen separately. Then the family should be interviewed as a group, in order to obtain as many facts as possible.

A complete physical examination with collection of evidence is essential. Orr (1980) related that "Up to 35 percent of girls and 50 percent of boys examined for alleged sexual abuse may have physical findings suggestive for abuse." (p. 1057) A complete physical examination, including examination of the genitals, by a family physician, pediatrician, or, in a complicated case, by a gynecologist is essential in order to assess the extent of injury and to collect materials for medicolegal purposes. All findings should be carefully documented in the patient's chart.

The physician needs to realize that his role is not only that of a clinician treating the child's symptom, but also that of the child's confidant and, above all, *advocate*. The clinician must be willing to testify openly and with conviction in court about the sexual abuse. Parents, the community, and to a great extent the legal system try to skirt the issue. The clinician's commitment to the total, comprehensive care of the child paves the way for prevention of further abuse and allows physical and emotional healing.

Frequently, younger or frightened children cannot directly talk about sexual abuse, because they fear reprisal from the abusing parent or person. The use of dolls, puppets, or drawings may help these children "play out" what happened to them.

Treatment and Management

We have seen a number of cases of children aged 3 to 4 years clearly and accurately play out their sexual abuse. Usually, the parents and legal authorities doubt the child's statements and want to believe that it is only the child's imagination. In our experience, we have not seen any child "make up" or invent stories regarding being sexually abused. Usually, the child's specific and concrete description is quite convincing, if one is willing to hear. For instance, a 4-year-old girl was referred to us by the mother's attorney for psychiatric evaluation, to determine whether the girl had been sexually abused by her father. In an interview in the playroom, the child "played out" the sexual abuse, while saying, "Daddy doll put his thing in her [referring to baby girl doll] mouth. He kissed her down there [pointing to the doll's genital area]. Then something gooey came out of his wee wee. It was icky. I was sick in my tummy." After further exploration, when she was playing the role of the daddy doll, she said to the girl doll, "Don't tell your mommy what happened. I'll kill you if you tell her." Then the child became agitated, started to touch her genital area, and began to hit the head of the daddy doll on the floor over and over, saying, "I hate you! I hate you!"

This vivid description convincingly documented sexual abuse and assisted the court in deciding that the father should not have visitation rights. The court ordered psychiatric evaluation and treatment for the father, in addition to further legal action.

The role of the clinician does not end with legal action or the removal of the abuser from the home. In this case, short-term psychotherapy for the child and the mother helped them to express their feelings and experiences within a supportive, protective, and therapeutic situation. Shortly afterward, the child's nightmares, agitated behavior, and driven masturbatory behavior decreased significantly. Taking the child's comments and behavior seriously, listening to her and helping her to "play out" experiences and feelings at her own pace, and working with the mother therapeutically helped the child re-establish some trust with grown-ups, and particularly her mother.

In most sexually abused patients, immediate removal of the abusing person from the family is strongly indicated. The abusing person, who is usually an adult male, needs to have psychiatric and psychological assessment, along with appropriate legal intervention and long-term follow-up. Evaluation, treatment, and follow-up are essential to determine whether sufficient changes have occurred within the abuser to allow a reunion of the family. Unfortunately, in most cases the abusing person initially acquiesces to intervention because of guilt and fear of legal reprisal, but soon resists treatment and is lost for follow-up. In this case, the parental rights of the abusing person should be terminated.

Assessment of the mother and home visits help to evaluate the physical and emotional climate of the home for the safety and protection of the child. If the climate is not suitable, the child should be removed from the home. Short-term hospitalization or placement in a residential setting may be indicated. Sadly, some of these children in foster homes or in residential settings again become the victims of sexual abuse.

Anxiety, phobia, depression, tendency toward sexual acting out and running away, delinquent behavior, drug and alcohol abuse, chronic feeling of low self-esteem, fragmentation, and disorganization are common.

Wathey and Densen-Gerber (1976) reported that in a population of 152 males and 85 females residing in "Odyssey Houses" for drug abusers across the nation, 25% of the males and 38% of the females had been involved in some type of incestuous relationship. Most of these relationships had been with members of the parental generation, and some had been with siblings. In most cases, the victim attempted to leave home before age 16. The authors concluded "...that parental generation or cross generational incest is far more traumatic to the 'victim'..." (p. 11) than peer age incest. Drug abuse, running away from home, and antisocial behavior, such as prostitution, were related to earlier traumatic incestuous relationships.

MacVicar (1979) reported on accidental and participating (willingly) victims of sexual abuse. She found that adolescent accidental victims responded favorably to short-term and crisis intervention therapy. However, all participating victims and latency-age accidental victims needed long-term psychotherapy. Acting-out behavior, in the form of seductive behavior toward male therapists and aggressive and provacative behavior toward female therapists, was prevalent. Depression in adolescents, phobia, behavioral disorders, and learning disturbances were most common in latency-age children. (p. 342)

Follow-Up

Some authors, such as Yorukoglu and Kemph (1966) and Weitzel et al. (1978), report that incestuous relationships do not have significant psychopathological impact on abused children and adolescents. Their reports are based on short-term follow-ups of a few months to one year. However, long-term follow-up of sexually abused children and adolescents does not support their findings.

Lewis and Sarrel (1969) reported on the frequent occurrence of psychopathology following sexual abuse. The manifestation of psychopathology was related to the developmental phase of the child, the frequency of the abuse, and whether or not the abuser was a relative. The longer the abuse, especially in the case of a parent or a relative, the more troublesome the outcome.

Conclusion

Sexual abuse of children and adolescents is a medical and psychiatric emergency. Reported incidence is significantly lower than actual incidence. Clinicians need to help increase parental vigilance in protecting children and adolescents from sexual abuse within the family and within the community. Child pornography and prostitution, rape, and murder of children are major psychosocial crises which speak of endemic violence toward and against children in our society. Clinicians, by working through their own personal feelings toward physical and sexual abuse and neglect and by being vigilant about diagnostic assessment, effective therapeutic intervention, and community education, play an important role in providing a relatively safe environment for our children and youth.

REFERENCES

Adams, P.L. (1978). Carnal aggression and abuse: Intervention strategies. Unpublished manuscript.

Altemeir, W.A., Vietze, P.M., Sherrod, K.B., Sandler, H.M., Falsey, S., O'Connor, S. (1979). Prediction of child maltreatment during pregnancy. *J. Am. Acad. Child Psychiatry, 18,* 205–218.

Brant, R.S.T., Tisza, V.B. (1977). The sexually misused child. *Am. J. Orthopsychiatry, 47,* 80–90.

Caffey, J. (1946). Multiple fractures in the long bones of infants suffering from chronic hematoma. *Am. J. Roentgenol., 56,* 163.

Caffey, J. (1957). Some traumatic lesions in growing bones other than fractures and dislocations: Clinical and radiological features. *Br. J. Radiol., 30,* 225.

Colwell, C. (1980). Grand jury urges reforms to fight child abuse. *The Courier-Journal,* November 8, p. B-1.

DeFrancis, V. (1963). *Child Abuse: Preview of a Nationwide Survey.* Denver: American Humane Association.

DeFrancis, V. (1969). *Protecting the Child Victim of Sex Crimes Committed by Adults.* Denver: The American Humane Assoc.

DeFrancis, V. (1971). Protecting the child victim of sex crimes committed by adults. *Federal Probation, 35,* 15–20.

deMause, L. (Ed.) (1974). *The History of Childhood.* New York: Harper and Row.

Durant, C. (1979). Violence: All in the family. *The Courier-Journal,* June 3, p. G-1.

Eisenberg, L. (1975). Normal child development. In Freedman, A., Kaplan, H., Sadock, B. (Eds.), *Comprehensive Textbook of Psychiatry-II,* Vol. 2. Second Edition. Baltimore: Williams and Wilkins, pp. 2036–2054.

Fontana, V.J. (1963). The "maltreatment syndrome" in children. *N. Engl. J. Med., 269,* 1389–1394.

Fontana, V.J. (1973). The diagnosis of the maltreatment syndrome in children. *Pediatrics, 51* (Suppl.), 780.

Fontana, V.J. (1980). Child maltreatment and battered child syndromes. In Kaplan, H., Freedman, A., Sadock, B.(Eds.), *Comprehensive Textbook of Psychiatry-III,* Vol. 3. Baltimore: Williams and Wilkins, pp. 2734–2744.

Freud, S., Breuer, J. (1895). Studies on hysteria. *Standard Edition of the Complete Psychological Works of Sigmund Freud,* Vol. 2, pp. 1–307.

Gil, D.G. (1970). *Violence against Children: Physical Child Abuse in the United States.* Cambridge: Harvard University Press.

Gray, J.D., Cutler, C.A., Dean, J.G., Kempe, C.H. (1977). Prediction and prevention of child abuse and neglect. *Child Abuse and Neglect, 1,* 45–58.

Green, A.H. (1978). Self-destructive behavior in battered children. *Am. J. Psychiatry, 135,* 579–582.

Helfer, R.E. (1976). Early identification and prevention of unusual child-rearing practices. *Pediatr. Ann., 5,* 184–190.

Herrenkohl, R.C., Herrenkohl, E.C., Egolf, B., Seech, M. (1979). The repetition of child abuse: How frequently does it occur? *Child Abuse and Neglect, 3,* 67–72.

Jones, M.P. (1976). *The Physician's Check-up on Child Abuse and Neglect.* Louisville: Norton-Children's Hospitals, Inc.

Kempe, C.H. (1969). The battered child and the hospital. *Hosp. Pract., 4,* 44–47, 52–53, 56–57.

Kempe, C.H. (1978). Sexual abuse, another hidden pediatric problem: The 1977 C. Aderson Aldrich Lecture. *Pediatrics, 62,* 382–389.

Kempe, C.H., Helfer, R.E. (Eds.) (1972). *Helping the Battered Child and his Family.* Philadelphia: Lippincott.

Kempe, C.H., Silverman, F.N., Steele, B.F., Droegemueller, W., Silver, H.K. (1962). The battered child syndrome. *J.A.M.A., 181,* 17–24.

Landis, J.T. (1956). Experiences of 500 children with adult sexual deviation. *Psychiatr. Q., 30,* 91–109.

Lewis, M., Sarrell, P. (1969). Some psychological aspects of seduction, incest, and rape in childhood. *J. Am. Acad. Child Psychiatry, 8,* 606–619.

MacVicar, K. (1979). Psychotherapeutic issues in the treatment of sexually abused girls. *J. Am. Acad. Child Psychiatry, 18,* 342–353.

National Center on Child Abuse and Neglect (1978). 1977 analysis of child abuse and neglect research. Washington, D.C.: U.S. Department of Health, Education, and Welfare.

Orr, D.P. (1980). Management of childhood sexual abuse. *J. Fam. Pract., 11,* 1057–1064.

Sarafino, E.P. (1979). An estimate of nationwide incidence of sexual offenses against children. *Child Welfare, 58,* 127–134.

Schmitt, B.D. (1980). The prevention of child abuse and neglect: A review of the literature with recommendation for application. *Child Abuse and Neglect, 4,* 171–177.

Silver, L.B., Dublin, C.C., Lourie, R.S. (1969). Does violence breed violence? Contributions from a study of the child abuse syndrome. *Am. J. Psychiatry, 126,* 152–155.

Solomon, T. (1973). History and demography of child abuse. *Pediatrics, 51,* 773–812.

Wathey, R., Densen-Gerber, J. (1976). *Incest: An Analysis of the Victim and Aggressor.* Paper presented at the Third Annual National Drug Abuse Conference, New York, New York, March.

Weitzel, W.D., Powell, B.J., Penick, E.C. (1978). Clinical management of father-daughter incest. *Am. J. Dis. Child., 132,* 127–130.

Yurokoglu, A., Kemph, J.P. (1966). Children not severely damaged by incest with a parent. *J. Am. Acad. Child Psychiatry, 5,* 111–124.

Chapter 16

PERVASIVE DEVELOPMENTAL, SCHIZOPHRENIC, AND OTHER PSYCHOTIC DISORDERS: In Infancy, Childhood, and Adolescence

From the early 1940's, the study of infantile autism, childhood psychosis, and childhood schizophrenias has captured the creative imagination of many clinicians, experimental scientists, and educators. Thousands of articles and many books have been written on these disorders. This awesome interest has been kindled by the severity of the psychopathological symptoms, the search for effective therapeutic modalities, and the hope for unraveling the mysteries of human development.

HISTORICAL PERSPECTIVE

Approximately 1,000 years ago, Avicenna (980-1037), a Persian physician and philosopher, treated an adolescent prince who was suffering from psychosis and symptoms of anorexia. (Shafii, 1972) Avicenna treated this patient by communicating with him within the metaphor of his delusional system, establishing a therapeutic alliance, and encouraging other physicians and relatives to communicate with the patient in the same manner. In this way, he created an effective therapeutic milieu that resulted in the patient's recovery.

In Western medical and psychiatric literature the following two cases are the earliest known references to psychosis in childhood and adolescence, and, particularly, to infantile autism. In 1799, Jean Marc Gaspard Itard beautifully recorded his observations of "The Wild Boy of Aveyron." (1801, 1807) This boy, subsequently named Victor, was either 11 or 12 years old. He was found in the woods of Aveyron, France, where he had apparently been surviving without human contact for many years. He was mute, did not show affection, and would bite or scratch others. Itard enthusiastically tried to rehabilitate Victor through a long-term, intensive, one-to-one relationship with a mothering person. Victor improved significantly in social relationships, but he remained mute and "... never became normal."(Wing, 1976, p. 6) Victor showed many symptoms of what we now call childhood autism.

John Haslam (1809), in his book *Observations on Madness and Melancholy,* described the case history of a 5-year-old boy who did not speak until age 4 years. The boy was admitted to Bethlem Royal Hospital in 1799. The child referred to himself in the third person and did not relate or become attached to anyone. Vaillant (1963) retrospectively diagnosed the case as early infantile autism.

In 1920, Lightner Witmer (1922) vividly described the clinical features of a young boy named Don, who was 2 years and 7 months old. Don was oblivious to people and would spend many hours gazing at a card in his hand and scratching it. He was mute, but would become totally absorbed in music. Witmer used a psychoeducational approach to help this young patient. He gained the child's attention by asking him to do something he could do and then something he could not do. After 1½ years of tedious and intensive work, Don improved to the extent that he could dress himself, talk, read, and attend the local school.

CLINICAL DESCRIPTION

These scattered case histories were flickers of light in a dark night. Potter (1933) was the first to discuss clearly schizophrenia in childhood. He reported six cases spanning ages 4 to 12 years. In regard to childhood schizophrenia, he stated, "It is necessary to bear in mind that children cannot be expected to exhibit psychopathology with all the elaborations of the adult." (p. 1253) The children he observed showed the following symptoms:

1. A generalized retraction of interest from the environment.

2. Dereistic [illogical] thinking, feeling and acting.

3. Disturbances of thought, manifested through blocking, symbolization, condensation, perseveration, incoherence and diminution, sometimes to the extent of mutism.

4. Defect in emotional rapport.

5. Diminution, rigidity and distortion of affect.

6. Alterations of behavior with either an increase of motility, leading to incessant activity, or a diminution of motility, leading to complete immobility or bizarre behavior with a tendency to perseveration or stereotypy.

p. 1254.

Bender and Lipkowitz (1940) wrote about the presence of hallucinations in emotionally troubled children. Bender (1942), who followed Potter at Bellevue Hospital in New York City, further elaborated on the clinical description of schizophrenia in childhood, which will be discussed later.

Leo Kanner (1943) wrote "Autistic Disturbances of Affective Contact," in which he described 11 cases (eight boys and three girls) ranging in ages from 2 to 8 years. Kanner conceptualized the psychopathology of these children as a unique syndrome "...not heretofore reported, which seems to be rare enough, yet is probably more frequent than is indicated by the paucity of observed cases." (p. 242) Some of these children were considered "feebleminded" or "schizophrenic." (ibid., p. 242)

The pathognomonic features of these cases were:

1. Extreme autistic aloneness
2. Perseveration of sameness
3. Excellent rote memory
4. Disturbance in language, such as muteness or delayed echolalia
5. Lack of spontaneous activities

Kanner (1944) coined the term "early infantile autism" to describe this psychopathological syndrome. Soon after, interest was focused on this syndrome and its relationship to childhood schizophrenia and other severe psychopathological disorders of childhood and adolescence.

ETIOLOGY

Kanner's (1946, 1949, 1951, 1952, 1965), Kanner and Eisenberg's (1955), and Kanner *et al.*'s (1972) contributions are monumental. In Europe, early infantile autism and early childhood autism (Wing, 1976) are referred to as Kanner's syndrome. Kanner attributed early infantile autism to constitutional factors and, more specifically, to "cold and refrigerating" mothers and obsessive intellectual parents.

Bender (1947, 1953, 1956, 1959, 1960, 1973; Bender *et al.* 1952) continued to write extensively on the etiology, clinical description, treatment, management, and long-term follow-up of childhood schizophrenia. She conceptualized the etiology to be organic factors, such as encephalopathy, deviation in the vasovegetative system, and, particularly, immaturity and plasticity of the nervous system on an embryonic level. Bender suggested that infantile autism is not a separate clinical entity, but is rather a pathological defense against catastrophic anxiety in schizophrenic children.

In addition to Bender's and Kanner's contributions, psychoanalysts began to write about childhood psychosis, emphasizing parental, particularly mother-child, interaction as a major contributing factor to the development of infantile autism and childhood psychosis. (Mahler *et al.*, 1949; Bettelheim, 1948)

Mahler (1952) divided childhood psychosis into autistic infantile psychosis and symbiotic infantile psychosis. She discussed extensively the psychotic child's relationship to the mother and emphasized the role of object relationship in the development of varieties of childhood psychosis:

...we may describe two clinically and dynamically distinct groups of early child psychosis: in one group of early child psychosis the mother, as representative of the outside world, never seems to have been perceived emotionally by the infant, and the first representation of outer reality, the mother as a person, as a separate entity, seems not to be cathected. The mother remains a part object, seemingly devoid of specific cathexis and not distinguished from inanimate objects. This type of infantile psychosis was first described by Kanner...and given the name of "Early Infantile Autism."

pp. 289–290.

According to Mahler, there is another form of psychosis, which she called "symbiotic infantile psychosis."

There is, however, another group of infantile psychosis in which the early mother-infant symbiotic relationship is marked, but does not progress to the stage of object-libidinal cathexis of the mother. The mental representation of the mother remains, or is regressively *fused with*—that is to say, is *not* separated from the self. It participates in the delusion of omnipotence of the child patient.

ibid., p. 292.

In symbiotic infantile psychosis children do not show disturbance of behavior in the first year of life, except that they may, perhaps, be overly sensitive, have some sleep disturbances, or be "cry babies." By ages 3 to 4 years, when there is a push toward separation from mother "...the illusion of the symbiotic omnipotence is threatened and severe panic reactions occur." (ibid., p. 292) Hallucinations, somatic delusion, delusions of fusion, death, and destruction, and extreme ambivalence are prevalent.

Mahler suggested that autistic and symbiotic children have a constitutional or heredity "anlage" for psychosis. The environment, particularly disturbance in the mother-child relationship, contributes to the development of these disorders.

Mahler et al.'s (1959), Mahler's (1965) and Mahler and Furer's (1972) studies of childhood psychosis led to the exploration of the normal mother-child relationship during the first 3 years of life, and culminated in her description of the phases of separation-individuation and the psychological birth of the self. (see chapters 2 and 3)

J. Louise Despert (1947–1948) suggested that the urge for language expression or *"la fonction appetitive"* is lacking in autistic or schizophrenic children. According to Despert, when symbolic language finally emerges it is associated with intensive emotional and affective charges, and this overwhelms the autistic child and further blocks the development of symbolic language.

Psychobiological Studies

Goldfarb (1956, 1958, 1961, 1962, 1964) and Goldfarb et al. (1972, 1973) extensively investigated childhood schizophrenia. Goldfarb divided childhood schizophrenia into organic and nonorganic disorders. He observed that schizophrenic children have a proclivity toward overdependence on proximal sensory receptors, such as touch, taste, and smell, and an aversion to distal receptors, such as vision and hearing. The sensory preference and basic perceptual dysfunction of autistic and schizophrenic children have important implications, not only for exploration of etiological factors, but also for possible development of treatment and rehabilitation programs.

Fish (1957, 1977), Fish et al. (1965, 1966) and Fish and Ritvo (1979) have followed, for a period of approximately 24 years, 16 children randomly selected from a maternity ward. Fish regularly plotted physical growth, gross motor function, visual-motor activities, cognitive development, muscle tone, and the proprioceptive and vestibular responses of these children. She found that in the preschizophrenic group there was significant "fluctuating dysregulation of maturation," which she referred to as "pandevelopmental retardation" (PDR). (Fish, 1977, p. 1297)

Fish suggested that PDR in infancy and early childhood is a predictor for future schizophrenic disorders in childhood, adolescence, or adulthood. She related PDR to "inherited neurointegrative defect in schizophrenia." (ibid., p. 1297)

Fish perceived infantile autism, childhood schizophrenia, and adult schizophrenia as part of the same continuum of schizophrenic disorders rather than as separate entities.

Studies by Onheiber et al. (1956), Ornitz et al. (1965), and Roffwarg et al. (1962) did not find any difference in the EEG dreaming and sleeping patterns between autistic and normal children. Later studies by Ornitz and Ritvo (1968) suggested that during the REM stage of sleep, auditory-evoked responses were overridden and showed larger responses in autistic children compared to normal. The authors suggested an equilibrium disruption in phasic excitation and inhibition of REM sleep in autistic children as compared to normal children, which may also continue during waking hours. Irregular spike, wave, and paroxysmal complexes in wakeful EEG of psychotic children is reported by White, et al. (1964).

Fowle (1968) found that in the blood studies of psychotic children 22.9% had several types of atypical lymphocytes and plasmocytes as opposed to 7.8% of normal children. These cells are usually associated with the production of antibodies in viral infections or with immature lymphocytes.

Gold and Seller (1965) found that spinal fluid of schizophrenic children injected into mice created seizures faster than the spinal fluids of a control group. Gold (1967), in a follow-up study, found a larger number of mice injected with the serum of psychotic children died as compared to the control group. He postulated the possibility of the existence of "epileptogenic factors" in the blood serum of psychotic children.

Heeley and Roberts (1965) found a defect in tryptophan metabolism in psychotic children as opposed to a control group. This defect was specific to the group of psychotic children who has shown deviant behavior from infancy as opposed to the ones who had a period of normal development and later regressed.

Campbell et al. (1974) found a higher blood serotonin level in severely psychotic children as opposed to the control group, although the difference was not statistically significant. They found "Low intellectual functioning was the only parameter which seemed to be clearly associated with higher serotonin levels." (p. 33)

Campbell et al. (1980) reported on the growth and development of 101 autistic children as compared with their normal siblings and a group of normal children. They found that, although the birth weight of autistic children did not differ from the normal population, the autistic children were on the whole shorter than the control group. Also, thyroid function studies (T3—triiodothyronine) and (T4—thyroxine) were significantly higher in autistic children than in the controls. A subclass of autistic children showed a variety of minor physical anomalies. Campbell *et al.* postulated that these findings may be related to elevated thyroid hormone levels, although none of the children were clinically hyperthyroid.

Early hyperthyroidism contributes to tissue resistance to the thyroid hormone, shortness in height, and the possibility of "...significant reduction of the DNA content of the brain, but, unlike in hypothyroidism, the cell size is not reduced." (ibid., p. 208) Minor physical anomalies, uneven development, and mental retardation, along with shortness of stature in autistic children may be related to fetal abnormalities in the first 3 months of gestation.

Rutter (1966, 1967, 1968, 1972, 1973, 1974), Rutter and Sussenwein (1971), and Rutter and Bartak (1973) perceived childhood autism as a specific, unique clinical entity different from childhood schizophrenia. Childhood autism, they felt, was related to organic brain disorder and deficiency in cognition, particularly language comprehension:

In schizophrenia the individual develops normally at first. It is only with the onset of illness that he loses touch with reality. The autistic child, on the other hand, shows abnormalities of development from early infancy. It is not that he loses touch with reality—he fails to gain it. About 4/5 of autistic children never show normal development and even in the 1/5 that do, the onset is about 30 months.

Rutter, 1974, p. 149.

In recent years, careful phenomenological and behavioral observations resulted in delineating infantile autism as a specific and distinct "pervasive developmental disorder" totally different from childhood schizophrenia or other forms of childhood psychosis. (Rutter, 1974) In this chapter, we will follow the present *DSM-III* (1980) format and describe infantile autism as a totally separate clinical entity from schizophrenia and other forms of psychosis.

PERVASIVE DEVELOPMENTAL DISORDERS IN INFANCY AND CHILDHOOD

Pervasive developmental disorders "...are characterized by *distortions* in the development of multiple basic psychological functions that are involved in the development of social skills and language, such as attention, perception, reality testing, and motor movement." (*DSM-III*, 1980, p. 86)

Previously the terms "early infantile autism" (Kanner, 1944), "atypical children" (Rank, 1955),

"symbiotic psychotic children" (Mahler, 1952), "childhood schizophrenia" (Potter, 1933; Bender, 1942; Goldfarb, 1961), "childhood psychosis," "infantile psychosis," and "childhood schizophrenia" (such as pseudoneurotic, pseudopsychopathic, pseudosomatic) (Bender, 1959) were used to describe what is now referred to as pervasive developmental disorders.

The term "pervasive" refers to the all-encompassing nature of the disorder, which includes disturbances in multiple psychological functions of human development. It is not a delay in a specific developmental area, such as speech, hearing, vision, or reading, but rather a distortion in many aspects of development and qualitatively different from any stages of normal development.

Pervasive developmental disorders are divided into:

1. Infantile autism
2. Childhood onset pervasive developmental disorder
3. Atypical pervasive developmental disorder

Infantile Autism

The word autism refers to "...a lack of responsiveness to other people." (*DSM-III*, p. 87) The child has gross difficulty and impairment in communication (verbal and nonverbal language).

Onset

By definition, infantile autism is a disorder that develops during infancy—the first 30 months of life.

Prevalence

Prevalence in the United States is not known. Lotter (1966), through an epidemiological study of 78,000 children aged 8 to 10 years in Middlesex, England, found that the prevalence of complete autistic syndrome was 2 per 10,000 children and partial autistic syndrome was 2.5 per 10,000.

Treffert (1970) reviewed the case histories of all children aged 12 years or younger in the State of Wisconsin who were diagnosed as having childhood schizophrenia, including childhood autism. The age-specific prevalence was 3.1 per 10,000 children. Strictly applying Kanner's criterion of childhood autism, the prevalence rate was 0.7 children per 10,000.

In summary, the prevalence of infantile autism is thought to be 4.5 per 10,000 children, and even this is a low estimate.

Sex Ratio

In most studies, the number of males is significantly higher than females. In Lotter's study, the ratio was 2.7 males to 1 female in children having complete autistic syndrome. In Treffert's study, the ratio was 3.4 males to 1 female in children diagnosed as having childhood schizophrenia. Kanner, in a study of 100 cases of infantile autism, found a ratio of 4 males to 1 female.

Clinical Features

Frequently, children with infantile autism come to the attention of clinicians, particularly child psychiatrists, between the ages of 2 and 4 years or older. At first, parents may be concerned about the child's hearing. They usually have consulted their pediatrician or family physician because of the child's lack of responsiveness to their communications. In most cases, hearing is normal. Along with concern about possible hearing loss, the parents are concerned about delay in language development or lack of speech. In the review of developmental history with the parents, the following clinical features usually unfold.

THE FIRST YEAR OF LIFE. Most autistic infants appear to be physically healthy following birth. Some are precocious and alert, and others are passive and unresponsive. Normal infants, soon after birth when they are picked up and held, "snug" to mother's body. Most mothers of autistic children say that they noticed a difference immediately after birth, in that picking up their infants was like picking up a mannequin or statue.

Eye Contact. Eye contact gazing, and following do not usually occur. The infant may have fleeting eye contact, but there is a strong tendency for gaze aversion. Later, the infant may look at another individual in a "pensive" manner, but often there is the feeling of "looking through" rather than "at" the person. Gaze aversion continues throughout early childhood and latency in most autistic children.

Eating. Some are voracious eaters, while others are fussy and "colicky" with nausea, vomiting, and gastrointestinal distress. Mothers may say that their infants were never content and always seemed dissatisfied, especially during the first few months of life. On the other hand, some infants, according to their mothers, were very "quiet, content, and happy" babies. Some autistic children have difficulty in accepting solid food and will only take liquids. The change from liquids to solids is difficult for them. Some may begin taking solid foods, but then regress to only liquid intake or soft mushy foods.

Social Smile. Parents frequently may retrospectively complain that the infant did not smile. The social smile by age 2 months and the recognition smile by age 4 months do not appear. Parents complain that "he did not know me," or "I might as well have not existed." Parents find this most disheartening. Lack of social and recognition smiles continues during childhood and early latency.

Anticipatory Posture. Most infants, according to Gesell and Amatruda (1941), by age 4 months or frequently earlier, make an anticipatory movement, such as lifting the arms and shoulders and have an expectant facial expression when being approached to be picked up. Autistic children do not.

Absence of Stranger and Separation Anxiety. Disturbance and lack of responsiveness to human beings manifests itself more clearly by the lack of development of apprehension toward strangers, which usually begins by age 4 to 5 months and, particularly, by the absence of stranger anxiety and separation anxiety, which usually begins between ages 7 and 10 months or older. This is an ominous sign.

Perseveration of Sameness. Some autistic children show severe anxiety or even panic in new situations or when a disturbance in their perseveration with sameness has occurred, such as moving from one place to another place, change of food, or the taking away of a favorite object. Autistic infants develop an intensive attachment to inanimate objects when they are between ages 6 and 12 months, rather than developing an attachment to their mothers.

Motility. Motility frequently develops fairly well. In some cases, the infant may be precocious, for instance, crawl, stand, or walk early. In other cases motility may be delayed. Rocking, head-banging, and extensive body stimulation may become pervasive. The infant may show plasticity or passivity or restlessness, agitation, or hyperactivity.

Disturbance in Communication. Nonverbal expression, such as anticipatory postures, smiles, facial expressions, or body gestures are usually minimal or do not exist for the sake of communication. The infant cries or shows agitation because of some distress or change in environmental routine, but body movement is usually related to tension discharge and not to communication.

Most infants begin to babble between ages 1 and 2 months and soon after begin to "coo"—a major step for language development. Approximately 50% of autistic children do not use language for any form of communication and they continue to be mute even at age 5 years. The other

50% may have shown some babbling and cooing and perhaps began to use a few words between ages 10 and 12 months. However, usually between ages 1 and 2 years an arrest in language development and regression or muteness occurs. The autistic infant may make gutteral sounds and cry, but does not seem to have the urge to speak or has given up trying.

Cognitive Functions. Although it is difficult to assess cognitive function in infants during the first year of life, approximately 50% of autistic children show evidence of mental retardation. There is disturbance in secondary circular reaction (effecting change in the environment) and disturbance in the development of object permanency. The infant does not show imitative behavior and has difficulty in generalizing sensory-motor input or schematas for new accomodations and equilibrium.

Affective Expression. Expression of emotion and affect is labile. Minor environmental changes may result in extreme and, at times, catastrophic reaction in the form of panic reaction and psychosomatic distress. The infant at times "tunes in" to minute sensory stimuli and at other times "tunes out" major stimuli, such as a loud noise. Abrupt sensory stimuli, such as turning a light on or a loud sound, may create an over-exaggerated startle reaction or even panic during the later part of the first year of life (usually the startle reaction disappears in normal infants by ages 3 to 4 months). (see chapter 2)

SECOND AND THIRD YEARS OF LIFE. Autistic aloneness and lack of responsiveness toward others becomes more prominent. The child does not show developmentally appropriate recognition of parents and does not manifest separation anxieties. There is delay, lack of development, or partial development in the separation-individuation process. A meaningful object relationship toward the mothering person does not exist or at most is partial.

The child relates to parents and strangers in the same manner by ignoring and avoiding them or relating to them when there is a specific need, such as wanting food or a favorite toy. These children avoid physical contact, such as hugging, but laugh when they are tickled and gain comfort when rocked. They relate to a part of the adult's body, such as taking mother's hand to get her to go to the refrigerator to open the door. Kanner refers to this process as part-whole confusion. For example, autistic children relate to a part of the body as though it were the whole.

Object constancy is not accomplished by age 3 years. There is lack of integration and synthesis of sensory, cognitive, and affective experiences.

Disturbance in Communicative Skills. During ages 2 to 3 years, lack of language development or lack of speech is most prominent. Approximately one-half of the children continue to be mute. Of the other half, some might use a few words to name objects, but often they are not able to use sentences, especially those containing pronouns. There is usually absence of the use of "yes." Language modulation and intonation is mechanical, and affective modulation of rhythm is disturbed. At times, language is quite explosive with overwhelming and inappropriate affective expression, and at other times it is "parrot-like," mechanical, and void of feeling. The child expresses negativism or dislike through temper tantrums, shrugging shoulders, grunting noises, or, at times, by saying "no." Deafness and receptive or expressive aphasia are frequently suspected, although clinical evaluation and careful observation do not usually reveal evidence of such disorders. These children do not respond to their names. There is lack of development of gender identity and family affiliation.

Bizarre Responses to the Environment. Sameness and obsessional preoccupation with repetitive behavior, such as whirling an object over and over, dominate the child's life. Carrying a card or ruler and scratching the surface of it or touching the edges of it repetitively is common.

Reliance on primitive forms of sensory-motor stimulation, such as rocking, head-banging, biting the self or others, kicking, licking—for example, the walls, floor, or toilet bowl—walking on tiptoes, and twirling occurs frequently. It is as though the child, through constant self-stimulating behaviors, shuts out external situations or fills the empty space within.

Affective Expression. Lability of mood and autistic withdrawal, along with explosive and volcanic expression of anger and destructive behavior, particularly at times of frustration, are prevalent. Self-destructive behavior, such as biting, kicking, throwing oneself to the ground, and impulsive momentary destructive attacks on others are common. Whining and crying at the time of need or distress of obliviousness to others predominate.

Response to Stimulation. Autistic children frequently respond to one part of a stimulation and then internalize that part by rote memory, and reproduce it over and over again without attention to other aspects of the same stimulus or accompanying stimuli. Lovaas refers to this process as "stimulus overselectivity." (Lovaas *et al.,* 1971, p. 305) For example, if there are two lights, one green and one yellow, an autistic child will perceive one light and totally ignore the other. This stimulus overselectivity limits the child's ability for learning and interferes with generalization.

Cognitive Development. Symbolic thought representation, which occurs in normal children at ages 18 months to 2 years, is absent or distorted. There is poverty of fantasy and imaginative play and extensive reliance on distorted cognitive functions of the sensory-motor period rather than the preoperational stage of intelligence. (see chapters 3 and 4)

Symbols do not have meaning or become concrete, metaphorical, and literal representations of reality. For example, when George was 2 years old, his grandfather encouraged him to speak by giving him a lollipop if he could say the word "lollipop." George enjoyed this game, and, even now at age 9 years, whenever he is happy or wants to do or eat something special, he says "lollipop." When people do not understand what he means by saying "lollipop," he becomes furious, has a temper tantrum, and attacks the person.

In the autistic child, the initial exposure to a stimulus, whether it is pleasant or traumatic, has a deep imprint on cognitive and affective memory. It is as though the child becomes the prisoner of such stimuli, and the only way to relate to the self and the environment is through the limited repertoire of these infantile sensory stimuli.

Toilet Training. Toilet training is delayed. Autistic children have difficulty understanding the nature of the process, although a few have been trained through a reflexive and automatic manner. Oppositional behavior in some cases emerges with and reinforces the child's tendency toward aloneness and sameness.

Play. Parallel play or meaningful play with children of the same age does not occur. However, the child might become quite agile and skillful in manipulating some objects, such as mechanical toys, balancing a ruler on the edge of a table, or building blocks in the form of high towers with exact sameness and careful balance.

AGES FOUR TO SIX YEARS. By this time, most parents have consulted a number of clinicians because of the child's lack of responsiveness to human contact, lack of language development, and possible retardation.

Pervasive Lack of Responsiveness to People. Autistic aloneness and lack of responsiveness toward others become prominent. The child may sit for hours motionless, stare into space, or appear deeply preoccupied. He shows no interest or little interest toward others and at times has an active aversion to people. Generally, he does not respond to his name. Favorite foods or toys are usually the only things that attract his attention. The child only relates to people momentarily to meet his own needs.

Gross Deficit in Language Development. The child is mute, although occasionally, under extreme stress or out of context, he may say a few words or a sentence. In the one-half of autistic children who do have language skills, the language has a peculiar quality. Kanner (1946) vividly described the language of autistic children as being literal and lacking proper synonyms or prepositions. The following are characteristics of the distorted language of an autistic child.

1. The tone is usually a mechanical, high-pitched, parrotlike monotone.
2. The modulation is whispering or explosive.
3. Naming objects instead of using complete sentences is frequent.
4. Asking or answering questions is quite rare.
5. Desires or wishes are communicated by, for instance, leading an adult by the hand to whatever is needed, rather than using words.
6. Negation is communicated by grunting, flapping the arms, and perhaps eventually by a simple "no." Saying "no" seems to have a magical or protective quality from unpleasant events.
7. There is lack of the use of "yes" or the pronoun "I."
8. If one asks the child a question such as "Do you want a cookie?" he will answer by repeating the question, saying "Do you want a cookie?" "You want a cookie?" or "Want a cookie?" Kanner refers to this as "affirmation by repetition." There is also pronominal reversal; for instance, instead of saying "I" the pronoun "you" is used. Frequently, the autistic child refers to himself as "he" or "she" or by a first name rather than "I, me, or mine."
9. In normal children, echoing of other peoples' voices is the first step toward speech development, which usually phases out by ages 2 to 2½ years. (Rutter, 1972) At least 75% of speaking autistic children continue to use echolalia, repeating and echoing other people's spoken words. (Rutter, 1965; Wing, 1971) Echoing can be immediate or delayed. If delayed, it may be for weeks, months, or years. In immediate echolalia, the autistic child repeats what he has heard over and over again, sometimes becoming very excited or stimulated by these repetitions. Delayed echolalia refers to the child's tendency to begin suddenly uttering a word or sentence repeatedly. At first, the utterance seems senseless, but later it is realized that the child has heard this word or sentence much earlier and then suddenly, for unknown internal or external reasons, begins to repeat it.
10. Autistic children often confuse the part for the whole or the whole for the part. For example, 9-year-old Coleen was asked, "What do you call this?" (referring to a 3M tape recorder). Coleen answered "3M," reading the label on

the machine. When she was again asked by the therapist saying "I mean this whole thing," she again said "3M."

11. The speech and thinking of the autistic child is literal and concrete. Kanner, for example, described a father who tried to teach his child to say "yes" by rewarding him with a ride on his shoulders. The boy learned to say "yes" only to indicate that he wanted a shoulder ride!

12. Kanner used the term "metaphorical language" to describe the concrete, specific personal experience of the child as a substitute for the names of real objects or events. For example, Paul, while playing, referred to a toy saucepan as "Peter Eater." This puzzled Kanner and the parents. Later, mother remembered that when Paul was 2 years old, she was reciting the nursery rhyme "Peter, Peter Pumpkin Eater" to him while she was working in the kitchen. Just at that moment, she dropped a saucepan. From then on, Paul called the saucepan "Peter Eater." At times, one needs the ingenuity of an archeologist to decipher the private metaphorical language of the autistic child.

Cognitive Function and Thought Process.

One of the major symptoms that differentiate autistic children from schizophrenic and other psychotic children and emphasizes the uniqueness of the autistic syndrome is the absence of hallucinations, delusions, and looseness of associations. The thought process of autistic children functions on a sensory-motor level before the development of symbolic thought representation, emergence of fantasy, and the development of the world of make-believe. When there is lack of development of symbol formation and fantasy, then there is less possibility of preoccupation with distorted symbolic thought representations in the form of hallucinations or delusions.

Special Ability.

Some autistic children have specific special abilities in limited and circumscribed areas. Extensive reliance on rote memory, sameness, and a fantastic ability for recall of remote memories can help in the development of isolated islands of special abilities, such as in music, in remembering detailed factual information about science, or special mechanical abilities. There is retardation and lack of development in many other areas. George, a 9-year-old autistic boy, was able to build carefully and meticulously a high tower with various colored blocks. The amazing thing was that each time the same color block was in the same place, position, and sequence as previous constructions. Susan, an 8-year-old autistic girl, was able to remember the birth dates of all the staff, childcare workers, teachers, therapists, and nursing students coming into the residential unit during the 4 years of her stay. She had significant deficits in reading, writing, arithmetic, and in human interactions. Frequently, the special ability or fantastic memory is irrelevant and useless because of inability to generalize for further adaptation. Some postulate that the *idiot savants* of the past may have been at one time in their lives autistic.

In some cases, with careful nurturing, the autistic child's special ability may become a source of vocational or professional training, and possible eventual employment. But successes are rare occurrences.

LATENCY AND ADOLESCENCE.

The relative improvement of the autistic child in latency and adolescence depends upon the child's ability to use language for some form of communication by age 5 years and also on the level of intellectual functioning. The less the child is able to use language, the more profound the autistic behavior, developmental retardation, and disturbance in social skills.

During latency and adolescence, all symptoms and behaviors discussed earlier, such as lack of responsiveness to people, gross deficit in language development, bizarre responses to the environment, resistance to change, and attachment to inanimate objects come to full expression or are modified. The symptoms may be intensified as a result of lack of proper psychoeducational programs, family upheaval, frequent environmental changes or inconsistencies, frequent hospitalizations, or lack of a consistent program in a long-term residential setting. The symptoms may be modified to a great extent in a supportive caring environment with special emphasis on helping the child and the family reinforce and enhance the child's positive behaviors.

Some autistic children who were mute at age 5, with proper therapeutic help, are able to use language in latency. They learn to read and write and some even become voracious readers.

Aggressive and self-destructive behaviors are directly related to the way the environment handles the child. If the child constantly experiences frustration and is not able to experience relative success, he will become more destructive and aggressive. On the other hand, realistic expectation and recognition of the fluctuations of ability increase affectionate behavior and encourage the child and the family to excel within the child's limitations.

Types of Infantile Autism

According to *DSM-III* (1980), infantile autism is divided into two types.

INFANTILE AUTISM, FULL SYN-DROMES PRESENT. At the time of assessment, the patient meets the diagnostic criteria of infantile autism, which were previously discussed.

INFANTILE AUTISM, RESIDUAL STATE. The patient at one time met the criteria for infantile autism, but at the time of assessment does not meet the full criteria. The patient has some signs of infantile autism, such as disturbance in communication and awkwardness in social relations.

Childhood Onset Pervasive Development Disorder

This disorder was previously referred to as symbiotic psychosis, childhood schizophrenia, or atypical child. Because this disorder bears "...little relationship to the psychotic disorders of adult life, the term 'psychosis' has not been used." (*DSM-III*, 1980, p. 86)

Onset

The onset by definition is after age 30 months and before age 12 years.

Prevalence

Prevalence is rare, and more common in boys than in girls, similar to infantile autism.

Clinical Features

PROFOUND DISTURBANCE IN HUMAN RELATIONSHIPS. There is intense and inappropriate clinging, lack of empathy, associality, and lack of appropriate affective responses.

INTENSE AND OVERWHELMING ANXIETY. The patient experiences severe panic attack, free-floating anxiety, and at times intense psychophysiological distress to everyday frustrations, such as separation from mother, disappointment, criticism, and minor physical illness. The patient's reactions are catastrophic in nature and the massive anxiety has a disintegrative and disorganizing quality. Usual comfort and assurances do not alleviate the anxiety and may intensify it. The anxiety frequently is traumatic in nature, as though the patient does not have or has not developed the ability for signal anxiety. This anxiety is similar to the anxiety in borderline personality disorder but with more intensity and catastrophic reaction. (see chapter 11)

AFFECTIVE RESPONSES. Emotional responses and affective expressions are inappropriate, constricted, and show extreme mood lability. The patient may be oblivious to realistic fears and, at the same time, afraid and react in panic to minor events.

IMPULSIVE BEHAVIOR. Aggressive, destructive, and unexplainable, impulsive behavior occurs frequently, such as scratching, biting, kicking, and attacking others and the self without outward provocation or for minor frustration. Autoerotic behavior, such as masturbation, mouthing objects, rocking, and rubbing occur without inhibition.

RESISTANCE TO CHANGE. The patient, similar to infantile autism, prefers sameness and resists change. For example, he rigidly follows exactly the same routine or eats the same food for a long period of time. Any change in routine results in catastrophic reaction and expression of massive anxiety or severely impulsive behavior.

MOTILITY. The patient is usually clumsy and awkward. Flapping of arms and hands, walking on tiptoes, whirling, and peculiar hand and finger movements and posturing are common.

SPEECH. Speech is fairly developed when compared to children with infantile autism. These children use pronouns and complete sentences, but their speech has a singsong, monotonous, mechanical, questionlike quality.

RESPONSE TO SENSORY STIMULI. These children are hypo- or hypersensitive to external stimuli. Frequently, they are extremely hypersensitive to noise (hyperacusis). A sudden, mild to moderate range of sound results in the child's automatically covering his ears with his hands or having a panic reaction. At the same time, these children may create a ruckus by pounding on drums or comparable things. Hypersensitivity to light is also reported, but less frequently.

DISTURBANCES OF BODY IMAGE. There is profound disturbance in body image and lack of ability to see the different parts of the body as a whole. Laura, age 10, was noticed staring at herself in the mirror, making different faces and watching her reflection in puzzlement. Then suddenly she pushed with all of her might against the mirror, saying angrily, "That girl is making faces at me!"

Larry, age 8, was finally toilet trained. After having a bowel movement in the toilet bowl, he was found putting his arm into the bowl while flushing the toilet and trying to make his hand and arm go down with his bowel movement. He was not able to differentiate between his excretions and a part of his own body. Imagine the constant fear and anxiety these children experience, if they feel that various parts of their body may also disappear, similar to the food they eat or their excretions. Fragmentation of body image and distortion in perception perpetuate the chronic but intense internal anxieties.

COGNITIVE ABILITY AND THOUGHT PROCESSES. Similar to infantile autism, these children have significant deficit in cognitive functioning. Approximately 40% have an IQ below 50, 30% between 50 and 70, and only 30% have 70 or above. Verbal intelligence is often far below age level, especially in the area of abstract thinking, logical reasoning, or symbolic thought representation. In visual-spatial tasks, manipulation of objects or immediate recall they may function age appropriately or even better.

Absence of hallucination, delusion, or loose association more or less differentiates these children from schizophrenic disorders in adolescence and adulthood.

Differentiation

These children resemble Mahler's infantile symbiotic psychosis or Bender's childhood schizophrenia. The differentiation between infantile autism and childhood onset pervasive developmental disorder may be difficult, but the guidelines listed in Table 16-1 are useful.

SCHIZOPHRENIC DISORDERS

Schizophrenic disorders are usually discussed extensively in adult psychiatric textbooks. The occurrence of schizophrenia in adolescents is similar to its occurrence in adults. Therefore, we will only briefly discuss schizophrenia in adolescence, and we refer the reader to adult psychiatric textbooks, such as Kaplan *et al.*'s *Comprehensive Textbook on Psychiatry* (1980) for a more detailed discussion.

Definition

Emil Kraeplin (1919) described dementia praecox, which begins in adolescence or early adulthood and eventually results in mental deterioration. He differentiated dementia praecox from manic-depressive psychosis, which begins in adulthood and does not result in deterioration. Hallucinations, delusions, disturbance in affect, and stereotypes were the clinical features of dementia praecox.

Eugen Bleuler (1911) in his classic book, *Dementia Praecox or the Group of Schizophrenias,* coined the term "schizophrenia" which means

Table 16-1 **Differentiation Between Infantile Autism and Childhood Onset Pervasive Developmental Disorder**

Criteria	Infantile Autism	Childhood Onset Pervasive Developmental Disorder
Onset	Birth to 30 months	30 months to 12 years
Human contact	Lack of responsiveness, prefers to be alone	Impairment in special relationships, inappropriate clinging
Language	Mutism, gross deficit	Speech present, but some abnormalities
Affect	Absent or explosive	Present but inappropriate, lack of empathy
Anxiety	Motoric expression	Catastrophic, unexplained panic reaction, psychosomatic distress
Thought processes	Lack of symbolic thought representation and absence of fantasy	Primitive forms of symbolic thought representations and bizarre ideas and fantasies
Delusions	Absent	Absent
Hallucinations	Absent	Absent
Loose associations	Absent	Absent
Resistance to change	Present	Present
Attachement to inanimate objects	Present	Relatively absent
Intelligence	Ranges from retarded to bright	Usually retarded range

"split-mindedness." He perceived fragmentation and splitting of the personality as essential aspects of schizophrenia, or dementia praecox, rather than deteriorative outcome. He conceptualized schizophrenia as an illness or a psychopathological syndrome consisting of the primary symptoms of disturbances in affects, thought associations, and volition, with the presence of autism and ambivalence. Hallucinations, delusions, stupor, and negativism were perceived as secondary symptoms. (Lehman, 1975, p. 853). Bleuler's significant contribution was the integration of Kraeplin's descriptive and phenomenological approach with Freud's psychodynamic concepts. In addition, he projected hope and optimism for the treatment of schizophrenia.

Schneider (1942) again brought into focus the phenomenological aspects of schizophrenia based on the integrative functions of normal personality. According to Schneider, "...identity feeling, continuity of psychic processes, and reality contact" are smoothly integrated in an average person. (Lehman, 1975, p. 854) Fragmentation and disturbance of these three major functions result in the expression of the pathognomonic symptoms of schizophrenia, which are now referred to as Schneiderian criteria of schizophrenia:

1. Thought withdrawal, such as "...thought stopping, thought insertion, thought hearing, perplexity, experience of being controlled, and speech disorders." (ibid., p. 854)
2. Derailment meaning "...lack of affect, inappropriate rage, depression, despair, depersonalization, and hallucinations." (ibid., p. 854)
3. *Faslin* is a German word which means "...rambling and talking in a disconnected manner, with the following symptoms: delusions, looseness of associations, inadequate emotional response, and ego-alien impulses." (ibid., p. 854)

Onset and Sex Ratio

Schizophrenic disorders begin in adolescence and early adulthood. The sex ratio is approximately equal.

Prevalence

The prevalence is estimated to be between 0.2 and 1% of the population, with significant increase in families with a history of schizophrenia.

Clinical Features

According to *DSM-III* (1980), the following are essential features of schizophrenic disorders.

Deterioration

The patient regresses from previous levels of functioning in the areas of human relationships, looking after the self, and performance in school or at work.

Disturbance in Thought Processes

Significant disturbances in thought process are related to thought content and forms. Delusion, such as persecutory (being spied upon) or reference (being made fun of by strangers) or deluson of negation (believing to be dead) are common.

Schneiderian criteria of thought broadcasting (others hear his thoughts), thought insertion (others put thoughts in his mind), thought withdrawal (others remove thoughts from his mind), or delusions of being controlled occur. Illogical thinking, magical delusions, grandiose thoughts and religious delusions, such as believing to be Christ, also occur, but less frequently. Looseness of association (moving from one subject to another without inherent logical connection) is quite common. Incoherence occurs when looseness of associations is severe.

Schizophrenic adolescents are concrete, but, at the same time, abstract and metaphorical. Repetition, stereotyped behavior, and thought blocking occur. In patients with low intellectual endowment and in patients with schizophrenic disorders, poverty of thoughts and ideas is profound. Neologisms (making new words), perseveration, and clanging (association to sound and rhythm of a word) occur, but less frequently.

Disturbance in Perception

Auditory hallucinations are most common. The patient hears voices coming from outside, insulting him or telling him what to do. Tactile and kinesthetic hallucinations, such as a burning sensation, tingling, feelings of electricity going through the body, worms or snakes crawling in the head, heart, stomach, or other parts of the body may occur. Visual, olfactory, and taste hallucinations occur less frequently. When they do occur, if they are not associated with auditory hallucinations, the possibility of psychomotor epilepsy, space-occupying brain lesion, drug abuse, or alcohol withdrawal (delirium tremens) should be considered.

Disturbance in Affect

Affective and emotional expression are one of the earliest signs of change in the acute phase of schizophrenic disorder. Affect is usually inappropriate and incongruent to the patient's thought processes or the reality of the situation. For example, the patient might smile or laugh aloud while saying, "Someone is here to kill me." Bluntness of affect (significant decrease in emotional expression) or flatness of affect (absence or lack of emotional expression) occurs frequently.

Perception of the Self

A schizophrenic adolescent feels fragmented, disjointed, and extremely confused about his own identity. The developmental task of establishing identity is hindered. The adolescent may be confused to the extent of not even knowing his own name. He might see himself as a devil one moment, an angel another moment, and nobody the next moment. Sexual identity also frequently shows significant signs of disturbance with panic concern about homosexual attack. Projection of inner turmoils and conflicts and forbidden wishes and impulses are common.

Disturbance in Human Contact

Autistic withdrawal and/or panic clinging behavior are common. The adolescent withdraws to the self, becomes preoccupied, and may spend many hours listening to music without any experience of joy and pleasure.

Impulsive Behavior

Extreme and unpredictable impulsive behavior, such as rage, destruction of property, and suicidal or homicidal behavior may occur under the influence of delusional thoughts or hallucinations. Minor frustrations or disappointments may result in catastrophic impulsive behavior.

Disorganizing Anxiety

Intense and overwhelming pathological anxiety of schizophrenic adolescents is contagious. Pacing, rocking, intense fear, dysphoric mood, depression, depersonalization, derealization, hypochondriacal concern about a variety of illnesses, and panic over death, dying, and annihilation are common, particularly in the acute phase of the disorder.

Duration

In order to meet the diagnostic criteria for schizophrenic disorders, the patient must have manifested "...continuous signs of the illness for at least six months at some time during...[his]life, with some signs of the illness at present." (*DSM-III*, 1980, p. 189)

Types of Schizophrenic Disorders

Disorganized Types

There is frequent incoherence in thought processes, absence of systematized delusion with blunted, inappropriate, or silly affects. This type usually has an early insidious onset and is associated with severe social impairment and poor progress. It was previously referred to as hebephrenic.

Catatonic Type

One or more of the following catatonic types may be present: catatonic stupor (significant decrease in reaction or spontaneous movement in the environment), catatonic rigidity (maintaining a rigid position), catatonic negativism (motionless, resistance to instruction or movement), catatonic excitement (motoric excitement or agitation not related to internal stimuli), and mutism. Self-inflicted injury, malnutrition, hyperpyrexia, or exhaustion may occur during catatonic stupor or excitation. Catatonic type is now less common in the United States. It appears to be more prevalent in rural areas or less industrialized countries.

Paranoid Type

The essential features are delusion or hallucinations of persecution, grandiosity, jealousy, doubt, mistrust, ambivalence, intense anxiety, outbursts of anger, argumentativeness, and tendency toward violence. The patient has concern about sexual identity, being a homosexual, or being coerced into sexual acts. The onset usually occurs in later life, although we have see schizophrenic disorder, paranoid type, not infrequently in adolescents. Paranoid schizophrenic disorder is more prevalent in industrialized societies, including the United States.

Undifferentiated Type

The patient has delusions, hallucinations, disturbances in thought processes, disturbance of affects and human relationships, but does not meet the criteria of the previous types.

Residual Types

The patient has a history of schizophrenic disorder with psychotic symptoms on at least one occasion. At the time of evaluation, there are no prominent psychotic symptoms, but there is a disturbance in affect, illogical thought, loose association, and withdrawal.

OTHER PSYCHOTIC DISORDERS

There are psychotic disorders in childhood and adolescence which do not follow the diagnostic criteria of pervasive developmental, schizophrenic, manic-depressive, or organic mental disorders. These psychotic disorders are usually of shorter duration, show less disturbance of premorbid personality, with less intensity of psychopathological disability following the psychotic episodes. In *DSM-III* (1980), these clinical conditions are referred to as "Psychotic Disorders Not Elsewhere Classified." (p. 199) Included are the following disorders.

Schizophreniform Disorder

This psychotic disorder is similar to schizophrenic disorder except that the duration is between 2 weeks and 6 months. The duration of the disorder includes the prodromal, active, and residual states.

In most of these cases, confusion and extensive affective and emotional turmoil, fear, and specifically "vivid hallucinations" occur. Schizophreniform disorder is acute and of short duration. The patient usually recovers and regains his earlier level of personality functioning. In the family history, the prevalence of schizophrenia is similar to the general population rather than increased, as it is in schizophrenia.

Brief Reactive Psychosis

Psychosocial stress, such as natural disaster, loss, unbearable disappointment, or physical injury may precipitate a brief psychotic reaction in children, adolescents, and adults, which lasts from a few hours to about 2 weeks. After recovery from the acute psychotic episode, the patient usually regains the premorbid level of psychic functioning. Clinical features include: extreme affective liability, such as depression and anxiety, fear, disorganization, and even momentary inappropriate joy and elation. Disturbance in reality testing, confusion, acute hallucination, or delusions may prevail. Bizarre behavior, muteness,

screaming, aggressive or self-destructive behavior may occur. Infantile behavior and acute regression, along with disorientation and loss of recent memory, are frequent.

During adolescence or young adulthood, brief reactive psychosis is more prevalent. In a short time, usually 2 to 3 days, the psychotic symptoms disappear. Usually, in 2 weeks, confusion, disorganization, and massive anxiety subside, although mild to moderate dysphoric moods or low self-esteem may continue for some time. Following recovery, the patient usually does not remember the episode or refers to it as a "scary nightmare."

Patients with narcissistic, histrionic, or, particularly, borderline personality disorder are more prone to episodes of brief reactive psychosis. In all of these cases, the possibility of organic mental disorders, such as psychomotor epilepsy, and alcohol and substance abuse should be considered before the final diagnosis is made.

Schizoaffective Disorder

The term "schizoaffective disorder" was originally used to describe schizophrenic disorder that expressed itself in the form of manic-depressive (affective) disorder. In recent years, the use of this category has been de-emphasized. It is important to evaluate the patient carefully to see whether he manifests the symptoms of major affective disorders, such as depression and manic-depressive disorder, or schizophrenic disorders, schizophreniform disorders, or brief reactive psychosis.

The clinical expression of the manifestation of schizoaffective disorder is the evidence of mood-incongruent delusion or hallucination, with the absence or disappearance of related affective symptoms, or, also, in cases in which affective symptoms exist but there is little information about the history of schizophrenia, schizophreniform, or affective disorders.

Atypical Psychosis

At times, some patients manifest psychotic symptoms that do not meet the criteria of the psychotic disorders discussed previously, for example, monosymptomatic delusion or hallucination, transient psychosis associated with the menstrual period, and some forms of postpartum psychosis.

There has been a tendency to underdiagnose or use the label of "autism" or "schizophrenic" loosely. Both of these tendencies jeopardize clinical accuracy and decrease the possibility of effective intervention.

The description and careful diagnosis of different types of psychotic disorders may help in clarifying various psychotic disorders of childhood and adolescence with the hope of facilitating further research in exploring the causative factors and finding effective and specific methods of management and therapeutic intervention.

MANAGEMENT AND TREATMENT

Management and treatment of infantile autism and pervasive developmental disorder in childhood, schizophrenic disorders, and other psychotic disorders depend on the following criteria:

1. The time of onset
2. The degree of developmental disturbances
3. The intensity of psychopathology
4. The degree of cognitive deficit and mental retardation
5. The ability to use language for communication
6 The family environment

There is no specific treatment approach. Management and treatment are tedious and long-term, associated with frequent therapeutic setbacks and limited progression. Patience, realistic expectations, a sober and optimistic attitude, and, above all, therapeutic agility are essential.

The fundamental requirements for therapeutic agility are acute sensitivity to the psychotic child's behavior, awareness of the range of therapeutic modalities, and the ability to use them when necessary.... The therapist working with the psychotic child, more than any other therapist, needs to remain curious, adventurous, and flexible.

Shafii, 1979, p. 556.

Integrating effective therapeutic methods from various therapeutic modalities, such as psychoanalysis and dynamic psychotherapies, behavior modification, cognitive and language training, educational activities, and psychopharmacotherapy, along with helping the parents to function as co-therapists, are important and essential for management and treatment of these disorders.

Short-term hospitalization might be indicated for extensive diagnostic assessment, temporary alleviation of the pressure on the family, and possible improvement of acutely distressing symptoms, such as disintegrative anxiety, destructive behavior toward the self or others, or overwhelming hallucinations or delusions in the case of schizophrenic disorders.

In most cases, long-term separation of the child from the family in a residential setting is not indicated, unless the family is not able to cope with the child's disturbing behavior or they contribute further to the child's deterioration.

For further information, see chapters 11, 21, and 23. For a more detailed discussion of special therapeutic consideration of childhood psychosis, see Shafii (1979), pp. 555–567.

REFERENCES

American Psychiatric Association (1980). *Diagnostic and Statistical Manual of Mental Disorders.* Third Edition. Washington, D.C.: American Psychiatric Association.

Bettelheim, B. (1948). *The Special School for Emotionally Disturbed Children.* Bloomington, Ill.: 47th Yearbook of the National Society for the Study of Education.

Bender, L. (1942). Childhood schizophrenia. *Nerv. Child, 1,* 138–140.

Bender, L. (1947). Childhood schizophrenia. *Am. J. Orthopsychiatry, 17,* 40–56.

Bender, L. (1953). Childhood schizophrenia. *Psychiatr. Q., 27,* 663–681.

Bender, L. (1956). Schizophrenia in childhood—its recognition, description and treatment. *Am. J. Orthopsychiatry, 26,* 499–506.

Bender, L. (1959). The concept of pseudopsychopathic schizophrenia in adolescents. *Am. J. Orthopsychiatry, 29,* 491–512.

Bender, L. (1960). Treatment in early schizophrenia. In Masserman, J., Moreno, J. (Eds.), *Progress in Psychotherapy.* New York: Grune and Stratton, pp. 177–184.

Bender, L. (1973). The life course of children with schizophrenia. *Am. J. Psychiatry, 130,* 783–786.

Bender, L., Lipkowitz, H. (1940). Hallucinations in children. *Am. J. Orthopsychiatry, 10,* 471–490.

Bender, L., Freedman, A., Grugett, A.E., Jr., *et al.* (1952). Schizophrenia in childhood: A confirmation of the diagnosis. *Trans. Am. Neurol. Assoc., 77,* 67–73.

Bleuler, E. (1911). *Dementia Praecox or the Group of Schizophrenias.* Translated by Zinken, J. New York: International Universities Press, 1950.

Campbell, M., Friedman, E., DeVito, E., Greenspan, L., Collins, P.J. (1974). Blood serotonin in psychotic and brain damaged children. *J. Autism Child. Schizophr., 4,* 33–41.

Campbell, M., Petti, T.A., Green, W.H., Cohen, I.L., Genleser, N.B., David, R. (1980). Some physical parameters of young autistic children. *J. Am. Acad. Child Psychiatry, 19,* 193–212.

Despert, J.L. (1947–1948). Delusional and hallucinatory experiences in children. *Am. J. Psychiatry, 104,* 528–537.

Fish, B. (1957). The detection of schizophrenia in infancy. *J. Nerv. Ment. Dis., 125,* 1–24.

Fish, B. (1977). Neurobiologic antecedents of schizophrenia in children: Evidence for an inherited, congenital neurointegrative defect. *Arch. Gen. Psychiatry, 34,* 1297–1313.

Fish, B., Shapiro, T., Halpern, F., Wile, R. (1965). The prediction of schizophrenia in infancy: III. A ten-year follow-up report of neurological and psychological development. *Am. J. Psychiatry, 121,* 768–775.

Fish, B., Shapiro, T., Campbell, M. (1966). Long-term prognosis and the response of schizophrenic children to drug therapy: A controlled study of trifluoperazine. *Am. J. Psychiatry, 123,* 32–39.

Fish, B., Ritvo, E.R. (1979). Psychoses of childhood. In Noshpitz, J. (Ed.), *Basic Handbook of Child Psychiatry,* Vol. 2. New York: Basic Books, pp. 249–304.

Fowle, A.M. (1968). Atypical leukocyte pattern of schizophrenic children. *Arch. Gen. Psychiatry, 18,* 666–680.

Gesell, A., Amatruda, C.S. (1941). *Developmental Diagnosis.* New York: Hoeber.

Gold, S. (1967). Further investigation of a possible epileptogenic factor in the serum of psychotic children. *Aust. N.Z. J. Psychiatry, 1,* 153–156.

Gold, S., Seller, M.J. (1965). An epileptic factor in the serum of psychotic children. *Med. J. Aust., 2,* 876–877.

Goldfarb, W. (1956). Receptor preferences in schizophrenic children. *A.M.A. Arch. Neurol. Psychiatry, 76,* 643–652.

Goldfarb, W. (1958). Pain reactions in group of institutionalized schizophrenic children. *Am. J. Orthopsychiatry, 28,* 777–785.

Goldfarb, W. (1961). *Childhood Schizophrenia.* Cambridge: Harvard University Press.

Goldfarb, W. (1962). Families of schizophrenic children. In *Mental Retardation.* Baltimore: Williams and Wilkins.

Goldfarb, W. (1964). An investigation of childhood schizophrenia. *Arch. Gen. Psychiatry, 11,* 620–634.

Goldfarb, W., Levy, D.M., Meyers, D.I. (1972). The mother speaks to her schizophrenic child: Language in childhood schizophrenia. *Psychiatry, 35,* 217–226.

Goldfarb, W., Yudkovitz, E., Goldfarb, N. (1973). Verbal symbols to designate objects: An experimental study of communication in mothers of schizophrenic children. *J. Autism Child. Schizophr., 3,* 281–298.

Haslam, J. (1809). *Observations on Madness and Melancholy.* London: Methuen.

Heeley, A., Roberts, G. (1965). Trytophan metabolism in psychotic children. *Dev. Med. Child Neurol., 7,* 46–49.

Itard, J.M.G. (1801, 1807). *The Wild Boy of Aveyron.* Eng. trans. of two reports by Humphrey, G., and Humphrey, M., 1932. New York: Appleton-Century-Crofts, 1962.

Kanner, L. (1943). Autistic disturbances of affective contact. *Nerv. Child, 2,* 217–250.

Kanner, L. (1944). Early infantile autism. *J. Pediatr., 25,* 211–217.

Kanner, L. (1946). Irrelevant and metaphorical language in early infantile autism. *Am. J. Psychiatry, 103,* 242–246.

Kanner, L. (1949). Problems of nosology and psychodynamics of early infantile autism. *Am. J. Orthopsychiatry, 19,* 416–426.

Kanner, L. (1951). The conception of wholes and parts in early infantile autism. *Am. J. Psychiatry, 108,* 23–26.

Kanner, L. (1952). Emotional interference with intellectual functioning. *Am. J. Ment. Defic., 56,* 701–707.

Kanner, L. (1956). Infantile autism and the schizophrenias. *Behav. Sci., 10,* 412–420.

Kanner, L., Eisenberg, L. (1955). Notes on the follow-up studies of autistic children. In Hoch, P.H., Zubin, J. (Eds.), *Psychopathology of Childhood.* New York: Grune and Stratton, pp. 227–239.

Kanner, L., Rodriguez, A., Aashenden, B. (1972). How far can autistic children go in matters of social adaptation. *J. Autism Child. Schizophr., 2,* 9–33.

Kaplan, H.I., Freedman, A.M., Sadock, B.J. (Eds.) (1980). *Comprehensive Textbook of Psychiatry-III.* Third Edition. Baltimore: Williams and Wilkins.

Kraeplin, E. (1919). *Dementia Praecox and Paraphrenia.* New York: Krieger, 1950.

Lehmann, H.E. (1975). Schizophrenia: Introduction and history. In Freedman, A.M., Kaplan, H.I., Sadock, B.J. (Eds.), *Comprehensive Textbook of Psychiatry-II,* Vol. 1. Second Edition. Baltimore: Williams and Wilkins, pp. 890–923.

Lotter, V. (1966). Epidemiology of autistic conditions in young children. I. Prevalence. *Soc. Psychiatry, 1,* 124–137.

Lovaas, O.I., *et al.* (1971). Selective responding by autistic children to multiple sensory input. *J. Abnorm. Psychol., 77,* 211–222.

Mahler, M.S. (1952). On childhood psychosis and schizophrenia: Autistic and symbiotic infantile psychosis. In Eissler, R.S., *et al.* (Eds.), *The Psychoanalytic Study of the Child,* Vol. 7. New York: International Universities Press, pp. 286–305.

Mahler, M.S. (1965). On the significance of normal separation-individuation phase: With reference to research in symbiotic childhood psychosis. In Schur, M. (Ed.), *Drives, Affects, Behavior,* Vol. 2. New York: International Universities Press, pp. 161–169.

Mahler, M.S., Ross, J.R., Jr., DeFries, Z. (1949). Clinical studies in benign and malignant cases of childhood psychosis (schizophrenic-like). *Am. J. Orthopsychiatry, 19,* 295–305.

Mahler, M.S., Furer, M., Settlage, C.F. (1959). Severe emotional disturbances in childhood: Psychosis. In Arieti, S. (Ed.), *American Handbook of Psychiatry,* Vol. 1. New York: Basic Books, pp. 816–836.

Mahler, M.S., Furer, M. (1972). Child psychosis: A theoretical statement and its implications. *J. Autism Child. Schizophr., 2,* 213–218.

Onheiber, P., White, P.T., DeMeyer, M.K., Ottinger, D.R. (1965). Sleep and dream patterns of child schizophrenics. *Arch. Gen. Psychiatry, 12,* 568–571.

Ornitz, E.M., Ritvo, E.R., Walter, R.D. (1965). Dreaming sleep in autistic and schizophrenic children. *Am. J. Psychiatry, 122,* 419–424.

Ornitz, E.M., Ritvo, E.R. (1968). Perceptual inconstancy in early infantile autism. *Arch. Gen. Psychiatry, 18,* 76–98.

Potter, H.W. (1933). Schizophrenia in children. *Am. J. Psychiatry, 12,* 1253–1270.

Rank, B. (1955). Intensive study and treatment of preschool children who show marked personality deviations or "atypical development," and their parents. In Caplan, G. (Ed.), *Emotional Problems of Early Childhood.* New York: Basic Books, pp. 491–501.

Roffwarg, H.G., Dement, W.C., Muzio, J.N., Fisher, C. (1962). Dream imagery: Relationship to rapid eye movements of sleep. *Arch. Gen. Psychiatry, 7,* 235–258.

Rutter, M. (1965). The influence of organic and emotional factors on the origins, nature and outcome of childhood psychosis. *Dev. Med. Child Neurol., 7,* 518–528.

Rutter, M. (1966). Behavioral and cognitive characteristics of a series of psychotic children. In Wing, J.K. (Ed.), *Early Childhood Autism.* Oxford: Pergamon Press, pp. 51–81.

Rutter, M. (1967). Psychotic disorders in early childhood. In Coppen, A., Walk, A. (Eds.), Recent Developments in Schizophrenia, *Br. J. Psychiatry,* Special Publication no. 1, 133–158.

Rutter, M. (1968). Concepts of autism: A review of research. *J. Child Psychol. Psychiatry, 9,* 1–25.

Rutter, M. (1972). Childhood schizophrenia reconsidered. *J. Autism Child, Schizophr., 2,* 315–337.

Rutter, M. (1973). The assessment and treatment of preschool autistic children. *Early Child Dev. Care, 3,* 13–29.

Rutter, M. (1974). The development of infantile autism. *Psychol. Med., 4,* 147–163.

Rutter, M., Sussenwein, F. (1971). A developmental and behavioral approach to the treatment of preschool autistic children. *J. Autism Child. Schizophr., 1,* 376–397.

Rutter, M., Bartak, L. (1973). Special educational treatment of autistic children: A comparative study. II. Follow-up findings and implications for services. *J. Child Psychol. Psychiatry, 14,* 241–270.

Schneider, C. (1942). *Die Schizophrenen Symptomverbande.* Berlin: Springer.

Shafii, M. (1972). A precedent for modern psychotherapeutic techniques: One thousand years ago. *Am J Psychiatry* 128: 1581–1584.

Shafii, M. (1979). Childhood psychosis. In Noshpitz, J. (Ed.), *Basic Handbook of Child Psychiatry,* Vol. 3. New York: Basic Books, pp. 555–567.

Treffert, D.A. (1970). Epidemiology of infantile autism. *Arch. Gen. Psychiatry, 22,* 431–438.

Vaillant, G.E. (1963). John Haslam on early infantile autism. *Am J. Psychiatry, 119,* 376.

White, P.T., *et al.* (1964). The neurologic status of children with early infantile autism: An EEG survey. *Electroencephalogr. Clin. Neurophysiol., 17,* 461–462.

Wing, L. (1971). Perceptual and language development in autistic children: A comparative study. In Rutter, M. (Ed.), *Infantile Autism: Concepts, Characteristics and Treatment.* London: Churchill.

Wing, L. (Ed.) (1976). *Early Childhood Autism.* Second Edition. Oxford: Pergamon Press.

Witmer, L. (1922). Don: A curable case of arrested development due to a fear psychosis in a 3 year old infant. *Psychol. Clinic 1919–22, 13,* 97.

Chapter 17

DEVELOPMENTAL RETARDATION: and Related Disorders

Nuhad D. Dinno, M.D.

INCIDENCE AND GENERAL CONSIDERATIONS

Mental retardation is one of the most handicapping of all childhood disorders. Its chief feature is intellectual subnormality associated with maladaptive behavior. The diagnosis of mental retardation implies onset at birth or during childhood.

Mental retardation, more appropriately referred to as developmental retardation, is estimated to be manifested in approximately 3% of the population at birth. This estimate of incidence is based on the following criteria: an IQ below 70, retardation identified in infancy, unchanging diagnosis, and a mortality similar to that of the general population. Applied to the United States population, this would suggest a population of 6 million. The actual population may be no higher than 2 million. (Tarjan *et al.,* 1973)

Considerations leading to the lower estimate for the clinical diagnosis of mental retardation are that at the same time the indiviudal shows impairment in intelligence there is a similar impairment in adaptive behavior, and that both of these symptoms manifest themselves during the developmental years. (Heber, 1959) Many pre-school children and adults, however, do not show major impairment in general adaptations, even with relatively low IQs. As a result, the clinical diagnosis of mental retardation, particularly when mild, is age dependent and usually not established before school age. Also, mortality in retarded individuals is inversely related to intelligence level, with only the mildly retarded having life expectancies that approximate those of the general population. Table 17-1, adapted from material supplied by the National Association for Retarded Citizens, sums up the extent of retardation in the United States more accurately. (National Association for Retarded Citizens, 1979)

Particular responsibilities of the medical profession have been clearly delineated in the *Report of the American Medical Association Conference on Mental Retardation* (1964): "The medical profession has a clearly defined responsibility in the early detection of retardation and in planning for and obtaining optimal care for the retarded." (p. xi) The report further emphasized that the physician may participate in many approaches, including improved methods of diagnosis and treatment, rehabilitation, and education.

Mental subnormality is one of the most incapacitating, lifelong handicaps a child or adult can have. Mental retardation, however, is a symptom, in the broadest sense, and not a diagnosis. (Wright and Tarjan, 1963) Most patients with an overt diagnosis of mental retardation are children or adolescents.

DEFINITION

The diagnosis of mental retardation requires that an individual manifest deficiencies in both adaptive behavior and intellectual functioning measured by intelligence. These same criteria are used to determine the degree or level of mental retardation. Four categories accepted by the American Association on Mental Deficiency (AAMD)(1977) are: Mild, Moderate, Severe, and Profound. Definitions for these levels are given in Table 17-2.

The 1977 AAMD classification system also included a level of Borderline Mental Retardation for individuals who scored between one and two standard deviations (s.d.) below the general population mean on intelligence tests. The borderline level, deleted in 1973, was based on data indicating that the large majority of persons in the borderline range of intellectual functioning are not signifi-

Table 17-1   **Estimates of Retardation by Age and Degree (1979)**

1970 Census	All Ages	Under 21 Years	21 Years & Older
General population	220 million	85.8 million	134.2 million
3% general population retarded	6.6 million	2.6 million	4.0 million
Profound retardation (IQ Below 20), about 1½% of retarded population	99 thousand	39 thousand	60 thousand
Severe (IQ 20-35), about 3½%	231 thousand	90 thousand	141 thousand
Moderate (IQ 36-50) about 6%	396 thousand	154 thousand	242 thousand
Mild (IQ 51-70), about 89%	5.9 million	2.3 million	3.6 million

Table 17-2   **Levels of Mental Retardation**

	Obtained Intelligence Quotient	
Levels	Stanford Binet & Cattel (s.d. 16)	Wechsler Scales (s.d. 15)
Mild	65-52	69-55
Moderate	51-36	54-40
Severe	35-20	39-25 (extrapolated)
Profound	19 and below	24 and below (extrapolated)

cantly impaired in adaptive behavior. However, a small minority of persons with IQs up to 10 points above the guideline ceilings of mild retardation in the older borderline classification are so impaired in their adaptive behavior that they may be classified as having mild mental retardation.

Utilizing the discussed criteria, one may define *mental retardation as significantly subaverage general intellectual functioning existing concurrently with deficits in adaptive behavior, and manifested during the developmental period.* (Kidd, 1964)

ETIOLOGY

The identification and diagnosis of mental retardation is one of the most challenging problems confronting the physician, whether the delayed motor development and hypotonia are early expressions of mental retardation or expressions of chronic systemic diseases, such as severe failure to thrive. Assessment of clinical symptoms is essential for establishing etiology, management, and prognosis.

The early identification of mental retardation is vital for success in remedial treatment. In an increasing number of instances, detection and diagnosis of an underlying biological abnormality can lead to the prevention of brain disease and consequent retardation or further organic deterioration, for example, congenital hypothyroidism and phenylketonuria (PKU).

The young child with slow development should have prompt pediatric evaluation. The diagnostic process is not an end in itself. It is the beginning of reality planning by parents and professionals.

The causes of mental retardation are numerous. More often than not, a careful investigation to determine specific causes may be unrewarding. More than 200 different factors have been identified as closely or casually related to mental retardation; yet there is no identifiable biological or organic cause for retardation in 65 to 70% of the cases.

The following etiological classification of mental retardation, including major organic causes, is adapted from *Nelson Textbook of Pediatrics.* (Vaughan, *et al.,* 1979) (see Table 17-3) Most disorders listed can be identified in early infancy. A significant number of these disorders have additional manifestations of central nervous system defect or damage, such as seizures, sensory defects, motor handicaps, and involvement of the skeletal, circulatory, and endocrine systems.

Table 17-3   **Etiological Classification of Mental Retardation**

I. Prenatal
  A. Genetically determined
    1. Metabolic disorders of protein, carbohydrates or fat
    2. Cerebral demylinating disorders
    3. Cranial anomalies
    4. Congenital ectodermosis
    5. Chromosomal abnormalities
    6. Endocrine—congenital hypothyroidism
  B. Maternal and fetal infections
    1. Rubella
    2. Toxoplasmosis
    3. Cytomegalic inclusion disease
    4. Syphilis
  C. Fetal irradiation
  D. Maternal medication or toxins
    1. Dilantin
    2. Alcohol
  E. Indefinite causes
    1. Placental abnormality
    2. Toxemia of pregnancy
    3. Nutritional deficiency
    4. Trauma
II. Perinatal
  A. Prematurity
  B. Postmaturity
  C. Anoxia at birth
  D. Birth trauma
III. Postnatal
  A. Kernicterus
  B. Cerebral infections: meningitis, encephalitis
  C. Cerebral trauma
  D. Cerebrovascular accidents
  E. Poisoning (e.g., lead, carbon monoxide)
  F. Postimmunization encephalopathy: pertussis, smallpox, and others
  G. Cultural—familial
  H. Psychogenic

DISORDERS OF AMINO ACID METABOLISM

Phenylketonuria

Phenylketonuria (PKU) is an inborn error of amino acid metabolism manifested by the inability of the body to convert phenylalanine to tyrosine. It produces a characteristic clinical picture, the most significant findings of which are mental retardation, seizures, light pigmentation of hair, eyes, and skin, and infantile eczema. It is an autosomal recessive disorder and its incidence in the general population of the United States is approximately 1 in 10,000. (Guthrie and Susi, 1962) Children with phenylketonuria are born with only slightly ele-

vated phenylalanine blood levels, but upon ingestion of protein, the amino acid accumulates in the serum and cerebrospinal fluid and is excreted in large quantities. In 1949, Jervis demonstrated the metabolic defect to be deficient hydroxylation of phenylalanine due to the absence of the enzyme phenylalanine hydroxylase.

Phenylketonuric infants appear normal at birth. During the first 2 months of life failure to thrive and irritability may frequently be observed. By 4 to 9 months, delayed development becomes apparent. In the untreated child, mental retardation is usually severe and seizures are common. A peculiar musty odor, attributed to phenylacetic acid, accompanies the patient and may suggest the diagnosis. A variety of EEG abnormalities have been found. The changes are either generalized slowing, dysrhythmia, or in the form of epileptogenic foci. Once developed, the cerebral defect is irreversible. The diagnosis of PKU depends upon the clinical picture, elevation of blood phenylalanine, and the presence of phenylpyruvic acid in the urine.

An increase in serum phenylalanine has been observed in premature infants which is associated with an increase in tyrosine. This usually is transient and is reversible with maturation. It has no clinical neurologic significance and does not warrant dietary management. There have been several varieties of nonphenylketonuric hyperphenylalaninemias that have been identified. The metabolic pathways of these lesser defects vary. Some differ from PKU only in degree, whereas others have basic differences in the details of the metabolic defect. (Blaskovics *et al.,* 1974)

In typical PKU, the diet, which contains a low level of phenylalanine, is initiated as soon as the diagnosis is established (at about 7 to 10 days of age) and should be maintained for at least 5 years. Although early dietary treatment is essential for the development of normal intellect, it does not necessarily prevent mental retardation. It is not clear why; however, there is speculation that CNS damage or impairment has already taken place prenatally and the changes are permanent. At present, there is no information as to the required duration of low phenylalanine intake, although resumption of a normal diet at about 5 years of age did not produce mental retardation.

Maple Syrup Disease

Maple Syrup Disease is an extremely rare autosomal recessive inherited disorder involving the oxidative decarboxylation of the branched-chain keto acids, neutral amino acids leucine, isoleucine, and valine. The condition was first described in 1954 by Menkes. The diagnosis is established by chemotographic study of blood and urine. Rapidly progressive neurological symptoms, principally seizures, depression of the consciousness, and motor disturbance appear in the first week of life. The keto acid derived from the just mentioned amino acids accumulate in blood and urine. Secondary accumulation of a derivative of alpha hydroxybutyric acid gives the characteristic maple syrup odor to the urine. Management by a diet low in branched-chain amino acids (leucine, isoleucine, and valine) is useful but only partially successful. Treated patients have survived longer and showed improvement in their intellectual functioning. Prenatal diagnosis is possible with this disorder, by a biochemical analysis of the cultivated amniotic fluid cells at about 15 weeks gestation.

Homocystinuria

Homocystinuria, first described in 1962 as a biochemical cause of mental retardation, appears to be second in occurrence after phenylketonuria. (Carson *et al.*, 1963) The clinical picture includes mental retardation, ectopia lentis, cerebral and extracerebral thrombosis, and fine sparse hair. A defect in hepatic cystathionine synthetase has been noted. Dietary management has not been successful. It is an autosomal recessive disorder.

A number of other, much rarer, inborn errors of amino acid metabolism have been described associated with mental retardation.

DISEASES OF CARBOHYDRATE METABOLISM

Galactosemia

Galactosemia is an autosomal recessive disease that has been recognized since the beginning of this century. Onset of symptoms may occur in the newborn period or within the first few months of life. Lethargy, vomiting, jaundice, hepatomegaly, cataracts, delayed motor development with hypotonia, and failure to thrive are the major clinical findings. Occasionally, recognition may be delayed until childhood when mental retardation may be the only overt clinical expression. The biochemical basis for the disorder is a deficiency of galactose-1-phosphate uridyl transferase, the enzyme catalyzing the conversion of galactose-1-phosphate into galactose uridine diphosphate. (Kalckar *et al.*, 1956; Isselbacher *et al.*, 1956)

Enzyme activity in parents of galactosemic infants is about 60% of normal.

Treatment with a diet low in galactose should be started as early as possible and continued throughout childhood. This has been relatively successful in preventing brain damage, with best results obtained in patients started at birth or early infancy. The majority will function in the normal range; however, visual motor difficulties are common. Prenatal diagnosis has been made by a biochemical analysis of cultivated amniotic fluid cells.

Mucopolysaccharidosis

Mucopolysaccharidosis is a syndrome of mental and physical retardation, multiple skeletal deformities, hepatosplenomegaly, and clouding of the cornea. The principal biochemical disturbance in all forms involves the metabolism of polysaccharides. First described by Hunter (1917), and later by Hurler (1919), there are now at least seven different variants recognized.

The clinical picture varies considerably in time of appearance, mode of expression, inheritance, and rate of progression. X-ray changes are quite extensive and usually consist of an omega-shaped sella turcica. The bodies of T12 and L1 vertebrae are hooklike. The ribs are spatulate. Changes of the long bones are observed. The metacarpals are broad and taper proximally. The mucopolysaccharides are inherited as autosomal recessive diseases with the exception of the form described by Hurler, which is an X-linked recessive disease. Prenatal diagnosis has been accomplished for most of these syndromes; unfortunately, no treatment presently has been successful.

DISORDERS OF LIPID METABOLISM

These are genetic diseases involving the accumulations of lipids in one or more of the body's organs. The enzyme deficiency is usually one of catabolism. Some of this group are associated with characteristic foamy histiocytes on examination of bone marrow as in Niemann-Pick disease, Gaucher's disease, GM1 gangliosidosis Type I, and fucosidosis. Others include Tay-Sachs disease, Krabbe's disease, and metachromatic leukodystrophy. The signs and symptoms for each disease vary with the enzymatic defect and site of lipid accumulation. When a diagnosis has been made in a child, other family members should be screened, since carriers of most of the lipidoses can be identified, and such studies can assist in genetic counseling. Prenatal diagnosis may also be possible by biochemical analysis of the cultured amniotic fluid cells.

Niemann-Pick Disease

First described in 1914, this autosomal recessive condition is rapidly progressive. During the first few months of life, the child presents with failure to thrive and delayed early motor skills. Hypotonia and listlessness become more marked coupled with hepatosplenomegaly. Petechiae may develop due to thrombocytopenia. A cherry red spot in the macula is present in over half the cases. The children are blind in the later stages of the disease. As a result of enzymatic defect sphingomeylin accumulates in the visceral organs and cerebral gray matter. The affected organs have the characteristic foam cells. Most patients die before 3 years of age.

Gaucher's Disease

In 1882, Gaucher described a patient who died from a chronic progressive illness and had an enlarged liver and spleen associated with an accumulation of large cells that appeared to contain an excess of fat. This autosomal recessive disease has at least two forms: the most common (noncerebral) form usually manifests in late adolescence because of splenomegaly, abnormal bruising, or pathological fractures. In the less common (cerebral) form, hepatosplenomegaly and neurological deterioration are usually seen during the first year of life. In both forms, there is accumulation of glucocerebroside due to deficient activity of glucocerebrosidase. Most patients with cerebral Gaucher's disease die before 2 years of age. Assay of beta-glucosidase activity in white blood cells or cultured skin fibroblasts may allow detection of the heterozygote state.

Tay-Sachs Disease

First described in 1881, this autosomal recessive condition is found predominantly in Ashkenazi Jews. It is associated with a deficiency of hexosaminidase activity. These infants are usually normal until 5 months of age. From there on, there is progressive failure to acquire new skills and loss of previously learned skills. Initially, there is an exaggerated response to sound. Focal or generalized convulsions are observed in almost all patients after the first year of life. Initially, there is

hypotonia and normal deep tendon reflexes. After 2 years, spasticity and rigidity are present and reflexes are hyperactive. Vision deteriorates rapidly after 9 to 11 months and atrophy of the optic nerve head usually develops after the first year. In the macula, a large white patch with a brownish red spot in its center is observed. Most children die between 2 and 4 years of age.

OTHER METABOLIC DEFECTS ASSOCIATED WITH MENTAL RETARDATION

Hyperuricemia

Hyperuricemia is characterized by mental retardation, self-mutilation, and choreoathetosis. It is an X-linked recessive disorder. The diagnosis may be confirmed by an elevated serum uric acid level. It can be diagnosed prenatally. Unfortunately, treatment has not been successful.

Trichopoliodystrophy

Trichopoliodystrophy, or kinky hair disease, has distinctive clinical features of coarse short hair, early onset of seizures, and severe developmental retardation. Bone x-rays show metaphyseal fractures and spurring. Serum copper level is decreased. Prenatal diagnosis of this X-linked disorder has been accomplished through amniocentesis.

NEUROCUTANEOUS SYNDROMES (PHAKOMATOSIS)

Diseases that affect both the skin and the nervous system are often classified as neurocutaneous disorders. The skin and the nervous system share a common embryological origin from the ectodermal layer. As many of the neurocutaneous diseases are due to single mutant genes, it seems likely that the primary genetic abnormality affects both the skin and the nervous system. Many, but not all, of the neurocutaneous syndromes ae associated with mental retardation.

Neurofibromatosis

Von Recklinghausen described this disease in 1882. It is the most common of the phakomatoses; associated mental retardation is milder and probably is present in about 10% of the cases.

Outstanding manifestations are those of hyper-hypopigmentation with *café au lait* spots in 94% of the cases. Multiple neurofibromata occur along nerves in subcutaneous tissues and sometimes in eyes and/or meninges. Along with these findings there may or may not be bone lesions. It follows an autosomal dominant pattern with variable penetrance and a fairly frequent mutation rate.

Tuberous Sclerosis

Bourneville is usually given credit for its recognition in 1880. Mental retardation in 62% of the cases together with convulsive disorder in 93% of the cases are the common neurological manifestations of this disease. Fibrous-angiomatous lesion varying in color from flesh to pink to brown develops in nasolabial folds, cheeks, and elsewhere in 83% of the patients. Areas of altered pigmentation are also found. Bone lesions have been described in about 66%. It is an autosomal dominant disorder with at least 25 to 50% of the cases representing a mutation.

Sturge-Weber Syndrome

This disease consists of the combination of predominantly unilateral upper facial vascular nevus, sometimes involving the choroid, and most commonly in a trigeminal facial distribution of the eye associated with hemangiomata of the arachnoid and pia, especially in the occipital and temporal areas. Seizures most commonly begin between ages 2 and 7 months and are grand mal in type, often asymmetrical. The degree of the central nervous system involvement is variable, with 30% having paresis and 50 to 60% having seizures. Not all patients are mentally retarded. (Chao, 1959)

The disorder is sporadic in inheritance. Occasionally, other family members may have hemangiomata to a lesser degree.

Von Hippel-Lindau Syndrome

Lindau recognized this by the association of the angiomatous retina (Von Hippel's disease) and angiomatous tumors of the cerebellum and other parts of the central nervous system. There is no association with mental retardation. It is inherited as an autosomal dominant disorder with varying expression.

Linear Sebaceous Nevi

This is a rare sporadic cutaneous lesion of infancy associated with variable degrees of mental retardation and seizure disorder. The cutaneous lesions occur over the head and neck. Its most common characteristic disposition is as a midline vertical linear patch over the forehead, lip, or chin. It is usually yellowish in color, elevated, and waxy in appearance. (Feurerstein and Mins, 1962)

CHROMOSOME ABNORMALITIES

Chromosome abnormalities are not rare. The incidence in unselected newborns is 0.5% and may be closer to 1%, if hidden mosaicism and minor abnormalities are detected.

Chromosome analyses can be done on lymphocytes from peripheral blood, cultured fibroblasts from skin biopsy, bone marrow, and amniotic fluid. Other tissues, such as thymus or gonads, may be used in selected cases. Current techniques for banding patterns of the chromosomes permit precise classification of many entities. These include reduplication, such as trisomy, partial trisomy, tetrasomy, and pentasomy, and deficiencies, such as deletions and monosomy X.

The most striking single clinical observation common to almost all the individuals with chromosomal anomalies is impaired intellectual function. This is associated with various abnormalities of both sex chromosomes and autosomes. Intellectual impairment is most marked in the autosomal trisomies.

Table 17–4 **Frequency of Some Chromosomal Abnormalities**

Condition	Frequency in Live Births
Trisomy 21—	
Down's syndrome	1/660
Trisomy 18	1/3500
Trisomy 13	1/5000
45X	1/2000 females
XYY	1/1000 males
XXY	1/1000 males

Down's Syndrome

The most common chromosomal abnormality associated with mental retardation was described by J. Langdon Down in 1860. This syndrome may be recognized at birth and the diagnosis can be confirmed by a cytogenetic study.

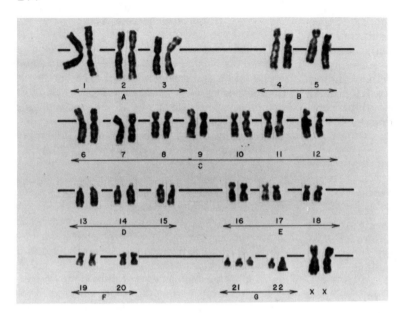

Figure 17-1 Female karyotype with trisomy 21.

The most common finding on chromosomal analysis is an additional third chromosome number 21. (Figure 17-1) This usually occurs as a sporadic defect, found in about 95% of patients with Down's Syndrome and increasing in incidence with maternal age. In 3 to 5%, a translocation defect occurs and the risk of recurrence is higher. Rarely, the cytogenetic study reveals a mosaic, or mixture, of cells containing 21 trisomy and cells that are normal. In the mosaic group, the clinical expression is more subtle and intelligence is somewhat less affected.

The most significant risk factor in Down's syndrome related to 21 trisomy is advanced maternal age. The incidence of this sporadic chromosome abnormality reaches nearly one in 50 births by age 45 years. The overall risk of recurrence in Down's syndrome is about 1%.

The translocation type imposes a certain higher risk of recurrence, depending on the chromosome group involved. If a translocation is found in a child with Down's syndrome, it is imperative that chromosome study of the family be performed. Genetic counseling is in order based upon the specific cytogenetic findings.

The chief clues to the diagnosis of Down's syndrome are the characteristic facies—flattened facial profile, upward slant of the eyes, epicanthal folds, and an inverted V-shaped upper lip—hypotonia, and abnormal hand configuration. The hand findings consist mainly of transverse palmar crease ("simean crease"), single flexion crease of the fifth finger with clinodactyly, and a distal axial tri-radius on the palms. Clinical diagnosis is possible at birth. The probabilities of mental retardation in the trainable or low educable range are relatively high, except in the mosaics where the degree is less predictable. Life expectancy is reduced by many factors, especially susceptibility to respiratory infection and the frequently associated congenital heart disease.

Trisomy 13

This chromosome abnormality is not only associated with severe or profound mental retardation, but has a high mortality rate in the first year of life. The infants are small for age at birth, usually having clinical features of cleft lip and/or cleft palate, eye defects, microcephaly, scalp defect, and polydactyly. Associated anomalies of the ears, heart, and kidneys are frequently present. Cytogenetic examination must be done to confirm the diagnosis and to reassure the parents that it is not inherited. The risk of recurrence is very small. (Figure 17-2)

Trisomy 18

This chromosome abnormality is similar in some ways to trisomy 13. The infants are small for age, and mortality is high during the first year of life. In fact, very few have survived beyond the first year. Common clinical findings include microphthalmia, overlapping fingers, micrognathia (smallness of the jaw), prominent occiput, low-set malformed ears, and hypoplasia of skeletal muscle, subcutaneous and adipose tissue. Other anomalies include congenital heart disease and genitourinary defects. Less common findings may be skeletal defects, omphalocele, and hemangio-

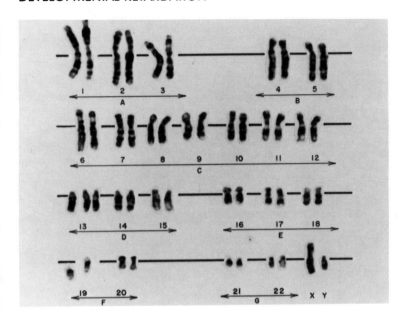

Figure 17-2 Male karyotype with trisomy 13.

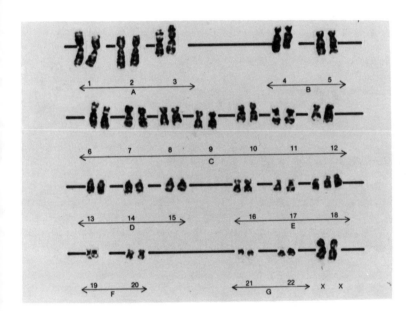

Figure 17-3 Female karyotype with trisomy 18.

ma. Mental retardation is usually profound. Trisomy 18 occurs sporadically. Cytogenetic study should be done to confirm the diagnosis. (Figure 17–3)

Cri du Chat Syndrome (5p–)

This chromosomal disorder is caused by loss of chromosomal material of the upper arms of chromosome number 5. There is moderate to severe mental deficiency associated with micro-cephaly. The most characteristic feature in the newborn period is a peculiar, soft mewing cry, which is usually restricted to infancy. Several minor dysmorphic features include rounded facies, hypertelorism, downward slant of the palpebral fissures, epicanthic folds, and malformed low-set ears. Most cases are sporadic, although balanced translocations of the parents with an increased risk of recurrence has been reported in a few cases. Like the previously described chromosomal abnormalities, most cases are sporadic. (Figure 17–4)

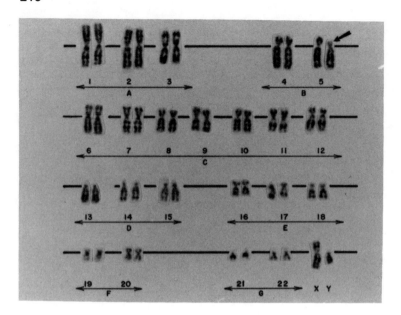

Figure 17-4 Partial deletion of short arm of chromosome number 5 (5p-).

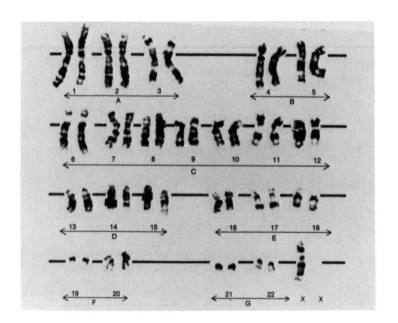

Figure 17-5 45X—Turner's Syndrome.

Turner's Syndrome

This sex chromosomal disorder is usually not associated with mental retardation. Several chromosomal abnormalities have been observed. The most common one is that of complete absence of one X chromosome. (Figure 17-5) Others may have XX/XO mosaic patterns, or only part of one X chromosome missing. Mosaicism or partial deletion generally has a lesser degree of malformations.

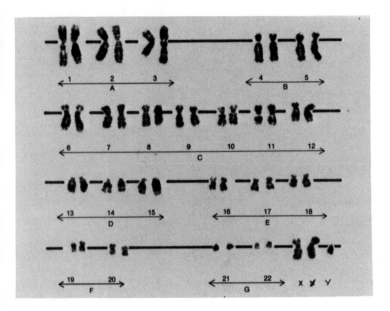

Figure 17-6 Male karyotype with XXY (Kleinfelter).

The most common feature is small stature. A broad chest with widely spaced nipples, low posterior hairline, and webbing of the neck are often evident at birth. Other findings include transient congenital lymphedema, with puffiness over the dorsum of the fingers and toes. Cardiac defects are frequent, the most common being coarctation of the aorta. Ovarian dysgenesis with hypoplasia to absence of germinal elements occurs in over 90% of the cases. Occurrence is generally a sporadic event and as yet no adequate data on risk for recurrence are available.

XXY Syndrome, or Klinefelter's Syndrome

Generally, there is a tendency toward dull mentality. About 20% of the patients have an IQ of less than 80. Behavior problems, insecurity, shyness, and poor judgment are common. Clinically, patients have long limbs with low upper to lower segment ratio from childhood and a relatively tall, slim stature. The child has a relatively small penis and testes persisting through adolescence and adulthood. Virilization is inadequate with gynecomastia occurring in about 40%. Infertility is the rule. Occasional findings are cryptorchidism, hypospadias, and adolescent scoliosis. Homosexuality may be more frequent than in the general population.

Cytogenetic study is essential for diagnosis. Most of the patients will be XXY (Figure 17-6), but some may have a mosaic pattern XXY/XY. Mosaic individuals have a better potential prognosis for testicular function and masculinization. Other variants, such as XXYY and XXXY, are more likely to have mental retardation and other minor anomalies.

XYY Syndrome

A pattern of variable anomalies has been observed which include acceleration of growth in mid-childhood, dull mentality, and explosive behavior that may be antisocial. Patients frequently have large teeth, prominent glabella, asymmetry, and severe acne in adolescence. Occasional findings are cryptorchidism, small penis, EEG and EKG changes. EEG shows a high amount of theta activity, which is usually found in younger children. Cytogenetics should be used to confirm the diagnosis. (Figure 17-7).

DRUG CONSUMPTION DURING PREGNANCY

Considerable attention to the problem of drug-induced congenital malformations resulted following the thalidomide tragedy of the early 1960s. (Mellin and Katzenstein, 1962) Since then, it has become increasingly clear that a number of factors may adversely affect the developing fetus, resulting in mental retardation, as well as other developmental abnormalities. Jones et al. (1973) first delineated the fetal alcohol syndrome. Other researchers have confirmed the observation that mental retardation, growth retardation, microcephaly, and some craniofacial abnormalities, such as ptosis, strabismus, and cleft palate, may

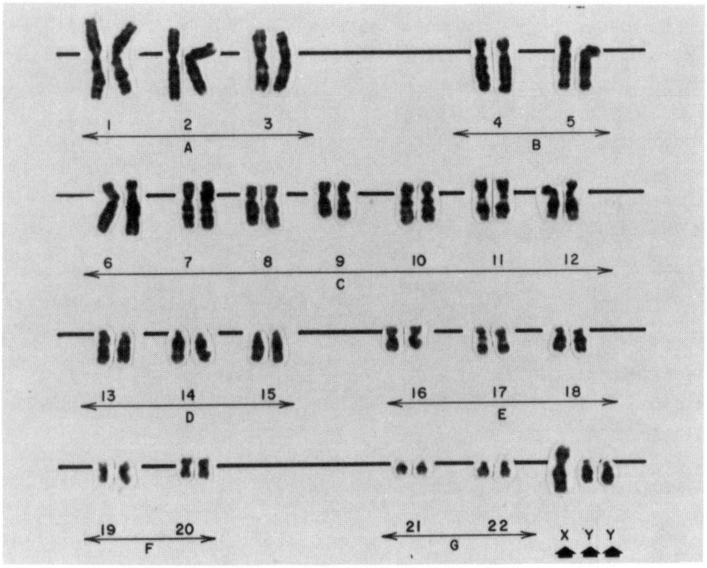

Figure 17-7 XYY—male karyotype.

occur in infants born to women with chronic alcoholism.

In recent years, other environmental agents have been recognized as playing roles in the etiology of several birth defects, many of which are associated with mental retardation and/or developmental disabilities. Possible teratogenic effects of anticonvulsants were first presented by Meadow in 1968. In mothers receiving anticonvulsive medications, such as Dilantin, during pregnancy the risk to the fetus of having dysmorphic features or mental retardation is approximately 10%. The risk of having some anomalies, such as microcephaly, congenital heart disease, limb abnormalities, and genitourinary and gastrointestinal abnormalities, is an additional 33%. (Hanson, et al., 1976) Other anticonvulsants have also been associated with significant congenital anomalies, including mental retardation.

Such problems point out the necessity for closely monitoring the effects of drugs and chemicals on the pregnant woman and her offspring in an attempt to help decrease potentially preventable causes of mental retardation and other associated birth defects.

INTRAUTERINE INFECTION

Prior to the rubella vaccine, epidemics of rubella occurred frequently. The last major epidemic was in 1964. Since then, there has been a progressive decline in the number of reported congenital rubella cases. In 1969, an effective rubella vaccine program was started and a dramatic decrease in the number of congenital rubella

and cases of rubella has occurred. (Krugman, 1977) Most common clinical manifestations of congenital rubella are growth retardation, mental retardation, microcephaly, cataracts, deafness, and congenital heart disease. Other findings may include genitourinary abnormalities, hemolytic anemia, delayed eruption of teeth, and dermatoglyphic alterations. With continued efforts and the cooperation of physicians, public health centers, and school officials, this important cause of mental retardation can be eliminated.

IRRADIATION

Concern over the effects of radiation, especially in pregnant women, has increased along with the public concern over other potentially toxic factors in the environment. Since the majority of radiation is from medical sources, prevention must focus upon the careful use of x-ray, not only during pregnancy, but also during the childbearing years.

EARLY RECOGNITION

Early diagnosis of intellectual, as well as physical, deficiencies is critical because many handicapped children may be significantly helped by early intervention. Some metabolic diseases can be treated by appropriate diet and medication. These include amino acid disorders (e.g., phenylketonuria) and endocrine disorders (e.g., hypothyroidism). Early diagnosis of genetic disorders may alter parental planning for future pregnancies. The increasing number of hereditary diseases being reported, some of which are diagnosable in utero, makes it essential for the physician to be knowledgeable.

Early diagnosis of the child in the comparatively privileged home may help prevent a situation in which uninformed parents have unrealistic expectations, exacerbating the child's condition and further depressing his function.

Early diagnosis is equally important for children experiencing environmental deprivation. There is evidence indicating that exposure to nursery school and other stimulating experiences may enhance the learning process, as well as the social adjustment, of many disadvantaged children.

The role of the physician is crucial since he is the chief professional person—with clinical training and skills to evaluate biological factors—coming in contact with children in the preschool period. Because of his relationship to the family, he is the appropriate person to coordinate and evaluate various diagnostic procedures, interpret findings to the parents, and plan for comprehensive care and treatment. Also, the physician's own expanding knowledge of the patterns of growth and development, and his skill in diagnostic method and learning to deal with high-risk groups, can facilitate early diagnosis.

Helpful in assessing young infants and neonates is the physical stigmata often associated with mental retardation. Certain combinations of observed anomalies of development with known mental retardation syndromes may be made using illustrated textbooks. (Holmes *et al.*, 1972; Smith, 1976; Gorlin *et al.*, 1976)

DIAGNOSTIC EVALUATION

The physician is frequently confronted with the problem of where to begin an evaluation process without resorting to an extensive evaluation that may not be warranted. There are certain guidelines available when added to clinical judgment that assist the physician in making such an evaluation.

As in all aspects of medicine, the history is exceedingly important. Several areas are especially significant in retardation. They include relevant developmental data, genetic information, fertility history, history of labor and delivery, blood group incompatibility, accidents, and history of seizures, including type of seizure. Most important is whether the child is progressing developmentally or shows neurological deterioration.

When the physical examination of the child does not reveal ongoing organic disease and there is past history of significant cerebral insult, such as asphyxia neonatorum with a low Apgar score of 6 and under, then extensive diagnostic search is unnecessary.

If there is no history of cerebral insult and no clinical findings on physical examination to suggest a specific disease entity, screening tests are in order. These would include:

1. Skull x-rays, x-rays for bone age (optional)
2. Urine for metabolic screening
3. Serum uric acid
4. Chromosome analysis
5. Thyroid studies in suspected hypothyroidism

Experience has shown that many retarded children are of small stature and may have delayed bone age. In some instances in patients with retardation, severe emotional and behavioral disturbance, or autisticlike qualities without clinically recognizable seizures, an EEG is indicated. A chromosomal analysis is certainly indicated when a patient has a recognizable pattern or stigmata, as in Down's syndrome.

Other tests may be indicated when the physician suspects a metabolic disease, progressive neurological disorder, or other generalized conditions. These tests may include:

1. X-rays of spine, long bones
2. Specific metabolic studies
3. CT scan
4. Muscle, brain, or rectal biopsy
5. Enzyme studies

The medical assessment is only a small part of the initial evaluation. Other studies, including psychological, social, and educational assessment, may be necessary, depending on the age of the child and the extent of the problems. In addition, consistent, comprehensive long-term management is essential for this chronic handicap.

PREVENTION

Since medical treatment of mental retardation offers little hope of complete alleviation, medical research efforts during the past century have focused on the prevention of mental retardation. (Sells and Bennett, 1977) Currently, the outlook for prevention is improving. New findings affecting early recognition appear almost daily, and anticipated future research should facilitate the physician's role by providing more practical tools. Prevention of mental retardation involves education of the medical profession, the pregnant mother, and the general public.

Heterozygote Detection

With the expansion of knowledge on meta-bolic diseases, the list of autosomal recessive disorders for which carrier identification for autosomal recessive and X-linked conditions is increasing. Very few, however, warrant mass population screening. Although there seems little justification or need for the widespread applica-tion of the methods for carrier detection in the general population, the techniques may be of value in high-risk subpopulations. (Milunsky, 1975) In situations where antenatal diagnosis is possible for the identification of a lethal or seriously incapaci-tating genetic disease, there is good reason for screening to identify couples at risk.

Tay-Sachs disease, which is a progressive neurodegenerative disorder is the first recessive condition in which a prospective approach to disease prevention has been applied. (Kaback *et al.,* 1974) The disease occurs in a defined popula-tion, specifically Ashkenazi Jews, where it is estimated that 1 in 30 is heterozygous for the gene that causes Tay-Sachs disease. Among non-Ashkenazi Jews and others, the heterozygote state is estimated to be 1/380. This makes effective screening possible. Carrier detection is by assay of the critical serum enzyme.

Phenylketonuria, more commonly encoun-tered in the general population, is also caused by deficiency of a specific enzyme in an identifiable asymptomatic carrier. (Griffin and Elsas, 1975) Because of heterogeneity in the general population for PKU, it is doubtful that heterozygote screening in the general population will be an effective means of ascertaining matings at risk for having an offspring with PKU. However, current methods allow the techniques available to provide im-proved genetic counseling of individuals at risk for PKU in selected families.

While heterozygote detection methods have proved to be useful in the conditions just men-tioned, there are limitations in screening methods for identification of heterozygotes for a variety of inherited inborn errors of metabolism associated with mental retardation. Milunsky summarized a list of several conditions, such a Tay-Sachs disease, PKU, and galactosemia, in which he discussed the feasibility and methods of identify-ing heterozygotes when the disorders are asso-ciated with mental retardation.

Prenatal Diagnosis

Diagnostic amniocentesis for the prenatal detection of genetic disorders is useful in monitor-ing high-risk pregnancies.

Prenatal diagnosis of most genetic defects requires amniocentesis, a procedure that must be preceded by appropriate genetic counseling. A family pedigree is essential. The counselor needs to verify the diagnosis of affected relatives, deter-mine risk factors, and recognize and deal with the psychosocial implications of prenatal diagnosis. The following are major indications for prenatal diagnosis:

1. Maternal age + 35 years
2. Previous child with Down's syndrome
3. If one of the parents has a balanced transloca-tion
4. Previous child with a neural tube defect
5. Hereditary metabolic errors
6. X-linked disorders

Biochemical, histological, and histochemical analyses of cultivated amniotic fluid cells remain the most reliable method for the intrauterine detection of familial metabolic disorders. Over 30 familial metabolic disorders are potentially de-tectable in cultivated amniotic fluid cells, and about one-half of these have been detected "in utero." (Nadler, 1972)

Maternal Phenylketonuria

The successful treatment program for PKU has resulted in increasing number of phenylketo-nuric girls, treated in their early years, but now on a normal diet, approaching a childbearing period and being "normal mentally." Current evidence suggests that the majority of children born to these women will be mentally retarded and microce-phalic, even though these children will not have PKU. It has been recommended by MacCready and Levy (1973) that, although further research is needed, dietary treatment during pregnancy of PKU mothers potentially can prevent mental retardation in their offspring. Several studies presently undertaken seem to support this view.

Newborn Screening

Newborn screening programs for PKU are ongoing in most states and are already defensible on economic as well as medical grounds. The relative frequency of the disorder, the simplicity of diagnostic testing, and the possibility for effective treatment in the neonatal period are the key factors in establishing screening programs.

Galactosemia is another inborn error of carbohydrate metabolism, significant because effective dietary therapy to prevent growth and developmental retardation is available. Several states have recently added galactosemia to their PKU screening programs.

Other amino acid disorders can be identified in the newborn period as demonstrated by the Massachusetts program. (Massachusetts Department of Public Health, 1974) However, these disorders, for the most part, are quite uncommon and not amenable to dietary therapy at the present time. Some of these conditions include maple syrup disease and homocystinuria.

The most recent important development in newborn screening is the availability of a convenient laboratory method for the detection of congenital hypothyroidism. (Dussault *et al.,* 1975) The ease of detection, the relative frequency (more common than PKU), and the critical need for treatment before age 3 months for having a greater chance of normal mental abilities warrant establishing such a program. (Fisher *et al.,* 1976)

Although progress has been made in the areas of prevention of mental retardation, for the majority of the retarded citizens the causes, and hence methods of prevention, remain unknown.

MANAGEMENT AND TREATMENT

As stated earlier, with the exception of a few metabolic errors and hypothyroidism, the treatment of mental retardation is predominantly nonmedical. It involves education to achieve maximum learning potential, vocational training habilitation, and normalization of social and recreational activities.

One extremely important component of the physician's role in the care of the mentally retarded, irrespective of etiology, is being a counselor for the family. This aspect of treatment can be successfully managed by a physician well informed about the relative importance of the organic, psychological, genetic, and environmental factors that may produce mental deficiency.

The physician's knowledge of available community resources and programs for the retarded is essential in guiding the family and in obtaining help for the child. Referrals to the local or state departments concerned with the mentally retarded or to parent-sponsored voluntary organizations, such as the National Association for Retarded Citizens, may be helpful in assisting families to obtain appropriate information about programs for their children. Programs for infants, preschool children, and special education classes for school-age children should be explored. Programs for the adolescent and young adult also need to be investigated. As the situation arises, the possibility of residential care facilities or alternatives can be explored with the family.

GENETIC COUNSELING

An important aspect of biomedical responsibility in the prevention of mental retardation is genetic counseling. In most situations, the disorder is sporadic and the recurrence rate is not much greater than the risk of mental retardation in the general population. This can be assuring to the family; however, this is altered if the specific diagnosis has genetic implications. When the disorder follows classic Mendelian genetics, the following occurrence rate can be shared with the family: 25% in autosomal recessive inheritance, 50% occurrence in autosomal dominant conditions, and 50% of males in X-linked disorders. Explanations should also be given of the unaffected potential carrier rate and detection in each condition.

Diagnosis is an essential component of the counseling process; it represents the beginning and not the end. Counseling parents regarding the presence of a developmental abnormality or a birth defect presents complex challenges to the physician who cares for the affected child and family. (Waisburn, 1980) Several issues are taken into consideration while providing genetic counseling that involves adaptation of the parents to the handicap and their response to uncertainty. Another point of equal importance is the parents' attitude about genetic counseling and whether telling them of a risk factor would influence their decision-making process. Such issues are an integral part of the genetic counseling process.

SUMMARY

Today the physician is in a particularly effective position to identify and initiate services to the retarded child early in life. The alertness of the physician through ongoing contact with the child may permit identification of the retarded child years before a diagnosis might otherwise have been made, and make possible the beginning of helpful therapy that may modify or reverse the cause of the disorder. Such identification is especially important in sociocultural retardation, in which current research indicates that enrichment of the child's environment early enough may save the child from a lifelong handicap.

Improved methods of fetal and infant salvage now permit survival of many handicapped infants who once would have succumbed at birth, presenting the physician with an increasing number of families who need guidance in managing a handicapped child.

The physician is apt to see more retarded patients because of the current emphasis on retaining handicapped children, when possible, in the community and allowing them to enjoy family life and the benefits of community services. The more comprehensive and effective the services, the greater the chance for the retarded person to achieve his maximum potential, to be a useful and productive citizen, and therefore to be less of a burden on his family and society. The physician will help to increase the status of the retarded person as a "human being" by proper counseling of the parents.

REFERENCES

American Association on Mental Deficiency (1977). *Manual on Terminology and Classification in Mental Retardation,* Special Report, No. 2.

American Medical Association (1964). Report of the American Medical Association Conference on Mental Retardation, Chicago, Illinois, April 9-11.

Blaskovics, M.E., Shaeffler, G.E., Hack, S. (1974). Phenylalaninemia: Differential diagnosis. *Arch. Dis. Child., 49,* 835.

Bourneville, D. (1880). Sclereuse tubereuse des circonvolutions cerebrales: Idiote et epilepse hemiplegique. *Arch. Neurol.* (Paris), *1,* 81.

Carson, N.A.J., *et al.* (1963). Homocystinuria: A new inborn error of metabolism associated with mental deficiency. *Arch. Dis. Child., 38,* 425.

Chao, D.H.C. (1959). Congenital neurocutaneous syndromes of childhood, III, Sturge-Weber disease. *J. Pediatr., 55,* 635.

Dussault, J.H. Coulombe, P. Laberge, C., Letarte, J., Guyda, H., Khoury, K. (1975). Preliminary report on a mass screening program for neonatal hypothyroidism. *J. Pediatr., 86,* 670-674.

Feurerstein, R.C., Mins, L.C. (1962). Linear nevus sebaceous with convulsions and mental retardation. *Am. J. Dis. Child., 104,* 675.

Fisher, D.A., Burrow, G.N., Dussault, J.H., Hollingsworth, D.R., Larsen, P.R., Man, E.B., Walfish, P.G. (1976). Recommendations for screening programs for congenital hypothyroidism. *J. Pediatr., 89,* 692-694.

Gorlin, R.J., Pindborg, J.J., Cohen, M.M. (1976). *Syndromes of the Head and Neck.* Second Edition. New York: McGraw-Hill.

Griffin, R.F., Elsas, L.J. (1975). Classic phenylketonuria: Diagnosis through heterozygote detection. *J. Pediatr., 86,* 512-517.

Guthrie, R., Susi, A. (1962). A simple phenylalanine method for detecting phenylketonuria in large populations of newborn infants. *Pediatrics, 32,* 338.

Hanson, J.W., Myrianthopolous, N.C., Harvey, M.A.S., Smith, D.W. (1976). Risks to the offspring of women treated with hydantoin anticonvulsant with emphasis on the fetal hydantoin syndrome. *J. Pediatr, 89,* 662-668.

Heber, R. (1959). A manual on terminology and classification in mental retardation. *Am. J. Ment. Defic., 64,* Suppl: 1-111.

Holmes, L.G., Moser, H.W., Halldorsson, S., Mack, C., Pant, S.S., Matzilevich, B. (1972). *Mental Retardation: An Atlas.* New York: Macmillan.

Hunter, C. (1917). A rare disease in two brothers. *Proc. R. Soc. Med., 10,* 104-116.

Hurler, G. (1919). Uber eine typ multipler Abartungen, vorwiegend am Skelettsystem. *Z. Kinderheilkd, 24,* 220-234.

Isselbacher, K.J., *et al.* (1956). Congenital galactosemia: A single enzymatic block in galactose metabolism. *Science, 123,* 635.

Jones, K.L., Smith, D.W., Ulleland, C.N., Streissguth, A.P. (1973). Pattern of malformation in offspring of chronic alcoholic mothers. *Lancet, 1,* 1267-1271.

Kaback, M., Becker, M.H., Ruth, M. (1974). Compliance factors in a voluntary heterozygote screening program. *Birth Defects, 10,* 145-163.

Kalckar, H.M., Anderson, E.P., Isselbacher, K.J. (1956). Galactosemia: A congenital defect in a nucleotide transferase. *Biochim. Biophys. Acta, 20,* 262.

Kidd, J.W. (1964). Toward a more precise definition of mental retardation. *Ment. Retard., 2,* 209-212.

Krugman, S. (1977). Present status of measles and rubella immunization in the United States: A medical progress report. *J. Pediatr., 90,* 1-2.

Lindau, A. (1926). Studien uber Kleinhirnsystem: Bon Pathogenese und Bezichungen zur angiomatosis Retinae. *Acta Pathol. Microbiol. Scand.* (Suppl.), *1,* 1.

Massachusetts Department of Public Health (1974). Cost benefit analysis of newborn screening for metabolic disorders. *N. Engl. J. Med., 291,* 1414.

MacCready, R.A., Levy, H.L. (1973). The problem of maternal phenylketonuria. *Am. J. Obstet. Gynecol.,* 113, 121-128.

Meadow, S.R. (1968). Anticonvulsant drugs and congenital abnormalities. *Lancet, 2,* 1296.

Mellin, G.W., Katzenstein, M. (1962). The saga of thalidomide. Neuropathy to embryopathy, with case reports of congenital anomalies. *N. Engl. J. Med., 267,* 1184-1192.

Menkes, J.H. (1954). Maple syrup disease: Isolation and identification of organic acids in the urine. *Pediatrics, 23,* 348.

Milunsky, A. (1975). *The Prevention of Genetic Disease and Mental Retardation.* Philadelphia: W.R. Saunders Co.

Nadler, H.L. (1972). In utero detection of familial metabolic disorders. *Pediatrics, 49,* 329.

National Association for Retarded Citizens (1979). *Facts on Mental Retardation.* Arlington, Texas: National Association For Retarded Citizens.

Sells, C.J., Bennett, F.C. (1977). Prevention of mental retardation: The role of medicine. *Am. J. Ment. Defic., 82,* 117-129.

Smith, D.W. (1976). *Recognizable Patterns of Human Malformations.* Second Edition. Philadelphia: W.B. Saunders Co.

Tarjan, G., Wright, W., Eyman, R.K., Keeran, C.V. (1973). Natural history of mental retardation. *Am. J. Ment. Defic., 77,* 369-379.

Vaughan, V.C., McKay, R.J., Behrman, R.E. (Eds.) (1979). *Nelson Textbook of Pediatrics.* Philadelphia: W.B. Saunders Co.

Von Recklinghausen, F. (1882). Uber die multiplen Fibroma der Haut und ihre Beziehung zu den multiplen Neuromen. Berlin: A. Hirschwald.

Waisburn, S.E. (1980). Parents reactions after the birth of a developmentally disabled child. *Am. J. Ment. Defic., 84,* 345-351.

Wright, S., Tarjan, C. (1963). Mental retardation: A review for pediatricians. *Am. J. Dis. Child., 105,* 511.

Part III

ASSESSMENT AND TREATMENT

Chapter 18

PSYCHIATRIC ASSESSMENT: How To Talk with Children

David Dolen, M.D.

Deign on the world to turn thine eyes,
And pause awhile from learning to be wise—
Samuel Johnson, 1749, line 157.

It comes to each trainee of children's psychotherapy, as inevitably as growth, that he or she will be responsible for conducting the initial evaluation of a child. For some, this event has been preceded by many hours of lecture and instruction, during which various dicta and doctrines have been expounded and then exempted or expelled. Others may be shown the water, given its depth, and told to swim. For all, this experience is accompanied by a certain amount of anxiety, and, if one is so inclined, intestinal turmoil. The following pages are not to be regarded as a rigid outline for conducting the initial interview and may, at times, be at variance with philosophies to which the reader has been previously introduced. However, it is the writer's hope, that at the end of this chapter, one will be able to ascertain what information is essential to an initial evaluation, and that the reader will begin to consider techniques that will expedite the collection of this information in a manner most likely to be comfortable for the evaluator and the evaluated.

THE INITIAL CONTACT

The first information one receives regarding the parents and child is usually in the form of a referral. The source of this referral—whether it is self-initiated, from social agencies, the school system, the pediatrician, or the court—may color the parents' attitudes toward the evaluation process. One should be mindful of this when contacting the parents to schedule the first appointment. This initial contact may well be in the form of a brief telephone call, which will serve several purposes. It introduces the evaluator in a more personal manner than does a letter and affords the evaluator the opportunity of collecting some vital statistics about the child, the family, and the presenting problems. It allows the evaluator to invite or insist that both parents participate in the evaluation, whereas, without specific invitation, the assessment is often conducted with a single parent (often mother) and child. Most importantly, this telephone contact may be utilized as an aid in triaging cases for possible emergency intervention. Situations that would qualify for such concern would include: suicidal action or ideation, harmful behavior or intent toward other, school refusal, psychosis, physical or sexual abuse, neglect, runaway behavior, fire-setting, or medical emergencies. (See chapter 13) When the evaluator becomes aware that any of the former possibilities exist, he is to see the child and family posthaste, or, if unable to do so, arrange a referral that will assure the most immediate evaluation and intervention. It is imperative that the evaluator be advised as to state and local legislation regarding such emergencies and the authorities to whom problems, such as suspected abuse or neglect, must be reported. (See chapter 15)

If it is the practice of the evaluator to mail family history questionnaires prior to the evaluation, the initial telephone contact affords an opportunity to describe and discuss the packet the family will receive, and its mode of return to the evaluator. It is also an opportunity for the parents to raise any misgivings or questions they may have, and, in so doing, possibly alleviate some of the anxieties of the first visit.

ANXIETIES OF ASSESSMENT AND ASSESSING

For all parties of the evaluation, pre-existing circumstances may dictate the behavior and attitudes of those involved and may create obstacles to the process. The child usually comes to the evaluation setting at the command of adults, whether they are his parents' or the courts'. He often lacks the power of veto and is placed on center stage with few options. His previous experiences with adults, including his parents, may greatly color his attitude and behavior. For example, an abused child may see all adults as potential abusers, and, therefore, as an adult, the evaluator may pose an immediate threat to the child.

Apprehension may also increase when the child learns that the evaluator is addressed as "doctor" (a title often bestowed on clinicians, regardless of educational degree). Memories of unpleasant injections and painful physical manipulations may surround such a title, as might also be the case of the evaluation setting when it is located within the confines of a hospital or pediatric clinic familiar to the child. Some of these anxieties may be lessened through informing the child and preparing him for a new experience. Poorly informed parents inform their children poorly. Anxious parents often come to the setting with anxious children. One should never underestimate the child's ability to read and interpret the apprehensions of those around him.

Several factors may contribute to parental anxiety, and families may enter into the evaluation process with many preconceived ideas reagarding the field of mental health. For some individuals, the clinician may loom as the omnipotent being, able to read minds and decipher one's innermost feelings at a glance (although some of us may strive for such a station, it is doubtful that it is ever attained). This belief escalates vulnerable feelings the family may have and may lead to a marked resistance to disclosure.

If the parents have a somewhat less ethereal view of the clinician, they may perceive him as mortal, but as a mortal with great intelligence, who, with verbal chicanery, will entice them to open all of the family closets and illuminate the ghosts and taboos of their childhoods and adult lives.

The parents may also have concern that the evaluator will reveal to them their greatest fear and that a position of self-doubt will be realized; namely, parental failure or guilt as the progenitors. With such self-doubts, they may enter the evaluation with a fear of loss of their parental rights. This can be exacerbated when their route to the evaluation is through a court request.

In families that are tightly bound and have histories of solving conflicts within the family unit, the evaluator may encounter guilt or resistance stemming from "the sin of support." Such families may be very reluctant to allow an "outsider" to become enmeshed and embroiled in its internal affairs. Another family set one may encounter are those individuals who believe in "the immediate cure." They suppose that their problems will be resolved by the sage advice and counsel obtained during their first encounter with the clinician.

Each of these preconceived ideas may contribute to anxiety or be a part of parental misconception. They should be considered by the evaluator, recognized, and defused.

The evaluator may also approach the evaluation with apprehension. The inexperienced evaluator may have serious self-doubt as to his capacity to perform as expected and should be cautious lest such anxiety hinder the observation process and his recognition of the fearfulness of the family. He must also be careful not to counter his insecurity with a bravado that will alienate the child and parents.

The young clinician may feel somewhat timorous when confronted by parents older than himself. Perhaps it will help to remember that being a trained professional may compensate for the desired years and experiences. It is of questionable value, however, to hide behind one's professional diplomas and garb when dealing with anxious and troubled children.

The anxious young physician may be tempted to retain his white coat and stethoscope as would Linus his blanket when embarking into unexplored territory. The physician must realize that removal of a jacket is not synonomous with the shearing of Samsonian locks and that retaining the medical vestment may further convince the frightened child that he will shortly experience all manner of painful medical probing and prodding. As to appropriate dress, Ginott (1964) advises "no tuxedoes," and then quotes Napoleon as saying, "...he who goes into a battle should not wear his best pants because they would interfere with his military zeal." (p. 129) So as to best preserve one's "military zeal," clothing is best suited that allows the evaluator to interact on a playroom floor, yet preserves a professional appearance.

THE WAITING ROOM

The old adage, "more is missed by not looking than by not knowing," certainly holds for the field of mental health. Above all else, one must first be an observer of human actions and interactions. If the setting so permits, a few minutes of unobserved observation in the waiting room may be of great value. If the parents are huddled closely in a corner, clinging tightly to their child, one could entertain several hypothetical pictures of the family unit. They may be extremely enmeshed, overprotective, or frightened. Conversely, if father is sitting on one side of the waiting room talking to other parents, mother has cornered the receptionist and is trying to convince her to join the local garden club, and the child is running at will through the halls, a totally different picture evolves. Such observations may influence the approach to the family and will certainly be taken into consideration during the final formulation.

Adams (1974) suggests that when approaching the family in the waiting room, attention first be focused on the child and introductions be made in a manner hopefully appropriate to the developmental level of the child. The evaluator may initiate his encounter with the preschool child by squatting down to the child's level and commenting on the child's activities. The clinician then introduces himself and extends an invitation to see where he works, informing the child that there will be toys there and other things he may find interesting (p. 99) It follows that such an introduction is modified with the increasing age and sophistication of the child, so that the approach to the adolescent may be a very brief introduction and a handshake. Whatever the age of the child, it holds that the primary attention is directed toward him during this first encounter and that the parents are only briefly acknowledged.

Having made some efforts to set the child at ease, the walk from the waiting room to the office is an ideal time to "break the ice" with the parents. Interjection of neutral material and recognition of effort may serve this purpose: for example, "I hope you didn't have too much difficulty getting here. The traffic is really bad this time of day." Parents often go to great trouble and major rescheduling in their search for help, and this should be recognized.

THE JOINT FAMILY INTERVIEW

Parents are important sources of data concerning the child. As such, a discussion of the interview of the parents will be included in our consideration of the assessment of the child. Several options exist as to how and when the parents will be involved in the evaluation. Some clinicians choose to see only the parents during the first session, with subsequent appointments made for evaluating the child. Others prefer to schedule large blocks of time that will allow for a joint family interview, including the parents and child, followed by a separate interview with the parents

and a separate interview with the child. If one's setting allows for a co-evaluator, it is sometimes felt to be expedient and to strengthen the sense of advocacy if simultaneous separate evaluations are conducted, with one clinician designated as the child's evaluator and the other as the parents' evaluator.

The advantages of an initial joint interview prior to these individual sessions are many. It allows the evaluator another opportunity to observe the family as a unit, to note their seating choices and possibly their alliances. It hopefully affords open discussion of the presenting problem and, through the inclusion of the child in such discussion, may initiate the child into the evaluation process and alleviate feelings of isolation and victimization.

If one opts for a joint interview, much of the information reserved for individual sessions may be obtained at this time. Again, the initial attention may be directed toward the child, hopefully relaying the attitude that this setting is not one in which children are seen and not heard. It is important to get an understanding of the child's understanding, or, in other words, to ascertain the reason the child thinks he has been brought for evaluation. Some children have been well informed and prepared for the session, while others may have been told they were going for "ice cream." Information such as this is important in evaluating family anxieties and the communication network. If the child appears anxious, one might recognize this and respond to the anxiety by comments such as "I know this must be a little frightening—being in a strange place and talking to someone you've never met before," or "I bet you wonder what's going to happen here today and maybe that's a little scary." One must always be aware of the developmental and intellectual level of the child, as it may be necessary to state things in several ways to be assured that the child fully understands what has been said.

After exploring the child's thoughts as to why he was brought for evaluation, the evaluator may then wish to make a statement of purpose and introduce a schedule of enactment. For the younger child, this may proceed as follows. If the setting is located in a hospital or pediatric clinic, the interviewer may inquire if the child has been there before and what his memories of the setting include. If the interview is being conducted by a "doctor," one might inquire as to the child's association with physicians. The evaluator may then make a statement such as, "I am a doctor, but not the kind that gives shots—I'm a talking doctor and this is a place where people come to talk about things that make them happy or things that make them sad, things that worry them, or things that get them into trouble. It's a place where we can play and talk about anything in the whole world you want to talk about." The evaluator may then inform the child that in a few minutes the two of them will go to a room with lots of toys, where they will have the opportunity to play and talk even more.

So doing, one is now able to turn the attention to the parents and find out if, in fact, the child's understanding of the visit is the same as their own. It is all too easy to isolate the child during one's interactions with the parents, and it may be wise occasionally to include the child in the conversation—for example:

Mother: "Paul's little sister was born last year when Paul was 3."
Evaluator: "What do you remember about that, Paul?"
Mother: "Paul's always getting beat up by the kids in the neighborhood."
Evaluator: "Mom says sometimes the kids in the neighborhood give you a hard time—could you tell me about that?"

It is important to remember that all questioning of the child and parents should be done in an open-ended fashion to obtain the most spontaneous responses and to avoid symptom suggestion.

During the joint interview, the evaluator should be alert to areas of exploration in which the parents appear reluctant to respond. In many cases, it is possible to conduct the entire parent interview with the child in the room. There are, however, some families who are reluctant to discuss certain issues in front of their children, and this line of information may be pursued by the parent evaluator during a separate interview. Keeping in mind that one may want to return to the parents in our search for understanding, let us proceed to the interview of the child.

INTERVIEWING THE CHILD

"The time has come," the Walrus said,
"to talk of many things:
Of shoes—and ships—and sealing-wax—
Of cabbages—and kings—
And why the sea is boiling hot—
And whether pigs have wings."
                                        Lewis Carrol, 1896, p. 59.

Indeed, the time has come to talk of many things and to explore the fantasies and wishes that are a part of the richness of childhood. Depending upon the child's age and maturity, the setting for this exploration will vary. One most likely would not invite a 16-year-old to the playroom, nor would one expect a 5-year-old to sit calmly in the chair of an office for a 45 to 50 minute interchange.

The playroom is for playing. It is for children who can enjoy and utilize toys and games as a means of expression and communication. Although most settings in which the evaluation of children occur will have a separate room for play, some evaluators have toys and games in their offices and effectively carry out the assessment in that setting.

After being prepared for play by the evaluator, most children will depart from their parents with enthusiasm and great expectation. The child with separation anxieties, however, may tear and become combative. In such cases, it may be necessary for mom to accompany the child to the initial session, where she may remain for all or a part of the time. As separation anxieties often involve both the child and the parent, the evaluator may want to spend time explaining the play process and reassuring all involved. It sometimes happens that, after several minutes of play, the younger child will suddenly miss mommy. At this time, a brief trip to the waiting room, or to whatever location mother inhabits, will often reassure the child, who is then able to return to play and a profitable session.

The evaluator may introduce the playroom or play setting in a number of ways, but the primary purpose of such introductions is to set an atmosphere that will allow for the most freedom of expression: for example, "This is a place where you can do anything you want to do and say anything you want to say. Most of the things you do and say will be between you and me, but if I want to tell mommy or daddy about anything we talked about, I will talk about it with you first." Not only does such a statement assure that child that he will have a certain amount of freedom, but it also implies that the clinician is someone who can be trusted.

Cohen (1979) wrote:

What most children need and can do rather quickly is to develop a sense of trust. They need to feel that the adult in question understands something about what it is like to be a child and can translate verbal and nonverbal messages into adult responses and signals; that the child is indeed being heard; and that even those parts of him which are "bad," painful, or ego dystonic are accepted without criticism or judgment.

p. 505.

Another feature of this type of introduction is the concept of limited confidentiality, or as Cramer (1975) called it, the "relationship of reasonable trust." (p. 2058) Confidentiality in the field of children's mental health, as in that of adult mental health, has some limitations. The child who informs the evaluator that he has intentions of setting his little sister's bed afire or that he is going to eat all of the pills in the medicine cabinet and sleep forever cannot be left to his own devices. In such cases, the evaluator has left himself an opening and may remind the child that this is one of the areas about which maybe his parents should be informed: for example, "Freddie, you seem like a really nice guy, and you and I have had a good time today. I wouldn't want you to do anything that would hurt you or get you into bad trouble. Maybe you and I could talk to mom and dad and see if we can't figure out a way for things to be better so you won't have to hurt yourself."

The reader is again reminded that observation is the primary key to understanding. The play session is a far less structured interview than that of the parents, in which specific historical data are obtained. The child should be allowed to initiate and enter into free play, with the evaluator following the pace of the child. The evaluator who presses too hard or too directly for information and/or rapport is likely to come up empty-handed on both counts. The evaluator who observes and listens may have most of his questions answered without direct intrusion and uncomfortable probing. In fact, if one is able to toss away a predesigned checklist and maintain an open mind and watchful eye, the play session can develop into an experience that is extremely enjoyable for most evaluators and children. If children are aware of the apprehension of those around them, as previously stated, be assured that they are as frequently aware of its counterpart. This ease on the part of the evaluator goes far in establishing rapport, and if toward the end of the session, the evaluator has unanswered questions, the child may be more readily responsive to requests that have come from a new-found friend than from a seemingly obsessed, intrusive stranger.

The assessment of the child begins with the observation of the child's appearance. How is he dressed? Is he smaller or larger than other children his age? Are there any particular physical characteristics that would distinguish him from his peer group?

Observation can also reveal information about the child's neurological processes. This is done by listening to his speech and by watching his play, observing which hand he uses to pick up the puppet and which foot is used to kick the ball, and observing his gait and gross motor coordination. If further investigation is needed at the end of the session, this can often be presented in the form of a game, in which the evaluator may demonstrate an act, such as "finger to nose," and request the child to follow (a neurological "Simon Says").

The House-Tree-Person Test can be of great value in exploring the graphic developmental level and fine motor coordination, as well as in eliciting fantasies from the child and aiding in the assessment of the child's self-image. Often, the introduction of such an activity requires no more than availability of the materials. Crayons and paper openly displayed on a table tend to draw attention before a session ends. Occasionally, the child will request that the evaluator draw. Again, it is important, as in all play with the child, to follow his lead and to gear your production toward his creation. If the evaluator is capable of producing Monets, for this exercise he should satisfy himself with Klees.

As will be discussed in the section on the parent interview, most of the information for the mental status examination can be obtained through observation or as a part of the evaluator's parallel play. For example, children learn by repetition, and this repetition extends into the playroom. A 5-year-old may find great glee in drawing a series of squares (a 5-year-old skill). The evaluator must constantly ask himself, "What do children this age do, and what is this child doing?" There are formal developmental tests and intelligence tests that are easy to administer and can be used in the playroom; however, these usually are not necessary, and through observation alone the evaluator should be able to make some assessment as to the need for formal psychological assessment at a later date.

Just as children learn by repetition, they often tend to repeat daily activities and traumas in the playroom. One may assume that the 5-year-old girl, who in play has the father doll request the little girl doll to pull down her panties so he can play with her "thing," has been exposed to inappropriate sexual stimulation. This is a good example of how play can facilitate the evaluation. If approached directly, the child might be too fearful to reveal her concerns, but in play, she is able to tell you about the dolls and her fear is one step removed. This is also a situation that requires going outside the bounds of the limited confidentiality as previously discussed.

The child will often offer fantasies freely in the playroom and develop elaborate plots and schemes limited only by his creativity. He may create new fantasies for this new environment or he may bring with him his imaginary friends and foes from his private world outside the playroom. Whatever the situation may be, the examination and interpretation of these fantasies must again take into account the age and developmental level of the child

Even if the same crocodile hides under the bed of one small boy between the ages of two to five, the crocodile of the two year old is not the same beast as the crocodile of the five year old—from the psychological point of view. He's had a chance to grow with the boy and is a lot more complex after three years under the bed than he was the day he first moved in. Furthermore, what you do about the crocodile when the boy is two is not the same as what you do about him when the boy is five.

Fraiberg, 1959, p. xi.

When fantasies are not forthcoming, there are several ways in which the evaluator may attempt to elicit them. One of the most popular techniques is asking the child for three wishes. These wishes and the exploration of the wishes not only tap into fantasy material, but also give the child a chance to describe his needs as he perceives them. For example, it is sometimes the case that the first wish for the child of divorced parents is for daddy to come home. This may be the first nonsymbolic information the child has given the evaluator concerning his conflicts, and, as such, the feelings of the child may be more openly explored. The evaluator must, however, develop a sense of how far to proceed with such exploration, lest the child become uncomfortable and end the communication. Reflecting with comments such as, "That must make you feel sad," is less intrusive than comments such as, "I wonder if you think he left because he didn't like you." One has discovered a problem area. It will not be resolved in the evaluation session, and one should be aware of this aspect in determining how deeply he should probe. Never open a wound when you are short of suture. Painful areas are to be recognized by the evaluator, but in-depth explorations are best handled in therapy, where time and a more supportive structure exist.

Another area the evaluator will want to pursue is the method of discipline used within the home. In so doing, one is open not only to the possibility of abuse, but is also evaluating the child's concept of right and wrong. Again, much of this information may be obtained through observation—as with the child who whips the doll and puts it to bed after it has stolen money from mommy. Other areas the clinician might want to investigate may include the child's attitude toward his family, his social relationships, and his thoughts about school.

If the child does not raise the presenting problem as a concern during the session, the evaluator may pick a time when the child seems to be at ease and relating to the interviewer to introduce the topic. After all, the child heard the

parents describe the presenting problem and might well expect that, at some point, this will be an issue. The evaluator's approach must be objective and relay to the child the clinician's desire to be understanding and nonpunitive: for example, "Freddie, I was just thinking, when mom said you hit your brother in the head with a baseball bat, you didn't have much to say. You must have been really angry at Bobby. I wonder what happened?"

Prior to entering the playroom, the evaluator may wish to inform the child of their time limitation. Shortly before the session is to end, the evaluator may remind the child that they have only a few minutes left for play. At this time, the child may be offered the opportunity to ask questions or comment on the session. If the evaluator has already determined that the child is in need of therapy, he may choose to introduce this decision to the child before he is returned to his parents: for example, "Freddie, we had a lot of fun today, and I really enjoyed talking with you and playing. Maybe we could come back to this room again and play and talk some more on another day."

THE PARENT INTERVIEW

The information to be obtained from the parents will vary with each child. There are, however, certain areas of questioning that are applicable and important to most cases.

The evaluator will be interested in hearing the parents' description and history of the presenting problem, and in eliciting any ideas they may have as to etiology. It is then important to explore other areas that may be problematic for the child. For example, parents come for evaluation with a 5-year-old boy with tantrum behavior. They are content and intent on describing how destructive and unmanageable the child has become. While exploring other problem areas, we learn that the child has also been enuretic for several months, after having been successfully toilet trained at age 2 years. Further exploration reveals that the parents have observed other regressed behaviors on the part of the child. He is often found with his 9-month-old sister's bottle and has been noted to scoot and crawl on the floor on occasion. Through exploration of areas the parents consider of little significance, the evaluator may learn a great deal about how this little boy accepted the birth of his sister and may now have a better understanding of the tantrum behavior.

It is important to elicit from the parents strengths they feel their child possesses and areas in which he excels. In so doing, one gets a sense of the parents' attitude and their expectations of the child. Parents who can describe no areas of excellence may well be disengaged from the child. Conversely, it may be the case that children, in whom the evaluator can find few excelling or endearing qualities, are described by the parents in the most glowing terms. Be aware that some families minimize their problems.

Next, one might pursue the developmental history of the child. It is the writer's experience that this pursuit often follows questions concerning the parental courtship when it is revealed that the parents married after a positive pregnancy test. It is important to obtain a clear history of the pregnancy and any problems that may have arisen during the gestation. It is also worthwhile to explore mom's and dad's attitudes upon learning that they were soon to become parents. Mom may have been very bitter that the pregnancy necessitated her dropping out of law school, and she may feel that Freddie is the reason she will never be self-fulfilled, or both parents may view the child as a gift from God, an unexpected, but long-sought blessing after 20 barren years.

Before reviewing the development of the child, it may be wise to familiarize oneself with each developmental stage as explored in earlier chapters, as this is basic and essential information for all individuals intent on working as evaluators and therapists of children. In assessing the pre-school-age child and infant, areas of particular concern would include any traumata of birth, the early mother-child contact and bonding process, and, related to this area, early mode of feeding. (Was the child breast-fed? How did the parents decide upon this particular choice of feeding?)

Table 18-1 may be of assistance in assessing some of the developmental milestones. The milestones and the approximate age of accomplishment are provided. The third column lists the chapter reference, should one desire a more in-depth exploration of development at these ages.

Table 18-1 **Milestone and Approximate Age of Accomplishment**

Milestone	Age	Chapter
Smile	2 months	2
First teeth	6 months	2
Sit	6 months	2
Crawl	10 months	2
Stand	10–12 months	2
Walk	10–14 months	2
First word	9–10 months	2
Sentence (3-word)	18 months	3
Feed self	18 months	3
Toilet trained	2–2½ years	3
Dress self	5 years	4

The evaluator is also interested in obtaining a thorough medical history of the child that will include the following: physical handicaps or disabilities, history of seizure disorders, any major illnesses, and injuries or operations—and the ages at which they occurred and whether or not they necessitated a physical separation from the family unit. The clinician would also seek any history of allergies and the names of any medication the child is taking or has been given in the past.

Likewise, one wants to explore the past psychiatric history of the child and obtain the names of any therapists or agencies who have worked with the child or family prior to this evaluation. One might consider obtaining a written consent from the parents that will allow the evaluator to contact other clinicians to collect data that may help in the final disposition of the case. It sometimes happens that in obtaining such histories, the evaluator learns that this family has sought professional assistance from a number of other clinicians over a brief period of time and were dissatisfied with the recommendations of all consulted. This is valuable information for the evaluator and may help him direct the child in need and his therapist-shopping parents along an appropriate therapeutic avenue.

In an attempt to get as complete a picture of the child as possible, the evaluator will want to explore the child's academic record and school behavior. He will be interested in the parents' description of the child's relationships with his siblings and peers. Through the parents, he will explore activities the child finds particularly fascinating or enjoyable, as well as fears and phobic behavior the child may exhibit. Throughout the interview, the evaluator should be alert to and explore all areas that might indicate that this child falls into the categories previously described as being emergencies.

Having obtained the parents' view of their child and a recounting of his history, one might go on to explore the environment of the child and to learn more about his guardians. A description of family routines, social life, occupations, income, location of the home, and sleeping arrangements will aid the evaluator in his attempt to piece together the tapestry of the child's life. An exploration of the parental relationship and the satisfaction or dissatisfaction found within the marital unit may cue the evaluator to problems that directly affect the child.

The evaluator will want to obtain a history and description of the family background of each parent and, in so doing, learn the child's place in the extended family. A history of family medical, legal, and psychiatric problems is an important part of this exploration, not only in the consideration of possible genetic transmission, but also as influencing factors to the child's development. For example, a 9-year-old boy with a chief complaint of deteriorating academic performance is brought for evaluation by his mother. Mother is intent on centering the exploration on his teacher and her son's peer relationships. Through the investigation of the father's family background, we learn that the father's family is of Eastern European origin and that he maintains very close ties with his mother. We also learn that the father and his family have long been associated with local covens and are deeply involved in "witchcraft." Mother tells us that her son often appears frightened of her husband and admits that the father's behavior sometimes seems irrational. She informs the clinician that, following the birth of their son, her husband fattened the family dog to three times its normal size and then slaughtered it as a sacrifice. We also discover that the 9-year-old has recently learned that following his grandfather's death, his grandmother retained parts of her dead husband's body, which are now preserved in jars and stored in her bedroom. This is a case where a fairly common presenting complaint develops into the macabre and the bizarre. Through routine exploration of the family's background, information was revealed that turned out to be very relevant to the child's behavior.

The evaluator will also want to explore the forms of discipline used within the home as to type, frequency, and effectiveness. One may discover rifts existing between the parents, with the child standing squarely in the middle. For example, after Freddie purposely destroyed the priceless family heirloom, mother sends him to his room for 15 minutes. While she is collecting the pieces from the floor, father enters the child's room, excuses his behavior, and tells him he may go outside to play.

The evaluator will want to make some judgment as to whether punishments are inordinately cruel and inhumane and to always be alert for possible indications of abuse.

Mental Status of the Parents

The primary foci of the parents' interview are the determination of the role of each parent in the child's life, the collecting of history, and determination of the effectiveness of the parenting. It is also necessary, however, to make a psychological assessment of each parent in search of blatant psychopathology that may be influencing the behavior of the child. This of course necessitates a mental status examination.

The inexperienced evaluator is tempted to pursue such an examination with a series of questions specifically designed to illuminate each aspect of the mental status, such as serial 7's, proverbs, and questions related to judgment. When dealing with anxious or guarded parents, such an examination may heighten their anxiety. With many parents, it is possible to obtain this needed information in the process of eliciting historical data. For example, one might remark to father, "What was it you said earlier about Paul's relationship with the neighborhood children?" When he informs you that it was, in fact, his wife who made the comment and then repeats her statement and then gives his own opinion as to the cause of the problem, the evaluator not only gains further insight into the father's perceptions, but also may assume that there is little reason to test father's memory for three objects after 5 minutes. Likewise, a mother who can adequately describe and date the developmental milestones of a 9-year-old in all likelihood would be able to name the last five Presidents.

This method of examination falls within the context of the dialogue and is not disruptive to the interview process. The means of obtaining such information will differ with the individual being interviewed and the style of the evaluator but appears to be effective in all but the most resistant and silent parents, in which case the yield from a formal mental status examination is also likely to be sparse.

DIAGNOSTIC FORMULATION

Having completed the parent and child assessment interviews, the evaluator may want some time alone (or with his co-evaluator if the duties have been shared) to sort through what he has learned, order this information, establish a diagnosis if possible, and arrive at recommendations to be offered the parents and the child. If therapy is seen as necessary, the evaluator must determine the therapeutic milieu that would be the most appropriate for this child and check to see that such therapy is available. He will need to gauge the severity of the problems and decide whether inpatient or outpatient therapy is to be recommended. If the choice is outpatient, he then must decide whether the child would progress most quickly in a day treatment program, individual therapy, or group therapy. The evaluator should also make a determination as to the therapeutic need of the parents. He must evaluate the completeness of his exploration and determine if there are questions that remain to be answered.

Is he satisfied with his neurological examination and medical history, or does the child need to be referred for laboratory testing or neurological or pediatric examination? He must determine whether psychological assessment is warranted and what areas might be explored through formal psychological testing. He must consider the possibility of medications and the benefits or hazards they might present for this particular child. During this brief absence from the family, the evaluator may want to review the initial referral and satisfy himself that he has explored areas that may have seemed particularly significant to the referring source. This is especially important in the case of a court referral, where often very specific (and sometimes impossible) requests are made of the evaluator. These tasks having been completed, the family is invited to rejoin the evaluator(s) in his office.

Presenting the Recommendations

This second joint session, in which the entire family is involved, is often a less tense, more amiable encounter than the first. It is a time when the evaluator will present his recommendations to the parents, and, hopefully, together they will arrive at the final disposition. If the evaluator feels the child and family have no problems that merit therapeutic attention, he will reassure them, tell them of his conclusions, and possibly offer suggestions as to how the family may deal with their concerns. He might then offer further services, if the family should need them at a later date.

When the evaluator has decided that therapy is necessary, he will inform the family of his conclusions and then briefly review the treatment possibilities and availabilities. If several treatment modalities or therapists are available and appropriate, he may want to discuss each with the parents to give them the chance to enter into the decision-making process. The family works best in therapy which is most agreeable to therapy.

The evaluator might then want to elicit the child's and family's views of his recommendations and make certain that they understand all that has

been said. He might want to share with them a "realistic" view of therapy. If this is a situation the evaluator believes will require many months or years of therapy to resolve, he probably would not want the family to depart believing that after the first five sessions their child will be "cured."

The process may end as it began—through contact with the referring source. A brief note acknowledging the referral, stating that the child and family have been evaluated, and then thanking the source for the referral will usually suffice. In some cases, it may be appropriate, with the consent of the family, to give a brief statement of disposition.

Having completed one's first evaluation and having survived the accompanying anxieties and panic, one might relax and take some time to review the entire process, considering the areas that were problematic and singling out techniques that seemed most beneficial in obtaining the desired information. In so doing, one will eventually develop an adeptness and ease that will prepare him for the most unusual and bizarre situations that are likely to be encountered along the road of his professional development.

REFERENCES

Adams, P.L. (1974). *A Primer of Child Psychotherapy.* Boston: Little, Brown & Co.

Carroll, L. (1896). *Through the Looking-Glass and What Alice Found There.* Special Edition. New York: Random House, 1946.

Cohen, R.L. (1979). The clinical examination. In Noshpitz, J. (Ed.), *Basic Handbook of Child Psychiatry,* Vol. 1. New York: Basic Books, pp. 505–508.

Cramer, J.B. (1975). Child psychiatry: Assessment. In Freedman, A.M., Kaplan, H.I., Sadock, B.J. (Eds.), *Comprehensive Textbook of Psychiatry—II,* Vol. 2. Second Edition. Baltimore: Williams and Wilkins.

Fraiberg, S. (1959). *The Magic Years.* New York: Charles Scribner's Sons.

Ginott, H.G. (1964). Problems in the playroom. In Hayworth, M.(Ed.), *Child Psychotherapy.* New York: Basic Books, pp. 125–130.

Johnson, S. (1749). Vanity of human wishes. In Brower, R., Ferry, A.D., Kalstone, D. (Eds.), *In Beginning with Poems—an Anthology.* New York: Norton, 1966, pp. 179–181.

Chapter 19

PARENTAL ASSESSMENT OF EMOTIONAL DISORDERS: In Childhood and Adolescence

Lovick C. Miller, Ph.D.

Assessment of an emotional disorder in childhood and adolescence is seldom based exclusively on information obtained directly from the patient. Generally in physical medicine, diagnosis depends to a great extent on information obtained from the patient (verbal, nonverbal, and laboratory analyses). In child psychiatry the diagnosis relies heavily on secondary and tertiary sources of information, particularly parents and teachers.

Often it is difficult to obtain much more than surface impressions from a diagnostic interview. The broad range of behavioral symptoms, indicative of psychopathology, are seldom directly expressed by the child. Enuresis, encopresis, night terror, stealing, temper tantrums, fighting, academic failure, and truancy, for instance, are behaviors generally known from other sources. Information about the child's ability to relate to others, mastery of social skills, and knowledge of deeper personality structures, such as psychosexual development, self-concepts, and identifications, are usually not forthcoming from the child himself. Empirical research has shown that clinical trainees' ratings of children's adjustment and need for treatment were influenced much more by parents' reports than by filmed segments of the children's playroom behavior. (McCoy, 1976)

Two principal sources of information about the child are parents and teachers. From parents, clinicians usually obtain information about the child's current symptomatic behaviors, history of presenting problems, and the developmental and family history. Teachers provide information on cognitive development, academic skills, relationships with peers and adults, and compliance with social norms. On the basis of all information gathered from the family, school, and child, the clinician arrives at a diagnostic formulation.

Since the 1960's, investigators have been developing systematic procedures for ascertaining the behavior of children at home and in the school.

The purpose of these scientific investigations was to identify empirically syndromes that could serve as a basis for the classification of childhood psychopathology. This research has resulted in the development of a number of inventories for parents and teachers to use to describe the behavior of children in the home and in the classroom. (Peterson, 1961; Dreger *et al.,* 1964; Spivak and Spotts, 1965; Rutter, 1967; Conners, 1969; Sines *et al.,* 1969; Miller, 1972; Achenbach, 1978; Achenback and Edelbrock, 1979)

OVERCONTROLLED AND UNDERCONTROLLED DIMENSIONS

Using multivariant statistics, researchers have been able to reduce a large number of pathological behaviors into their basic dimensions. Achenbach and Edelbrook (1978) have reviewed over 90 scientific articles investigating parent and teacher observations of children's pathognomic behavior. These studies have revealed two broad categories of pathological behavior; overcontrolled and undercontrolled syndromes. Within the overcontrolled syndrome, most studies have isolated the subdimensions of anxiety, depression, social withdrawal, and somatization, while the undercontrolled syndrome includes aggressive, hyperactive, and delinquent behaviors.

In an number of studies, overcontrolled children, as compared with undercontrolled children, performed better in school, on standardized tests, in teacher and peer ratings, and on experimental measures of impulsivity, delay of gratification, and foresight. (Achenbach, 1966; Achenbach and Lewis, 1971; Rolf, 1972; Weintraub, 1973; Rolf and Garmezy, 1974)

Reliability

The test-retest reliability and stability of these syndromes have been acceptable, but the specific behavior symptoms are not constant in different situations. For example, the hyperactive child may be placid in a one-to-one interview, but hyperactive in the classroom. (See chapter 10) Even though children often behave differently in various situations, validity studies have verified the dimensions of these syndromes.

Ross *et al.* (1965) compared the psychopathological classification of boys obtained by using a teacher rating scale and an assessment by clinical psychologists. They found a high level of agreement on the extent of psychopathology in 94% of the aggressive boys and 61% of the withdrawn boys. None of the "well-adjusted" boys (control group) showed psychopathology.

Follow-Up

A follow-up study by Hafner *et al.* (1975) found that overcontrolled children, when matched on demographic variables to undercontrolled ones, performed better in school, completed more grades, more frequently finished high school, had more friends, and were rated higher on mental health ratings. Overcontrolled males as adults had better job stability, higher socioeconomic status, fewer encumbrances, fewer marriages and divorces. Thus, it would seem that the behavioral patterns isolated by parent and teacher ratings of children's behavior have demonstrated a strong reliability and validity based upon empirical research and have provided a base for an empirical classification system for children's emotional disorders.

LOUISVILLE BEHAVIOR CHECKLIST (LBC)

The Louisville Behavior Checklist (LBC) (Miller, 1967, 1977) is an inventory of behaviors designed to help parents identify and communicate concerns about their children. The inventory covers an extensive range of social and emotional behaviors, from competency to deviancy, for assessing psychopathological disorders. The outcome of the parental responses provides clinicians with an overview of the child's deviant behavior and significant information for arriving at a clinical diagnosis.

LBC is available in three different forms covering ages 3 to 18 years:

1. Form E1—age range 3 to 6 years
2. Form E2—age range 7 to 12 years
3. Form E3—age range 13 to 18 years

LBC consists of 164 items of deviant and prosocial behavior, 97 of which appear in all three forms. Items have been written to be answered either true (T) or false (F) by the child's parent. Personal pronouns are not used except for sex-specific items, so that the same checklist is used for both boys and girls. The sex-specific items have parts designated "For Boys Only" and "For Girls Only." Currently, 35 scales have been constructed for the three forms of the LBC. These scales are as follows:

A. *Scales available for Forms E1 and E2:*
   1. Infantile aggression (Ia)—describes egocentric, emotionally demanding, and interpersonally belligerent behavior.
   2. Hyperactivity (Ha)—refers to impulsive and constant motion involving both large and small muscles.
   3. Antisocial behavior (As)—describes illegal and destructive behavior where the main thrust is against property, person, self, and others.
   4. Aggression (AG)—a broad-band factor scale composed of items from the previous three narrow-band factor scales (scales 1, 2, and 3).
   5. Social withdrawal (Sw)—describes an apparent reluctance to interact with others and a preference for social isolation and lack of involvement.
   6. Sensitivity (Sn)—describes a disability characterized by a subjective sense of "unlikeableness," combined with a tendency to cope with stress with a combination of somatizing, impulsive, immature, and rivalrous behaviors.
   7. Fear (Fr)—refers to manifest anxiety focalized around multiple objects with special concern over sleep, death, and assuring the availability of a companion.
   8. Inhibition (IN)—a broad-band factor scale composed of items from the previous three narrow-band factor scales (scales 5, 6, and 7).
   9. Immaturity (Im)—refers to both social and physical processes; for example, babyishness, dependency, whining, slow physical growth, and clumsy, poor coordination.
   10. Normal irritability (Ni)—describes noxious behaviors reported to occur in at least 25% of the general population.
   11. Prosocial deficit (Pd)—scale composed of behaviors highly valued by society, such as "relaxed and able to concentrate," "able to study and meet school requirements," and "has a good sense of right and wrong." Items are counted when marked "False" to show a deficit in prosocial behavior.

12. Rare deviance (Rd)—describes noxious behaviors reported to occur in less than 1 to 3.5% of the general population.

13. Neurotic behavior (Neu)—contains items traditionally assumed to indicate a psychoneurotic process, such as phobias, obsessions, compulsions, depression and the use of tranquilizers.

14. Psychotic behavior (Psy)—contains items traditionally assumed to indicate a psychotic process, including uncontrolled behavior, such as smearing of feces, echolalia, lack of speech, excessive seclusiveness, and unresponsiveness.

15. Somatic behavior (Som)—indicates somatic dysfunction related to brain damage or psychic stress; for example, epilepsy, periods of unconsciousness, headaches, stomachaches, or asthma. The scale includes items reflecting both structural and functional disability.

16. Sexual behavior (Sex)—indicates unusual and generally unacceptable sexual behavior.

17. Severity level (SL)—a broad-band scale composed of all noxious and pathogenic behaviors on the inventory minus the normal irritability and intellectual deficit items.

B. *Scales available for Form E1 Only:*

18. Intellectual deficit (Id)—reports failure to master age-specific cognitive tasks, such as color recognition, knowing right from left hand, being able to read simple words and to add simple number.

19. Cognitive disability (CD)—a broad-band factor scale composed of items from the two previous narrow-band factor scales Im (no. 9) and Id (no. 18).

20. School disturbance predictor (SDp)—composed of items that describe children whom teachers are most likely to consider disturbed or disturbing.

Form E2: this scale is under construction and is not currently available.

C. *Scales available for Form E2 only:*

21. Academic disability (Ad)—reports specific deficits in academic skill and abilities commonly associated with learning failures.

22. Learning disability (LD)—broad-band factor scale composed of items from the previous two narrow-band factor scales Im (no. 9) and Ad (no. 21).

D. *Scales available for Form E3 only:*

23. Egocentric-exploitive (E-E)—a bipolar dimension ranging from an egocentric, exploitive pole to an allocentric, altruistic pole.

24. Destructive-assaultive (D-A)—measures anger expressed physically and verbally against persons and property. A person high on this scale would be potentially dangerous or violent.

25. Social delinquency (SD)—classifies illegal behavior as well as behavior that flouts social norms and mores.

26. Adolescent turmoil (AT)—describes an agitated state frequently associated with the adolescent years. This scale combines a mixture of internalizing and externalizing mechanisms for handling internal tensions and conflicts.

27. Apathetic isolation (AI)—describes a tendency to withdraw into oneself and to avoid participation in social activities.

28. Neuroticism (Neu)—a general neuroticism scale that combines manifest anxiety, obsessive-compulsive mechanisms with depression and somatic complaints.

29. Dependent-inhibited (D-I)—describes dependent, inhibited, immature behaviors that combine a lack of self-confidence with a tendency to give in to others.

30. Academic disability (AD)—reflects a lack of interest and poor performance in school.

31. Neurological or psychotic abnormality (NPA)—combines items reflecting central nervous system instability and symptoms of psychosis. The scale describes diverse and bizarre behaviors.

32. General pathology (G)—a scale made up of items that are associated with most forms of pathology, but do not define any specific type.

33. Longitudinal (Lon)—traces the longitudinal course of manifest symptoms from ages 3 to 18 years.

34. Severity level scale (SL)—a scale made up of all items which a panel of expert clinicians judged to reflect a moderate to severe level of pathology.

35. Total pathology (TP)—answers to all 164 items on the inventory are summed to provide a total score for pathology.

Scoring for Behavioral Dimensions

Many professionals will simply wish to scan the protocol quickly to gain an overview of the child's behavior and to insure that significant deviant behaviors have not been overlooked during the initial interviews. For those who wish to scan the checklist, prosocial items have been located at numbers ending in the digit "5," with the exception of items 15, 65, and 115. By scanning the numbers ending in "5," an examiner can gain an insight into the parent's view of the child's positive assets.

Thirty items in Form E1 and 30 in Form E2, reflecting more extreme deviant behaviors, have been selected for particular scrutiny and appear on the back of the answer sheet.

To obtain behavioral dimensions, the protocols can either be scored by hand or optical scan machines. Scores on each scale are transformed to standard scores and plotted to obtain a behavioral profile. This profile provides a picture of the child's emotional and behavioral pathology.

Two different norm groups are available for LBC scales, a General Population norm (Miller *et al.*, 1971) and a Standard Clinical Population norm. The General Population norms reflect the amount of pathology in the average child of the same age and sex in the general population. Most children referred for clinical evaluation will place above the 90th percentile of the general population on many scales.

The reader is referred to the Louisville Behavior Checklist manual (Miller, 1981) for a detailed discussion of test development and development of General Population norms. Standard Clinical Population norms were obtained by taking all available protocols referred to the Child Psychiatric Services, University of Louisville School of Medicine, and to the Psychology Section of the Jefferson County Juvenile Detention Center. This sample included 941 children for E1, 634 for E2, and 272 for E3. Several studies of referrals to the clinical service in subsequent years have shown the norms to be stable. The Standard Clinical Population norm appears to be a stable index of pathological symptoms for children referred for psychiatric care.

Reliability

Research has shown that the scales are also reliable within acceptable limits. (Miller *et al.*, 1972) Two methods for assessing reliability have shown that the items within the scales are internally consistent and that when the child is re-evaluated 6 weeks after initial assessment, parents report the same pathology. There is one exception to these general findings, and that is that some children's pathology is variable, so that for a few children there is considerable change within a very short period of time. Whether this is due to instability of behavior within children or parent judgment cannot be determined with this instrument.

Validity

How do we know that what the parents say about their children is valid? Parents are biased about their children's positive and negative behaviors and lack experience with large groups of children for comparison. Observations reported on the checklist represent to a certain extent the prejudices of the parents. The score on any scale is at once a reflexion of the parent as well as the child.

On the other hand, the parent has information about the child which is totally unknown to any other adult. The parents observe the child in the intimacy of the family over a 24-hour period, 7 days a week, over a period of years. This knowledge of the child is very valuable, for not only is some of it not available from any other source, but it represents bits of personality that emerge in close, intimate relationships. Thus, parents are not only biased about their children, but they also know their children in very personal ways and know things about their children known to no one else.

So, back to the original question! How do we know that the parents' observations are valid? A number of studies have been done to answer some of the validity questions. For example, we would expect that children diagnosed at a psychiatric clinic as emotionally disturbed would be rated higher on the checklist than children in the general population. This turns out to be true. We would also expect children treated on an inpatient service to manifest more problems than those treated on an outpatient basis, and this is also true. We would also expect that children sent to juvenile court would manifest more aggressive behavior than would patients on an inpatient psychiatric service, while those on a psychiatric ward would manifest more anxiety, neurotic and psychotic behavior than adjudicated delinquents. All of these expectations turn out to be so.

In a study, the LBC's of 18 autistic children were abnormally high. The primary disturbances were in the areas of social withdrawal, academic disability, immaturity, and rare deviance, behavioral deficits most typically reflecting the primary symptoms of infantile autism. In this study, the findings lend strong support to the validity of the LBC.

It would be expected that children rated disturbed by a teacher or clinician would also be rated disturbed by a parent. However, children often manifest serious problems at school that are not seen in the home, and vice versa. The correlation between parents' and teachers' observations about children are generally positive, but they also tend to be low. Observers also tend to agree more on some types of behaviors, like academic performance, than on others, like anxiety. This is to be expected, because anxiety is usually evoked in specific situations, while the failure to acquire academic skills is generally recognized by both parent and teacher alike.

Clinicians have found it necessary to take information from many sources from which a mosaic of the child's behavior and attitudes can be formed. Such a behavioral profile is compiled only after an extensive diagnostic study. In so doing, it is assumed that the truth does not lie in one particular source, but in multiple sources of information. The LBC is one way to obtain information about the child.

In general, parents will rate children diagnosed as disturbed higher on LBC scales than parents of children from the general population. However, some parents of disturbed children will not report disturbances in their child. One of the least pathological protocols ever reported was given by a parent of a severely abused child. This parent, who was under court investigation for abuse, checked all prosocial items "yes," and did not check one single pathognomic response on the entire checklist. Parents also for other reasons minimize pathology in their children. Parents are a valuable source of information about their children in general, but in specific instances, this might not be the case.

Clinical Usefulness of the LBC

The LBC has proved useful in many situations. It is excellent as a screening device for identifying emotional disturbances in children. When a problem is suspected, a checklist that covers the universe of emotional and behavioral problems is extremely helpful, since it takes too much time to ask parents about all aspects of a child's behavior. The general efficiency of a diagnostic evaluation can be increased by having the parents fill out the checklist at home and return it by mail, so that symptomatic behavior can be ascertained before the initial contact. In intact families, the viewpoints of both the father and the mother can be compared. Sometimes these are congruent and other times at variance, a fact that alerts the clinician to differences of opinion between parents which might constitute a significant aspect of the child's problem. Children over 12 can also fill out the checklist themselves, which gives still another view of the child's behavior. Often there are real surprises because children will admit to behaviors unknown to their parents, but which need to be known to a professional. On the other hand, children will deny many things that parents observe. The instrument is particularly useful for busy pediatricians or social case workers who need to know about the emotional and behavioral life of the patient, but has neither the time nor clinical training to ascertain this information in depth.

Clinical Studies

The following cases were selected from approximately 2,000 patients with completed LBC's at Child Psychiatric Services, University of Louisville School of Medicine. The cases have been selected to show a wide range of disorders over the entire age span from 3 to 18 and to indicate the variety of patterns of childhood psychopathology that emerges on the LBC. In addition, the cases are illustrative of personality types that clinical experience and cluster analysis have indicated to represent types of childhood psychopathology.

The profiles are based upon the clinical population norms on which a scale score of 50 represents the average score for a child referred to a psychiatric service and a score of 45 represents the beginning range of pathology.

An Oppositional-Aggressive Child

Clara is a 6-year-old white female, the only child from a divorced family. She is currently living with her mother who has been divorced twice. She was referred for extreme aggressiveness toward peers, having tried to strangle a playmate. She spends most of her time with babysitters. She is described as "driven" and thought to have strong unmet dependency needs. There is evidence that her mother's second husband was abusive, both to Clara and her mother. Clara has developed good cognitive skills, obtaining a Full Scale IQ of 105, and has acquired academic skills up to the middle of the first grade. Her clinical diagnosis was *oppositional disorder.*

In the LBC, Clara presents a profile with elevations on all the aggressive scales (Figure 19-1). Only 16% of the children presenting to the Psychiatric Service have been seen as more aggressive. She is most aggressive in an infantile and oppositional way, but she is also hyperactive and manifests considerable antisocial behavior. She shows few inhibition symptoms, indicating that there is very little internalized conflict. She also shows few signs of intellectual or emotional immaturity. Her total disability scale is 48, suggestive that her aggressive behaviors are quite representative of her way of coping with stress and solving interpersonal conflicts. Prognosis for this type of profile is not good and the elevated social disability predictor scale (not shown) suggests high probability of behavior problems at school. Offsetting these dour predictions is her good cognitive development in the face of considerable deprivation, which may help her to deal with difficulties as she grows older.

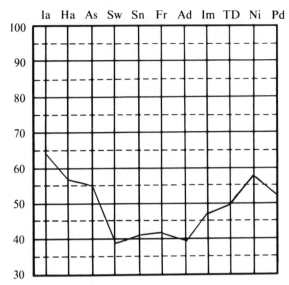

Figure 19-1 LBC profile of Clara, a 6-year-old white aggressive female.

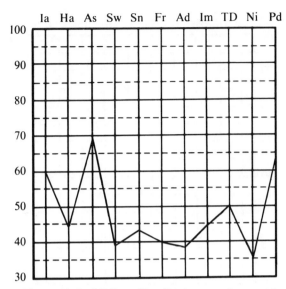

Figure 19-2 LBC profile of Robert, an 8-year-old white aggressive male.

An Unsocialized-Aggressive Child

Robert is an 8-year-old white male referred to a child psychiatric inpatient setting for fire-setting, aggressive behavior, and running away. He had been removed from his home because of possible abuse. He "hates" his mother, who deserted the family when he was very young. He has been placed in a series of foster homes, including his grandmother's, which did not work out because of her drinking. He was diagnosed as *unsocialized aggressive.* After discharge from the hospital, while he was placed in a "Behavior Disorder" school, he adapted well and made good grades. However, when discharged to his father, they both dropped out of recommended outpatient therapy.

The LBC showed the highest elevations in *antisocial behavior, infantile aggression,* and *prosocial deficit* (Figure 19-2). All forms of aggressive behavior, except hyperactivity, are exhibited by this child, including the failure to develop adequate interpersonal coping skills. He steals, sets fires, runs away, disobeys, and is abusive to others. He is not inhibited nor does he have academic or immaturity problems. He seems to believe that to survive in this life, it is necessary to suppress one's emotions and take what is needed or wanted.

A Hyperactive-Anxious Child

Jan, a 10-year-old black female, was referred for rebellious and aggressive behavior as well as fear of the dark. She is the seventh of eight children, whose father recently died of a heart attack. Also, her mother was recently hospitalized

for by-pass surgery because of obesity. Jan has many friends and is very popular with her classmates. She still has unresolved anger over the death of her father. She was diagnosed as having an *adjustment disorder with mixed emotional features.*

This is a rather unusual LBC profile, for it combines *hyperactivity* with *fear* (Figure 19-3). Hyperactivity is more typically associated with aggressive behavior, but Jan does not appear aggressive at home. Rather, she is perceived as more socially withdrawn, sensitive, and anxious. Her mother also notes that she is having problems in the academic area. Overall, the number of symptoms is below average for a clinical population.

Hyperactivity accompanied by elevation in the inhibition area suggests that the hyperactivity is not related to organicity, but reflects internal conflicts. Further, the nature of the problem does not appear to be severe and the prognosis is good if proper treatment is utilized.

A Case of Adolescent Turmoil

Elaine is a 15-year-old white female from a wealthy, intact family. Elaine was referred for being out of control, having violent and at times dangerous temper tantrums, and running away from home. The last time, she stayed out all night with a boyfriend. She is described as being charming out of the home, but a devil at home. She opposes everything her parents stand for, dresses and talks crudely, and makes friends with peers having antisocial values. She is failing in school.

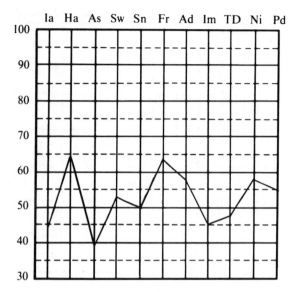

Figure 19–3 LBC profile of Jan, a 10-year-old black hyperactive-anxious female.

Elaine is in constant conflict with her younger sister and goes out of her way to break parental rules.

According to her parents, as an infant she had a terrible temper, which was aggravated by the birth of her younger sister. She would scream for 6 to 7 hours at a stretch, refuse to sleep or to be touched, become rigid, red in the face, and glassy-eyed. Pediatric evaluation revealed no physical basis for her behavior, but she convinced her parents that she was a "special" child. She was reared with her parents being constantly afraid to cross her, lest they activate her temper. By age 5, she was a model child, which continued until age 12. Father said she was so beautiful and charming that the parents constantly exhibited her to family and friends before excusing her from adult company. Around puberty, Elaine made what her father called a "180-degree change."

Elaine was in a private school with high academic standards, which she found difficult to reach. This was understandable, since her verbal IQ was 105. However, she was able to read on a 12th grade level, although her arithmetic skills were limited.

Elaine received outpatient psychotherapy, which helped for a while, but she became more involved with drugs and a delinquent male. She passed out on drugs one night on the street and was taken by police to a psychiatric hospital. She was diagnosed as manic-depressive, but removed on the advice of her outpatient therapist, rehospital-ized, and diagnosed as *adolescent turmoil.* She stabilized, went away to a boarding school, and then one year later returned improved to her family. Two years later, she was maintaining successful gains.

Figure 19-4 shows the LBC profile of Elaine as completed by her and her father. Elaine's self-profile approximates her clinical picture and contrasts sharply with her father's rating. Elaine admits to a total pathology considerably above the clinical mean with a high level of severity. Her highest score was on the NP scale, which indicated a lack of impulse control and considerable impulsive acting out, perhaps at a psychotic level. This was associated with elevation of the *neurotic scale* and *social delinquency scale.* She also showed mild elevations on *egocentrism* and *destructive-assaultive,* but denied problems in the academic area and said that she was not apathetic or dependent. This is a record of an impulsive, anxious, socially delinquent adolescent who is crying for help, but biting the hands that extend that help.

Her father, despite his plea for help, sees very few problems. His profile of Elaine is marked by low total disability and severity scores. He sees the primary problem as academic and admits to some lack of impulse control with an NP Scale of 50. However, every other scale is below the pathological range. It is particularly striking how unaware the father is of his daughter's internal pain and

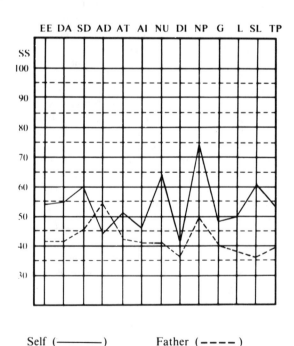

Self (———)   Father (– – – –)

Figure 19–4 LBC profile of Elaine, a 15-year-old female, with self- and father's rating.

conflicts. In a diagnostic interview, the father admitted to suspicions of most of the behaviors that Elaine described on the LBC, but he would not codify them on the checklist. It is difficult to know why the father denied so much of his daughter's behavior, but the profile is presented to illustrate that false negative protocols can be obtained even when parents recognize problems and seek help for their children.

A Case of Withdrawal and Depression

Tom is a 12-year-old white male referred for being generally apathetic and underachieving at school. Tom is the older of two brothers and lives with his mother and adoptive father. He used to like school, but now does not. He particularly dislikes mathematics. He has had no friends until last year, when he finally developed a relationship with another youngster. He is seen as having strong dependency needs and was diagnosed as *withdrawing reaction of childhood*. He had a Full Scale IQ of 109 and was reading at a seventh grade level, but only doing 5th grade work in arithmetic.

The LBC suggests a severe social withdrawal and immaturity accompanied by academic disability (Figure 19-5). There is little indication of aggressive problems or of manifest anxiety or sensitivity. Tom appears to be a child who is very inhibited in interpersonal relationships and this inhibition also affects his ability to invest himself in academic learning. From psychological testing, it was possible to rule out central nervous dysfunction, which lends support to the hypothesis that his learning problems are an indication of an underlying depression.

A Case of Academic Disability

Mike is a 7-year-old white male referred for school failure, compounded by a speech impediment. He is the youngest of four children in an intact, middle-class family. He has failed the first grade twice. He worries about his parents' fights, but otherwise manifests no serious personality problems. He has a Full Scale IQ of 90 and showed severe visual-motor impairment on the Visual-Motor Integration test. Achievement tests indicated a reading and spelling capacity in the middle of the first grade, with a second grade achievement level in arithmetic.

The LBC indicates that the primary problem is in the *academic area* with elevations on the *normal irritability* and *prosocial deficit* (Figure 19-6). This indicates he is manifesting an above-average number of behaviors that are quite typical of this age group and that he has not developed adequate social coping skills. He shows some immature behaviors that are frequently associated with learning disabilities. He demonstrates no problems in the areas of aggression or inhibition, except for a very slight tendency toward social withdrawal. Currently, Mike is having problems acquiring academic and social skills. Prognosis is not good, although in recent years, educational specialists have made considerable progress diagnosing and treating these types of disorders.

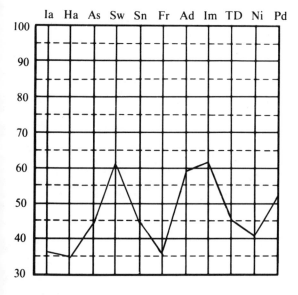

Figure 19-5 LBC profile of Tom, a 12-year-old white depressed male.

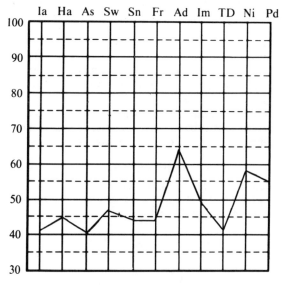

Figure 19-6 LBC profile of Mike, a 7-year-old white male with a learning disability.

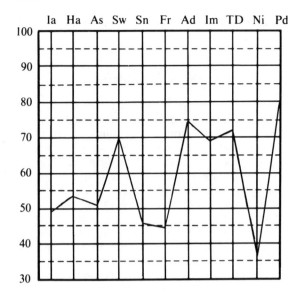

Figure 19-7 LBC profile of Susan, a 4-year-old retarded epileptic female with autistic features.

A Case of Autism-Psychosis

Susan, a 4-year-old white female, was referred for neglect, deprivation, and abuse. She is currently living in a foster home, following removal from the care of her divorced mother. Susan does not talk, has poor eye contact, eats everything, walks on toes, appears unaware of her surroundings, smears feces, and does not like to be touched. Epilepsy was diagnosed at age 11 months and mental retardation at age 3 years. She also manifested many features that suggested a diagnosis of *Autism*.

In the LBC profile, almost every scale is above 45 (Figure 19-7). This indicates severe pathology. In addition, the total disability scale is 71 and the prosocial deficit 80. This means that Susan has fewer social skills than 100% of the children evaluated in this psychiatric service. What cannot be seen from this profile is that the *rare deviance scale* was 60, the *psychotic scale*, 73, and the *somatic scale*, 82. These elevations suggest extreme disturbance, although the *aggressive* and *anxiety scales* are comparably low.

REFERENCES

Achenbach, T.M. (1966). The classification of children's psychiatric symptoms: A factor-analytic study. *Psychol. Monogr., 80,* (whole #615).

Achenbach, T.M. (1978). The child behavior profile: I. Boys aged 6–11. *J. Consult. Clin. Psychol., 46,* 478–488.

Achenbach, T.M., Lewis, M. (1971). A proposed model for clinical research and its application to encopresis and enuresis. *J. Am. Acad. Child Psychiatry, 10,* 535–554.

Achenbach, T.M., Edelbrock, C.S. (1978). The classification of child psychopathology: A review and analysis of empirical efforts. *Psychol. Bull., 85,* 1275–1301.

Achenbach, T.M., Edelbrock, C.S. (1979). The child behavior profile: II. Boys aged 12–16 and girls aged 6–11 and 12–16. *J. Consult. Clin. Psychol., 47,* 223–233.

Conners, C.K. (1969). A teacher rating scale for use in drug studies with children. *Am. J. Psychiatry, 126,* 884–888.

Dreger, R.M., Lewis, P.M., Rich, T.A., Miller, K.S., Reid, M.P., Overlade, D.C., Taffel, C., Fleming, E.L. (1964). Behavioral classification project. *J. Consult. Psychol., 28,* 1–13.

Hafner, A.J., Quast, W., Shea, M.J. (1975). The adult adjustment of one thousand psychiatric and pediatric patients: Initial findings from a twenty-five-year follow-up. In Wirt, R.D., Winokur, G., Roff, M. (Eds.), *Life History Research in Psychopathology, 4.* Minneapolis: University of Minnesota.

McCoy, S.A. (1976). Clinical judgments of normal childhood behavior. *J. Consult. Clin. Psychol., 5,* 710–714.

Miller, L.C. (1967). Louisville behavior checklist for males, 6–12 years of age. *Psychol. Rep., 21,* 885–896.

Miller, L.C. (1972). School behavior checklist: An inventory of deviant behavior for elementary school children. *J. Consult. Clin. Psychol., 38,* 134–144.

Miller, L.C. (1977, 1981). *Louisville Behavior Checklist Manual.* Los Angeles: Western Psychological Services.

Miller, L.C., Hampe, I.E., Barrett, C.L., Noble, H. (1971). Children's deviant behavior within the general population. *J. Consult. Clin. Psychol., 37,* 16–22.

Miller, L.C., Hampe, E., Barrett, C.L., Noble, H. (1972). Test-retest reliability of parent ratings of children's deviant behavior. *Psychol. Rep., 31,* 249–250.

Peterson, D.R. (1961). Behavior problems of middle childhood. *J. Consult. Psychol., 25,* 205–209.

Rolf, J.E. (1972). The social and academic competence of children vulnerable to schizophrenia and other behavior pathologies. *J. Abnorm. Psychol., 80,* 225–243.

Rolf, J.E., Garmezy, N. (1974). The school performance of children vulnerable to behavior pathology. In Ricks, D., Thomas, A., Rolf, M. (Eds.), *Life History Research in Psychopathology, 3.* Minneapolis: University of Minnesota.

Ross, A.O., Lacey, H.M., Parton, D.A. (1965). The development of a behavior checklist for boys. *Child Dev., 36,* 1013–1027.

Rutter, M. (1967). A children's behavior questionnaire for completion by teachers: Preliminary findings. *J. Child Psychol. Psychiatry, 8,* 1–11.

Spivack, G., Spotts, J. (1965). The Devereux child behavior scale: Symptom behaviors in latency age children. *Am. J. Ment. Defic., 69,* 839–853.

Sines, J.O., Pauker, J.D., Sines, L.K., Owen, D.R. (1969). Identification of clinically relevant dimensions of children's behavior. *J. Consult. Clin. Psychol., 33,* 728–734.

Weintraub, S.A. (1973). Self-control as a correlate of an internalizing and externalizing symptom dimension. *J. Abnorm. Child Psychol., 1,* 292–307.

Chapter 20

PSYCHOLOGICAL ASSESSMENT OF CHILDREN AND ADOLESCENTS

Richard J. Cowen, Ph.D.

Billy R., the 8-year old son of Mr. and Mrs. R., has been having difficulties in many areas: he sometimes wets his bed at night, he does not obey his parents, he fights with siblings and peers, he is disruptive and unable to sit still in class, and he does not perform up to academic potential. From his parents' and teacher's viewpoints, Billy's problems span several key areas: interpersonal, academic, and familial.

As a result of her concerns, Mrs. R. contacts a child guidance clinic to request an evaluation, with the hope that her family and Billy's school may ultimately be helped in dealing with Billy's problems. The remainder of this chapter deals with intermediary steps in the evaluation process (i.e., between the time Billy is referred to when a final disposition is made), from the standpoint of *psychological assessment*.

To maximize chances of devising an effective and meaningful intervention for Billy, it is first necessary to have a thorough understanding of his presenting problems and the circumstances under which they occur. Psychological assessment is one important means of gathering such data.

There are two major approaches to psychological assessment: traditional and behavioral, each with somewhat different assumptions. The traditional approach assumes that each child has a unique "personality," consisting of a core of relatively stable characteristics, and that one must go beyond observed behavior to understand the child. By contrast, behavioral assessment emphasizes current behavior and seeks to identify and understand variables "...currently maintaining an individual's maladaptive thoughts, feelings, and behaviors." (O'Leary and Wilson, 1975)

TRADITIONAL PSYCHOLOGICAL ASSESSMENT

Maloney and Ward (1976) describe psychological assessment as "...*a process of solving problems (answering questions)* in which psychological tests are often used as *one* of the methods of collecting relevant data." (p. 5) The clinician, rather than particular tests, is at the center of the traditional psychological assessment process. The ultimate task is to conceptualize questions to be answered, techniques to be used, and to integrate findings into a meaningful, coherent whole to promote maximally effective intervention on the child's behalf. (Korchin, 1976) In addition to psychological testing, other relevant assessment procedures include: obtaining the parent interview and history material, the mental status examination, and getting additional information from relevant community sources (e.g., school, scouting). (See chapters 18 and 19)

Parent Interview

This is a frequent first step in traditional child psychological assessment. Initially the child and his or her parents (and, perhaps, siblings) are asked to come in for an evaluation. Although different clinics vary in their format, one is to have the whole family seen together for a "joint interview" in order to begin exploring presenting problems. During the interview the reaction of each family member to the situation is observed. The clinician notes such factors as patterns of communication and interaction, who leads the family conversation, who is excluded, and who sits where to understand the family better from a systems perspective.

Next, the parents are interviewed alone to obtain a history of presenting problems. Additional information, for example, might be needed about the nature, frequency, and severity of Billy's fighting, how long it has been going on, when it started, and how it is handled.

The developmental history is another important piece of data, focusing on such areas as the mother's pregnancy and delivery, whether there were complications at birth, early infancy and developmental milestones, play patterns, social relations during childhood, traumas or crises for the child and other family members, moves, hospitalizations, and deaths. A medical history of the child (and that of other family members) is also desirable, including operations, accidents, illnesses, current medications and dosages. Hereditary conditions in the extended family are documented, as is any past psychiatric history, with dates, names, outcomes, and social and community agencies involved. Finally, a social family history is obtained, including information about the parents' own childhoods, their marriage, their communication patterns, and their methods of discipline.

In addition to factual material obtained, it is important to form subjective impressions of the parents as people, such as their capacity for parenting and their motivations for bringing their child to the clinic at this time. These impressions ultimately contribute to a final understanding of the patient's presenting problem within a total context.

Child-Interview—Mental Status Examination

Next in the assessment process, the child is seen individually by the examiner. Although such an interview may be conducted in the examiner's office, it is frequently more useful to see children Billy's age and younger in a playroom equipped with various toys and play materials. Young children tend to express themselves more naturally through play than by words. Developmentally, children are not at a stage where their thoughts and feelings are as readily accessible to them as are adults. A strategically equipped playroom includes such items as dolls (male and female) and a dollhouse, paper, crayons, an easel and paints, a blackboard, a telephone, a stuffed Bobo doll, water, guns with rubber tipped darts, trucks, and cars. The nature of the child's play, the toys he chooses, his play sequence, and shifts in his play or talk are all relevant to understanding him.

The mental status examination is an important way of organizing and summarizing information obtained about the child in the interview setting. Clinical impressions and judgments are made on the basis of appearance and behavior, relationship with the examiner, the nature of the child's thought processes, mood and affect, judgment and insight, orientation and intellectual functioning. Although the mental status examination is subjective and nonstandardized, it nevertheless yields important information on the

patient's "mental systems" and current functioning levels.

Other Data

Wherever feasible, it is helpful to collect additional relevant information from the school and other community agencies about the child. This information may come via verbal report, direct observation, or written records. For example, teacher accounts and descriptions of classroom behavior, peer relations, and academic performance may be useful in extending the boundaries of the diagnostic formulation to another significant domain. Equally relevant, particularly with developmentally delayed children, are findings provided by other professions, e.g., audiology, nutrition, reading, speech and hearing. This is of prime importance in developing a comprehensive treatment plan. (Magrab, 1976)

Psychological Tests

Psychological tests represent *one* method of collecting important information in the overall assessment process of children. Maloney and Ward (1976) consider that psychological testing is to psychological assessment as a tool is to a process (pp. 35–36), and they caution about equating the two. From one case to another, the relative importance of psychological tests in the overall assessment procedure may vary greatly, in that psychological tests represent only one of a series of different procedures.

Traditional approaches to psychological assessment include both cognitive and projective tests. The former consist primarily of intelligence and academic achievement measures, most of which are objective and standardized, with empirically determined norms for interpretation of individual scores. The assumption behind this type of test is that children are different on different measurable dimensions, which can be described and measured by particular tests. For purposes of clarity, tests of visual-motor coordination and integration will also be included in this general category.

Projective tests and tests of personality and emotional functioning are necessarily more subjective and less well-structured instruments. They are based on the premise that children reveal important aspects of their personality in the unique way they respond to and structure relatively unstructured material.

Given Billy's presenting difficulties, and assuming that mental status (child interview), parent interview and history, and other data have already been obtained, it is important to have additional information regarding his visual-motor, intellectual, academic, and personality functioning. Particular questions or hypotheses include: "Is there an organic component to Billy's difficulties?" or "Is there a discrepancy between his potential and achievement levels?"

An appropriate test battery might include a Bender-Gestalt or Developmental Test of Visual-Motor Integration (DTVMI), Wechsler Intelligence Scale for Children-Revised (WISC-R), Wide Range Achievement Test (WRAT), Rorschach, Thematic Apperception Test (TAT), or Children's Apperception Test (CAT), and human figure drawing. Below is a brief description of these and other psychological tests employed with children.

Visual-Motor and Visual-Perceptual Tests

BENDER VISUAL-MOTOR GESTALT TEST. (Bender, 1938) This measure is used to assess the degree of intactness and integration of visual perception and motor behavior in children. The Bender-Gestalt is also often used in screening for oganicity. It consists of nine cards, each containing an abstract geometrical design. The child is presented the cards, individually and in sequence, and told to copy the designs on a blank sheet of paper. The nature and frequency of "errors" made (typical ones include rotation of the figures, perseveration, and defects of integration) give a measure of visual-motor coordination and often an index of possible neurological dysfunction. Normative data are available (Koppitz, 1964) for children from age 5 upward.

DEVELOPMENTAL TEST OF VISUAL-MOTOR INTEGRATION. (Beery and Buktenica, 1967) This test is sometimes used in lieu of the Bender-Gestalt to assess the same abilities, especially in younger children or in cases of suspected mental retardation. The DTVMI can be administered by cards or in booklet form. However, the figures are at lower (less complex) levels than those of the Bender-Gestalt. Hence, DTVMI norms are also lower than the Bender's, extending between ages 2 and 10 to 16.

FROSTIG DEVELOPMENTAL TEST OF VISUAL PERCEPTION. (Frostig *et al.,* 1966) This test is used to assess nonverbal functions, such as spatial relations, eye-hand coordination, and figure-ground relations, which are not extensively tapped by conventional intelligence tests.

Intelligence Tests

Although there is no universally accepted definition of the concept of "intelligence," Wechsler has proposed measuring *abilities* that combine to make up intelligence, i.e., "...the aggregate or global capacity of the individual to act purposefully, to think rationally and to deal effectively with his environment." (1958, p. 7) The WISC-R is one of the major current tests of intelligence, or general ability, for children between the ages of 6 and 17.

WECHSLER INTELLIGENCE SCALE FOR CHILDREN-REVISED. (Wechsler, 1974) A recently revised version of the WISC, the WISC-R, is an intelligence scale originally published by Wechsler (1949).

The WISC-R consists of twelve subtests, six which comprise the verbal scale (information, similarities, arithmetic, vocabulary, comprehension, and digit span) and six of which make up the performance scale (picture completion, picture arrangement, block design, object assembly, coding, and mazes). each subtest measures a different ability and contributes toward an overall measure of "intelligence."

Below follows a description and rationale of the individual WISC-R subtests.

A. Verbal scale
1. Information—consists of 30 items covering a wide range of general factual information (e.g., "What are the four seasons of the year?"; "Who invented the electric light bulb?"; "How tall is the average American male?"). Performance on this subtest is associated with natural endowment, richness of early environment, degree of schooling and cultural interests, and tends to correlate with academic achievement.
2. Similarities—consists of 17 items asking for a statement of how two things are alike (e.g., apple–banana, anger–joy). Similarities measures verbal concept formation and abstract reasoning.
3. Arithmetic—includes 14 orally presented problems, whose solutions require concentration, numerical reasoning ability, and effective use of previously learned arithmetical skills.
4. Vocabulary—probably the best single measure of general intelligence, this subtest requires the definition of 32 words of increasing difficulty. Scores are associated with learning ability and early educational environment and give a rough index of academic potential. Vocabulary is the most stable subtest over time and most resistant to interference from neurological and emotional factors. Although it is also the most frequently used WISC-R subtest for quick screening and research, neither this nor any

other subtest should be used *per se* as a substitute for a comprehensive measure of overall intelligence.

5. Comprehension—consists of 17 items requiring the use of practical judgment about what should be done in certain circumstances, why certain practices are followed in particular situations (e.g., "What should you do if you see thick smoke coming from the window of your neighbor's house?"). This subtest taps common sense and the ability to use meaningfully facts and relationships already known to the child. Difficulty on the comprehension test may suggest impaired judgment.

6. Digit span—measures short-term memory for numbers (from 3 to 9, depending on accuracy) which are orally presented by the examiner and then must be repeated by the child. On the second half of the subtest, the child is asked to repeat the digits in reverse order. Since digit span is particularly sensitive to attentional problems, it is often a difficult subtest for distractible, anxious children.

B. Performance scale
1. Picture completion—consists of 26 incomplete drawings where the child must tell which part is missing. Close attention to the environment, concentration, and remote memory are required. Vigilant, obsessive-compulsive, and, in certain cases, paranoid children often do well on this measure.

2. Picture arrangement—consists of 12 sets of drawings on separate cards which must be arranged in a coherent sequence so that the cards tell a story. This task taps perception of cause and effect relationships, interpretation of social situations, and ability to anticipate consequences. Along with block design, it is considered to be among the best performance measures of general intelligence.

3. Block design—a visual-motor test requiring reproduction of up to 11 designs printed on cards, using a set of blocks whose sides are red, white, or half-red and half-white. This subtest taps concept-formation, along with perceptual analysis (breaking down the stimulus card into block-sized units), synthesis, and visual-motor reproduction (reconstructing the patterns with the blocks). This is a relatively difficult task for children with neurological impairment, such as right hemisphere or right parietal dysfunction, and/or those experiencing emotional disruption, such as anxiety.

4. Object assembly—consists of four separate, fragmented puzzles requiring assembly into

their original wholes. It is considered primarily as a test of perceptual organizational ability and visual-motor coordination. Object assembly also provides information about a child's problem-solving abilities and work habits.

5. Coding—contains nine symbols that are paired with nine numbers (or five shapes paired with five special marks, for children below age 8). The child fills in as many of the blanks as possible on the answer sheet within 2 minutes. Coding measures ability to work in a concerted fashion on a basically rote task; for example, visual-motor speed. Low scores are associated with psychomotor retardation and/or neurological impairment.

6. Mazes—has nine increasingly difficult mazes, which measure planning ability or foresight in the context of visual-motor coordination and perceptual organization.

The child's performance on each subtest (raw score) is converted into a scaled score with a mean of 10 and a standard deviation of 3; hence, all subtest scores are expressed in comparable units. The verbal score is computed by summing scaled scores for the first five verbal subtests (i.e., all except digit span) or by prorating the sum of all the verbal subtests (i.e., multiplying by 5/6). Actual IQ (intelligence quotient) equivalents are found in the WISC-R Manual (Wechsler, 1974); they are based on normative populations of children at a given age. The same procedure is followed for performance scores; add the first five performance subtest scaled scores (all except mazes) or prorate all six. Overall, or Full Scale, IQ is found by summing verbal and performance scores and converting the total into an IQ score based on Wechsler's norms.

The range of children's WISC-R IQ scores is roughly normally distributed, covering the full intellectual spectrum, as seen in Table 20-1.

The pattern or profile of the child's performance across different WISC-R subtests is often of particular interest. Since the norms are constructed so that there are essentially no differences between verbal and performance IQs and since each subtest has items scaled in order of increasing difficulty, patterns of "scatter," both intra- and inter-test, take on special meaning. Passing more difficult items while failing relatively simpler ones on the same subtest may suggest attentional problems and interference and/or disruption from emotional factors, particularly anxiety. Cultural and motivational factors are also relevant along these same lines. If verbal IQ is significantly (i.e., by more than 10 to 15 points) greater than performance IQ, one might at least wonder about the role of such factors as neurological involve-

Table 20-1 **The Range of WISC-R Scores**

IQ Score	Range	Percentage of Population
130 and above	Very superior	2.3
120 129	Superior	7.4
110 119	High average	16.5
90 109	Average	49.4
80 89	Low average	16.2
70 79	Borderline	6.0
Below 70	Mental retardation (mentally deficient)	2.2
55 69	Mild retardation	
40 54	Moderate retardation	
25 39	Severe retardation	
24 and below	Profound retardation	

Wechsler, 1974

ment, depression, or even psychotic thinking. On the other hand, with performance IQ significantly greater than verbal IQ, one is more inclined to hypothesize "acting-out" tendencies, possible sociopathy (usually in delinquents), families not oriented to education, and/or poor academic achievement, such as "doers," as opposed to "thinkers."

WECHSLER PRESCHOOL AND PRIMARY SCALE OF INTELLIGENCE (WPPSI).
(Wechsler, 1967) Constructed for children ages 4 to 6½ years, this scale is similar, but not identical, to the WISC-R. Eight of the 11 subtests are essentially downward extensions of the following WISC-R scales: Information, picture completion, similarities, block design, arithmetic, vocabulary, comprehension, and mazes. In addition:

1. Animal House (replaces coding)—requires the placing of different colored pegs in appropriate holes in a form board. Although still sensitive to attentional, concentrational, and learning factors, animal house does not require pure form perception and reproduction as does coding and hence is less sensitive to neurological interference.
2. Sentences—measures immediate auditory memory for sentences or thoughts. Since sentence recall is affected by other than memory factors (e.g., vocabulary level), sentences and digit span should not properly be considered to be interchangeable.

3. Geometric design—consists of 10 items (geometric designs) which the child is asked to copy. This subtest measures perceptual and visual-motor organization similarly to the DTVMI and Bender-Gestalt. It is also sensitive to interference from organic factors.

STANFORD-BINET. (Terman and Merrill, 1973) This is an updated version of a general intelligence test first published in 1905 by the French psychologist, Alfred Binet (Binet and Simon, 1905) and later revised several times. (Terman, 1916; Terman and Merrill, 1937; Terman and Merrill, 1960) This measure was initially designed to assess children's intellectual capabilities, and identify children who would be most likely to benefit from public school education. Although the age range is from 2 through adulthood, the Stanford-Binet is designed primarily for children (it is mainly verbal at the older levels). It has different combinations of verbal and nonverbal subtests at each age level, with age intervals of 6 months from ages 2 to 5 years and of one year thereafter. From 2 to 5 years, the Stanford-Binet is more heavily weighted with items measuring nonverbal reasoning, visual-motor skills, and social intelligence. For school-age years, more emphasis is placed on cognitive functions, such as memory and abstract reasoning. The IQ is given as a single score based on the child's mental age, which is computed by summing the child's performance across subtests from a basal to a ceiling level. Although the Stanford-Binet does not provide as comprehensive a subtest profile as the Wechsler scales, it is often useful with retarded children whose ability levels in certain areas may be either below basal limits of the WISC-R or above ceiling limits of WPPSI subtests.

OTHER INTELLECTUAL MEASURES.
Sometimes for reasons of time and/or convenience, certain scales are used as "quick screening" measures of intelligence when it is not practical or feasible to administer one of the three major tests described. Frequently employed are the Peabody Picture Vocabulary Test and Columbia Mental Maturity Scale, both of which are helpful in "breaking the ice" and establishing rapport with children, and are particularly relevant for children with difficulty in expressive language. It must be remembered, however, that these measures tap only *one* aspect of the complex domain of "intelligence;" hence, global judgments regarding intelligence from any single of these tests is unwise. They are more useful as supplements to or corroboration of information obtained from the Binet or Wechsler scales.

Peabody Picture Vocabulary Test (PPVT) (Dunn, 1965) measures receptive vocabulary and hence does not require expressive skills. It is appropriate for children as young as 2½ years. It consists of 150 plates, each with four drawings and merely requires correct identification of visually presented items. The PPVT is untimed, and hence a power rather than a speed test.

Columbia Mental Maturity Scale (CMMS) (Burgemeister *et al.*, 1972)—for children 3½ years and older—consists of 100 plates, each with three to five drawings of objects that either do or do not bear a relationship to each other. The child's task is to select the one that "does not belong" with the others in the group. Variables sampled include form, color, size, and number.

Infant Assessment. The following measures are relevant, particularly for infants suspected of developmental delay or a specific intellectual handicap.

Bayley Scales of Infant Development (Bayley, 1969) consists of a mental scale *and* a motor scale, in addition to descriptive material about the infant's behavior. The Bayley may be used with infants up to age 2½ years.

Cattell Infant Intelligence Scale (Cattell, 1940) is often used as a downward extension of the Stanford-Binet. The appropriate age range of the Cattell is from 2 to 30 months. Its relative advantages include a large number of subtest items at each age level and small intervals between age levels.

Merrill-Palmer Scale of Mental Tests (Stutsman, 1931) covers the age range of 18 to 71 months and is particularly useful with hearing-impaired children and/or children with language delays, due to its emphasis on nonverbal tasks. The Merrill-Palmer gives a picture of the child's motor functioning; it is often used in conjunction with the Stanford-Binet, which is more sensitive to language functioning, to give a more complete picture or profile of the child's overall abilities.

Academic Achievement Tests

WIDE RANGE ACHIEVEMENT TEST (WRAT). (Jastak *et al.*, 1965) This is a relatively brief, standardized instrument of academic functioning, consisting of three achievement tests: reading (i.e., letter and/or word recognition), spelling, and arithmetic. Grade levels, standard scores, and percentiles ranging from prekindergarten through college are provided in the manual. More detailed, specific measures of academic achievement may be obtained by using the Gray Oral Reading Test (Gray, 1963), the Woodcock Reading Mastery Tests (Woodcock, 1973), and Key Math (Connolly *et al.* 1974), to name a few.

Projective Tests

The rationale for projective techniques is spelled out in the "projective hypothesis," which essentially says that the nature and content of a child's response to an unstructured situation reflect his or her underlying personality characteristics and dynamic traits. Two widely used projective tests with children are the Rorschach Inkblot Test (Rorschach, 1942) and the TAT. (Murray, 1943) Although the two are different, both have ambiguous structures and place relatively few restrictions on the child's mode of response.

RORSCHACH. The Rorschach Inkblot Test consists of 10 cards each with a printed symmetrical inkblot. Of the 10, five are achromatic (composed of shades of gray and black), two primarily black with blotches of red, and three mutlicolored. The child is presented with the cards, one by one, and asked to say what each card looks like.

The administration is divided into two major phases: "free association" and "inquiry." During the first, the examiner records verbatim the child's responses to each card, also noting reaction time and total time for each card, behavioral observations (gross and subtle), incidental comments, such as "Is it all right to turn the card?," and visible expressions of feelings.

The second or inquiry phase begins after the child has finished responding to each card (with older children the inquiry is typically done after the entire free association part of the test is over). In the inquiry, the examiner asks general questions to determine the exact location of each response, how the child arrived at it, and what aspect(s) of the blot contributed to the particular response. In order to give a satisfactory inquiry, the examiner must have a thorough understanding of the scoring procedures.

An optional third phase, "testing the limits," is sometimes given to determine whether or not the child is capable of other sorts of responses, i.e., by calling attention to particular areas of the blot ("Might it also be...?").

Most scoring systems follow Rorschach's (1942) guidelines. Five characteristics are commonly used:

A. Location—where on the card the percept was seen. Although scoring systems vary somewhat, four basic location scorings are widely used:
   1. the whole, or nearly whole, blot (W or W̶);
   2. a large, distinctly, segmented area of the blot, or "normal detail" (D);
   3. a small or "rare detail" (Dd);
   4. a white space (S) instead of the inked areas.
B. Determinants—how the percept was seen and the particular characteristics or qualities of the blot used in the response. There are four major determinant categories:

1. form (F)—shape or contour of the blot determines the response;
2. movement (M, if human, e.g., "two people dancing," FM, if animal, e.g., "a bird flying," m, if inanimate, e.g., "falling rock")—movement is seen in the static blot;
3. color (C)—color is used to determine a response;
4. shading (c for texture, e.g., "fur," K for vista or three-dimensional effects, e.g., "a mountain gorge," k for a three-dimensional concept projected onto a two-dimensional plane, e.g., "x-ray").
C. Form level—level of accuracy of the percept, usually depicted by adding a "+" or "−." Both Beck (1944) and Klopfer et al., (1954) have extensive response lists for all ten cards, and the corresponding accuracy levels for each response.
D. Content—content of the response (such as animal, human, fire).
E. Popular-original—frequency of occurrence (in a normative sense) of the response. Some popular responses include "bat" or "butterfly" on card V, and "spiders" or "crabs" on card X. An original response is one occurring less than once in 100 times in the examiner's experience.

Interpretation of the Rorschach is a complex task. It takes into account the child's total pattern of responses and involves formulation of hypotheses based on responses to combinations of several different categories. Although a comprehensive review of Rorschach interpretation systems is beyond the scope of this chapter, several major interpretive hypotheses related to basic scoring categories are presented. It should be remembered that these are not "cookbook" interpretations. Interpretation ultimately depends not only on the particular score, but also on its relation to other variables, such as quality and sequence of responses. All frequency percentages reported in the following are from Ames et al. (1974).

A. Location—relates to cognitive orientation or intellectual manner of approach. W responses (40 to 50% of the total responses is average) show a capacity for abstraction, integration, and organizing abilities. Protocols with D (30 to 40% is average) often indicate conventional thought, practical common sense, and an interest in the concrete. Dd (less than 10% is average) suggests the ability to make refined judgment requiring critical observation. An excessive emphasis on Dd may typify a child who is insecure and/or anxious, or an obsessive-compulsive child who feels comfortable with the conventional. S responses may be associated with oppositional or negativistic tendencies, with original or creative children,

and/or with neurological impairment (e.g., figure-ground reversals).
B. Determinants—generally relate to emotional aspects of personality.
1. Form (F) responses—relate to intellectual or ego control, for instance reasoning ability or critical facility. Unlike adults, where percentages of F usually range from 20 to 50, younger children average between 50 to 80% of F responses. A lower proportion of F may imply either inadequate control and impulsivity (particularly if there are many F responses) or creativity and sensitivity, if the form quality is good.
2. Movement (M, FM, or m) responses—indicate capacity for fantasy, reflection, and richness of inner life. Human movement (M) responses of good form level suggest a capacity for creativity, thoughtfulness, and good intellectual endowment; about 5 to 10% M responses is average for children. Animal movement (FM) responses are similar to M, but on a less mature developmental level. Whereas M responses are often associated with ego control, FM responses suggest more spontaneous, relatively unrestrained emotional impulses; approximately 8 to 10% FM responses are average. Inanimate movement (m) responses are thought to represent a state of tension or anxiety, such as helplessness in coping; 2 to 4% m is average for children.
3. Color (C) responses—relate to emotional responsiveness to stimuli in the environment (interpersonal relationships). Since form can be involved, in varying degrees in color (as well as shading) responses, it is indicated in the scoring by the addition of F. Thus, FC would be given to a colored percept of definite form ("yellow canary"). Such a scoring suggests an ability for controlled responsiveness to emotional demands as well as the potential for warmth and relating well to others; 1 to 4% FC is considered average for children. CF responses refer to instances where the child does not integrate color in the percept of a definite form ("a landscape"). Such scores may indicate spontaneity or impulsivity, depending upon their quality; 3 to 7% is average. A pure C response is completely color-determined with no form quality ("a sunset") and suggests a (sometimes pathological) lack of control in handling the emotional aspect of situations; 1 to 4% is average. The use of achromatic color (FC', C'F, or C'), a response based on the black, gray, or white quality of the blot, is often suggestive of

tension or depression and, in some cases, anxiety.

4. Shading (c, K, or k) responses—generally relate to anxiety. Texture responses (Fc, cF, or c) refer to awareness of one's need for dependency and affection. A high number of texture responses suggests overdependence or an immature need for closeness. Diffuse shading or vista responses (FK, KF, or K) suggest the presence of anxiety related to frustration of affectional needs; the (form) quality tends to indicate the child's success in coping with these issues. Fk, kF, or k responses are believed to pertain to anxiety the child tends to cover up by intellectualization.

C. Form level—see before.

D. Content—includes an extensive list of categories. In addition to reflecting cultural and background factors, content responses give useful information about personality structure, interests, and conflicts. The most common content categories, for chidren, are animal responses, A, comprising from about 40 to 50% of the total protocol. Such responses often indicate stereotypy or conventionality. Other common content includes H, or human, responses (thought to indicate interest in persons or the self), Hd and Ad (human and animal detail responses), said to represent social anxiety and/or concern with body parts, and Anat, or anatomy responses suggestive of excessive concern or anxiety with bodily integrity, or hypochondriasis.

E. Popular-original—popular (P) responses typically occur about 20 to 25% of the time in children's protocols. Excessive P may indicate stereotypy and overconformity. Original (O) responses, although considered a measure of creativity, are often not scored for children due to the wide variability of responses, especially at the lower age levels.

Although the Rorschach has been criticized both from methodological and psychometric (reliability, validity) standpoints, it remains a useful instrument. Various interpretive approaches (Beck, 1944; Klopfer, *et al.*, 1954) have been developed for the Rorschach; however, clinicians use the test in different ways for different purposes. Often the clinician's personal style or needs, along with his or her experiences with the test and personal "clinical norms," determine the way in which the Rorschach is used.

THEMATIC APPERCEPTION TEST.
(Murray, 1943) With the Rorschach, the TAT is one of the most widely used projective devices. It consists of 31 cards (one of which is blank) of either scenes or interpersonal events, some clear, some ambiguous. Examples of scenes include: a boy sitting at a table, looking at a violin; a young girl holding a doll, sitting next to an older lady on a couch.

The child is administered a subset of cards, usually preselected, according to potentially relevant content, by the examiner and told to make up a story about each, indicating what is currently happening, what led up to it, and how the story ends. The examiner records each story verbatim and may also "probe" ("What happens then?") if sections are omitted by the child.

The TAT, unlike the Rorschach, has no formal scoring procedure, although Murray and others (Bellak *et al.,* 1949) have proposed different approaches. The assumption is that the child will identify with the figures in the picture and will thus provide information about how he or she thinks or feels across various situations. From themes or patterns noted, the examiner may make inferences and hypotheses regarding the child's thought and emotional organization, self-concept, conflicts, aspirations, needs, interpersonal relations, modes of problem solving, and other important personality attributes.

TAT interpretation relates to the clinician's expertise, ability to make observations and inferences, and familiarity with the instrument. The TAT is frequently used in conjunction with the Rorschach. Whereas the latter provides a picture of the child's underlying personality structure, the TAT develops more substantive, "closer-to-consciousness" data, which add meaningfully to the total diagnostic picture.

CHILDREN'S APPERCEPTION TEST.
(Bellak and Bellak, 1949) This is sometimes used in lieu of the TAT; it has animal rather than human figures on each of its 10 cards. The authors reason that children can more readily identify with animal characters. Interpretation, as with the TAT, must be done within a total context.

HUMAN FIGURE DRAWINGS.
Children's figure drawing techniques have been in use for more than 50 years. (Goodenough, 1926) The Draw-a-Person (DAP) task is relatively brief and easily administered to children, requiring only a piece of paper, a pencil, and instructions to draw a picture of a person. Instructions are usually as unstructured as possible. One important advantage of the DAP is that it can be given to children of almost any age, intellectual level, or level of artistic ability.

Initially, the task was used as a measure of intelligence; in her book, Goodenough (1926) presented a detailed system of scoring and norms for interpretation. Later, with the publication of Machover's (1949) work, the DAP test was used more extensively as a projective technique. The basic assumption is that human figure drawings represent one's body image and self-perception, and that the ultimate production will reflect the child's own life experiences.

Children's figure drawing interpretation takes into account numerous factors (size of drawings, the relative size of different bodily parts, and the level of detail). As with other projective techniques, however, one cannot assume that a single sign represents a certain quality, for example, that an unusually small head necessarily signifies feelings of inadequacy. Rather, one needs to consider the configuration of signs and relate these to other material from the child's total protocol. In brief screening, children's human figure drawings are used as rough estimates of intellectual level and/or degree of psychological differentiation and organization.

Discussion

The traditional approach to child psychological assessment seeks to gather as much relevant data as possible during the assessment process. Each new perspective provides additional and different types of information about presenting problems in a specific context. A broad-based approach such as this is essential in establishing a more complete clinical understanding of contributing factors and in making future treatment decisions.

After all the assessment data have been collected, the next step is to integrate them in a clinically meaningful way. By organizing and classifying the assessment data, the clinician arrives at a final "diagnosis." This is important not only in describing the nature of the child's condition, but also in determining how the problems may be most effectively treated. Treatment recommendations established at the end of the assessment procedure are typically shared with the child and his parents.

In Billy's case, psychological assessment reveals that academically he is functioning 1½ to 2 years below grade level in arithmetic, despite an overall IQ in the high average range. His parents, although well-meaning, are lax and often inconsistent in their discipline. His teacher has 28 students in her third grade classroom, and not enough time to give Billy the attention he needs, either academically or for his disruptions. Projective data reveal that Billy is an anxious, insecure youngster with many fears and doubts about his own abilities. He is noted to have difficulty in appropriately expressing his impulses, especially anger and aggression, particularly within the context of his family situation.

Based on this, Billy's problem might be diagnosed as an overanxious disorder, with a specific learning disability. Given this diagnosis, appropriate treatment recommendations might include: (1) outpatient play therapy for Billy—individual or group—with concurrent parent counseling sessions for Mr. and Mrs. R., (2) family therapy (for the whole R. family), (3) individualized tutoring in arithmetic for Billy in a resource classroom at school.

BEHAVIORAL ASSESSMENT

Behavioral assessment differs from traditional assessment both in its underlying assumptions and methods. Mischel (1973) points out that: "The focus [in behavioral assessment] shifts from attempting to compare and generalize about what different individuals are like to an assessment of what they *do*—behaviorally and cognitively—in relationship to the psychological conditions in which they do it." (p. 265) Hence, rather than assuming overt behavior is merely an indication of underlying dynamics, the behavioral approach: "...entails more of a direct sampling of the criterion behaviors themselves." (Goldfried and Kent, 1972)

Although there are different methods of child behavioral assessment (self-report measures, physiological measures), the primary ones involves observation in the natural environment.

The basic behavioral assessment paradigm is as follows:

1. Describe or pinpoint the problem—operationalization of the problem or "target" behaviors (those needing to be changed), as well as identification of those variables—antecedent and consequent—currently maintaining and controlling the target behaviors.
2. Record its rate of occurrence—to know the frequency of occurrence of the target behaviors, baseline data are taken.
3. Pinpoint critical reinforcers—determining what is reinforcing to the child, i.e., something for which the child will work.
4. Reconsequate target behaviors—rearranging the consequences of behavior such that they generate appropriate behavior for reinforcement.

Assessment of Billy's bedwetting behavior, for example, begins with a behaviorally oriented interview designed to obtain a further description or pinpointing of the problem. Such interviews seldom ask "why" questions. Rather, the focus is on "how," "what," "when," and "where" questions to help ascertain "...relevant personal and situational variables which are maintaining the client's problems." (O'Leary and Wilson, 1975, p. 25) This is important in order to select an appropriate treatment strategy and evaluate treatment outcomes.

In the interview with Billy's parents, it is determined that organically based causes of his enuresis have been ruled out in previous visits to the family pediatrician. A detailed examination of the morning routine reveals the following pattern: Billy's bed is wet (an average of five mornings per week), Billy dawdles in his room instead of getting ready for school, Mrs. R. comes into the room and makes Billy's bed for approximately 15 minutes during which time they talk. After the bed is made, Mrs. R. proceeds to dress Billy because it is getting late. Finally they go downstairs and she fixes him breakfast.

Further questioning determines that Billy enjoys reading and talking with his mother after breakfast; moreover, he wants very much to be able to sleep in the top bunk bed.

As events are now occurring, there is a payoff for Billy in wetting his bed (getting to talk with his mother, having her dress him), and hence it is likely to continue. Behavioral assessment seeks to develop a program to deliver reinforcing events to Billy contingent on *appropriate,* not inappropriate, behavior (cf., reconsequation of the target behaviors).

Accordingly, the following program is designed: If Billy's bed is dry, he earns the privilege of sleeping in the top bunk bed every succeeding "dry" night, along with verbal positive reinforcement or praise from his parents for keeping his bed dry. Mrs. R. is told to have Billy's clothes laid out and to instruct him that when he has dressed himself he can come down for breakfast. After finishing breakfast, Billy is free to read and talk to his mother.

On the other hand, if Billy wets his bed, Mrs. R. is instructed to say something like: "That's too bad. Here are the new sheets," and then leave the room, with the understanding that Billy is to strip his wet bedding, bring it down to the washing machine for washing, and return to his room to make his bed with the new sheets. About 10 minutes after Mrs. R. has left the room for the first time, she may come back and give Billy a "prompt" (i.e., message telling the time and place of reinforcement), such as: "As soon as you're done, you can come down for breakfast and stories."

The program is set up so that Billy has a high chance of earning positive reinforcement at the beginning. Ongoing monitoring of the system through the use of charts and descriptive data collected by the parents is necessary to determine if that program is working optimally or if additional adjustments need to be made, such as adding bonuses to strengthen the system, or fading reinforcers that are no longer necessary.

Billy's school behavior is also monitored concurrently. Behavioral assessment includes a school visit, where it is determined, from talking with Billy's teacher, that Billy is most disruptive during reading circle when the teacher works with a small group of children at the front of the room on basic reading skills while the remainder of the class is left to do assigned seat work. During this time, Billy is frequently out of his seat and also talks with his neighbors. Direct classroom observation, in fact, bears out the teacher's complaints (i.e., a high baseline rate of the two target behaviors maintained largely by the amount of attention they attract both from peers and teacher). Further talking with the teacher brings to light that free time for preferred activities (for instance, eraser tag, alphabet bingo, musical chairs) is a reinforcer for her class.

One way to reconsequate Billy's target behaviors is for the teacher to use a group contingency procedure based on "Grandma's Rule" (Becker, 1971; Homme, 1971), which states: "First you work, then you play." Hence, Billy's teacher is told to designate a half-hour time slot for reading circle. For that period, Billy and the rest of the class outside of the reading circle must do 15 minutes of "good work" in order to earn free time for the remaining 15 minutes. The teacher then keeps track of total amount of "good work" with a stop watch; whenever Billy, or any other child, engages in any of the target behaviors, the teacher stops the stop watch, announces the child's name and says that he or she should be working now. The watch is kept stopped until the child is back on-task. At the end of 15 minutes of "good work" by the whole class, reading circle is terminated and the students are allowed to spend the remainder of that day's 30-minute period in free time activities of their choice.

Such a program also needs to be monitored and analyzed continuously over time to be sensitive and adjust to any changes in effectiveness. Its major advantage is in bringing group contingencies to bear on Billy's target behaviors. Whereas previously they were reinforced by classmates' and the teacher's responses, the new program essentially reverses the contingencies such that now the opposite behavior, "good work," is rewarded by the class, the teacher, and by the free time it ultimately earns.

Discussion

Behavioral assessment concerns itself primarily with those variables or behaviors that are directly observable. It involves selection of treatment techniques based on direct observation of presenting problems. Assessment and treatment are more integrally related in this format than with traditional techniques. Continuous monitoring and evaluation is crucial, so that treatment itself can be modified at any time, if necessary.

CONCLUSION

Although the *methods* of assessment used in traditional and behavioral approaches differ greatly, the two approaches share similar *goals*. Each strives, via its own technology, to provide a maximum of useful, relevant data to help obtain as thorough an understanding as possible of the child. Such information, in turn, facilitates the development and implementation of an effective treatment plan.

Finally, although two essentially different approaches (traditional and behavioral) to psychological assessment of children are presented, it does not necessarily follow that they are mutually exclusive. For example, direct classroom observation may be a very helpful adjunct to the traditional assessment of a hyperactive child. By the same token, an important aspect of certain behavioral assessment approaches includes consideration of a child's cognitive processes (which are certainly not observable) as mediating factors. Indeed, one of the more promising directions of the future is pointed out by Lazarus (1976), who proposes a "multimodal" approach to assessment and treatment. This particular approach takes into account information from the following modalities: behavior, affect, sensation, imagery, cognition, interpersnal, and drugs—for which Lazarus uses the acronym of "BASIC ID." By combining elements from both the traditional and behavioral approaches, Lazarus feels the multimodal technique offers a comprehensive, systematic alternative, not constrained by the limitations of either one.

REFERENCES

Ames, L.B., Metraux, R.W., Rodell, J.L. Walker, R.N. (1974). *Child Rorschach Responses: Developmental Trends from Two to Ten Years.* New York: Brunner/Mazel.

Bayley, N. (1969). *Bayley Scales of Infant Development: Birth to Two Years.* New York: Psychological Corporation.

Beck, S.J. (1944). *Rorschach's Test: Vol. I, Basic Processes.* New York: Grune and Stratton.

Becker, W.C. (1971). *Parents Are Teachers: A Child Management Program.* Champaign, Ill.: Research Press.

Beery, K., Buktenica, N. (1967). *Developmental Test of Visual-Motor Integration.* Chicago: Follett.

Bellak, L., Bellak, S.S. (1949). *Manual of Instruction for the Children's Apperception Test.* New York: C.P.S. Co.

Bellak, L., Pasquarelli, B.A., Braverman, S. (1949). The use of the Thematic Apperception Test in psychotherapy. *J. Nerv. Ment. Dis., 110,* 51–65.

Bender, L. (1938). *A Visual Motor Gestalt Test and Its Clinical Use.* New York: American Orthopsychiatric Association, Research Monograph, No. 3.

Burgemeister, B.B., Blum, L.H., Lorge, I. (1972). *Columbia Mental Maturity Scale,* Third Edition. New York: Harcourt Brace Jovanovich.

Cattell, P. (1940). *The Measurement of Intelligence of Infants and Young Children.* New York: Psychological Corporation.

Connolly, A.J., Nachtman, W., Pritchett, E.M. (1974). *Keymath Diagnostic Arithmetic Test.* Circle Pines, Minn.: American Guidance Service.

Dunn, L.M. (1965). *Expanded Manual for the Peabody Picture Vocabulary Test.* Minneapolis: American Guidance Service.

Frostig, M., Lefever, W., Whittlesey, J.R.B. (1966). *Administration and Scoring Manual for the Marianne Frostig Developmental Test of Visual Perception.* Palo Alto: Consulting Psychologists Press.

Goldfried, M.R., Kent, R.N. (1972). Traditional versus behavioral personality assessment: A comparison of methodological and theoretical assumptions. *Psychol. Bull., 77,* 409–420.

Goodenough, F. (1926). *Measurement of Intelligence by Drawings.* New York: World Book.

Gray, S. (1963). *Gray Oral Reading Tests.* Indianapolis: Bobbs-Merrill.

Homme, L. (1971). *How to Use Contingency Contracting in the Classroom.* Champaign, Ill.: Research Press.

Jastak, J., Bijou, S.W., Jastak, S. (1965). *Wide Range Achievement Test.* Wilmington: Guidance Associates.

Klopfer, B., Ainsworth, M.D., Klopfer, W.G., Holt, R.R. (1954). *Developments in the Rorschach Technique, Vol. I, Technique and Theory.* New York: World Book.

Koppitz, E. (1964). *The Bender Gestalt Test for Young Children.* New York: Grune and Stratton.

Korchin, S.J. (1976). *Modern Clinical Psychology: Principles of Intervention in the Clinic and Community.* New York: Basic Books.

Lazarus, A.A. (1976). *Multimodal Behavior Therapy.* New York: Springer.

Machover, K. (1949). *Personality Projection in the Drawing of the Human Figure.* Springfield, Ill.: Charles C Thomas.

Magrab, P.R. (1976). Psychology. In Johnston, R.B., Magrab, P.R. (Eds.), *Developmental Disorders: Assessment, Treatment, Education.* Baltimore: University Park Press.

Maloney, M.P., Ward, M.P. (1976). *Psychological Assessment: A Conceptual Approach.* New York: Oxford University Press.

Mischel, W. (1973). Towards a cognitive social learning reconceptualization of personality. *Psychol. Rev., 80,* 252–283.

Murray, H.A. (1943). *Thematic Apperception Test Manual.* Cambridge, Mass.: Harvard University Press.

O'Leary, K.D., Wilson, G.T. (1975). *Behavior Therapy: Application and Outcome.* Englewood Cliffs, N.J.: Prentice-Hall.

Rorschach, H. (1942). *Psychodiagnostics: A Diagnostic Test Based on Perception.* (Translated by P. Lenkau and B. Kronenberg) Berne: Hans-Huber. (First German Edition, 1921; U.S. Distributor, Grune and Stratton).

Stutsman, R. (1931). *Merrill-Palmer Scale of Mental Tests.* New York: Harcourt, Brace, and World.

Terman, L.M. (1916). *The Measurement of Intelligence.* Boston: Houghton Mifflin.

Terman, L.M., Merrill, M.A. (1937). *Measuring Intelligence.* Boston: Houghton Mifflin.

Terman, L.M., Merrill, M.A. (1960). *Stanford-Binet Intelligence Scale.* Boston: Houghton Mifflin.

Terman, L.M., Merrill, M.A. (1973). *Stanford-Binet Intelligence Scale: Manual for the Third Revision—Form L-M.* (1972 Norms Edition) Boston: Houghton Mifflin.

Wechsler, D. (1949). *Manual for the Wechsler Intelligence Scale for Children.* New York: Psychological Corporation.

Wechsler, D. (1958). *The Measurement and Appraisal of Adult Intelligence*. Fourth Edition. Baltimore: Williams and Wilkins.

Wechsler, D. (1967). *Manual for the Wechsler Preschool and Primary Scale of Intelligence*. New York: Psychological Corporation.

Wechsler, D. (1974). *Manual for the Wechsler Intelligence Scale for Children—Revised*. New York: Psychological Corporation.

Woodcock, R.W. (1973). *Woodcock Reading Mastery Tests: Manual*. Circle Pines, Minn.: American Guidance Service.

Chapter 21

PSYCHOTHERAPY IN CHILDHOOD AND ADOLESCENCE

David Dolen, M.D.

The mouse that gnawed the oak-tree down
Began his task in early life.
He kept so busy with his teeth
He had no time to take a wife.

The mouse that gnawed the oak-tree down,
When that tough foe was at his feet—
Found in the stump no angel-cake
Nor buttered bread, nor cheese nor meat—

The forest-roof let in the sky.
"This light is worth the work," said he.
"I'll make this ancient swamp more light,"
And started on another tree.

Vachel Lindsay (1914), p. 502.

Having reckoned with milestones in the sea of development and battled the myriad philosophies in the fields of theorem, the victorious trainee, armed with the knowledge gained in his previous pursuits, is now ready for perhaps his most exciting engagement. He is ready to assume his unique fortune: the intimate exploration of the fantasies, the excitement of discovery, the joys, the pains, and the hopes of another human being. He is ready to don a new robe as a psychotherapist and stand at the child's side as an advocate and healer and witness the felling of the "oak-tree" and the opening of the "forest-roof" that lets in the sky of the future.

Many definitions are available for psychotherapy, and many conflicts exist as to what constitutes a justifiable treatment procedure. Ranging from Actualism to Zone Therapy, a preponderance of philosophies and techniques have arisen during the past century, each defining the role of the therapist and the therapy in a somewhat different light. Jerome Frank (1961) in *Persuasion and Healing* offers the following broad-based definition:

Attempts to enhance a person's feeling of well-being are usually labeled treatment, and every society trains some of its members to apply this form of influence. Treatment always involves a personal relationship between healer and sufferer. Certain types of therapy rely primarily on the healer's ability to mobilize healing forces in the sufferer by psychological means. These forms of treatment may be generically termed psychotherapy.

p. 1.

As it is beyond the scope of this chapter to examine each of the schools of psychotherapy and the application of their techniques, an approach will be assumed that allows the therapist to examine some of the more commonly employed procedures used in the therapy of children in each developmental stage from infancy to adolescence, with occasional detours along the way to discuss the relationships and processes of psychotherapy.

AXLINE'S EIGHT BASIC PRINCIPLES

Although the therapist's approach will vary for children of different developmental levels, the principles and guidelines followed will usually remain constant. Virginia Axline (1947) provided the following eight basic principles that she believed should be followed "sincerely, consistently, and intelligently."

1. The therapist must develop a warm, friendly relationship with the child, in which good rapport is established as soon as possible.
2. The therapist accepts the child exactly as he is.
3. The therapist establishes a feeling of permissiveness in the relationship so that the child feels free to express his feelings completely.
4. The therapist is alert to recognize the feelings the child is expressing and reflects those feelings back to him in such a manner that he gains insight into his behavior.
5. The therapist maintains a deep respect for the

255

child's ability to solve his own problems if given an opportunity to do so. The responsibility to make choices and to institute change is the child's.

6. The therapist does not attempt to direct the child's actions or conversation in any manner. The child leads the way; the therapist follows.

7. The therapist does not attempt to hurry the therapy along. It is a gradual process and is recognized as such by the therapist.

8. The therapist establishes only those limitations that are necessary to anchor the therapy to the world of reality and to make the child aware of his responsibility in the relationship.

p. 93–94.

As therapy with children of varied developmental stages is discussed, one may want to be aware of these guidelines and consider how they might best be maintained. It will soon become apparent that such maintainance will require some flexibility and that in certain cases, such as the therapy of infants, some principles are more applicable to the work with the parents than to that of the child.

THERAPY OF THE INFANT

Tom was seen by a pediatrician at 4 months of age and identified as a "failure to thrive" infant. (see chapter 7) Laboratory and physical examination revealed no organic cause for delayed development. A referral was made for psychotherapy as the pediatrician believed the primary cause of the infant's delays to be emotionally based.

Such a case may be immediately perplexing and the source of much consternation for the new therapist. The infant is apparently the identified patient, and this may not fit into one's preconceived ideas as to the process of psychotherapy. After all, infants do not often enter into long philosophical discussions or enumerate the many disappointments of their lives. They do very little when placed in a playroom and fail to comply with the mode of intervention most frequently identified as the domain of children's psychotherapy. Yet, when one considers the presenting problem, it is difficult to arrive at a more qualified intervener that the child psychotherapist, who understands the physical and intellectual development of children and is able to use this knowledge in gauging the problems and progress of the child, who understands the awesome powers of emotions and is able to relate disturbances of that realm to the more apparent physical functionings of the body, and who understands the "unspoken dialogue" of affect and actions.

Fraiberg *et al.* in *Clinical Studies in Infant*

Mental Health—The First Year of Life (1980) described three treatment modes she uses in infant psychotherapy. The first is "brief crisis intervention."

This mode of treatment is chosen when in our assessment the problem is largely reactive to a circumscribed set of external events and when the parents' psychological capacities suggest that they can make use of a brief focused intervention.

p. 60.

The second is "developmental guidance—supportive therapy." Fraiberg *et al.* choose this approach when the parents are seen as having good parenting skills but illness or neonatal difficulties are seriously straining the parenting capacities. She also uses this approach in cases where the infant has serious emotional impairment and the parents have severe psychological problems and "limited capacity" to deal with internal conflicts. In both these situations "... our objective is to provide emotional support and to strengthen parenting capacities, while simultaneously providing developmental guidance in the form of information and discussion about the baby's needs." (ibid., pp. 60–61)

The third mode of intervention is "infant-parent psychotherapy." This is the treatment choice when the parents have integrated the infant symbolically into their own neurosis so that the child represents a part of the "parental past" or "an aspect of the parental self that is repudiated or negated." Fraiberg *et al.* refer to this pathological process metaphorically as "old ghosts" invading "the nursery." (ibid., p. 61) For example: Tom, the "failure to thrive" infant, presented at the beginning of this chapter, was found to have great symbolic significance for his mother. Mother was observed to be very ill at ease holding her baby, and she was able to state after several sessions that she had some ambivalence toward Tom. She recalled her own mother telling her as a child that she only married because she was pregnant with her. Tom's mother remembered only a few occasions when her mother had ever hugged or touched her. She stated that her father provided the only "love" she knew. She remembered being ill as a child and her father staying home from work to care for her.

The therapist was suddenly reminded that Tom's father, a military professional, had returned from Germany to be with his wife and ailing son. Tom's mother had unknowingly allowed her own maternal deprivation to surface as anger toward her own infant, whom she could neither caress nor nurse. She was eventually able to realize that Tom's "failure to thrive" was a powerful force in bringing her husband (love object) home from

Germany, similar to the way her father would stay home when she was ill. Helping the mother, through psychotherapy, to work through her internal conflicts and decrease the unconscious symbolic attachment of her own childhood experiences to those of her baby, along with providing specific suggestions for effective parenting, helped to alleviate the pathological situation. "Undo the impediments to forward movement and the baby takes off! It's a little bit like having God on your side." (ibid., p. 53)

Fraiberg *et al.* suggested that in the treatment of infants, both parents and the infant should be part of the therapy session; the child is the focus of the session. It is preferable to have therapeutic sessions within the child's home. The therapist should observe the infant's reactions to the stimuli around him and utilize the infant's and parents' reactions to those stimuli for therapeutic and growth enhancing purposes.

PLAY THERAPY

If he [Tom Sawyer] had been a great and wise philosopher, like the writer of this book, he would now have comprehended that Work consists of whatever a body is *obliged* to do, and that Play consists of whatever a body is not obliged to do.

Mark Twain (1876), p. 29.

Play is an important consideration in the psychotherapy of preschool and latency-age children. Melanie Klein and Anna Freud introduced "play therapy." They believed that children's free play bore great similarity to adult free association—one of the vital ingredients of psychoanalysis. Maintaining this perspective, these post-Freudian pioneers set out to discern the inner functionings of the minds of children through observation of their play. (Harrison, 1975, p. 2214)

In retrospect their theory appears somewhat obvious and very logical. What mother has not witnessed the spontaneous eruption of monsters from the id destroying the castles in the backyard sandbox or the creation of fantasy environments so detailed and real for the child as to be suggestive of the primary process of dreams?

Play affords opportunities for therapy found in no other mode. It is the language of the child and often his self-created balm. Through play, he learns by repetitively enacting newly discovered ideas and physical skills. Through play, the child does battle with his universe, attempting to defeat the foes of his narcissism. Through play, the child may find some means of self-nurturance. In no realm can the child feel quite as safe as in the world of fantasy and play. He is the totalitarian ruler of a kingdom without dimension. It is this security and control, when undisturbed by the therapist, that will often allow admission into the child's world and the establishment of rapport. The therapist who intrudes too quickly, interprets too directly, or attempts to force his assimilation can be quickly and silently exiled from this totalitarian state. On the other hand, one who is able to abide by Axline's eight principles, one who is warm, accepting, tolerant of free expression, patient, and respectful of the child will often be offered an honorary citizenship. No efforts should be made, in any way, to obligate the play, for as Twain suggests, obligated play is no longer play.

A more detailed discussion of play as a developmental phenomenon can be found in chapter 3 and 4. The introduction of the child to play and the playroom is discussed in chapter 18.

The Playroom

As mentioned in chapter 18, some clinicians utilize an area of their office for play therapy; others have a specially designated room that is the setting of the therapeutic sessions. As a matter of convenience, the term "playroom" will be used to describe both. There is thought to be an advantage in maintaining the same setting from one session to another. The familiarity of the setting will hopefully help the child feel more at ease and more open to free expression. Any clinician, who has been working with a child over a period of months and one day departs for the playroom to find that another therapist and child are already occupying the facilities, knows that the playroom assumes a significance beyond that of just familiarity. The anger expressed by the 6-year-old that someone else is using "our" room is a clue to the symbolic importance of the setting. The playroom is for some children one of the few stable entities in their lives. It represents a very special relationship with an adult whom they have grown to trust and respect. It represents a privileged freedom of expression and confidentiality. It represents something that is shared by two individuals with no room for intrusion. In this light, the child's anger can be easily understood, and all attempts should be made to insure that the setting remains the same from session to session.

With similar concerns, the child may wonder if other children use the room and share a special relationship with the therapist the way he does. Toward the end of a session, a 6-year-old boy was observed carefully arranging toys in patterns and secreting tiny cars in the corners of the room. When this behavior was reflected aloud by the clinician, the boy stated, "The next time I'll know if you and some other kid have been in here." The child was informed that many children used the room, after which he requested that the cabinets "be ours, special, so no one but you or me can touch the toys." The therapist then replied, "I play with other kids in the playroom but our relationship is very special, and we do things that no one else does and talk about things that no one else talks about." The boy appeared reassured by the therapist's verbal recognition of their special relationship.

Stocking the Playroom

The choice of toys for the playroom is made with several considerations in mind. The toys should lend themselves to creative activity. There should be toys that are appropriate for the developmental level of the child, as well as toys that allow for regressions.

A room laden with boxes and closets of expensive toys is sometimes more distracting than beneficial. Often the more simple and modest toys lend themselves to the most productive sessions. A typical playroom stock might include the following:

1. Crayons and paper: Above all other items, these are perhaps the most versatile and most essential. They lend themselves to all manner of expression. Many therapists have been "mortally wounded" with jumbo red crayons utilized as guns! The most complex of games can develop with a crayon and piece of paper, as well as the most enlightening drawings from fantasy and reality.
2. Clay: This medium offers the child the opportunity for three-dimensional expression.
3. Puppets: Hand puppets lend themselves to active and verbal expression and allow for aggressive battling, one puppet against another.
4. Dolls: The most overtly symbolic of the toys, dolls are often given the character traits of the child and his family. A set of family dolls can be very illustrative of the family life style and alliances when used by the child in routine play.
5. Dollhouse: The dollhouse represents the home of the child and is a toy that offers a microcosm of the family setting.
6. Water (optional): Water play is often utilized by autistic children, preschoolers, and obsessive-compulsive children.
7. Gun (optional): Obviously a symbol of aggression, it is utilized in the playroom. However, when this article is absent, children appear to

have little difficulty locating other toys on which they bestow destructive powers.
8. Toy telephone: The telephone, symbolic of communication within our culture, is often used for fantasy conversations with significant figures outside of the playroom.

THERAPY WITH THE PRESCHOOL CHILD

> The wolf also shall dwell with the lamb, and the leopard shall lie down with the kid; and the calf and the young lion and the fatling together; and a little child shall lead them.
>
> The Old Testament, Isaiah 11:6

Although it is doubtful that Isaiah's prophecy was directed toward the psychotherapy of children, he could easily be describing the impulses and ambivalences that bring the child to psychotherapy in the parents' search for "The Peaceable Kingdom." More importantly, the last line of the prophecy reminds one of perhaps the most important dictum of play therapy—the child takes the lead. (Hopefully, the therapist's acceptance of this advice will lead to better results than did the thirteenth century interpretation of this prophecy, which led to the disastrous Children's Crusade.)

Allowing the child to take the lead in play requires that the therapist understand what normal play is for that particular developmental stage and to have some awareness of how he (the therapist) might appropriately be a part of the play. Play as an interaction between two children is said to begin between ages 18 and 24 months. At this age, play is described as parallel, with children playing side by side. (see chapter 3) As the child approaches the age of 3 and until around age 6, the play becomes more thematic, centering around oedipal concerns and fears. (see chapter 4) Fantasy abounds and the child is more able to engage in cooperative play.

Understanding the normal play of a preschool child can alleviate some of the anxieties of the beginning therapist. When a 5-year-old boy appears intent on tearing the head off the father doll or repeatedly runs over the doll with a toy truck, the therapist is less tempted to interpret these actions as signs of social maladjustment and to see them in a more realistic framework as an acceptable way of dealing with the conflicts of this developmental stage.

The preschool child is often very fluid in fantasies, making for a play session that is ever changing, unpredictable, and filled with delightful surprises. Preschool children will often enter into adult role play as a mother, father, nurse, doctor, or fireman. They show great concern as to their position of power in the world (family) and not uncommonly will enact fantasy scenes in which all major decisions and actions evolve as per their dictate.

Consider the following example. Melanie, a frightened 4½-year-old has been occupied for some time in feeding, diapering, and bedding the three baby dolls in the playroom. She has portrayed her mothering role in the kindest, most nurturing manner imaginable. Suddenly, she spies a hand puppet of a clown in the corner of the room. She immediately labels the clown as mother and assumes a fetal position next to the dolls with her thumb in her mouth. Very shortly, Melanie decides that she and her three sisters can have more fun if mother is not around and begins to plot, with the dolls, the means of mother's demise, which happens to be locking mother in the bedroom. Although much of this play is clearly oedipally oriented and apparently normal play, the therapist should always be aware of the content of such play in his search for conflicts that go beyond those of normal development.

This case is illustrative of such conflicts. Melanie, for the first time, mentions being locked in a room as a horrible punishment. It was later learned that mother did, in fact, use this form of punishment and, on other occasions, had locked Melanie in her room when she was having overnight guests. Melanie has subtly communicated a trauma and in later sessions repetitively played out the trauma with numerous variations. Her final working through of the conflict occured long after mother had eliminated this frightening isolation technique. Melanie entered the playroom, turned out the lights, and announced, "No one can see me. No one can hurt me," and in her own somewhat omnipotent manner, informed the therapist that her fear was diminishing.

Throughout therapy with preschool children, direct interpretation can be kept to a minimum. The child often does not have the abstract abilities to understand and utilize the interpretation, and when the interpretation brings painful material out of fantasy into reality, the thematic play will often cease. For Melanie, simple reflections and comments such as, "Ooh, that sounds scary," or "I wonder what's going to happen now?" were all the encouragement she needed to continue her exploration and eventually create her own corrective experience.

THERAPY WITH THE OVERCONTROLLED CHILD

Most children, like Melanie, enter into the world of play readily and with little pause. There are, however, those shy, frightened, inhibited children who are able to sit for sessions on end, secluded mutely in a corner of the playroom. Such a child is certainly a challenge to the beginning therapist. Whatever the reason for this withdrawn behavior, whether it is from fear and the perception that one is defenseless in the presence of an adult or whether it is from repeated sexual or physical abuse, the therapist will probably be most successful by approaching whatever cinders of the normal child that remain aglow in his isolation. This approach, if too direct or too enthusiastic, will only drive the child further into his corner. The therapist is like a young boy sitting quietly in the grass in hopes of petting a frightened kitten. When he makes a sudden move, the kitten runs farther away. When he remains still and appears unconcerned, the kitten comes closer to investigate. Through patience, the boy is eventually able to establish himself as a nonthreatening, trustworthy companion.

An approach to the remnants of normality in the child can take several forms. The therapist is aware that play is a normal function of childhood and a means of communication for the child, so perhaps the least threatening way of involving the child is to communicate on his own turf. For example, a 5-year-old boy compliantly enters the playroom as though ordered to do so. He immediately stations himself next to the sink and refuses to move until the session has ended and he is returned to his mother. Toward the end of the first session, the therapist, who had attempted direct contact earlier with the child, seated himself a "safe" distance from the child and engaged in puppet play with a puppet on each hand. He created a dialogue between the two puppets that was both emotionally laden and humorous. He made no direct moves toward the child. Much to the disappointment of the therapist, the child also made no direct moves toward him or the puppets. The second session, as the first, began in silence on the part of the child. The only difference this time was that he positioned himself closer to the puppets which happened to be lying on the floor. After a few minutes, he hesitantly kicked the puppets toward the therapist, who took the cue and entered into animated puppet dialogue. Feeling somewhat more confident this time, the therapist allowed the puppets to occasionally address their comments toward the child. By the end of the session, the child had softly requested to be "Mr. Groucho."

One might be accused of having seduced the child into play and having directed and led the course of the session. Be that as it may, it was an effective means of involving the child, after which the therapist quickly reverted to parallel play allowing the child to create the fantasies and secure his proper status in the session.

Another sort of inhibition can be witnessed in the playroom. This is the child who consciously avoids material he has already identified as painful. Although this is seen more commonly in older children, this seems an appropriate point for discussion. There are occasions when the therapist is aware of major traumas or conflicts that have recently occurred in the life of the child. The therapist waits for the child to disclose the painful events but finds that, during these periods, the child's play becomes void of overt fantasy, and he (the child) insists upon engaging in a repetitive activity, such as tossing a ball against the wall. If the therapist or the child can arrive at a non-threatening basis of communication, a pattern can be established that affords the child a specific instrument for communicating and working through a specific problem. For example: Donald was a 7-year-old boy who was abandoned by his mother shortly after birth and left in the care of his father, a gentleman who had been diagnosed as schizophrenic. Donald's father had avoided all treatment for his illness with the exception of three forced hospitalizations in a state institution and was believed by the community to be delusional the majority of the time. Donald's welfare was closely guarded by two social agencies that were attempting, for well-founded reasons, to maintain the father and son as a family unit. The father's paranoid disposition had forced Donald to promise never to discuss him (the father) with anyone at anytime. When information filtered down to the therapist of particularly irrational escapades that had involved the father and son, and the therapist confronted the child with his knowledge, he (the therapist) was faced with a verbally noncommunicative, frightened little boy. The solution to this dilemma came in a most unusual way. Knowing, through the teacher, that Donald had recently been publicly and harshly chastised by his father, the decision was made not to confront the child with this information; rather, he was allowed to avoid the topic completely. In the course of his play, still giving no clues as to any conflicts, he mentioned going to a movie and then recounted the entire plot of the film. The therapist, greatly modifying the storytelling technique of Richard Gardner (1971), then suggested that perhaps Donald would like to write the script for a movie. Donald entered into the activity with glee as the clinician recorded the story word for word as Donald told it. Donald drew illustrations for the book. The document that evolved was filled with the fears and confusions that Donald had previously been unable to express. Its characters were so thinly disguised that, at times, even Donald would correct himself as he mistakenly used his or his father's name instead of that of the characters. The book would go untouched for months until a conflict arose at home or father would become more blatantly ill, at which time Donald would suggest that another chapter be added to the book. He completed the book one month before therapy was to be terminated and one week after the therapist had decided their work was done. Donald had not yet been informed of the impending termination.

THERAPY WITH THE UNDERCONTROLLED CHILD

Another type of child who may bring awe to the beginning therapist is the one who is aggressive, destructive, and undercontrolled. With the overcontrolled child, it is usually unnecessary to mention limitations on play or behavior. With the undercontrolled child, limit setting becomes a major concern. Various theories suggest different solutions for treating such a child. Some present criticisms that limits and formal structuring destroy the permissiveness of the session and impede the freedom of expression. It is the belief of this therapist that every effort should be made to assure free expression and that every effort by made to extinguish physical aggression directed toward other people. If it is the responsibility of the therapist to see that no physical harm comes to the child during therapy, it is also his responsibility to see that the child inflicts no physical harm on others. With a child who has a history of assaultive behavior, it may be wise to begin therapy with a somewhat more structured approach. The child is offered the same freedoms to "talk about anything he wishes and to play whatever he wants to play." He is informed, as are the other children, that "this is a very special place." In addition, he is told that no one will hurt him here nor will he be allowed to hurt anyone else. For some children, this statement turns the playroom into a special place, for it is the first place they have encountered restrictions. Such an introduction may provide comfort for some of these children, as they are often fearful of being harmed and often terrified of their lack of self-control and desirous or even demanding that limits be established to help them gain mastery over their impulses.

Having made such a promise to the child, the therapist must then maintain the promise. When a child threatens to throw a building block at the therapist, the therapist must respond. He may reflect, "Charles, you look angry and when you get angry, you want to hurt people, but remember this is a place where you don't get hurt and you don't hurt anyone else. Maybe you can punch the dummy and show me how mad you are." If the child throws the block, a more direct approach is merited. With children in tantrum or children who impulsively break the rules, physical restraint can sometimes be of value. Holding the child firmly, but in a manner that causes no physical pain, gives him time to regain control and reflect upon the source of his impulses. If, when released, the child immediately resumes his attack, he is again restrained. During each restraint, the same phrase is repeated, "This is a place where no one will hurt you and you will not be allowed to hurt anyone else." When the child has regained his composure, the session can proceed.

Sending the child from the playroom in times of dyscontrol can be misinterpreted by the child. It may appear that the therapist is saying that these are emotions that cannot be dealt with in therapy. It may also appear that the therapist is rejecting the child. It is sometimes the case that such behaviors develop as a means of testing whether one will accept or reject the child. It is also the case that these behaviors may be a part of the child's initial resistance to therapy. Sending him away from the site of therapy does little to confront this resistance.

This sort of behavioral problem, more than any other, demands the most immediate examination of the therapist's countertransference to the child. The playroom is not the site for sadistic reprisals against the child, and the therapist should be alert to any such tendencies he may have. He is to accept and attempt to understand the behavior but, at the same time, aid the child in rechanneling his emotions and modifying his activities.

The therapist, who, in the name of permissiveness, allows the child physically to batter and abuse him (the therapist), cannot long maintain a respect for the child or himself. Limit setting is sometimes necessary, and when limits have been established, testing of those limits is recognized and pointed out to the child without delay. As the child learns through repetition, it may be expected that one will be required to restate and enforce the limits on several occasions.

Having alluded to the issue of countertransference, perhaps a digression to discuss briefly transference and countertransference will be of value.

TRANSFERENCE

What are transferences? They are new editions or facsimiles of the impulses and phantasies which are aroused and made conscious during the progress of analysis; but they have this peculiarity, which is characteristic for their species, that they replace some earlier person by the person of the physician.

Freud (1953), p. 116.

Thus was transference defined by the progenitor of psychoanalysis. Transference for the early analysts was seen as a connection between the preconscious and the unconscious. It was viewed as an entirely intrapsychic phenomenon with minimal or no rational basis.

During psychoanalytic treatment, the repressed unconscious material is revived, and since the material contains many infantile elements, the infantile strivings are reactivated and seek gratification in the transference. As the most important relationship of the child is that with his parents, the relationship between patient and analyst established in the transference becomes analogous to, or, at times, even similar to the patient's relationship with his parents in childhood. The patient endows the analyst with the same magic powers and omniscience which in childhood, he attributed to his parents. The traits of submissiveness and rebellion, in transference, likewise reflect the attitude of the child to his parents. The patient behaves irrationally in the psychoanalytic situation; it often takes a long time to make him see the irrationality of his behavior, which is deeply rooted in his unconscious infantile life.

Nunberg (1955), p. 781.

Helping the patient see the irrationality of his behavior through the examination and interpretation of the transference is a major goal of the analytic process. Through such examination, the patient will hopefully recognize the source of conflicts and, upon recognition, be able to alter his behavior toward the analyst, arriving at a more realistic relationship. The analyst has acted as a catalyst for the re-enactment of infantile experiences in the analytic situation. Once this phenomenon is recognized by the patient as a re-enactment and is dealt with on a conscious level, hopefully the transference will have been utilized as a corrective experience for the past in the present.

Although this phenomenon is widely recognized and accepted among the analysts and dynamically oriented psychotherapists of adults, adolescents, and older children, there are theoretical camps that battle as to the ability of a child to form a transference relationship. Some argue that such a process is possible only after the ego has surfaced and has begun to mature, which they believe is certainly not the case in the preschool child. Others maintain that the ego is present from infancy, and children are, in fact, capable of forming transference relationships.

Whether or not either side is correct is not the purpose of this discussion. What is important is that a phenomenon exists with even preschool children that resembles transference and can be utilized by the clinician to make advances in the therapy. For example: A 4-year-old boy, in play, sets a table with the toy dishes. He proceeds to prepare all of his favorite foods, describing each and how wonderful they will taste. When his preparations are complete and the dinner is to be served, he informs the therapist, "This is for me. You've been bad." This child, through play, is providing much information that is valuable to the therapy. He is describing his own needs for nurturance and is beginning to realize that these needs may not always be met. He is relating to the therapist as he wishes to and sometimes *does* relate to his own father, who has noted of late that his son responds to him with much ambivalence. One can discern in the child anger, omnipotence, and the frustrations of the oedipal phase. His behavior differs from the adult in that the adult often re-enact the oedipal conflicts of the past; the child, on the other hand, is re-enacting more recent conflicts, as he is presently entrapped within the oedipal phase.

This case is void of much of the complexity and shrouded behavior of the adult transference. The child has not yet developed the intricate meshwork of defenses that necessitate the obliqueness of the adult, yet considering the developmental stage of this patient and the concreteness of his intellectual functioning, his behavior toward the therapist is, in many ways, comparable to that of the adult patient toward his therapist. The honesty and forthright manner of the child may greatly abbreviate the therapist's task of understanding the type and source of conflicts.

The therapist is faced with an important decision when confronted with material that stems from conflictual origins. He must determine whether or not to make a verbal interpretation and, in so doing, hopefully bring the conflict into the open for a more conscious resolution, or whether to allow the play to continue as an emotional release, or in some way to alter the play, so as to help create a corrective experience.

Verbal interpretations for preschool children often fall on deaf ears or, if partially understood, may disrupt the play and subsequently interrupt or terminate the flow of information and expression. The same is true of interpretations made incautiously or in a manner that would threaten the latency child or adolescent. In the case presented,

interpretation is unnecessary and probably ill advised. The child is presenting material that is conflictual; however, the conflict is normal for his age. Through play, he is exploring his alternatives and "acting in" the conflict. The therapist's attempt in any way to disrupt this exploration may inhibit the work the child has already initiated and, in fact, counter the advantages of play as a therapeutic modality.

The process of displacement is an essential feature of play therapy. The child in play therapy is offered the opportunity to transfer his emotions not only onto the therapist but also onto the objects of play that surround him. The child has the option of identifying a doll as "mother" and then defiantly burying her in a sandbox or of shooting a puppet and, in so doing, momentarily removing a troublesome father. The guise of play allows the child a safe exploration of forbidden impulses. Similarly, he can react to the therapist as a parent and express hatred or love and yet do so in the context of a game or play and never threaten his "real world" relationship with the therapist. The child is often able to create his own corrective experiences without ever undergoing the intense emotions, insecurity, and fear of alienation that is often a part of the exploration of the irrational adult transference.

COUNTERTRANSFERENCE

Broadly defined, countertransference occurs when "The patient's personality, or the material he produces, or the analytic situation as such represents an object from the...[therapist's] past, onto which past feelings and wishes are projected," (Annie Reich, 1951, p. 26) or "...where the patient serves merely as a tool to gratify some need of the analyst, such as alleviation of anxiety or mastery of guilt feelings." (Hinsie and Campbell, 1970, p. 167)

Countertransference plays an important role in the therapist's understanding of the child. It is through momentary identifications with the child that the therapist is able to comprehend and recognize the complex productions of the child's psyche. It is important that the therapist examine these identifications and understand their origins in his own past, lest the therapist lose his objectivity and relate to the child as though the child is the primary source of these emotional productions. For example: The therapist, earlier described, who follows a dictum of permissiveness and allows the child to batter or abuse him in the playroom, may one day find that he wishes to retaliate physically against the child. In examining the source of these emotions, he may discover that he has re-created in the playroom a situation reminiscent of his own childhood. He has given the child full voice and has constrained himself to accept whatever behavior is directed toward him. The situation and behavior of the child invokes feelings from his own childhood of being insignificant and helpless, of being overpowered and squelched by his own parents, of rebellion and of the desire to fight his way to liberation. Recognition of the countertransference allows the therapist consciously to adjust his behavior toward the child. The failure to explore the origin of the countertransference may result in an antitherapeutic relationship and hinder therapeutic progress.

PSYCHOTHERAPY AND THE LATENCY CHILD

During latency, from onset at approximately 6 years of age, characterized by the fluidity and unpredictability of the oedipal period, to the closure of the period with the early stirrings of genital sexuality, which heralds the onset of adolescence at around age 12 years, the child experiences what might be termed an "intellectual quickening." (see chapter 5) The child, for the first time, understands the concepts of time and death and is capable of mathematical calculations and deductive reasoning. The superego is defined, and the child develops a sense of ethics and morality. The ego is strengthened and the defenses become firmly entrenched. The child not only enters into cooperative play but solicits peer interaction and understands the concepts of loyalty and friendship. The child is confronted by the concept of reality and is able to test reality accurately. All of these factors affect play.

With this new sense of reality and strengthened defenses, primary process material of fantasy is more closely guarded. The rigid superego serves to tighten and order activities. The spontaneity of the preschool child is not readily apparent. The child becomes concerned about rules and their interpretations. He chooses formally prescribed games and calculated activities over the more loosely defined, open play of the oedipal period.

For the latency child, one may wish to add board games to the playroom stock. Although fantasies are not freely elicited, the child's approach to the game can tell you about his self-image. He may be a fierce competitor who undauntedly strives to establish his position in a manner not dissimilar to the oedipal child who assumes an omnipotent role in his fantasies, or he may make little effort to win and present as a disillusioned, broken individual who sees himself as weak and incapable.

The fantasies remain, the format is different, and the therapist must learn how to decipher new codes. For example: Michael, a 10-year-old, informs the therapist he has recently been involved in serious research to perfect a "stink bomb." He has combined all manner of vile ingredients from the family medicine chest and the refrigerator and is presently aging them in an underground vat in the backyard. When asked how he planned to use this concoction, he hesitated and then replied that he would spread it around the house of a girl who lived down the street. One might interpret this interchange as a statement of the latency male's purported fear or dislike of the opposite sex; however, there seemed to be more involved. Michael's enthusiasm made it appear as though he were on the verge of a great discovery. It was then the therapist's task to determine what Michael wished to discover. The question posed by Michael's research is "What makes foul odors?" As it turns out, Michael's question was of great personal significance. If he understood the source of fetid odors, he might more readily understand the functioning of his own body and the odors of elimination. With this understanding under his belt, he believed that he was only a step away from deciphering his sexual being. How very different from the oedipal child who lays his cards on the table and asks, "Where do babies come from?"

The overt interpretation of Michael's account would have been far too threatening to this well-defended young man, and yet a response to the material seemed indicated. The therapist asked Michael how he believed the stink bomb would smell. Michael replied, "like the worst smell in the world." The therapist then wondered aloud what the worst smell in the world might be. Michael replied with much hesitancy, "the bathroom." Through discussion, it was learned that Michael believed that the odor of feces was created by chemicals combining with food; therefore, he had taken chemicals from the medicine cabinet and combined them with the contents of the refrigerator. He was scientifically testing reality. The therapist commented that many amazing things happen in the human body and that Michael seemed interested in understanding the science and chemistry of the body. Michael was able, with little show of embarrassment, to proceed with questions related to the penis (not to his own, but the "universal concept of penis") and urination, thereby, giving the therapist the opportunity to introduce and explore sexuality and genital functioning. Michael's interest was apparent and he would occasionally ask for clarification or raise new questions. The fact that all of his questions were academically cloaked seemed to ease his approach to the subject. At no time was he able to ask a question which might imply that his interest was in his own body as opposed to that greater body known as science!

Special problems of latency, such as over-controlled and undercontrolled behaviors, can be approached in a manner similar to that described in the previous section on the preschool child. One must, however, adopt an approach and language that is no way patronizing to the child. For example: With the overcontrolled child where puppets were used to evoke participation, one might substitute a deck of cards or a checker board which might have more appeal for the middle and late latency child.

PSYCHOTHERAPY WITH THE ADOLESCENT

Saturday, 30 January 1943
Dear Kitty,
I'm boiling with rage, and yet I mustn't show it. I'd like to stamp my feet, scream, give Mummy a good shaking, cry, and I don't know what else, because of the horrible words, mocking looks, and accusations which are leveled at me repeatedly each day, and find their mark, like shafts from a tightly strung bow, and which are just as hard to draw from my body.
Anne Frank (1952), p. 75-76.

Anne Frank's entry into her diary is a statement that development can proceed and stages reached at the appropriate age even under the most horrible circumstances and in the most painful settings. This brief excerpt reveals many features characteristic of adolescence. It shows exquisite sensitivity to criticism, the tendency toward rebellion and self-liberation, as well as the hesitancy to disturb the family unit. It demonstrates the frustrations of indecision and the romance of martyrdom. Adolescence is a period of marked physical and emotional development. It is a time for many when physical changes and sexual drives appear too quickly for emotional acceptance. The early adolescent (12 to 14 years) often finds himself in the habitus of the adult with the attitudes of a latency child. By middle adolescence (14 to 16 years), he begins to dabble in the world of ideals in search of an environment he can identify as adult and his own. He may show great interest in international affairs, the question of legal abortion, and political reform. He delves headfirst into a world he has previously identified as the domain of adults. The side he chooses to support of defend

is not infrequently the opposite of that espoused by his parents. He is well on his way to the process of emancipation—the task of late adolescence. For a review of the psychological and physiological changes of adolescence, refer to chapter 6.

Anna Freud (1958) recognizes a similarity between the adolescent and two other types of patients—those involved in unhappy love affairs and those in mourning.

To my mind the libidinal position of the adolescent has much in common with the two states described above. The adolescent too is engaged in an emotional struggle, and moreover in one of extreme urgency and immediacy. His libido is on the point of detaching itself from the parents and of cathecting new objects. Some mourning for the objects of the past is inevitable; so are the "crushes," i.e., the happy or unhappy love affairs with adults outside the family, or with other adolescents, whether of the opposite or of the same sex; so is, further, a certain amount of narcissistic withdrawal which bridges the gap during periods when no external object is cathected.

pp. 262-263.

The therapist who wishes to work with the adolescent must be alert and aware of the fluctuations and potential volatility of this age group, from the withdrawal noted by Anna Freud to the most aggressive of verbal assaults. The therapist is often met with strong resistance and immediately discredited. Confidentiality becomes a prime consideration at this time. How can one reveal his innermost thoughts to someone who may betray him to the ultimate adversary, his parents? Above all else, the therapist must be accepting. The adolescent often expects, and moreover even elicits, criticism that is then used as a basis for rejecting the therapist. Interpretations should be guarded and limited, as they are often perceived as criticism.

Most adolescents fear the loss of autonomy. Unlike the younger child who comes to therapy because his parents bring him, the adolescent may refuse therapy because it is suggested by his parents. He interprets the suggestion as coercion that is directed toward his enslavement in childhood. Likewise, the transference to the therapist is often one of an overpowering parent, an individual intent on maintaining the adolescent's behavior within certain guidelines and controlling his thoughts. Fraiberg (1955) suggests that therapy with the adolescent begins by assuring him that he, in fact, has the control. She cites Aichhorn's approach to delinquents as a model for introducing therapy, "'You don't need to tell me anything you don't wish to,' to which one can safely add, 'Though when you know me better you may *want* to tell me some things so that I can help you better.'" (p. 279)

The therapist listens to the adolescent, understands his dilemma, and accepts his approach—with the realization that the method the adolescent uses to resolve a conflict today may differ markedly from the method he will use tomorrow. The therapist is supportive and yet not zealously so. Reassurance to a young lady that her choice to engage in intercourse is a justified decision may be interpreted differently on different days. The therapist would fare better to recognize the sexual urges of the patient and leave the resolution of moral issues in her hands.

It is very important that the therapist recognize the discontent, emotional fluctuations, suspiciousness, and narcissism of normal adolescence and differentiate these characteristics from significant adolescent pathology. It is important to be able to assure and reassure the adolescent of the normality of his developmental conflicts, while at the same time helping him work through pathological conflicts.

In many cases, what the therapist provides is the possibility of a relationship with a sensitive adult—a species heretofore identified as rare or nonexistent by the adolescent. The adolescent often perceives himself as an emotionally laden being, burgeoning with the most intense feelings. As such, once a relationship of trust is established, he may willingly share these feelings as they pass the screen of consciousness in rapid succession. The therapist may facilitate the sharing by noting the postures of the patient, his gestures, and verbal hesitations. Many adolescents are not only willing, but eager, to explore these aspects of their selves that provide further knowledge as to their identity and add to their accumulation of narcissistic wealth.

The adolescent, even in the early stages, is not usually a candidate for the playroom, and, as such, a different approach to uncovering the primary process must be used. He is more able to provide the therapist with free associations and to recount his dreams. Although again, warning against inappropriate and premature interpretation should be heeded.

Occasionally the adolescent will spontaneously select an expressive medium to utilize within the therapeutic setting. (When the therapist suggests the use of drawings or writing as a form of expression, he is often confronted with resistance.) Two brief cases may be illustrative of this phenomenon. Gary, a somewhat obsessive-compulsive 14-year-old male anorexic entered therapy by immediately informing the therapist "I hate you, I would like to see you hang from this hospital and rot." Although his verbal expression of disdain lessened, any overt attempt on the part of the therapist to explore feelings was met with incredible resistance. Gary, a collector of tropical fish, in an effort to maintain silence within the session, began drawing pictures of fish and marine life. It became clear that asking questions about fish (about which he was very knowledgeable) was permissible, whereas questions regarding himself were not. He produced hundreds of drawings during therapy—big fish eating smaller fish, smaller fish dying of hunger because there were no fish smaller than they to consume, and sharks emerging from the sea to devour islands. Gary was able to describe the feelings and intents of every fish. He drew male fish and female fish and discussed the sexual lives of fish. Over time, two fish began to appear repetitively: one, a large fish that had to be caged and controlled to prohibit his indiscriminate devouring of the entire world; and the other, a small fish, always alone, always pictured in a corner of an otherwise void ocean. During the investigation of the "Kingdom of Fishes" and the discussion of fish growth and fish alternatives, Gary gained weight and progressed. Although he was never able to express any strong feelings of affection for the therapist, he was eventually able consciously to relate the marine world to his own world and to realize that if a fish had alternatives, so did he.

Another case is that of a 15-year-old boy with a 2-year history of court involvement for delinquent acts. His "street-wise" manner and "tough guy" exterior were such integral parts of his defense system that any attempt on the part of the therapist to go beneath that exterior was met with profanity and threats. Much to the therapist's surprise, this young man turned out to be a very talented and sensitive poet. In his poetry, he was able to reveal many childhood conflicts, fears, insecurities, and not infrequently, suicidal ideation. As the relationship of trust grew, the poetry became more revealing, and it became apparent that he was working on a conscious level to deal with his problems. Both he and the therapist were aware of the significance of the poetry, and yet he remained resistant to discussing his feelings and life outside of that context. One day, suddenly concerned that his feelings might be exposed, he informed the therapist, "You know, if you ever showed those poems to anyone, it wouldn't mean anything. They are just poems."

Although work with the adolescent is often frustrating and may require great flexibility as well as restraint on the part of the therapist, there are few more satisfying cases for a therapist than that of the successfully treated adolescent. The therapist is privileged to witness the Aristotelian metamorphosis. He enters therapy with a child and sees that child give birth to the adult—a functioning, independent future-oriented person.

FAMILY THERAPY

Having focused primarily on the individual therapy of the child and his reactions and interactions in a playroom or, in the case of the adolescent, in the therapist's office, one is reminded that the cures of psychotherapy are determined by the behavioral changes that occur in the "real world" environment, rather than in the therapeutic setting. There are many therapists who maintain that an effective way of treating the child is to center the therapy more closely within the environment—the family. When various members of a related group undergo simultaneous interaction with a therapist, the term "family therapy" is applied.

Family therapy is regarded by some of its leading proponents as a school of ordered principles with specific rules and procedures. However, many other clinicians view family therapy as a continuously evolving and adaptable process: ". . . not a treatment method but a clinical orientation that includes many different therapeutic approaches." (Haley, 1975, p. 1881)

What most hold in common is the view of the family as a unit, and, as such, the behaviors, pathology, and strengths of its individual members affect all other members of the unit. The unit is the active participant in therapy. The family is seen as being able to create, maintain, or extinguish pathology. Tseng and McDermott (1979) described a family unit as follows:

The concept of family involves a complicated biopsychosocial organization with multiple dimensions of functions. A family is not merely an aggregate of related yet separate individuals; it is a matrix of a special group with a special bond to live together and which has the potential to develop, grow, and contract. As a matrix a family is involved in the functions of communication, role division, and transactions.

p. 23.

Some of the advantages of therapeutic work with the family as a unit are readily apparent. It can serve to diminish the possible isolating effect of labeling, as is sometimes seen when one child is in therapy, and his siblings, in their rivalrous manner, attempt to provoke him by calling him "crazy."

Sometimes great progress is made in therapy only to be followed by regression when the child returns to an unaltered environment. Consider the depressed, abused child who is hospitalized and then returns to a setting where the potential of abuse remains. Family therapy in this situation can support the child's progress, deter the regression, and hopefully help the family in its attempt to overcome pathology. Family therapy delegates to each family member a responsibility for communicating with and advancing the growth of its individual components.

The approaches to family therapy are varied. Ackerman (1966), one of the pioneers of family therapy, approached the family in an unplanned manner, observing the interactions and alliances of each member and then interpreting the behavior. Satir (1964) placed great emphasis on the marital unit and centered her work with the family around restructuring, defining, and hopefully, obtaining a healthy marital dyad. Minuchin (1974) attempted to help the family cure itself by advocating that the therapist join with the family to transform the structure of "the family system" through a feedback process. Bowen (1966) utilized several techniques from hospitalizing the entire family to seeing multiple families in groups.

Some therapists act as negotiators among family members. (Zuk, 1969) Others prefer less direct involvement in family crisis. Some therapists, such as Villeneuve (1979), chose to use techniques of child psychotherapy, such as drawing and puppet play, in the family session. For most therapists, the time of the session ranges between 45 minutes and one hour. MacGregor *et al.* (1964), on the other hand, opted for extended sessions of many hours or days. The list of theories and techniques is almost without limit, each having merits and points of much contention and debate.

If one is to accept Haley's premise that all therapeutic endeavors, whether with an individual, with selected family members, or with the family as a unit, have an impact on the family and are a means of doing therapy with the family (Haley, 1975), then each psychotherapist is, in certain aspects, a family therapist.

Indications and Contraindications for Family Therapy

Extensive debate exists concerning the indications for family therapy. Kolb (1968) stated, "Family psychotherapy has found its greatest application in the treatment of those neurotic, psychotic, and personality disorders in which individuals 'act out,'" for instance, aggressive behavior, maladaptation of children or adolescents at school, and the addictive states. (p. 520) He also suggested that family therapy is of value in situations where psychotic defenses are aggravated or perpetuated by "conflict-ridden" family interactions.

Kolb believed that family therapy is contraindicated for children or adolescents, especially when

...one or both parents is known to have an established paranoid psychosis or has a history of a personality disorder with traits of dishonesty, deceitfulness, untruthfulness or current antisocial behavior.

ibid., p. 570.

Haley (1975) treated the controversy of indications and contraindications for family therapy as a "non-question." (McDermott, 1981, p. 411) He viewed individual sessions as a necessity in some cases—particularly in families of great conflict and violence—for preparing groundwork for later therapy with the family as a unit. (Haley, 1975, p. 1881)

McDermott (1981) outlined the indications and contraindications for family therapy as suggested by Ackerman (1966), Kramer (1970), Wynne (1965), Brown (1972), Malone (1979), and Schechter (1980). The following is a composite of those outlines.

Indications

1. Disturbance in family relationship; interpersonal and intrapersonal conflicts, marital disturbances, fixed patterns of distancing with threats and episodes of destructive eruptions, overstimulation of aggressive and sexual impulses, and acute family crises.
2. Disturbance in communication; amorphous communication, collective chaos in cognition and erratic distancing, failure to develop effective speech.
3. Emotional disorders in children and adolescents; developmental delays, hyperactivity, severe aggressive behavior, functional enuresis and encopresis, overwhelming sibling rivalry, severe froms of separation anxiety, problems of separation in adolescents, acting out behavior, such as delinquency, sexual promiscuity and drug abuse, and reducing secondary gains of emotional disorders.
4. Chronic physical illness and psychophysiological disorders; for example, anorexia nervosa, asthma, diabetes, cystic fibrosis, and hemophilia.

5. Failure of individual therapy or preparation for intensive individual psychotherapy or psychoanalysis.

Contraindications

1. Disruption or threat of disruption in family relationships; divorcing families and refusal of significant family members to participate.
2. Dishonesty; tendency toward lying and deceit within the family and inability to be honest, psychopathic destructiveness.
3. Focusing on family transaction may result in increased resistance, intensify sadomasochistic tendencies among family members, or increase the threat of physical violence within the family.
4. In severe forms of emotional disorders, such as severe depression, acute schizophrenia, paranoid schizophrenia, progressive deterioration of one member of the family toward paranoid conditions or severe psychophysiological disorders.
5. In cases of late adolescents who are attempting to separate themselves psychologically from the family.
6. Unavailability of skilled therapists.

The Case of Lisa

Lisa, a 13-year-old girl, was referred for tantrum behavior and destruction of family possessions. She had broken doors in the home, destroyed the family television, and, most recently, had thrown her sister's birthday cake onto the floor. Lisa had had a neurological examination, including an electroencephalogram, which was normal. During several individual psychotherapy sessions, Lisa expressed guilt feelings about her behavior but continued to act out.

Family sessions were scheduled and attended by Lisa, her mother, father, and two younger sisters. In the course of family therapy, information was obtained that had not surfaced in the individual sessions. Although in the individual sessions, it had been noted that Lisa often complained of being "bored," it was not until the family sessions that this word took on a special significance. Each family member, at some point, described his or her "boredom"; for example, the father stated that he was "bored" by Lisa's watching television rather than playing chess with him. It soon became apparent that the word "bored" was a family idiom used in lieu of the word "angered." In fact, the family had invested much energy in denying that anyone was ever angry. Lisa's behavior was totally unacceptable in this home of preordained pacifism. It was noticed and pointed out to the family that Lisa seemed to be the one who expressed the anger of the whole family, and often the parents or sisters would subtly cue her outbursts. For example, during the course of therapy, mother learned that she was again pregnant. She was experiencing some angry feelings toward her husband whom she blamed for the pregnancy. The day she learned that the pregnancy test was positive, Lisa requested to go swimming with friends. Rather than make a decision as to her daughter's activities, she told Lisa that she should contact her father at work and ask his permission. The mother already knew that the father was experiencing a particularly trying day and had requested that the family not interrupt his work. When Lisa telephoned her father, she was met with an immediate refusal. Lisa reacted by destroying several of her father's power tools with a wrench. This sort of interaction was noted time after time. Lisa was frequently the "scapegoat" of the family.

Part of the therapist's responsibility was to prevent a continuous scapegoating of Lisa or any other family member and to interpret the isolating effect such action can have. The family sessions proceeded along lines similar to group therapy, with the therapist shifting the focus from one member to another. The therapist had constantly to evaluate his own feelings to safeguard against any tendencies he might have to ally himself with one family faction and alienate the other. The goal of the therapy was to improve the interfamily communication and to explore healthy ways for each member to express feelings that had previously been taboo.

In this case, the therapist assumed a far more active role than he usually took with his individual cases. Interpretations were made more freely, based on the family members' interactions with each other in the therapeutic session, rather than on past memories and events. Seldom was the phrase, "How did that make you feel?" used; rather, a more common approach was "What are we doing now? or "Let's take a look at how what you are saying is affecting everyone else." Attention was paid to postures, gestures, and seating choices and then interpreted to the family in an effort to help them more easily define their alliances and positions within the family.

Although theoretical frameworks, methods, and approaches may differ extensively, family therapy is an essential component of therapeutic work with children and adolescents. Effective inclusion of the family or other significant people in the therapeutic process helps immensely in recognizing subtle aspects of healthy and pathological relationships. Family therapy mobilizes the resources of the child and the family as a whole for enhancement of healing and for progress on the infinite path of human development.

TERMINATION

Having touched on psychotherapeutic techniques for children of varying ages, it seems appropriate to discuss briefly the termination of therapy. Unlike the adult or even the adolescent who is able to see therapy as a goal-oriented process that, if successful, will eventually spell its own termination, the younger child is often unaware of goals and grows to view the therapy sessions as a part of a very special relationship. Suddenly to threaten that relationship or suddenly to sever the bonds that have grown over a period of months or years is a trauma that is not easily understood. The announcement of a planned termination should provide for an adequate number of therapy sessions to assure the resolution of conflicts that arise as a result of the impending termination. Once the plan for termination is announced, it is not uncommon for the child's behavior to regress and for the presenting symptoms to reappear. When the termination is perceived as a loss by the child, he may also express very direct anger toward the therapist for his feelings of rejection. There is a danger during this period that the family will also react to the termination with anger and remove the child from therapy before a satisfactory resolution is made.

A frequently expressed concern of the child is that the therapist might forget him after he is gone. This is sometimes followed by efforts on the child's part to attach drawings to the playroom wall or similar behaviors in which an attempt is made to leave behind a permanent reminder of his existence. Termination anxiety can sometimes be alleviated by the therapist by letting the child know that he will not forget him, and although the therapist will not see him as he has in the past, he will always remember the things that they did and the special times they had together. The therapist might recount some of the achievements and memories of therapy that each might maintain.

Termination with a patient also affects the therapist, for he, too, often develops emotional attachments, and after a long period of frequent contact during which he is updated and informed of the child's progress and conflicts, the prospect of no communication as to the child's welfare can be very sad. In some cases arrangements with the child to contact each other on special occasions through telephone calls or letters can be reassuring to both the patient and therapist.

Having completed one's work with the child, hopefully the therapist will be able to reflect and echo the statement of Lindsay's mouse and say most assuredly, "This light *is* worth the work."

REFERENCES

Ackerman, N. (1966). *Treating the Troubled Family.* New York: Basic Books.

Axline, V. (1947). The eight basic principles. In Haworth, M. (Ed.), *Child Psychotherapy.* New York: Basic Books, 1964, pp. 93–94.

Bowen, M. (1966). The use of family theory in clinical practice. *Compr. Psychiatry, 7,* 345–374.

Brown, S. (1972). Family group therapy. In Wolman, B. (Ed.), *Manual of Child Psychopathology.* New York: McGraw-Hill Book Co., pp. 969–1009.

Fraiberg, S. (1955). Some considerations in the introduction to therapy in puberty. In Eissler, R. (Ed.), *Psychoanalytic Study of the Child,* Vol. 10. New York: International Universities Press, pp. 264–286.

Fraiberg, S., Shapiro. V., Cherniss, D.S. (1980). Treatment modalities. In Fraiberg, S. (Ed.), *Clinical Studies in Infant Mental Health: The First Year of Life.* New York: Basic Books.

Frank, A. (1952). *Anne Frank: The Diary of a Young Girl.* Garden City, New York: Doubleday.

Frank, J. (1961). *Persuasion and Healing—A Comparative Study of Psychotherapy.* New York: Schocken Books, 1963.

Freud, A. (1958). Adolescence. *Psychoanal. Study Child, 13,* 255–278.

Freud, S. (1953). A fragment of an analysis of a case of hysteria. *Standard Edition of the Complete Psychological Works of Sigmund Freud,* Vol. 7, 3–122.

Gardner, R. (1971). *Therapeutic Communication with Children: The Mutual Storytelling Technique.* New York: Science House.

Haley, J. (1975). Family therapy. In Freedman, A., Kaplan, H., Sadock, B. (Eds.), *Comprehensive Textbook of Psychiatry-II,* Vol. 2, Second Edition. Baltimore: Williams and Wilkins, pp. 1881–1886.

Harrison, S. (1975). Individual psychotherapy. In Freedman, A., Kaplan, H., Sadock, B. (Eds.), *Comprehensive Text-*

book of Psychiatry-II, Vol. 2. Second Edition. Baltimore: Williams and Wilkins, pp. 2214–2229.

Hinsie, L.E., Campbell, R.J. (1970). *Psychiatric Dictionary.* New York: Oxford University Press.

The Holy Bible. Isaiah 11:6.

Kolb, L.C. (1968). *Noyes' Modern Clinical Psychiatry.* Seventh Edition. Philadelphia: W.B. Saunders Co.

Kramer, C. (1970). *Psychoanalytically Oriented Family Therapy.* Chicago: Family Institute of Chicago, Pub. No. 1, pp. 1–42.

Lindsay, V. (1914). The mouse that gnawed the oak-tree down. In Sanders, G., Nelson, J. (Eds.), *Chief Modern Poets of England and America.* New York: Macmillan, 1930, p. 502.

MacGregor, R., Ritchie, A.M., Serrano, A.C., Schuster, F.P., MacDonald, E.G., Goolishian, H.A. (1964). *Multiple Impact Therapy With Families.* New York: McGraw-Hill Book Co.

McDermott, J. (1981). Indications for family therapy: Question or non-question? *J. Am. Acad. Child Psychiatry, 20,* 409–419.

Malone, C. (1979). Child psychiatry and family therapy. *J. Am. Acad. Child Psychiatry, 18,* 4–21.

Minuchin, S. (1974). *Families and Family Therapy.* Cambridge: Harvard University Press.

Nunberg, H. (1955). In Hinsie, L.E., Campbell, R.J., Psychiatric Dictionary. New York: Oxford University Press, 1970, p. 78.

Reich, A. (1951). On counter-transference. *Int. J. Psychoanal., 32,* 25–40.

Satir, V. (1964). *Conjoint Family Therapy.* Palo Alto: Science and Behavior Books.

Schechter, M. (1980). Indications and contraindications for marital and family therapy. In Holfing, C., Lewis, J. (Eds.), *The Family.* New York: Brunner/Mazel, pp. 240–270.

Tseng, W.-S., McDermott, J. (1979). Triaxial family classification: A proposal. *J. Am. Acad. Child Psychiatry, 18,* 22–43.

Twain, M. (1876). *The Adventures of Tom Sawyer.* Special Edition. New York: Heritage Press.

Villeneuve, C. (1979). The specific participation of the child in family therapy. *J. Am. Acad. Child Psychiatry, 18,* 44–53.

Wynne, L. (1965). Some indications and contraindications for exploratory family therapy. In Boszormenyi-Nagy, I. (Ed.), *Intensive Family Therapy.* New York: Harper and Row, pp. 289–322.

Zuk, G. (1969). Triadic based family therapy. *Int. J. Psychiatry, 8,* 539–548.

Chapter 22

GROUP PSYCHOTHERAPY: In Childhood and Adolescence

James F. Kennedy, Ph.D.

Mental health clinicians are often unaware that the field of group psychotherapy had its beginnings, in 1934, when Slavson initiated psychotherapy groups for children. (Slavson and Schiffer, 1975) Developmental ego psychology has provided clinicians with a theoretical basis for identifying the indications for group psychotherapy in childhood and adolescence. Despite the impressive accumulation of clinical data during these past 45 years, group psychotherapy for children is still surprisingly nonexistent in some areas of the country and poorly understood in others.

Questions arise by clinicians about differences and similarities between group activity and group psychotherapy, merits of individual versus group psychotherapy, indications and contraindications for group psychotherapy, and issues of transference and countertransference within a group setting.

PRINCIPLES OF GROUP PSYCHOTHERAPY IN CHILDHOOD AND ADOLESCENCE

Definition

Scheidlinger and Raush (1972) have defined group psychotherapy as a method within the broader realm of psychotherapy "wherein a practitioner utilizes the interaction in a small, carefully-planned group to effect repair of personality malfunctioning in individuals specifically selected for this purpose." Careful diagnostic assessment, taking into consideration age and developmental factors, is essential for determining the appropriateness of group psychotherapy for each patient.

Preparation for Group Psychotherapy

Adult patients in group psychotherapy are usually cognizant of the psychotherapeutic purpose of the group and accept participation in the group as a means of obtaining help for modifying their pathological mode of functioning. Children and adolescents, on the other hand, are often unwilling patients brought for psychotherapy at the insistence of parents or other adults. They need to become aware of the therapeutic nature of the group for modifying their attitudes and behaviors. While some practitioners who work with children will explain their role as that of a friend who is going to spend time playing games with them, this is not accurate and does a disservice to the child. Even preschool children are able to understand the therapeutic aims of psychotherapy. In preparing a child for group psychotherapy, the explanation should be in a language that the child can understand, such as, "Children come to this group because they are sad, have worries, feel unhappy, get mad easily, or have bad feelings toward others." The therapist should be described as a person who is specially trained to understand children's problems and to help them become happier people. An honest explanation engenders trust in the therapist and creates the kind of therapeutic group atmosphere where cohesion and peer identification around a common purpose may develop.

Types of Psychotherapy Groups

Several different forms of therapy groups for children have evolved since Slavson developed the original activity group therapy (AGT). Those first activity groups were designed for prepubertal children. In this form of group therapy, children are enabled to express conflicted feelings through a sustaining relationship with a permissive therapist over an extended period of time up to 3 to 4 years. It is an ego level form of treatment in which interpretations of behavior are avoided and resistance and other defense mechanisms are not explored. (Schiffer, 1969, p. 11) AGT is defined as "a method of group treatment of specially selected latency children where the corrective modality is experiential, flowing from significant activities and interactions in a group."(Slavson and Schiffer, 1975, p. 463)

While Slavson's groups were for children between ages 9 years and puberty, Schiffer (1969) began to adapt AGT to young latency-age children from ages 6 to 9 years. He discovered that the therapist had to be more involved with these more active children. He developed a form of group therapy within the New York City public school system for emotionally deprived children. It is an experiential, noninterpretive form of group therapy that offers a corrective reexperience for the children and is called the therapeutic play group (TPG). (Slavson and Schiffer, 1975, pp. 425-437)

Although AGT has been the treatment of choice for the largest number of emotionally disturbed children of latency age, it requires special space and materials that are often unavailable in most clinical settings. Consequently, a modified form of AGT, called activity-interview group psychotherapy (A-IGP), has evolved and is the form of group therapy for children utilized in many clinical settings. (ibid., pp. 297–313) A-IGP is defined as a "treatment method drived from AGT with latency children presenting neurotic features or traits, that includes individual and group interviews based on patients' play, manual activities, and verbalization." (ibid., p. 463)

Schiffer also began to work with younger, preschool-age children and developed the method of play group therapy (PGT). PGT is

...a group treatment method for prelatency children where various types of age-appropriate play materials are supplied and where the therapist may speak with individual children and/or the group, at opportune times, explaining and interpreting their feelings and behavior on their level of understanding; includes also dyadic, triadic, and total group interactions and attitudes."

ibid., p. 465.

Groups for adolescents tend to be discussion and interview focused, although activities may be included, particularly with the early adolescent. (Sugar, 1975a, p. 51)

Space and Equipment

Slavson has extensively discussed the space and room requirements for group therapy with children. (Slavson and Schiffer, 1975, pp. 55–85) Activity group therapy is geared toward anxiety-binding and ego progressive growth through age-appropriate activities, such as building with tools.

Since most psychotherapy groups for children must adapt to the physical facilities of the clinical setting, the classical method of activity group therapy is not often practical or realistic in terms of the space available. Many groups are conducted according to the modified activity-interview format.

The size and furnishings of the room dictate the maximum number a well-balanced group can accommodate. The type of room, as well as the materials, should reflect the developmental needs of the child. For preschool groups, sandboxes, watercolors, tricycles, wagons, large balls, blocks, building materials, dollhouses, and dolls are the materials that should be available. Latency-age children require a room that has both tables and chairs where they may sit and talk as well as a variety of both age-appropriate activities, as well as some younger age materials that allow for periodic regression. Groups for children who have reached puberty and early adolescence meet in rooms similar to the adult group therapy room with chairs and a table in the middle. Toys may be distracting and are not included, and the emphasis is on talk and discussion. However, because of the restlessness and anxiety of the early adolescent, games, such as chess, checkers, and a deck of cards, may be needed to provide a channel to discharge anxiety.

Size of Group and Length of Sessions

The literature is quite clear regarding the number of children that can be effectively accommodated for responsible practice. The traditional AGT consists of six to eight children (Slavson and Schiffer, 1975, p. 64), while five children are considered the maximum for the preschool and nursery groups (ibid., p. 377); Schiffer (1977, p. 386) further states that five or six children are optimum for A-IGP for latency-age children, whereas Ginott (1961, p. 33) stated that five is the maximum, and that beginning group therapists should start with three children in a group. Other clinicians generally agree that six is the maximum for A-IGP for latency-age children.

The number will also vary with the diagnosis and presenting problem of the child. If one or two children have impulse control problems, then the number should be lower, while a withdrawn, isolated child could be added as a seventh member of a balanced, cohesive group.

The length of time for the A-IGP session also varies, with the usual recommended practice being between 90 minutes and 2 hours. (Schiffer, 1977, p. 386) AGTs are planned to meet for 2-hour sessions with 90 minutes for activity and 30 minutes for refreshments. (Slavson and Schiffer, 1975, p. 259)

Because preschool children have short attention spans, PGT sessions should be no longer than 75 minutes. (ibid., p. 412) In some clinical settings, constraints of time, costs, and conflicting clinical demands necessitate that group sessions, particularly of the activity-interview type, be no more than 50 to 60 minutes.

The usual frequency of group sessions is weekly, although twice-weekly group therapy meetings are not uncommon. With cost effectiveness of clinical services a present reality, group therapy should not be viewed as an administrative shortcut to treat more children in less time. While the process of human growth and development cannot be speeded up, group psychotherapy with children requires a similar leavening process dependent on the internal clock of human change. Besides the time allotted for the group sessions, additional professional time is required for recording and the essential collaborative telephone calls that must be made to parents, teachers, and absent children.

Factors of Group Balance

Slavson and Schiffer (1975) and other group therapists discussed the importance of psychological balance in a group and have identified such roles as instigators, neutralizers, and neuters. Group balance is "a judicious blending of aggressive and passive children with a number who fall between these categories [and] will set in motion interactions of mutual benefit, bringing the group under self-control through that blending." (p. 112)

Selection and Screening: Indications and Contraindications for Group Psychotherapy

Most group therapists emphasize careful selection, screening, and preparation of children for group psychotherapy. Slavson and Schiffer (1975) stated that the effectiveness of group therapy with children is "in direct relation to the care taken in selecting and grouping children correctly." (p. 111) The principles of the therapist's autonomy and group balance are essential to selection and screening. The therapist knows the group and when an opening occurs can determine what type of child would meet the criteria for group balance, how much preparation is needed for that child as well as the group, and the timing of entry.

Slavson and Schiffer (1975) emphasize that children with primary behavior disorders, neurotic traits, mild neuroses, and some schizoid personalities profit from AGT. (pp. 107–108)

Children who are negativistic, lack a minimal superego, and manifest regressive infantalism are not appropriate for AGT. Contraindicated for PGT are preschool children who are hostile, destructive, impulsive, and narcissistic. (Schiffer, 1969, p. 104)

MacLennan (1977) described those children for whom AGT is indicated as those latency-age children who are experiencing problems in ego development, such as defiance, dependence, social fearfulness, constrictiveness, aggressiveness, compulsiveness, and withdrawal. (p. 86) MacLennan identifies children who are totally self-absorbed and children who regress severely in unstructured settings as poor candidates for group psychotherapy. Imber (1979) and Sugar (1974) described some of the problems that arise because of improper selection and assignment of children to psychotherapy groups. Sugar is more restrictive and more specific in terms of the indications for group psychotherapy for latency-aged children in the activity-interview type of group or the interpretive psychotherapy group. A basic requirement is that the child have the ability to use play or language to express his conflicts and fantasies and be able to profit from interpretations.

Group psychotherapy is contraindicated, according to Sugar, for the deprived or severely antisocial child, the child who is totally action-oriented, and the child with severe disorganization of ego functions who cannot attend to or concentrate on many stimuli. Sugar does indicate that some of these children might be included in a heterogenous group with neurotic children after a lengthy preliminary period of intensive individual psychotherapy. According to Sugar, the most suitable child for an interpretive type of group is the one who has a behavior disorder that is in the neurotic range or who has a psychosomatic disorder, neurotic symptoms, inhibitions, or sexual problems that are treatable and responsive to verbalizations.

In contrast, Frank (1976) has reported on her exploratory work in treating ego-impaired children in psychotherapy. The children she described are considered inappropriate for group therapy by many group therapists.

A word of caution about selection of children for group psychotherapy is based on the child's developmental level, ego growth, and the nature of his object relation. The development of the capacity for peer grouping is also viewed as a phase-specific development of the personality. The developing child must first incorporate control and self-esteem in a parent-child relationship before attempting the give-and-take of peer relations. Children who are not ready for a peer group because of unresolved residuals within the parent-child relationship fall into two extreme groups. On the one hand are the shy, anxious, self-conscious children who are still attached to parents and unable to reach out to peers. At the other extreme are the anxious, uncertain, needy children who are starved for acceptance and love, but who provoke rejection in their attempts for peer acceptance by challenging behavior, clowning, bragging, and other efforts to be the center of attention. Because of nurture gaps or symbiotic attachments, these two groups of children need a period of individual psychotherapy to increase self-esteem and build frustration tolerance and impulse control before they can tolerate the less structured setting of a peer group. Some clinicians inappropriately refer a child for group therapy because of the manifest behavior of poor peer relationships without taking into consideration developmental perspectives and earlier difficulties in object relationship.

Phases of Group Development

Like adult groups, children and adolescent groups have the following definite phases of development:

1. Initial phase of getting to know each other.
2. Gradual subgroupings and subgroup play.
3. Development of autonomy through games and imagination.
4. Middle phases of therapy where play is symbolic, reflecting individual and group conflicts, interspersed with verbalization by the children.
5. Separation and termination of individual children as their problems are resolved.

Schiffer (1969) described four phases in the TPG: preparatory phase; therapeutic phase; re-educational phase; and termination. (pp. 2–3)

Five stages of group development have been identified by Kolodny, Garland, and Jones: (Bernstein, 1970)

1. Pre-affiliation stage. This is the initial meeting of an aggregate of individuals with various feelings who are not really a group and in whom avoidance-approach patterns of testing are prominent.
2. Power-control stage. The drop-out rate is the highest during this stage, not because of the greater need to formalize relationships, but because competition may be strong and the risks of self-revelation, intimacy, rejection, and hurt are the most prominent.
3. Intimacy stage. Personal involvement of group members is intensified with greater sharing and satisfying relationships. This stage appears to develop earlier in latency-age groups due to the natural formation of gangs and subgroups, accompanied by the excitement and goal-directedness of peer play.
4. Differentiation stage. There is increased freedom to express individual feelings and enhance individuality through cooperation and working on common problems and common age-appropriate and age-specific developmental conflicts.
5. Termination stage. The time for evaluating the experience of group therapy as well as identifying behavioral changes.

As in adult group psychotherapy, the latency or adolescent group should play a part in evaluating a person's readiness to terminate therapy.

One boy in a latency-age group had been suspicious, distrustful, had isolated himself and reacted with aggressive behavior toward peers in the initial phases of the group. However, he eventually became an integral member of the group as he felt accepted by the other members. The group enabled him to gain self-esteem as well as to understand some of his parents' marital conflict, Over a 3-year period he significantly improved his ability to tolerate frustration, interact and reciprocate on a peer level, and showed marked improvement in school and at home. Despite the suggestions by the therapist and other group members that it was time for his termination, he was very reluctant to leave the group and needed support and encouragement of the group over a period of time in order to terminate.

Absent Members and Decisions for Termination

Every group develops a life and history of its own, and every person who enters or leaves that group becomes a part of the psychological life of each child. The care, concern, and preparation shown by the therapist for additions or terminations carry many messages to the child. Experienced group therapists are always struck by the curiosity expressed by one child about another who may have only attended a few sessions. Many of the children that are seen for emotional difficulties have experienced significant object losses and separations. Entry and departure of group members must be dealt with carefully in order for the child to work through some of the anxiety associated with separation. Children are particularly perceptive and alert to the concern and the interest 'shown by the therapist about absent children.

When a group has been carefully selected and group balance prevails, the child's absence from the group is usually related to parental resistance. Parental resistance is difficult to deal with unless the parent is in therapy at the same center. (Soo, 1979)

The departure of a therapist reactivates the experience of the loss of a parent. It requires at least 4 to 5 weeks to prepare the children for the therapist's departure and at least the same amount of time afterward to master the separation.

In a group of 10-year-old boys, the female co-therapist was completing her training and would be leaving the service. The boys had regressed in their behavior, and for several weeks were more disorganized and disruptive, with fighting and mutual provocation. When this behavior was pointed out as a reaction to the loss of the female therapist, they were usually able to talk about how they felt and the anxiety would be reduced. At the last session in which the female therapist would be present, the boys were restless and lethargic and had difficulty organizing games and activities and sticking with them. One of the boys who had verbalized concerns about his mother's hospitalizations during previous sessions, and also had been reacting to the separation from his father because of divorce, dramatically played out his feelings toward the therapist. He took blocks and built a coffin on the floor and then climbed into it. Some of the other boys then entered into his dramatic play by pretending to call his mother and telling her that he had died.

Another interesting reaction to the loss of the therapist occurred in a 9-year-old girls' group.

The male co-therapist was completing his training and was moving to another part of the country. The girls in this group had experienced considerable anxiety toward men because of the uncertain relationships they had with fathers and stepfathers. Fear and anxiety with fantasies of punitive power were prevalent. However, they only began to verbalize these feelings after the therapist had left the group, and their difficulty decathecting the male therapist lingered on for several months after he had left. During subsequent sessions, they would often wonder about what Dr. C. might be doing at that very hour.

In both of these examples, the reactions of the children were opportunities to relate the loss of the therapist to other significant losses in their lives and to discuss the related painful and mixed feelings.

Single Therapist Versus Co-Therapist

There are advantages and disadvantages to the co-therapy dyad. Levine and Dang (1979) reviewed the literature regarding co-therapists in group psychotherapy and identified some of the difficulties and complexities that may arise, such as rivalry, dominance-submission patterns, and re-creating parental conflicts for children. In order to keep such conflicts under control, it is important that the co-therapists have the opportunity

for joint supervision. If the co-therapists can deal with issues in their relationship through individual or peer group supervision, it can become a growth experience, as discussed by Benjamin (1972). The importance of a good working relationship is particularly important in group psychotherapy with children because of the stresses and demands on the group therapists.

QUALIFICATIONS OF GROUP PSYCHOTHERAPISTS FOR CHILDREN AND ADOLESCENTS

Before becoming a group therapist for children and adolescents, training and experience in adult individual and group psychotherapy and child individual psychotherapy is essential. Group psychotherapy with children is a highly complex and sensitive mode of psychotherapy, requiring not only a thorough grounding in the theory of child development and child psychopathology, but also the theory of the group dynamics and techniques of group psychotherapy. The American Group Psychotherapy Association (1978) has recently described a curriculum program with specific minimum education and training requirements for the individual undertaking group psychotherapy. A number of group therapists, Slavson and Schiffer (1975), Sugar (1974), Rosenthal (1977), have detailed the qualifications and training required for work with children and adolescents. One of the most important qualities of the group therapist working with children and adolescents is having the technical skill to deal with the patients' resistances and transferences and the therapists' countertransference reactions.

Resistance

Resistance is a major issue in psychodynamic psychotherapy. However, in work with children, resistance can be minimized. Slavson and Schiffer (1975) stated that the preschool child as well as the latency-age child readily accepts therapy if the therapist creates a climate of freedom and safety where the child can grow and is encouraged by the therapist's interpreting the underlying meaning of some of his play. (pp. 368–369) The child patient can rapidly demonstrate a lack of resistance by quickly producing highly regressive, libidinal content through symbolic play. Children oppose treatment not so much because of unconscious resistance, but because they are unwillingly brought to the therapist by their parents and they have realistic concerns and fears about meeting a strange adult. Groups actually have the potential of reducing fear and suspicion of the beginning child patient because it is comforting for them to be in the presence of other children who are more familiar than adults. The ease with which children take to group therapy is in contrast to the difficulties adolescents and adult patients have in beginning to make use of psychotherapy. Slavson and Schiffer attribute this to the fact that children lack the rigid built-up discriminations of what is proper or improper, what is permissible or taboo, and the absence of strong feelings of shame that plague adults. Slavson and Schiffer point out that some children who have been abused react to other adults or children defensively, but it is not because of resistance, but rather from a pervasive fear of being hurt or punished.

Sugar (1974) points out that attention should always be given first to the most superficial levels of resistance, and what is conscious and troublesome should be managed before proceeding to unconscious matters. Sugar discusses missed appointments as a form of resistance in latency-age children's groups, not in the psychodynamic sense, but as a reaction to the conflicts between the child's world and the parents' world. For instance, scheduling a group for a Friday afternoon created irregular attendance, but after the group was rescheduled to a morning, the children returned to the group and a cohesive working unit was re-established. In like manner, Soo (1979) emphasizes parental resistance as the real reason for missed appointments and premature termination of children in group therapy.

Although latency-age children can acknowledge the problems that brought them to the clinic for help and can talk about them in the context of the group, adolescents have much greater difficulty. However, as noted by Rosenthal (1971), the impetus for growth, change, and further development keeps adolescents in therapy. Their overt protestations to therapy, couched in open denials, such as, "I have no problems," "You are my problem," directed toward the therapist, belie the cohesiveness of the group and the attachments that maintain ongoing group therapy. However, adolescent groups do manifest other forms of resistance, as identified by Rosenthal. Groups offer opportunities to avoid participation that are not available in individual treatment. The sub-groupings that occur may be utilized as a way to avoid dealing with problems. Scapegoating is another form of behavior that diverts the group from its therapeutic purpose. Rosenthal also identifies the craving for excitement which occurs in adolescent groups as a means to avoid anxiety-provoking issues. Rosenthal emphasizes that the foregoing forms of resistance must be identified and dealt with directly by the therapist in order to maintain the therapeutic focus as well as to avoid the disintegrating effect on the group.

Transference

Transference reactions are not as intense or clear-cut in children in latency and preschool years because these children are dependent on parents or guardians. A clear-cut transference neurosis does not develop, but intense transference reactions are regularly present and should eventually be interpreted when appropriate. Examples of transference reactions were described in the earlier section dealing with the termination of a co-therapist. Sugar (1974) gave similar examples of transference reactions when the therapist announced an impending vacation. Sugar points out that any interpretations of transference reactions may be to the individual or the group as a whole.

Slavson and Schiffer (1975) discussed the differences in transference reactions in AGT versus A-IGP. In AGT, because the therapist remains passive and uninvolved rather than active and interpretive, a positive transference to the good adult figure develops. These authors emphasize that the activity group therapist must make every effort to maintain a positive transference with the children, for only then can he or she serve in a supportive role, as a model for identification and ride the crest of transient negative feelings toward him or her. It is relatively easy to acheive this in AGT, since no exploration or interpretation is employed and no verbal clarifications are sought. The neutrality and passivity of the therapist demand consistency. In contrast, in A-IGP, the therapist does evoke, to some degree, active or suppressed negative feelings. (Schiffer, 1977, p. 387) Catharsis is a goal of this type of therapy, with the discharge of more deeply affected emotions occurring through both the activities as well as the interview or discussion segment of the group session. In A-IGP materials are selected and provided to touch on affective components of the personality and are employed symbolically to represent elements in the inner life of the child and other persons and create anxiety within the child.

Countertransference

Being aware of and controlling countertransference reactions requires objectivity for the therapist treating groups of children. A number of authors have discussed the special difficulties for the therapist in dealing with groups of acting-out, aggressive children (Schreiber, 1969). This is one of the major reasons that most therapists prefer to work with adults rather than with children. There are both physical as well as emotional demands made on the therapist. Individual psychotherapy with children is taxing enough, as described by

Chethik (1969). Slavson and Schiffer (1975) emphasize that much of children's conduct, particularly in its primitiveness, is implicitly directed against adults. (p. 124) The therapist should be aware of his or her own vulnerable spots and not react personally to the behavior of the child. The therapist should not only remain in control of his or her own feelings, but also convey to the children that he or she is in control of the group and the session. The loss of this control creates anxiety in the children with the potential for regression and disintegration of that group.

Slavson and Schiffer emphasized the neutrality of the therapist in maintaining emotional objectivity regarding all the patients in the group. They also point out that this is very difficult for the therapist, but, if it is not achieved, jealousy, rivalry, and competition among the children will increase with either aggressive acting-out toward each other or withdrawal. The extremely provocative and negative child is a particular challenge for the therapist, testing the therapist for any sign of implicit or explicit rejection.

In contrast, the dependent, vulnerable child may evoke protective feelings in the therapist. If the other children sense this, they may assume that the vulnerable child is the therapist's favorite, become jealous, and attempt to scapegoat that child. The sensitivity and impartiality that the therapist demonstrates in dealing with the vulnerable child also conveys a positive and reassuring message to the other children, namely, that the therapist will not allow any child to be hurt, physically or emotionally, in the group. The rivalry, jealousy, and concerns about favoritism may occur if the therapist sees one or more of the children for individual therapy outside of the group. In many settings where a child may need individual therapy, he will be assigned to another therapist who is not the group therapist for that child.

Slavson and Schiffer (1975) discuss countertransference reactions in preschool PGT. (pp. 395–397) Preschool children are more open in displays of emotion, both positive and negative. It is important that when the therapist is lonely or depressed he or she not encourage clingy and affectionate displays by children or, on the other hand, replicate the punitive control of some parents in reaction to more regressed behavior of preschoolers, such as sand, water, and smearing with paints and clay.

Sugar (1975a) described the difficult countertransference reactions that may occur with groups of early adolescents. (p. 62) The group therapist is exposed to a heavy bombardment of emotional stimuli, such as name-calling, projection of sexual anxiety, or ignoring the therapist. The therapist's calmness in accepting these emotionally charged reactions without a reprisal is reassuring and comforting to the children. Rosenthal (1971), Rachman (1975), Spruiell (1975), and Stierlin (1975) described countertransference reactions in group therapy with middle and older adolescents.

A final comment must be made about the stresses on group therapists in general and specifically on those who treat groups of children. The beginning group therapist often feels exposed and vulnerable as described by Williams (1966). It is crucial that beginning group therapists receive support through clinical supervision and institutional acceptance, or many become frustrated and decide that group therapy is not for them. Group therapists tend to feel more visible and more responsible for cancellations and drop-outs than individual therapists do. If a patient drops out of individual therapy, it is explained away in terms of resistance and lack of motivation, but if a group has poor attendance, there is the suggestion that the therapist is doing something wrong.

DEVELOPMENTAL PERSPECTIVES IN GROUP PSYCHOTHERAPY

The natural clusters and groupings that evolve spontaneously among children bear close resemblance to shared developmental needs and tasks. This phenomenon has been reported by clinicians as well as formalized by society by grouping children according to age in scouting, little league athletics, dancing, drama, and within school systems. (Buxbaum, 1945) Children of a specific age identify with children of a similar age in terms of psychological needs as well as physical maturation, and feel threatened by older children and look down on younger children. This phenomenon aids in the development of group cohesion for group psychotherapy. The literature supports the planning of psychotherapy groups according to the following stages and substages of psychosexual development.

Preschool (Ages 4 to 5 Years)

The preschool-age child is in the oedipal stage of psychosexual development, which precedes the latency age with its tendency toward natural gang formation. Consequently, since mother and father issues are predominant and peer relations secondary, this form of group resembles the family, with male and female co-therapists and children of both sexes. Peer relations are not as intense, parallel play predominates, and subgroupings are temporary and more in the realm of testing out peer relations. The children shift between seeking out the individual attention of one or both therapists, with sibling rivalry a common feature. The types of play materials reflect age-specific needs and consist of expressive, regressive, and control-building toys and activities. Since children of this age are still incorporating controls, testing limits with the therapist is common. Schiffer describes this from of group therapy as PGT. (Slavson and Schiffer, 1975)

The following is an example of a preschool group consisting of three boys and three girls with psychopathology, ranging from withdrawn, shy, and passive, to aggressive, provocative, and restless.

The group interaction was generally a mixture of solitary play with some pairings with a peer or therapist, but rarely subgroups of three. Rivalry for the therapist's attention was obvious and expressed by pushing in front of another child, grabbing the therapist's hand, and pulling the therapist away from another child. In order to get to the group therapy room, it was necessary to go down a stairwell one flight and open the door to the floor with a key. The key represented control and power to the children. Rivalry for the therapist's key became intense, with begging for the key, grabbing and pushing other children, and pouting if not selected to be the favored one to open the door with the magical key.

The next clinical example demonstrates preschool group interaction with both diagnostic and therapeutic implications.

A 4-year-old girl was added to a group consisting of three boys and two girls, aged 4 and 5 years old. This 4-year-old girl separated from her mother with great reluctance and continued to sob and cry for mother in the group room. A 5-year-old boy with autistic features, who rarely interacted with the other children and was withdrawn and isolated, approached the crying child and put his arm around her to comfort her.

This was one of the first indications that this boy could respond appropriately to other human beings and provided important prognostic data. The empathic gesture by him demonstrates the group dynamics of peer identification and nonverbal response leading to the development of group cohesion.

Early Latency (Ages 6 to 7 Years)

Children of this age are experiencing the transition from the safety and protection of parents and home to the increased expectations of new adult models and peers. During the early latency period, consolidation of ego defenses is incomplete and peer and teacher performance pressure cause periodic regression to the oedipal period. Children observed in free play as well as in psychotherapy groups will shift from peer competition and gang formation to playing house and re-creating family themes through role playing or doll play. Buxbaum (1945) points out that children aged 5 to 6 years use the support of the peer group to deal with feelings of disappointment and loss in regard to oedipal rivalry.

An example of displaced oedipal feelings from parents to teacher occurred when my wife invited me to have lunch with her kindergarten class. Because of my uncertain schedule, the children had not been prepared for my arrival. After I approached the group and was introduced, the children became restless and began giggling. Several boys and girls began pointing out a small, wiry, sullen-looking boy to me with excited shouts of, "This is Richard," "Here's Richard!", and after some anxious giggling reported that "Richard loves Mrs. K.," and then the children waited in anxious expectation. The support of the peer group in this challenge to an adult rival, as well as the vicarious identification with Richard in this oedipal drama, was striking.

Children of early latency age seek out same sex gangs and groups at school in the neighborhood. This coincides with ego efforts to repress oedipal anxiety and to reinforce sexual identification through peer support. The same sex group is found to work very well in group therapy with children of this age. A male-female co-therapy team has advantages for this age, since it allows the security of the symbolic family to continue, as well as continued consolidation and working-through of lingering oedipal issues.

A psychotherapy group consisted of 6-year-old boys whose symptoms of oedipal anxiety consisted of counterphobic aggression, phobic anxiety, shyness, and passivity. During a session, a counterphobic boy spontaneously and assertively hugged the female co-therapist and said he loved both her and his school teacher. This prompted a passive boy to identify and cautiously say he loved his teacher, also. Two phobic boys began to act out anger toward their mothers by suddenly hitting and throwing the mother doll across the room. The male co-therapist commented how sometimes the children loved their parents and wanted to hug them, and other times they were mad at their parents and wanted to hit them.

This example demonstates how a well-balanced group assists children in expressing and dealing with both the positive and negative sides of ambivalence. The phobic boys could reveal repressed anger, while the shy boy could reveal his suppressed love and affection within the safety of the peer group, and with the approval of the symbolic parents, the co-therapists. However, the presence of the male and female co-therapists creates anxiety as well. Children in groups will displace anger for the therapist by scapegoating another child. This occurs most often if the therapist must intervene or set limits with a provocative child. Identification with the aggressor is a common ego defense in childhood, but when it takes the form of scapegoating in a group, the therapist should point out that the child is really angry at the therapist and can talk about it in the group without fear of reprisal. (A. Freud, 1946)

Mid-Latency (Ages 8 to 10 Years)

Children in this age range are in a period of rapid ego growth and consolidation of adaptive ego defenses. The same sex group provides support and identification to enhance progressive ego development. Pros and cons exist concerning the choice between a single therapist of the same sex or the symbolic parents exemplified by the male-female co-therapists (Levine and Dang, 1979). The latter provides the continued reworking of oedipal identifications and rivalries, as well as opportunities to regress to preoedipal stages for nurturance and protection. Progressive-regressive shifts in behavior occur between sessions, as well as within a session, and may be precipitated by events within the group or within the personal lives of the children. The associative themes are dramatically manifested through the shifts from verbal, and cognitive expression to physical, motor discharge and symbolic play. A common example of this phenomenon occurs when a group of children discuss experiences of separation and loss of a parent or friend and then decide to play a game, such as hide-and-seek. This physically active game provides a channel for mastering separation anxiety when the cognitive capacity of the immature ego falters. In contrast, older adolescents have access to a wider range of sophisticated ego defenses and may not need to discharge anxiety through physical activities within the group. A psychotherapy group of six boys aged 9 and 10 years demonstrated these age-specific psychological issues and the progressive-regressive shifts in behavior.

The boys selected for this group represented a range of presenting problems: shy, withdrawn, phobic, anxious, immature, restless, competitive, angry, and provacative. Relationships were both cooperative and competitive with a strong desire to achieve and excel. Competitive activities, such as boxing matches and sports, provided an opportunity to demonstrate strength as well as achievement. In this group, one means of channeling aggression was through simulated wars and combat. Although these were very noisy, physically active episodes, there was a definite order and organization with specific rules that all of the boys adhered to. For instance, if a boy was told that he had been shot,

then he had to fall down on the floor and count to ten before he could get back up and begin shooting at the other boys. The subgroupings that formed for these combat activities reflected needs for peer identification and safety as well as competition between subgroups. Subgroupings for similar psychological reasons occurred in building forts and hide-outs. The furniture would be moved quickly and rearranged for both the battles as well as the forts. The building of the forts and the hide-outs often involved either placing furniture within a very small closet, or piling several pieces of furniture in such a way as to build a shelter. As the boys crowded inside of these small play structures, the emotional need of the child of this age for physical closeness as well as safety was demonstrated. When the therapist indicated that only 5 to 10 minutes remained in the session, it was impressive how quickly the boys would rearrange the furnishings and have everything in the exact order it had been when they entered the room. While the previous examples have demonstrated age-appropriate activities for this age child, this same group demonstrated regressive psychological themes through other types of play. Since parents of some of the boys were divorced and others had been hospitalized or seriously ill, discussions of separation feelings would be followed by a game of hide-and-seek. At other times there would be a need for more regressive play, such as subgroupings that sat on the floor and built houses with blocks and created family themes much as the preschooler does. All of these activities were under the protective eye of the symbolic parents, the co-therapists. Another interesting pattern occurred in this group when one of the therapists was absent because of a vacation, a professional meeting, or for illness. The content would shift according to which therapist was present. For instance, in this boys' group, if the female therapist was absent, then the boys began to discuss sexual ideas, whereas if the male therapist was absent, the content took the form of cooperative protection of the female therapist and anger toward the absent male.

The importance of opportunities for spontaneous, freely organized, peer-group play during latency cannot be overemphasized. Progressive emotional development is aided when children are afforded opportunities to organize their play creatively to channel aggression, master anxiety, and consolidate ego defenses. Playing out competitive feelings within the safety of the planned psychotherapy group enhances self-esteem and confidence building.

Late Latency and Puberty (Ages 11 to 12 Years)

The behavior described for mid-latency continues to be evident during late latency. However, the internal disruption occasioned by the onset of puberty creates stress on the ego to defend against the increasing strength of impulses and maintain equilibrium. The progressive-regressive fluctuations in behavior and content in the psychotherapy group become more pronounced as evidenced by momentary shifts from anxious curiosity about sex to preschool play with toys. Oedipal anxiety and ambivalence toward adults increases and the need for identification and support of the same sex peer group becomes extremely important.

A 12-year-old boys' group included Robert, a withdrawn, isolated boy, and Mark, a passive boy, who because of a thyroid disorder, was small for his age and overprotected by his divorced mother and dominant grandmother. Both of these boys shied away from competitive physical activities. In the course of group therapy, Mark gradually became more comfortable in the interaction within the group and would risk himself in short boxing matches with boys of similar physical stature. He finally discovered a means to excel and compete with the larger boys by jumping rope. As rope jumping became a major activity in the group, Mark began to practice at home and took great pride when he became the champion of the group by jumping 400 times consecutively without a miss. The confidence he gained within the group helped him to become active in a neighborhood recreation program, initially starting with rope jumping and then moving into other athletic activities. Robert also gained status within the group through jumping rope and gained confidence in being able to assert himself and to risk competition activity.

Because of the re-emergence of oedipal anxiety during this period of development, the presence of the co-therapist of the opposite sex creates ambivalence for the child and inhibits the discussion of sexual concerns and questions.

James, age 12, entered the group 6 months after his mother had died. His presenting problem was getting into fights when other children teased about his mother. In the group he was readily accepted by the other boys. He had a colorful imagination and gained status in the group by his exaggerated account of various incidents in his life. He was never a behavior problem in the group and was liked by the other boys. He related positively to them, was supportive and empathetic, offering suggestions for some of their problems. He related positively to both the male and female co-therapists. He was a catalyst for the group because he could talk openly about some of his frightening dreams concerning his dead mother, as well as the sadness and the sense of loss he felt following her death. He was protective and positive toward the female co-therapist and appropriate in his behavior. On those occasions when the female therapist was absent due to a vacation, he quickly revealed his sexual curiosity and confusion. When this was commented upon, he explained that he would be embarrassed to talk about such thoughts and feelings if the female therapist was present.

The latter example demonstrates the importance of understanding developmental theory as well as the individual dynamics of each child in order more accurately to time the decision to discontinue the co-therapy team in favor of the therapist of the same sex.

Early Adolescence (Ages 13 to 14 Years)

Group psychotherapy with adolescents aged 13 to 14 is extremely difficult, demanding, and trying for the therapist. Blos (1971) emphasized that early adolescence is a time for protection from disturbing sexual stimulation and consolidation of identification with the parent of the same sex. Consequently, the therapist in the group should be of the same sex. Heterosexual curiosity and anxiety can be dealt with in a safe manner on the reality level through vicarious discussions of the needs and behavior of the opposite sex. This allows the consolidation of ego defenses against disturbing impulses and prepares the early adolescent for the risk-taking with the opposite sex that occurs in later adolescence. The following case example demonstrates the disrupting effect on a group when developmental theory was not followed:

A female medical student was added as an observer to an ongoing group of early adolescent boys. The addition of the female was very disturbing to this group, and one boy in particular, whose defenses against sexual curiosity were impaired, became disorganized to the point of making obscene comments and becoming restless and unable to sit still. Needless to say, the rest of the group became upset and anxious by this lad's behavior. After the female observer left, the group settled back down to deal with heterosexual issues on a verbal, cognitive level without intense anxiety or acting-out behavior.

In early adolescent groups, both boys and girls can deal with sexual anxiety and curiosity through group interaction. Boys make provocative heterosexual and homosexual comments toward other boys in the group and the therapist. Girls of this age, in a same-sex group, will talk about their feelings about boys and deal with their own self-doubt in a more benign, cooperative manner. The boys' groups are provocative in other ways as well, as the boys are trying to deal with their own feelings about masculinity by acting them out often in hostile, confrontive, and testing ways. (Sugar, 1975a, pp. 49-67) It is important for the therapist not to be threatened by these forms of rebellious behavior, but to maintain the control of the group by emphasizing firm reality limits, such as the time of the group sessions, the same meeting room, and the rules against damaging furniture or fighting with others in the group. The therapist must remind himself or herself that these provocative and testing behaviors are efforts to play out disturbing anxiety in a safe and controlled setting and that the consistency of the therapist is reassuring to the young adolescent.

Middle Adolescence (Ages 15 to 16 Years)

Psychotherapy groups for this age adolescent begin to resemble adult groups with verbalization and discussion the principle mode of communication. Developmental changes and growth have resulted in a wider range of ego defenses so that anxiety is not as disrupting to the ego as during the previous stages. Increased cognitive skill and the development of abstract reasoning ability enhance both defensive and coping capacities. There is a greater sense of security about sexual identity leading to risk-taking with the opposite sex. The question of sexual homogeneity in planning psychotherapy groups for middle adolescents is less of a problem and these groups generally include both males and females. Decisions about group therapy composition at this age must be related to patients' needs, age span, psychosexual levels, levels of integration, positive attributes, and diagnosis. (Sugar, 1975b, pp. 42–43) The extremely immature adolescent would not be included in this age group until the ego growth described had taken place. The therapist of this age group may be male or female, operating singly or as co-therapists. Adhering to group rules in terms of maintaining confidentiality, as well as discouraging relationships outside the group, is important in all groups, but particularly so for this age range because of the issues of dating and heterosexual attraction that are occuring at this time.

A mixed group of adolescents consisted of three boys and three girls. One of the girls, Sue, a 16 year old, masked her insecurity and self-doubt by relating in a manipulative, seductive, hysterical manner. She had experienced loss and rejection through a series of foster home placements and protected herself from close relationships. Fifteen-year-old Andrea was more attractive physically but was a depressed, dependent girl who became involved in questionable male relationships as a means to gain love and affection. One of the boys, Bruce, was an insecure, isolated boy who compensated for feelings of inadequacy by an intellectual, critical approach to other people. As would be expected in the interaction between those three, Bruce attacked Sue self-defensively, and Sue in turn would provoke these attacks. Andrea, who could empathize with both, would make an effort to be the peacemaker and to support each one of them. Over the course of therapy, both Bruce and Sue became more secure and accepted in the group. They gradually began to talk about their distrust of others, their wish for acceptance, and their fear of rejection by peers. At times there were some subtle pairings by some of the boys and the girls in the group, and the therapist needed to be particularly alert so that the heterosexual attractions were not acted out outside of the group rather than discussed within the therapy session.

SUMMARY

The three major components that are considered essential in planning and implementing an effective and successful group psychotherapy program for children have been reviewed and discussed. These are: planning based on group therapy practice principles; planning based on child development theory; and training and supervision requirements for the demanding therapeutic task of group psychotherapy with children and adolescents.

REFERENCES

American Group Psychotherapy Association (1978). *Guidelines for the Training of Group Psychotherapists*. New York: American Group Psychotherapy Association.

Benjamin, S.E., Jr. (1972). Cotherapy: A growth experience for therapists. *Int. J. Group Psychother., 22*, 199–209.

Bernstein, S. (1970). Personal communication.

Blos, P. (1971). The child analyst looks at the young adolescent. *Daedalus, 100*, 961–977.

Buxbaum, E. (1945). Tranference and group formation in children and adolescents. *Psychoanal. Study Child, 1*, 351–365.

Chethik, M. (1969). The emotional "wear and tear" of child therapy. *Smith College Stud. Soc. Work, 39*, 147–156.

Frank, M. (1976). Promoting Ego Capacities in Impoverished Latency-Age Children. Presented at the 33rd annual conference of the American Group Psychotherapy Association, Inc., Boston, Mass., February 4.

Frank, M. (1979). Group Psychotherapy with Ego-Impaired Children. Presented at the 36th annual conference of the American Group Psychotherapy Association, Inc., New York, New York, February 16.

Freud, A. (1936). *The Ego and the Mechanisms of Defense*. New York: International Universities Press, pp. 117–131. 1960.

Ginott, H. (1961). *Group Psychotherapy with Children*. New York: McGraw-Hill Book Co., p. 33.

Imber, S.D. (1979). Uses and abuses of the brief intervention group. *Int. J. Group Psychother., 29*, 46.

Kauff, P.F. (1977). The termination process: Its relationship to the separation-individuation phase of development. *Int. J. Group Psychother., 27*, 3–17.

Levine, C.O. and Dang, J.C. (1979). The group within the group: The dilemma of co-therapy. *Int. J. Group Psychother., 29*, 175–184.

MacLennan, B.W. (1977). Modification of activity group therapy for children. *Int. J. Group Psychother., 27*, 85–96.

Rachman, A.W. (1975). *Identity Group Psychotherapy with Adolescents*. Springfield, Ill.: Charles C Thomas, pp. 182–191, 295–296.

Rosenthal, L. (1971). Some dynamics of resistance and therapeutic management in adolescent group therapy. *Psychoanal. Rev., 58*, 353–365.

Rosenthal, L. (1977). Qualifications and tasks of the therapist in group therapy with children. *Clin. Soc. Work, 5*, 191–199.

Schamess, G. (1976). Group treatment modalities for latency-age children. *Int. J. Group Psychother., 26*, 455–473.

Scheidlinger, S. and Raush, E. (1972). Psychoanalytic group therapy with children and adolescents. In Wolman, B.B. (Ed.), *Handbook of Child Psychoanalysis*. New York: Von Nostrand, pp. 364–398.

Schiffer, M. (1969). *The Therapeutic Play Group*. New York: Grune and Stratton.

Schiffer, M. (1977). Activity-interview group psychotherapy: Theory, principles and practice. *Int. J. Group Psychother., 27,* 377–388.

Schreiber, S.C. (1969). Some special forms of aggressiveness in activity group therapy and their impact on the therapist. *Smith College Stud. Soc. Work, 39,* 138–146.

Slavson, S.R. and Schiffer, M. (1975). *Group Psychotherapies for Children: A Textbook.* New York: International Universities Press.

Soo, E.S. (1979). Premature terminations in activity group therapy. *Int. J. Group Psychother., 29,* 115–118.

Spruiell, V. (1975). Adolescent narcissism and group psychotherapy. In Sugar, M. (Ed.), *The Adolescent in Group and Family Therapy.* New York: Brunner/Mazel, p. 33.

Stierlin, H. (1975). Countertransference in family therapy with adolescents. In Sugar, M. (Ed.), *The Adolescent in Group and Family Therapy.* New York: Brunner/Mazel, p. 165.

Sugar, M. (1974). Interpretive group psychotherapy with latency children. *J. Am. Acad, Child Psychiatry, 13,* 648–666.

Sugar, M. (1975a). Group therapy for pubescent boys with absent fathers. In Sugar, M. (Ed.), *The Adolescent in Group and Family Therapy.* New York: Brunner/Mazel, pp. 49–67.

Sugar, M. (1975b). The structure and setting of adolescent therapy groups. In Sugar, M. (Ed.), *The Adolescent in Group and Family Therapy.* New York: Brunner/Mazel, pp. 42–43.

Williams, M. (1966). Limitations, fantasies and security operations of beginning group psychotherapists. *Int. J. Group Psychother., 16* 150–162.

Chapter 23

PEDIATRIC PSYCHOPHARMACOLOGY

The use or abuse of mind-influencing drugs in children and adolescents reflects the prevalent use of these drugs in adults. de Mause (1974) examined the treatment of children in Western cultures. (p. 25) Children, from antiquity to the present time, were beaten, tortured, drugged, or killed for a variety of reasons, such as crying too much. The use of drugs to calm agitated, restless, and whiny infants has been prevalent in most cultures. In early Mesopotamia and Greek cultures, wine and beer were common tranquilizing agents for quieting crying babies. In Asia, even now, opium is used as a tranquilizing and sedating agent. American Indians and early European immigrants to this continent used tobacco to calm their agitated children.

At the present time, there are two schools of thought concerning the use of drugs in the treatment of emotionally troubled children. One group perceives the use of drugs, especially in the treatment of hyperactive children, as societies' action to suppress and drug the children of minorities and the poor, to make them "docile robots" in the classroom. The other group advocates the extensive use of drugs for even minor illnesses or misbehavior. A careful and concerned clinician falls somewhere between these two extremes. (Gittelman-Klein, 1975, p. 9)

GENERAL CONSIDERATIONS

Psychotropic agents are the most widely prescribed drugs, not only in this country but in the world. In the United States, primary care physicians are the most frequent prescribers. They write 40% of all prescriptions for psychotropic drugs; psychiatrists write 12%.

Often, after listening to a "complaining" mother for a short time, the busy clinician feels that he *has to do* something immediately. The easiest thing to do is to write a prescription. The drug may temporarily settle the child and quiet the anxious mother; however, in the long run, it may be a detriment to the psychological and emotional development of the young patient.

It is essential for clinicians to be well-versed in the psychological and psychophysiological effects of psychotropic agents on the child and the family. Before writing any psychopharmacological prescription for a young person, a physician should consider the temperament of the child, the tempo of the family, and the symbolic meaning of the drug.

Temperament of the Child

The child's constitutional temperament is directly related to his and his parents' biological rhythm. (Chess *et al.,* 1967; Thomas and Chess, 1977; Luce, 1970) For instance, some children are more active and exuberant in the early morning, whereas their parents might be more active in the late afternoon or evening. Knowledge of biological rhythms within the family may help in assessing variations in the child's behavior and the parental responses.

A brief psychological assessment, with emphasis on understanding the child's temperament and biorhythms, can be helpful. The following questions may elicit relevant information: Has the child always been very active and highstrung? Was the child colicky? Has the child been comforted by eating or does he continue to be fussy? Has the child been a picky eater? Have sleep patterns been regular? At what time of the day is the child at his best or his worse? A complete physical examination to rule out organicity, physical abnormality, developmental milestone lag, or biochemical imbalance is essential.

Tempo of the Family

The child is the barometer of the family because he expresses the climate of family life through his behavior. Unhappy or quarrelsome parents often displace and project their difficulties onto one or more of their children without being aware of it. Frequently, this child becomes withdrawn, restless, aggressive, defiant, and unmanageable. When verbal and physical punishment and home remedies fail to bring the child "into line," the parents reluctantly consult a physician, asking him to give them "something to calm the child down and make him mind."

In our experience, many parents of preschool children who ask for medication to calm their children down are indirectly communicating a state of high tension, instability, anger, or depression within the family unit. A sensitive clinician, by asking a few nonjudgmental but caring questions, will find that these troubled parents will confide their difficulties. Listening with empathy for a short time may help the parents to see that tranquilizing their child is not a real solution to troubles within the family.

It is a must for any physician who is considering administering a psychotropic medication to a child to ask the following questions.

1. Was the child planned?
2. Were the parents looking forward to the baby?
3. Did the mother have any major emotional or physical problems during pregnancy?
4. How are the parents getting along?
5. Is there any physical or financial stress in the family; for example, sickness of one of the parents or grandparents, loss of a job?
6. Is there a drinking problem or drug abuse?
7. Are the parents emotionally together so that they can support each other in times of stress?
8. Is there a possibility of separation or divorce?
9. Has the family moved recently?
10. Is mother pregnant again or has there been a new baby in the family?
11. Does mother or father appear to be anxious, depressed, or irrational?
12. Is anyone physically abusing the child?
13. If the mother is working, is the caretaker neglecting or mismanaging the child?
14. Have the parents themselves or any of the children used prescribed psychotropic medications, and, if so, what was their response?
15. What do the child and the parents expect from the drug?

Symbolic Meaning of Drug Use

The recommendation for drug treatment has a number of symbolic meanings for the young person and his family. The child may think: "I am so bad off that nothing else can help me but drugs."; "Thank God, someone finally is trying to help me!"; "The kids in school will think I'm a weirdo or wacky."; "Now the drug will solve all of my problems."; "The drug may do something to my body or my mind."; and/or "Mom and Dad are punishing me for being bad."

The parents may feel relief, shame, embarrassment, or guilt concerning the use of drugs. They may wonder if their child will become a drug abuser or suffer from the long-term effects of drug use. They may feel that the drug will magically solve all of their problems.

A sensitive physician will briefly explore the parents' and child's feelings about the use of drugs, dispel their misconceptions, and reassure them concerning their unrealistic worries and expectations. He should emphasize that drug treatment is only a part of the total treatment program.

INDICATIONS FOR PSYCHOTROPIC DRUGS

Research in the efficacy of psychopharmacological agents in pediatric populations is limited as opposed to the studies of adult populations. Bradley (1937), Bradley and Green (1940), Bender and Cottington (1942), Eisenberg et al. (1961), Eisenberg (1972), Conners (1969), Fish (1960, 1968, 1971), Fish et al. (1966), Campbell (1975, 1976), Campbell and Shapiro (1976), Winsberg et al. (1976), Greenberg and Yellin (1975), Rapoport et al. (1974, 1978), Zrull et al. (1964), Shaw and Lucas (1970), and McAndrew et al. (1972) are a few of those who have done naturalistic or careful quantified studies in pediatric psychopharmacology.

From these studies, the only proved effective drugs are dextroamphetamine (Dexedrine) and methylphenidate (Ritalin) for the management of hyperactive children (attention deficit disorders). Antipsychotic agents and anxiolytic agents contribute to the patient's symptomatic relief but have not proved to be therapeutically effective with children as compared to adults.

In prescribing drugs for children and adolescents, one must not only consider the child's temperament and the family tempo, but also must take into account the age and weight of the child, the intensity of his behavioral problems, and the coping ability of the family.

Table 23-1   **Common Neuroleptics for Children and Adolescents**

Trade Name	(Generic Name)	Dose/Lb.	Daily Dose	IM(Maximum)	Mode of Use
Sedating Major Tranquilizers					
Phenothiazines					
Thorazine	(Chlorpromazine)	1/4 mg. to 1.5 mg.	10-200 mg. or more	Up to 5 yr: 40mg. 5-12 yr.: 75 mg.	Tablets: 10, 25, 50 mg. Syrup: 2 mg./1cc. Ampules: 25 mg./1cc.
Vesprin (Not for children under 2½ years)	(Triflupromazine)	1 mg. oral 1/10 mg. IM	10-150 mg.	10 mg.	Tablets: 10, 25, 50 mg. Ampules: 20 mg./cc. 10 mg./1 cc.
Piperizines					
Mellaril (Not for children under 2 years)	(Thioridazine)	1/4 mg. to 1.5 mg.	10-200 mg. or more		Tablets: 10, 25, 50, 100 mg. Concentrate: 30 mg/1cc.
Stimulating Major Tranquilizers					
Stelazine (For children 6 years and older)	(Trifluoperazine)		1-15 mg.	2 mg.	Tablets: 1, 2, 5, 10 mg. Concentrate: 10 mg/1 cc. Vials: 2 mg/1cc.
Haldol	(Haloperidol)		1½-15 mg.		Tablets: ½, 1, 2, 5, 10 mg. Concentrate: 2 mg/1cc.
Taractan (Not to be used in children under 12 years)	(Chlorprothixene)		10-100 mg.		Tablets: 10, 25, 50, 100 mg. Concentrate: 20 mg/1cc. Ampules: 12.5 mg/1cc.

COMMON USE OF NEUROLEPTIC DRUGS IN CHILDREN

Neuroleptic drugs are generally divided into sedating and stimulating agents (Table 23-1). Sedating neuroleptics are used in the case of severe agitation, aggression, and destructive and unmanageable behavior. They are particularly useful in the following categories: childhood psychosis (childhood schizophrenias, the acute and agitated autistic child), severe acting-out behavior in the mentally retarded child, a moderate to severe form of behavioral disorders, and in severe anxiety disorders. For the sake of brevity, refer to Table 23-1 regarding detailed information on neuroleptics.

Side Effects of Major Neuroleptics

Autonomic

Because of the anticholinergic and antiadrenergic effects of these drugs, the most frequent side effects are: dry mouth and throat, blurred vision, photophobia, cutaneous flushing, photosensitivity, constipation, postural hypotension (usually the first few days), and weight gain.

Extrapyramidal

ACUTE DYSTONIC REACTION. This side effect is the most distressing to children. It occurs more frequently with the use of stimulating neuroleptics. The symptoms include:

1. Bizarre movements of tongue, neck, face, lips, and mouth; salivation
2. Torticollis
3. Oculogyric crisis
4. Opisthotonus

TREATMENT. The treatment of acute dystonic reaction is of an emergent nature, and includes:

1. Discontinuation of medication
2. Reassurance of the patient and the family
3. In severe cases, intramuscular or intravenous antiparkinsonism agents, such as benztropine

(Cogentin) 0.5 to 1 mg. or diphenhydramine (Benadryl) 25 to 50 mg.

PARKINSONIAN SYNDROME. Masked faces, tremor at rest, rigidity, and motor retardation occur.

AKATHISIA. The patient is not able to sit still.

PARADOXICAL EFFECT. The patient's symptoms become worse. Increase of medication will usually improve paradoxical side effects; if no improvement occurs, medication should be discontinued and a different class of neuroleptic should be prescribed.

Cardiovascular

Sedating neuroleptics, such as chlorpromazine and thioridazine, particularly thioridazine, are reported to have quininelike effect on the heart muscle. They may induce tachyarrhythmia, ventricular fibrillation, and sudden death. In children with a history of heart disease, especially those who are taking quinine, sedating neuroleptics— particularly thioridazine—are contraindicated.

Other

Seizures, insomnia, leukopenia, leukocytosis, suppression of bone marrow, agranulocytosis, and impaired liver functions may occur. Thioridazine in high doses of 800 mg. or more may create retinitis pigmentosa and blindness.

Generally, child psychiatrists use thioridazine more frequently than adult psychiatrists. Thioridazine has less extrapyramidal side effects in children and does not usually potentiate seizure disorders. (Goodman and Gilman, 1970, p. 165; Shader, 1976, pp. 90–94)

Tardive Dyskinesia

One of the most debilitating side effects of the neuroleptics is tardive dyskinesia. The word tardive means "late" or "gradually appearing," and the word dyskinesia means "disorder of movement." Tardive dyskinesia refers to involuntary movements of the tongue, mouth, face, or jaw, such as smacking of the lips, tongue, protrusion, cheek puffing, and chewing movements. Choreoathetoid movements of the extremities, tics, dystonia, and facial grimacing may also be present, the triad of buccolingual masticatory involuntary movements are most common and have significant diagnostic value.

According to Jeste and Wyatt (1981), the prevalence of tardive dyskinesia in psychiatric patients treated with neuroleptics has been increasing steadily during the last 30 years, ever since the introduction of the use of neuroleptics for the treatment of various psychopathological disorders, particularly schizophrenia. In the long-term use of neuroleptics approximately 25% of patients manifest signs of tardive dyskinesia.

Tardive dyskinesia is divided into three types.

1. Spontaneous dyskinesia—this type occurs spontaneously in individuals, particularly psychiatric, institutionalized patients who have never been treated with neuroleptics.
2. Withdrawal or reversal dyskinesia—this type is directly related to the decrease or withdrawal of neuroleptics. It usually lasts a few weeks to a year. Approximately 40 to 50% of neuroleptically related tardive dyskinesia cases are of this type.
3. Persistent tardive dyskinesia—the dyskinesia persists and continues for many years following the use of neuroleptics. Decrease or withdrawal of neuroleptics may precipitate or worsen the condition. Persistent tardive dyskinesia can become debilitating because of its intensity and chronicity.

The American Psychiatric Association Task Force on Late Neurological Effects of Antipsychotic Drugs (1980) reported that 10 to 20% of patients on prolonged use of antipsychotic drugs develop tardive dyskinesia. The prevalence is much higher in the elderly population. Jeste and Wyatt (1981) calculated the prevalence of persistent tardive dyskinesia attributed to neuroleptics as 13%, including both inpatients and outpatients of all ages.

TARDIVE DYSKINESIA IN CHILDREN AND ADOLESCENTS. It was thought that children and adolescents did not develop tardive dyskinesia while on neuroleptics. McAndrew *et al.* (1972) reported on the presence of dyskinesia in 10 hospitalized children after phenothiazines were discontinued. The symptoms appeared 3 to 10 days following discontinuation of the medication and subsided 3 to 12 months later. The symptoms were, to some extent, different from tardive dyskinesia in adults, involving rhythmical and myocloniclike movement of the upper extremities. These movements were more prominent in the distal rather than proximal area. Some of these children also showed facial tics and akathisia.

Engelhardt (1974) reported that 48% of children showed signs of neurological withdrawal symptoms following discontinuation of neuroleptics. "Oral dyskinesia, the most common symptom in adult patients, occurred in only 16% of the children, whereas ataxia was found in 52 of the 68 instances of drug withdrawal." (Winsberg and Yepes, 1978, p. 257) In 38% of the cases, spontaneous remission occurred.

Withdrawal from fluphenazine, haloperidol, thiothixene, trifluoperazine, thioridazine, and chlorpromazine all resulted in tardive dyskinesia. Fluphenazine and haloperidol showed the highest occurrence of symptoms and thioridazine and chlorpromazine the lowest.

Paulson *et al.* (1975), in a 4-year follow-up of 16 children with mild to moderate symptoms of tardive dyskinesia, reported that these children continued to show persistent tardive dyskinesia similar to adults.

TREATMENT. There is no specific treatment. The clinician needs to weigh the risk for tardive dyskinesia carefully and discuss this with the child and the family openly before prescribing neuroleptics on a long-term basis. Even the use of neuroleptics for 3 to 6 months may result in persistent tardive dyskinesia in vulnerable and high-risk cases. The history of tardive dyskinesia, Huntington's chorea, or dyskinetic disorders in the family may increase the risk.

It is hypothesized that tardive dyskinesia occurs because of hyperreactivity or hypersensitivity of postsynaptic neurons in the corpus striatum to dopaminergic neurotransmitters, especially in the basal ganglia. It appears that dopamine supersensitivity of the postsynaptic neurons may play an important role in the development of tardive dyskinesia. Antipsychotic effects of neuroleptics are postulated to be related to the antidopamine effects in the limbic system and the forebrain portion of the cerebral cortex.

The following guidelines may be helpful for the prevention and treatment of tardive dyskinesia.

1. The indications for neuroleptics should be carefully weighed against the side effects.
2. It should be kept in mind that all neuroleptics have neurological effects and side effects, and it is because of this that they are called neuroleptics.
3. The possibility of tardive dyskinesia should be considered even in the early phase of treatment.
4. A trial reduction of the dosage of neuroleptics may be helpful to see if the patient shows early signs of tardive dyskinesia. Tardive dyskinesia is frequently reversible if neuroleptics are withdrawn in the early phase of treatment. Then a decision needs to be made concerning either the discontinuation of the neuroleptic, or a change to another neuroleptic, or the use

of other antipsychotic agents, or discontinuation of all medication.
5. Careful follow-up, along with a supportive and therapeutic relationship with the child and the family, will help significantly to alleviate anxiety, provide realistic reassurance, and find an effective way to decrease the intensity of and possible remission of symptoms.
6. The lowest possible dose should be used in the treatment of children.
7. Polypharmacy should be avoided.
8. We do not recommend the use of routine antiparkinsonism agents along with neuroleptics in children and adolescents.
9. In the case of early signs of tardive dyskinesia, antiparkinsonism agents, neuroleptics, and anticholinergic medications should be discontinued.
10. Discussions with the child and the family concerning the pattern and severity of tardive dyskinesia should be documented in the medical record.
11. Re-evaluate the patient at least every 3 to 6 months.
12. The following medications are experimental. (Adapted from The American Psychiatric Association Task Force on Late Neurological Effects of Antipsychotic Drugs Report, 1980) They may partially suppress the symptoms of tardive dyskinesia.
    a. Cholinergic agents: choline, lecithin, physostigmine, deanol
    b. GABA-ergic agents; benzodiazepines, sodium valproate, baclofen, muscimol
    c. Dopamine antagonists: apomorphine, butyrophenones, clozapine, papaverine, phenothiazines, pimozide
    d. Amine depleting agents: reserpine, tetrabenazine
    e. Blockers of catacholamine synthesis: alpha-methyldopa, alpha-methytyrosine
    f. Blockers of catacholamine release: lithium salts
    g. Others: Amantadine, antihistamines, pyridoxine (vitamin B6), tryptophan
13. The following agents intensify or worsen tardive dyskinesia:
    a. Anticholinergic agents: antiparkinsonism agents, such as benztropine
    b. Dopamine agonists: amphetamines, L-Dopa (recently small and repeated doses of L-dopa are used to gradually desensitize the patient to L-dopa, with the hope of treating or preventing tardive dyskinesia)
    c. Others: phenytoin (Dilantin)

COMMON USE OF STIMULANTS AND ANTIDEPRESSANTS FOR CHILDREN

Hyperactivity as a diagnostic label is extensively abused. Eight to 10% of all school-age children are diagnosed hyperactive. Only 20% of these children can truly be considered hyperactive, which includes attention deficit disorder, restlessness, destructiveness, poor frustration tolerance, and soft neurological signs, such as mixed dominance, clumsiness, poor eye-motor coordination, minor physical anomalies, and dysrhythmic brain electrical activity. Many children who are labeled hyperactive by parents, teachers, pediatricians, and family physicians may really be showing transient childhood reactions to loss, fear, separation, physical illness, or family upheaval. (see chapter 10)

Following Bradley's report in 1937, amphetamine sulfate (Benzedrine), dextroamphetamine (Dexedrine), and methylphenidate (Ritalin) have been used extensively for the treatment of hyperactive children. (Bender and Cottington, 1942; Zrull *et al.*, 1964; Conners, 1969; Fish, 1971; Eisenberg, 1972; Rapoport *et al.*, 1974, 1978, 1980; Spring *et al.*, 1976, Shih *et al.*, 1976; Nahas and Krynicki, 1977)

Dextroamphetamine (5 to 10 mg.) could be used as a test dose to see whether the child who is manifesting hyperactive symptoms can benefit from psychostimulant medication. Usually, dextroamphetamine will calm the hyperactive child within one-half to one hour, with the effect lasting for 2 to 4 hours. Some children may worsen with psychostimulant, especially when hyperactivity is covering underlying anxiety disorders, childhood psychosis, or borderline psychosis. For some of these children, a major neuroleptic drug may be indicated.

Studies by Rapoport *et al.* (1978, 1980) have shown that, even with one test dose (0.5 mg./kilogram of body weight) of dextroamphetamine, cognitive and behavioral improvements occurred in normal prepubertal boys, similar to the effects of dextroamphetamine on hyperactive children. These studies raised serious doubts concerning the unique and specific action of dextroamphetamine on hyperactive children.

Antidepressant agents, such as imipramine (Tofranil) and amitriptyline (Elavil) are not generally used for hyperactivity in children under age 12 years. Some physicians have used imipramine for school phobia, anorexia nervosa, or depression. One needs to be very cautious in the use of antidepressant agents in adolescents because of the paradoxical effects, the potential for abuse, and the possibility of drug overdose to commit suicide. These tricyclic antidepressant agents are extremely dangerous because an overdose results in death more frequently than with other psychotropic drugs (Table 23–2).

Imipramine is prescribed for enuresis in children aged 6 years or older. The enuretic child can be given 25 to 50 mg. of imipramine one hour before bedtime. If enuresis does not decrease significantly or stop within 2 weeks, medication should be discontinued. (Poussaint and Ditman, 1965; Kales *et al.*, 1977)

Side Effects of Psychostimulants and Antidepressants

The side effects of psychostimulants and antidepressants are basically similar to the neuroleptics, but also include loss of appetite, anorexia, and insomnia. Safer and Allen (1973) reported on the long-term effects of dextroamphetamine and methylphenidate in hyperactive children. They observed a significant suppression of growth in height and weight in hyperactive children who had been on dextroamphetamine for 2 or more years. In children who were taking daily doses of 20 mg. or more of methylphenidate, growth suppression in height and weight also occurred but to a lesser degree. Dextroamphetamine and methylphenidate may contribute to the suppression of the secretion of prolactin and the growth hormone.

Satterfield *et al.* (1979), in a study of 72 hyperactive boys treated continuously with methylphenidate, showed that, in the first year of treatment, a temporary reduction in growth rates of height and weight occurred, but in the second year of treatment, a larger than expected growth rate occurred which offset the slow rate of the first year. According to the authors, the "...growth rate reduction is of such minor magnitude (less thn 1% deficit in expected full height) that it has little clinical significance." (p. 217) Now, it is generally accepted "...that stimulants produce a temporary retardation in the rate of growth in weight and possibly a temporary slowing of growth in height, but no effect on adult height or weight." (ibid., p. 217)

COMMON ANXIOLYTIC AND SEDATIVE DRUGS FOR CHILDREN

The most popular anxiolytic and tranquilizing agents for adults, chlordiazepoxide (Librium) and diazepam (Valium), are not effective for children and, in fact, may worsen anxiety, hyperactivity, rage, aggression, and psychosis. This is also true of barbiturates (Table 23–3).

Table 23-2   Common Stimulants and Antidepressants for Children and Adolescents

Trade Name	Generic Name	Daily Dose	Mode of Use
For Attention Deficit Disorders			
Benzedrine (Not for children under 3 years)	Amphetamine sulfate	2.5–40 mg.	Spansules: 15 mg. Tablets: 5, 10 mg.
Dexedrine (Not for children under 3 years)	Dextroamphetamine sulfate	2.5–40 mg.	Spansules: 5, 10, 15 mg. Tablets: 5 mg. Elixir: 1 mg./1 cc.
Ritalin hydrochloride (For children 6 years & older)	Methylphenidate hydrochloride	10–60 mg.	Tablets: 5, 10, 20 mg. Before breakfast and lunch
Cylert (For children 6 years & older)	Pemoline	37.5–112.5 mg.	Tablets: 18.75, 37.50, 75 mg.
For Enuresis			
Tofranil (For children 6 years & older)	Imipramine	25–50 mg.	Tablets: 10, 25 mg. One hour before sleep
For Depressive Disorders			
Tofranil (For children 12 years or older)	Imipramine	25–100 mg.	Tablets: 10, 25 mg.
Elavil (For children 12 years or older)	Amitriptyline	25–100 mg.	Tablets: 10, 25 mg.
Sinequan (For children 12 years or older)	Doxepin hydrochloride	25–100 mg.	Tablets: 10, 25, 50 mg.
For Manic-Depressive Disorders			
Eskalith (See chapter 8)	Lithium carbonate		

An antihistaminic agent, diphenhydramine (Benadryl), and an anxiolytic agent, hydroxyzine (Atarax, Vistaril), are effective for decreasing anxiety, hyperactivity, agitation, and for bedtime sedation. Chloral hydrate is the oldest, safest, and most widely used effective sedative for children and adults.

Side Effects of Anxiolytic and Sedative Drugs

Side effects are basically related to the antihistaminic, atropinelike, and sedating effects of these drugs. The most common side effect is sedation. Others are dizziness, tinnitus, lethargy, fatigue, nervousness, blurred vision, diplopia, incoordination, tremor, and sleeplessness. Also, dryness of the mouth, urinary frequency, and hypotension occur.

Gastrointestinal side effects are common in the pediatric population, i.e., loss of appetite,

nausea, vomiting, abdominal pain, constipation, and diarrhea. When medication is given with meals, gastrointestinal side effects are reduced.

HYPERSENSITIVITY REACTIONS FOR ALL DRUGS

Rash, urticaria, allergic dermatitis, leukopenia, and, rarely, anaphylactic shock (in the case of parental administration), and agranulocytosis may occur.

GENERAL GUIDELINES

1. The physician should *know* the drugs he is prescribing. Knowing one or two drugs in each major category very well is better than knowing all of them superficially.

Table 23-3 Common Anxiolytic and Sedative Drugs for Children and Adolescents

Trade Name	Generic Name	Dose/Lb.	Daily Dose		Mode and Indication
			Oral	IM	
Benadryl	Diphenhydramine Hydrochloride	2.5 mg.	25–300 mg.	25–50 mg.	Capsules: 25, 50 mg. Elixir: 2.5 mg./1cc. Ampules: 10, 50 mg./1 cc. Effective: behavioral disorder, hyperactivity, anxiety disorders bedtime sedation, acute dystonic reaction.
Atarax Vistaril	Hydroxyzine Hydrochloride		Under 6: 10–50 mg. Over 6: 50–100 mg.		Tablets: 10, 20, 50, 100 mg. Syrup: 2 mg./1cc. Effective: hyperactivity, anxiety, agitation,
Chloral hydrate (Noctec)	Chloral hydrate	5–25 mg.	250–1000 mg.		Capsules: 250, 500 mg. Noctec Syrup: 100 mg./1cc. Effective sedation.
Donnatal (Mebaral, Numbatal)	Barbiturate preparations				May worsen anxiety, agitation, and aggressive behavior. No use in pediatric psychiatry.
Librium (Not recommended for children under 6 yr.)	Chlordiazepoxide Hydrochloride				May evoke rage and aggression and worsen psychosis. Not usually prescribed.
Valium	Diazepam				May increase anxiety in severely disturbed child. Not usually prescribed.

2. Polypharmacy should be avoided.
3. Begin with a low dosage, and after 2 to 3 days increase the dosage until the desired effect is achieved or until side effects, such as dry mouth or drowsiness, are seen.
4. Most major tranquilizers become effective in 2 to 4 weeks. Occasionally, the patient will have to be on medication for 3 months before the optimal effect is achieved.
5. In the case of psychostimulants, such as dextro-amphetamine or methylphenidate, the effects can be seen within a few hours. If the optimal dose of medication is not effective within a period of 2 weeks, the medication should be discontinued.
6. It is advisable in the case of the long-term use of major tranquilizers or stimulants for the child to be seen by a child psychiatrist for a careful psychiatric evaluation.
7. *Any drug that could interfere with the child's physical or emotional growth and development should not usually be prescribed,* but in the case of *absolute necessity,* the risk of administration should be explained carefully and openly with the parents and the child.

PREPARATION OF THE CHILD AND THE FAMILY

Psychological

1. Children should be included in discussing the possible prescription of a drug.
2. The more the child and the parents understand the nature of the drug and its possible usefulness, the more the drug will be effective.
3. The possible side effects should be discussed openly and honestly with the child and the family, and they should be advised as to how they can cope with the side effects when they occur.

Physical

1. Thorough physical examination of the child is necessary.
2. The clinician should inquire about any history of allergies in the child or family members concerning the specific drug or class of drugs to be prescribed.

3. Pretreatment laboratory studies are indicated, including:
   a. a complete blood count and differential
   b. serum alkaline phosphotase
   c. serum glutamic-oxaloacetic transaminase (SGOT)
   d. serum glutamic-pyruvic transaminase (SGPT)
   e. urinalysis.

Campbell and Shapiro (1976) recommend that "blood and liver function" studies be repeated weekly during the first month of treatment, and once a month thereafter, or as often as clinically indicated. (pp. 155–156)

DRUG HOLIDAY

It is a prudent practice to encourage patients who need to take medications for a long period of time to plan free drug periods (drug holiday) at regular intervals, if this will not create a major health hazard. This is particularly necessary for children and adolescents on psychopharmacological agents. A drug holiday could be scheduled in the following ways.

1. Weekend abstinence—during the weekend, the child does not have peer and school pressures and could skip Saturday and Sunday doses, especially of psychostimulants.
2. Every 3 to 4 months for a period of 2 weeks, the child could be free from taking medications, particularly in the long-term use of neuroleptics.
3. Summer holiday—when school is out and the child is freer in motor expression and under less pressure, medication should be decreased or discontinued. This is particularly true in the use of psychostimulants in the hyperactive child, or the use of haloperidol in Tourette's disorder (chronic multiple tics).

Benefits of a Drug Holiday

1. Allows the physician, patient, and the family to assess the child's present functioning without medication. Frequently, the initial symptoms for which the child was placed on medication have subsided or disappeared because of maturation, effective therapeutic management, and/or change in the family tempo.
2. Allows the body, especially the neuroendocrine system, to function free from drug influence. This is particularly indicated for hyperactive children who take dextroamphetamine or

methylphenidate for long periods of time. In children taking psychostimulants it is believed that drug holidays are helpful in aborting chronic suppression of prolactin and growth hormone.
3. After the drug holiday, the body in some cases becomes more responsive to the effects of the medication and smaller doses are possible.
4. From a psychological point of view, drug holidays can be interpreted by the family and the child as a sign that they are coming along well and can be an impetus for the child and family to work more effectively in modifying their behavior and improving their attitude toward each other.

REFERENCES

American Psychiatric Association Task Force on Late Neurological Effects of Antipsychotic Drugs (1980). Tardive dyskinesia: Summary of a task force report of the American Psychiatric Association. *Am. J. Psychiatry 137*, 1163–1172.

Bender, L., Cottington, F. (1942). The use of amphetamine sulfate (Benzedrine) in child psychiatry. *Am. J. Psychiatry, 99*, 116–121.

Bradley, C. (1937). Behavior of children receiving Benzedrine. *Am. J. Psychiatry, 94*, 577–585.

Bradley, C., Greene, E. (1940). Psychometric performance of children receiving amphetamine (Benzedrine) sulfate. *Am. J. Psychiatry, 97*, 388–394.

Campbell, M. (1975). Pharmacotherapy in early infantile autism. *Biol. Psychiatry, 10*, 399–423.

Campbell, M. (1976). Drug effects in youth poorly understood. *Psychiatr. News*, Oct. 1, p. 26.

Campbell, M., Shapiro, T. (1976). Therapy of psychiatric disorders of childhood. In Shader, R.I. (Ed.), *Manual of Psychiatric Therapeutics, Practical Psychopharmacology and Psychiatry*. Boston: Little, Brown & Co., pp. 137–162.

Chess, S., Thomas, A., Birch, H.G. (1967). Behavior problems revisited: Findings of an anterospective study. *J. Am. Acad. Child Psychiatry, 6*, 321–331.

Conners, C.K. (1969). A teacher rating scale for use in drug studies with children. *Am. J. Psychiatry, 126*, 884–888.

deMause, L. (1974). *The History of Childhood*. New York: Harper and Row.

Eisenberg, L. (1972). Symposium: Behavior modification by drugs, 3. The clinical use of stimulant drugs in children. *Pediatrics, 49*, 709–715.

Eisenberg, L., Gilbert, A., Cytryn, L., Molling, P.A. (1961). The effectiveness of psychotherapy done and in conjunction with perphenazine or placebo in the treatment of neurotic and hyperkinetic children. *Am. J. Psychiatry, 117*, 1088–1093.

Engelhardt, D. (1974). CNS consequences of psychotropic drug withdrawal in autistic children: A follow-up report. Paper presented at ECDEU meeting. Miami, Florida, May 23–24.

Fish, B. (1960). Drug therapy in child psychiatry: Pharmacological aspects. *Compr. Psychiatry, 1*, 212–227.

Fish, B. (1968). Methodology in child psychopharmacology. In Efron, D.H., Cole, J.O., Levine, J., Whittenborn, J.R. (Eds.), *Psychopharmacology: A Review of Progress*, Public Health Service Publication No. 1836. Washington, D.C.: U.S. Government Printing Office, pp. 989–1006.

Fish, B. (1971). The 'one child, one drug' myth of stimulants in hyperkinesis; importance of diagnostic categories in evaluating treatment. *Arch. Gen. Psychiatry, 25,* 193–202.

Fish, B., Shapiro, T., Campbell, M. (1966). Long-term prognosis and the response of schizophrenic children to drug therapy: A controlled study of trifluoperazine. *Am. J. Psychiatry, 123,* 32–39.

Gittelman-Klein, R. (Ed.) (1975). *Recent Advances In Child Psychopharmacology.* New York: Human Sciences Press.

Goodman, L.S., Gilman, A. (1970). *The Pharmacological Basis of Therapeutics.* Fourth Edition. New York: Macmillan.

Greenberg, L.M., Yellin, A.M. (1975). Blood pressure and pulse changes in hyperactive children treated with imipramine and methylphenidate. *Am. J. Psychiatry, 132,* 1325–1326.

Jeste, D.V., Wyatt, R.J. (1981). Changing epidemiology of tardive dyskinesia: An overview. *Am. J. Psychiatry, 138,* 297–309.

Kales, A., Kales, J.D., Jacobson, A., Humphrey, F.J., II, Soldatos, C.R. (1977). Effects of imipramine on enuretic frequency and sleep stages. *Pediatrics, 60,* 431–436.

Luce, G. (1970). *Biological Rhythms in Psychiatry and Medicine.* Chevy Chase, Md.: U.S. National Institute of Mental Health, U.S. Government Printing Office, Publication No. 2088.

McAndrew, J.B., Case, Q., Treffert, D.A. (1972). Effects of prolonged phenothiazine intake on psychotic and other hospitalized children. *J. Autism Child. Schizophr., 2,* 75–91.

Nahas, A.D., Krynicki, V. (1977). Effect of methylphenidate on sleep stages and ultradian rhythms in hyperactive children. *J. Nerv. Ment. Dis., 164,* 66–69.

Paulson, G.W., Rizvi, C.A., Crane, G.E. (1975). Tardive dyskinesia as a possible sequ   if long-term therapy with phenothiazines. *Clin. Pediatr., i4,* 953–955.

Poussaint, A.F., Ditman, K.S. (1965). A controlled study of imipramine (Tofranil) in the treatment of childhood enuresis. *J. Pediatr., 67,* 283.

Rapoport, J.L., Quinn, P.O., Bradbard, G., *et al.* (1974). Imipramine and methylphenidate treatment of hyperactive boys. *Arch. Gen. Psychiatry, 30,* 789–793.

Rapoport, J.L., Buchsbaum, M.S., Zahn, M.S., Weingartner, H., Ludlow, C., Mikkelson, E. (1978). Dextroamphetamine: Cognitive and behavior effects in normal prepubertal boys. *Science, 199,* 560–563.

Rapoport, J.L., Buchsbaum, M.S., Weingartner, H., Zahn, T.P., Ludlow, C., Mikkelson, E.J. (1980). Dextroamphetamine: Its cognitive and behavioral effects in normal and hyperactive boys and normal men. *Arch. Gen. Psychiatry, 37,* 933–943.

Safer, D.J., Allen, R.P. (1973). Factors influencing the suppressant effects of two stimulant drugs on the growth of hyperactive children. *Pediatrics, 51,* 660.

Satterfield, J.H., Cantwell, D.P., Schell, A., Blaschke, T. (1979). Growth of hyperactive children treated with methylphenidate. *Arch. Gen. Psychiatry, 36,* 212–217.

Shader, R.I. (Ed.) (1976). *Manual of Psychiatric Therapeutics, Practical Psychopharmacology and Psychiatry.* Boston: Little, Brown & Co.

Shaw, C.R., Lucas, A.R. (1970). *The Psychiatric Disorders of Children.* Second Edition. New York: Appleton-Century-Crofts, pp. 436–456.

Shih, T.M., Khachaturian, Z.S., Barry, H., III, Hanin, I. (1976). Cholinergic mediation of the inhibitory effect of methylphenidate on neuronal activity in reticular formation. *Neuropharmacology, 15,* 55–60.

Spring, C., Yellin, A.M., Greenberg, L. (1976). Effects of imipramine and methylphenidate on perceptual-motor performance of hyperactive children. *Percept. Mot. Skills, 43,* 459–470.

Thomas, A., Chess, A. (1977). *Temperament and Development.* New York: Brunner/Mazel.

Winsberg, B.G., Yepes, L.E., Bialer, I. (1976). Pharmacological management of children with hyperactive/aggressive/inattentive behavior disorders: Suggestions for the pediatrician. *Clin. Pediatr., 15,* 471–477.

Winsberg, B.G., Yepes, L.E. (1978). Antipsychotics (major tranquilizers, neuroleptics). In Werry, J.S. (Ed.), *Pediatric Psychopharmacology.* New York: Brunner/Mazel, pp. 234–273.

Zrull, J.P., Westman, J.C., Arthur, B., Rice, D.L. (1964). A comparison of diazepam, d-amphetamine and placebo in the treatment of the hyperkinetic syndrome in children *Am. J. Psychiatry, 121,* 388–389.

INDEX

INDEX